THE DARWIN READER

FIRST EDITION

THE DARWIN READER

EDITED BY

MARSTON BATES

AND

PHILIP S. HUMPHREY

LONDON
MACMILLAN & CO LTD
1957

MACMILLAN AND COMPANY LIMITED
London Bombay Calcutta Madras Melbourne

THE MACMILLAN COMPANY OF CANADA LIMITED
Toronto

ST MARTIN'S PRESS INC
New York

PRINTED IN GREAT BRITAIN

CONTENTS

CHAPTER PAGE

Introduction vii

Part One

THE AUTOBIOGRAPHY

1. Recollections of the Development of My Mind and Character 3

Part Two

THE VOYAGE OF THE 'BEAGLE'

2. Tierra del Fuego 37
3. Galapagos Archipelago 57
4. Coral Formations 79
5. Reflections on the Voyage 94

Part Three

THE ORIGIN OF SPECIES

6. The Darwin-Wallace Essays of 1858 103
7. The Variation of Organisms 120
8. Natural Selection 136
9. Difficulties of the Theory 165
10. Geology and Geography 200
11. Recapitulation and Conclusion 244

Part Four

THE DESCENT OF MAN

12. Outline of the Evidence 271
13. The Races of Man 296
14. Principles of Sexual Selection 315
15. Secondary Sexual Characters of Birds 325
16. Secondary Sexual Characters of Man 344
17. General Summary and Conclusion 356

Part Five

THE EXPRESSION OF THE EMOTIONS

CHAPTER PAGE
18. The Expression of the Emotions in Monkeys 369
19. Special Expressions of Man: Blushing 380
20. Concluding Remarks on Emotions 403
21. Biographical Sketch of an Infant 415

Part Six

PLANTS AND WORMS

22. The Movements and Habits of Climbing Plants 427
23. Insectivorous Plants 437
24. The Formation of Vegetable Mould 449

Appendix: The Darwinian Literature 459

Index 469

INTRODUCTION

THE TWO editors of this volume are associated in an experiment in teaching biology at the University of Michigan. We are trying, like many others all over the country, to find ways of giving some appreciation of science to students who will never be scientists themselves, but who will be living in a world shaped in many ways by the ideas of science as well as by the material products of scientific technology. We have found no formula for accomplishing this, but the search explains how we happened to undertake the present anthology of Darwin's writings.

When the biographical study of Darwin and Huxley by William Irvine (*Apes, Angels and Victorians*) appeared, we thought that this might be used to build up an illuminating case history in the development of science. Here was a fascinating account of the personalities and events involved in one of the great revolutions of Western thought—a revolution that has affected every aspect of the intellectual world in which we live today. But if we were to ask the students to read about Darwin, shouldn't we also require them to read some of the basic writings of Darwin himself? The most important books have always been readily available in reprint form: but they comprise a considerable bulk of verbiage, a mass of material that we would hesitate to inflict on anyone with only a general interest in science.

The *Origin of Species* and the *Descent of Man* will hold the interest of any biologist, and should be read in their complete form by every biologist. But our experience, when we have tried to persuade non-scientist friends to read them, has not been encouraging. Why not, then, attempt to extract the most important and the most interesting parts? Why not try to make up a *Darwin Reader*? So we were off, soon forgetting about students, and thinking instead of the needs of the educated citizen in the world today. But the needs are really the same, whether one thinks of the undergraduate today, or of the man who was an undergraduate twenty years ago.

We have tried, then, to include material that would illustrate Darwin's most important ideas—selecting, at the same time, for the most readable prose. Sometimes these two objectives have coincided; when they have not, the decision on what to include has been arrived at by argument—sometimes protracted—between ourselves. Each student of Darwin will probably object to some of our decisions, but these are perhaps less arbitrary in that they have been arrived at jointly by two people with somewhat different backgrounds and tastes.

Darwin was a prodigious worker and a voluminous writer. His output is almost incredible when one thinks also of the amount of time he spent in being ill. He was, further, interested in almost everything—and he tended to form generalizations about everything that interested him. We thought, at one time, of trying to illustrate this breadth of interest by including at least a sample from each of his books: but we could see no way of doing this and at the same time producing an anthology that was readable in itself.

Thus there is nothing here from his longest book, *The Variation of Animals and Plants under Domestication*. It is an important book for anyone interested in the subject, but it is also a very dull book. Darwin himself was appalled at its length and dullness, and was rather surprised that Murray would publish it—though it sold well enough. Darwin developed, in this book, one of his pet theories, an explanation of inheritance by means of 'pangenesis'. The elusiveness of the laws of variation and inheritance always bothered Darwin, and he got some peace of mind by working out this elaborate theory according to which all parts of the body continually gave off ultra-microscopic 'gemmules' which accumulated in all other parts of the body, including the germ cells, so that each cell included a sort of representation of the whole organism. He could thus explain how the fertilized egg combined traits from both parents, how lost parts could be regenerated, how a whole plant could grow from a cutting of the stem, leaf or root, and the like. The whole concept has been rendered obsolete by the gene theory of modern genetics, but the nature and development of science is perhaps just as well illustrated by theories that have been abandoned as by theories that have been retained and substantiated. The pangenesis story would make a nice case history in the philosophy of science, but we could see no way of dealing with it within the confines of the present book.

We have in general tried to limit editorial intrusion to the absolute minimum required for the articulation of the various selections—another reason for not including material, like pangenesis, that would require editorial comment. This is Darwin's book, not ours. Such editorial notes as are included have been indicated by square brackets.

We have removed all of Darwin's footnotes, since they are of interest only to scholars who, in any case, will want to work with the original books. Minor cuts in the text have been indicated by extra periods. Longer omissions, of a paragraph or more, have been indicated by four asterisks set between paragraphs.

Anthologies, we notice, generally begin with a biographical sketch and critical appraisal of the man who is the subject of the anthology. It seems to us that Darwin has written the best possible introduction to his own work in his *Autobiography*, with which we start this volume. In the matter of critical appraisal, it would be difficult to write anything fresh and interesting. The subject is well covered by several books currently in print, such as those by William Irvine, Jacques Barzun and Paul Sears. We have tried to open this literature to the reader in the brief survey of books about Darwin at the end of our anthology.

PART ONE

THE AUTOBIOGRAPHY

CHAPTER 1

RECOLLECTIONS OF THE DEVELOPMENT OF MY MIND AND CHARACTER

[The Darwin autobiography was first published by his son, Sir Francis Darwin, in 1887. It was written in 1876, six years before Darwin's death. Darwin wrote the 'Recollections', as Sir Francis noted, for his children, without any thought that they would ever be published. The son consequently thought it desirable to omit a few passages 'of a personal and intimate kind' in preparing the manuscript for publication. It remains, however, a charmingly personal document; and although it was one of the last things written by Darwin, it seems the most appropriate introduction to his work. It is a short document, but for present purposes it was necessary to shorten it further by the omission of occasional paragraphs and pages of rather special or technical interest. About three-fourths of the original is here included.]

A GERMAN Editor having written to me for an account of the development of my mind and character with some sketch of my autobiography, I have thought that the attempt would amuse me, and might possibly interest my children or their children. I know that it would have interested me greatly to have read even so short and dull a sketch of the mind of my grandfather, written by himself, and what he thought and did, and how he worked. I have attempted to write the following account of myself, as if I were a dead man in another world looking back at my own life. Nor have I found this difficult, for life is nearly over with me. I have taken no pains about my style of writing.

I was born at Shrewsbury on February 12th, 1809, and my earliest recollection goes back only to when I was a few months over four years old, when we went to near Abergele for sea-bathing, and I recollect some events and places there with some little distinctness.

My mother died in July 1817, when I was a little over eight years old, and it is odd that I can remember hardly anything about her except her deathbed, her black velvet gown, and her curiously constructed work-table. In the spring of this same year I was sent to a day-school in Shrewsbury, where I stayed a year. I have been told that I was much slower in learning than my younger sister Catherine, and I believe that I was in many ways a naughty boy.

By the time I went to this day-school my taste for natural history, and more especially for collecting, was well developed. I tried to make out the names of plants, and collected all sorts of things, shells, seals, franks, coins, and minerals. The passion for collecting which leads a man to be a systematic naturalist, a virtuoso, or a miser, was very strong in me, and was clearly innate, as none of my sisters or brother ever had this taste.

One little event during this year has fixed itself very firmly in my mind, and I hope that it has done so from my conscience having been afterwards sorely troubled by it; it is curious as showing that apparently I was interested at this early age in the variability of plants! I told another little boy (I believe it was Leighton, who afterwards became a well-known lichenologist and botanist) that I could produce variously coloured polyanthuses and primroses by watering them with certain coloured fluids, which was of course a monstrous fable, and had never been tried by me. I may here also confess that as a little boy I was much given to inventing deliberate falsehoods, and this was always done for the sake of causing excitement. For instance, I once gathered much valuable fruit from my father's trees and hid it in the shrubbery, and then ran in breathless haste to spread the news that I had discovered a hoard of stolen fruit.

I must have been a very simple little fellow when I first went to the school. A boy of the name of Garnett took me into a cake-shop one day, and bought some cakes for which he did not pay, as the shopman trusted him. When we came out I asked him why he did not pay for them, and he instantly answered, 'Why, do you not know that my uncle left a great sum of money to the town on condition that every tradesman should give whatever was wanted without payment to any one who wore his old hat and moved [it] in a particular manner?' and he then showed me how it was moved. He then went into another shop where he was trusted, and asked for some small article, moving his hat in the proper manner, and of course obtained it without payment. When we came out he said, 'Now if you like to go by yourself into that cake-shop (how well I remember its exact position), I will lend you my hat, and you can get whatever you like if you move the hat on your head properly.' I gladly accepted the generous offer, and went in and asked for some cakes, moved the old hat, and was walking out of the shop, when the shopman made a rush at me, so I dropped the cakes and ran for dear life, and was astonished by being greeted with shouts of laughter by my false friend Garnett.

I can say in my own favour that I was as a boy humane, but I owed this entirely to the instruction and example of my sisters. I doubt indeed whether humanity is a natural or innate quality. I was very fond of collecting eggs, but I never took more than a single egg out of a bird's nest, except on one single occasion, when I took all, not for their value, but from a sort of bravado.

I had a strong taste for angling, and would sit for any number of hours on the bank of a river or pond watching the float; when at Maer I was told that I could kill the worms with salt and water, and from that day I never spitted a living worm, though at the expense probably of some loss of success.

Once as a very little boy whilst at the day-school, or before that time, I acted cruelly, for I beat a puppy, I believe, simply from enjoying the sense of power; but the beating could not have been severe, for the puppy did not howl, of which I feel sure as the spot was near the house. This act lay heavily on my conscience, as is shown by my remembering the exact spot where the crime was committed. It probably lay all the heavier from my love of dogs being then, and for a long time afterwards, a passion. Dogs seemed to know this, for I was an adept in robbing their love from their masters.

I remember clearly only one other incident during this year whilst at Mr. Case's daily school,—namely, the burial of a dragoon soldier; and it is surprising how clearly I can still see the horse with the man's empty boots and carbine suspended to the saddle, and the firing over the grave. This scene deeply stirred whatever poetic fancy there was in me.

In the summer of 1818 I went to Dr. Butler's great school in Shrewsbury, and remained there for seven years till Midsummer 1825, when I was sixteen years old. I boarded at this school, so that I had the great advantage of living the life of a true schoolboy; but as the distance was hardly more than a mile to my home, I very often ran there in the longer intervals between the callings over and before locking up at night. This, I think, was in many ways advantageous to me by keeping up home affections and interests. I remember in the early part of my school life that I often had to run very quickly to be in time, and from being a fleet runner was generally successful; but when in doubt I prayed earnestly to God to help me, and I well remember that I attributed my success to the prayers and not to my quick running, and marvelled how generally I was aided.

I have heard my father and elder sister say that I had, as a very young boy, a strong taste for long solitary walks; but what I thought about I know not. I often became quite absorbed, and once, whilst returning to school on the summit of the old fortifications round Shrewsbury, which had been converted into a public foot-path with no parapet on one side, I walked off and fell to the ground, but the height was only seven or eight feet. Nevertheless, the number of thoughts which passed through my mind during this very short, but sudden and wholly unexpected fall, was astonishing, and seem hardly compatible with what physiologists have, I believe, proved about each thought requiring quite an appreciable amount of time.

Nothing could have been worse for the development of my mind than Dr. Butler's school, as it was strictly classical, nothing else being taught, except a little ancient geography and history. The school as a means of education to me was simply a blank. During my whole life I have been singularly incapable of mastering any language. Especial attention was paid to verse-making, and this I could never do well. I had many friends, and got together a good collection of old verses, which by patching together, sometimes aided by other boys, I could work into any subject. Much attention was paid to learning by heart the lessons of the previous day; this I could effect with great facility, learning forty or fifty lines of Virgil or Homer, whilst I was in morning chapel; but this exercise was utterly useless, for every verse was forgotten in forty-eight hours. I was not idle, and with the exception of versification, generally worked conscientiously at my classics, not using cribs. The sole pleasure I ever received from such studies, was from some of the odes of Horace, which I admired greatly.

When I left the school I was for my age neither high nor low in it; and I believe that I was considered by all my masters and by my father as a very ordinary boy, rather below the common standard in intellect. To my deep mortification my father once said to me, 'You care for nothing but shooting, dogs, and rat-catching, and you will be a disgrace to yourself and all your family.' But my father, who was the kindest man I ever knew, and whose memory I love with all my heart, must have been angry and somewhat unjust when he used such words.

Looking back as well as I can at my character during my school life, the only qualities which at this period promised well for the future, were, that I had strong and diversified tastes, much zeal for whatever interested me, and a keen pleasure in understanding any complex subject or thing. I was taught Euclid by a private tutor, and I distinctly remember the intense satisfaction which the clear geometrical proofs gave me. I remember with equal distinctness the delight which my uncle gave me (the father of Francis Galton) by explaining the principle of the vernier of a barometer. With respect to diversified tastes, independently of science, I was fond of reading various books, and I used to sit for hours reading the historical plays of Shakespeare, generally in an old window in the thick walls of the school. I read also other poetry, such as Thomson's

Seasons, and the recently published poems of Byron and Scott. I mention this because later in life I wholly lost, to my great regret, all pleasure from poetry of any kind, including Shakespeare. In connection with pleasure from poetry, I may add that in 1822 a vivid delight in scenery was first awakened in my mind, during a riding tour on the borders of Wales, and this has lasted longer than any other æsthetic pleasure.

Early in my school-days a boy had a copy of the *Wonders of the World*, which I often read, and disputed with other boys about the veracity of some of the statements; and I believe that this book first gave me a wish to travel in remote countries, which was ultimately fulfilled by the voyage of the *Beagle*. In the latter part of my school life I became passionately fond of shooting; I do not believe that any one could have shown more zeal for the most holy cause than I did for shooting birds. How well I remember killing my first snipe, and my excitement was so great that I had much difficulty in reloading my gun from the trembling of my hands. This taste long continued, and I became a very good shot. When at Cambridge I used to practise throwing up my gun to my shoulder before a looking-glass to see that I threw it up straight. Another and better plan was to get a friend to wave about a lighted candle, and then to fire at it with a cap on the nipple, and if the aim was accurate the little puff of air would blow out the candle. The explosion of the cap caused a sharp crack, and I was told that the tutor of the college remarked, 'What an extraordinary thing it is, Mr. Darwin seems to spend hours in cracking a horse-whip in his room, for I often hear the crack when I pass under his windows.'

I had many friends amongst the schoolboys, whom I loved dearly, and I think that my disposition was then very affectionate.

With respect to science, I continued collecting minerals with much zeal, but quite unscientifically—all that I cared about was a new-named mineral, and I hardly attempted to classify them. I must have observed insects with some little care, for when ten years old (1819) I went for three weeks to Plas Edwards on the sea-coast in Wales, I was very much interested and surprised at seeing a large black and scarlet Hemipterous insect, many moths (Zygæna) and a Cicindela, which are not found in Shropshire. I almost made up my mind to begin collecting all the insects which I could find dead, for on consulting my sister, I concluded that it was not right to kill insects for the sake of making a collection. From reading White's *Selborne*, I took much pleasure in watching the habits of birds, and even made notes on the subject. In my simplicity, I remember wondering why every gentleman did not become an ornithologist.

Towards the close of my school life, my brother worked hard at chemistry, and made a fair laboratory with proper apparatus in the tool-house in the garden, and I was allowed to aid him as a servant in most of his experiments. He made all the gases and many compounds, and I read with care several books on chemistry, such as Henry and Parkes' *Chemical Catechism*. The subject interested me greatly, and we often used to go on working till rather late at night. This was the best part of my education at school, for it showed me practically the meaning of experimental science. The fact that we worked at chemistry somehow got known at school, and as it was an unprecedented fact, I was nicknamed 'Gas'. I was also once publicly rebuked by the head-master, Dr. Butler, for thus wasting my time on such useless subjects; and he called me very unjustly a 'poco-curante', and as I did not understand what he meant, it seemed to me a fearful reproach.

As I was doing no good at school, my father wisely took me away at a rather earlier age than usual, and sent me (October 1825) to Edinburgh University with my brother, where I stayed for two years or sessions. My brother was completing his medical studies, though I do not believe he ever really intended to practise, and I was sent there to commence them. But soon after this period I became convinced from various small circumstances that my father would leave me property enough to subsist on with some comfort, though I never imagined that I should be so rich a man as I am; but my belief was sufficient to check any strenuous effort to learn medicine.

The instruction at Edinburgh was altogether by lectures, and these were intolerably dull, with the exception of those on chemistry by Hope; but to my mind there are no advantages and many disadvantages in lectures compared with reading. Dr. Duncan's lectures on Materia Medica at 8 o'clock on a winter's morning are something fearful to remember. Dr. Munro made his lectures on human anatomy as dull as he was himself, and the subject disgusted me. It has proved one of the greatest evils in my life that I was not urged to practise dissection, for I should soon have got over my disgust, and the practice would have been invaluable for all my future work. This has been an irremediable evil, as well as my incapacity to draw. I also attended regularly the clinical wards in the hospital. Some of the cases distressed me a good deal, and I still have vivid pictures before me of some of them; but I was not so foolish as to allow this to lessen my attendance. I cannot understand why this part of my medical course did not interest me in a greater degree; for during the summer before coming to Edinburgh, I began attending some of the poor people, chiefly children and women in Shrewsbury: I wrote down as full an account as I could of the case with all the symptoms, and read them aloud to my father, who suggested further enquiries and advised me what medicines to give, which I made up myself. At one time I had at least a dozen patients, and I felt a keen interest in the work. My father, who was by far the best judge of character whom I ever knew, declared that I should make a successful physician,—meaning by this, one who would get many patients. He maintained that the chief element of success was exciting confidence; but what he saw in me which convinced him that I should create confidence I know not. I also attended on two occasions the operating theatre in the hospital at Edinburgh, and saw two very bad operations, one on a child, but I rushed away before they were completed. Nor did I ever attend again, for hardly any inducement would have been strong enough to make me do so; this being long before the blessed days of chloroform. The two cases fairly haunted me for many a long year.

My brother stayed only one year at the University, so that during the second year I was left to my own resources; and this was an advantage, for I became well acquainted with several young men fond of natural science. One of these was Ainsworth, who afterwards published his travels in Assyria; he was a Wernerian geologist, and knew a little about many subjects. Dr. Coldstream was a very different young man, prim, formal, highly religious, and most kind-hearted; he afterwards published some good zoological articles. A third young man was Hardie, who would, I think, have made a good botanist, but died early in India. Lastly, Dr. Grant, my senior by several years, but how I became acquainted with him I cannot remember; he published some first-rate zoological papers, but after coming to London as Professor in University College, he did nothing more in science, a fact which has always been inexplicable to me. I knew him well; he was dry and formal in manner, with much enthusiasm beneath this outer crust. He one day, when we were walking together, burst forth in high admiration of Lamarck and his views on evolution. I listened in silent astonishment, and as far as I can judge, without any effect on my mind. I had previously read the *Zoonomia* of my grandfather, in which similar views are maintained, but without producing any effect on me. Nevertheless it is probable that the hearing rather early in life such views maintained and praised may have favoured my upholding them under a different form in my *Origin of Species*. At this time I admired greatly the *Zoonomia*; but on reading it a second time after an interval of ten or fifteen years, I was much disappointed; the proportion of speculation being so large to the facts given.

Drs. Grant and Coldstream attended much to marine Zoology, and I often accompanied the former to collect animals in the tidal pools, which

I dissected as well as I could. I also became friends with some of the Newhaven fishermen, and sometimes accompanied them when they trawled for oysters, and thus got many specimens. But from not having had any regular practice in dissection, and from possessing only a wretched microscope, my attempts were very poor. Nevertheless I made one interesting little discovery, and read, about the beginning of the year 1826, a short paper on the subject before the Plinian Society. This was that the so-called ova of Flustra had the power of independent movement by means of cilia, and were in fact larvæ. In another short paper, I showed that the little globular bodies which had been supposed to be the young state of *Fucus loreus* were the egg-cases of the worm-like *Pontobdella muricata*.

* * * *

During my second year at Edinburgh I attended Jameson's lectures on Geology and Zoology, but they were incredibly dull. The sole effect they produced on me was the determination never as long as I lived to read a book on Geology, or in any way to study the science. Yet I feel sure that I was prepared for a philosophical treatment of the subject; for an old Mr. Cotton, in Shropshire, who knew a good deal about rocks, had pointed out to me two or three years previously a well-known large erratic boulder in the town of Shrewsbury, called the 'bell-stone'; he told me that there was no rock of the same kind nearer than Cumberland or Scotland, and he solemnly assured me that the world would come to an end before any one would be able to explain how this stone came where it now lay. This produced a deep impression on me, and I meditated over this wonderful stone. So that I felt the keenest delight when I first read of the action of icebergs in transporting boulders, and I gloried in the progress of Geology. Equally striking is the fact that I, though now only sixty-seven years old, heard the Professor, in a field lecture at Salisbury Craigs, discoursing on a trap-dyke, with amygdaloidal margins and the strata indurated on each side, with volcanic rocks all around us, say that it was a fissure filled with sediment from above, adding with a sneer that there were men who maintained that it had been injected from beneath in a molten condition. When I think of this lecture, I do not wonder that I determined never to attend to Geology.

From attending Jameson's lectures, I became acquainted with the curator of the museum, Mr. Macgillivray, who afterwards published a large and excellent book on the birds of Scotland. I had much interesting natural-history talk with him, and he was very kind to me. He gave me some rare shells, for I at that time collected marine mollusca, but with no great zeal.

My summer vacations during these two years were wholly given up to amusements, though I always had some book in hand, which I read with interest. During the summer of 1826, I took a long walking tour with two friends with knapsacks on our backs through North Wales. We walked thirty miles most days, including one day the ascent of Snowdon. I also went with my sister on a riding tour in North Wales, a servant with saddle-bags carrying our clothes. The autumns were devoted to shooting, chiefly at Mr. Owen's, at Woodhouse, and at my Uncle Jos's, at Maer. My zeal was so great that I used to place my shooting-boots open by my bed-side when I went to bed, so as not to lose half a minute in putting them on in the morning; and on one occasion I reached a distant part of the Maer estate, on the 20th of August for black-game shooting, before I could see: I then toiled on with the gamekeeper the whole day through thick heath and young Scotch firs.

I kept an exact record of every bird which I shot throughout the whole season. One day when shooting at Woodhouse with Captain Owen, the eldest son, and Major Hill, his cousin, afterwards Lord Berwick, both of whom I liked very much, I thought myself shamefully used, for every time after I had fired and thought that I had killed a bird, one of the two acted as if loading his gun, and cried out, 'You must not count that bird, for I fired at the same time,' and the gamekeeper, perceiving the joke, backed them up. After some hours they told me the joke, but it was no joke to me, for I had shot a large number of birds, but did not know how many, and could not add them to my list, which I used to do by making a knot in a piece of string tied to a button-hole. This my wicked friends had perceived.

How I did enjoy shooting! but I think that I must have been half-consciously ashamed of my zeal, for I tried to persuade myself that shooting was almost an intellectual employment; it required so much skill to judge where to find most game and to hunt the dogs well.

One of my autumnal visits to Maer in 1827 was memorable from meeting there Sir J. Mackintosh, who was the best converser I ever listened to. I heard afterwards with a glow of pride that he had said, 'There is something in that young man that interests me.' This must have been chiefly due to his perceiving that I listened with much interest to everything which he said, for I was as ignorant as a pig about his subjects of history, politics, and moral philosophy. To hear of praise from an eminent person, though no doubt apt or certain to excite vanity, is, I think, good for a young man, as it helps to keep him in the right course.

* * * *

Cambridge, 1828–1831.—After having spent two sessions in Edinburgh, my father perceived, or he heard from my sisters, that I did not like the thought of being a physician, so he proposed that I should become a clergyman. He was very properly vehement against my turning into an idle sporting man, which then seemed my probable destination. I asked for some time to consider, as from what little I had heard or thought on the subject I had scruples about declaring my belief in all the dogmas of the Church of England; though otherwise I liked the thought of being a country clergyman. Accordingly I read with great care *Pearson on the Creed*, and a few other books on divinity; and as I did not then in the least doubt the strict and literal truth of every word in the Bible, I soon persuaded myself that our Creed must be fully accepted.

Considering how fiercely I have been attacked by the orthodox, it seems ludicrous that I once intended to be a clergyman. Nor was this intention and my father's wish ever formally given up, but died a natural death when, on leaving Cambridge, I joined the *Beagle* as naturalist. If the phrenologists are to be trusted, I was well fitted in one respect to be a clergyman. A few years ago the secretaries of a German psychological society asked me earnestly by letter for a photograph of myself; and some time afterwards I received the proceedings of one of the meetings, in which it seemed that the shape of my head had been the subject of a public discussion, and one of the speakers declared that I had the bump of reverence developed enough for ten priests.

As it was decided that I should be a clergyman, it was necessary that I should go to one of the English universities and take a degree; but as I had never opened a classical book since leaving school, I found to my dismay that, in the two intervening years, I had actually forgotten, incredible as it may appear, almost everything which I had learnt, even to some few of the Greek letters. I did not therefore proceed to Cambridge at the usual time in October, but worked with a private tutor in Shrewsbury, and went to Cambridge after the Christmas vacation, early in 1828. I soon recovered my school standard of knowledge, and could translate easy Greek books, such as Homer and the Greek Testament, with moderate facility.

* * * *

Public lectures on several branches were given in the University, attendance being quite voluntary; but I was so sickened with lectures at Edinburgh that I did not even attend Sedgwick's eloquent and interesting lectures. Had I done so I should probably have become a geologist earlier than I did. I attended, however, Henslow's lectures on Botany, and liked them much for their extreme clearness, and the admirable illustrations;

but I did not study botany. Henslow used to take his pupils, including several of the older members of the University, on field excursions, on foot or in coaches, to distant places, or in a barge down the river, and lectured on the rarer plants and animals which were observed. These excursions were delightful.

Although, as we shall presently see, there were some redeeming features in my life at Cambridge, my time was sadly wasted there, and worse than wasted. From my passion for shooting and for hunting, and, when this failed, for riding across country, I got into a sporting set, including some dissipated low-minded young men. We used often to dine together in the evening, though these dinners often included men of a higher stamp, and we sometimes drank too much, with jolly singing and playing at cards afterwards. I know that I ought to feel ashamed of days and evenings thus spent, but as some of my friends were very pleasant, and we were all in the highest spirits, I cannot help looking back to these times with much pleasure.

* * * *

I also got into a musical set, I believe by means of my warm-hearted friend, Herbert, who took a high wrangler's degree. From associating with these men, and hearing them play, I acquired a strong taste for music, and used very often to time my walks so as to hear on week-days the anthem in King's College Chapel. This gave me intense pleasure, so that my backbone would sometimes shiver. I am sure that there was no affectation or mere imitation in this taste, for I used generally to go by myself to King's College, and I sometimes hired the chorister boys to sing in my rooms. Nevertheless I am so utterly destitute of an ear, that I cannot perceive a discord, or keep time and hum a tune correctly; and it is a mystery how I could possibly have derived pleasure from music.

My musical friends soon perceived my state, and sometimes amused themselves by making me pass an examination, which consisted in ascertaining how many tunes I could recognize, when they were played rather more quickly or slowly than usual. 'God Save the King', when thus played, was a sore puzzle. There was another man with almost as bad an ear as I had, and strange to say he played a little on the flute. Once I had the triumph of beating him in one of our musical examinations.

But no pursuit at Cambridge was followed with nearly so much eagerness or gave me so much pleasure as collecting beetles. It was the mere passion for collecting, for I did not dissect them, and rarely compared their external characters with published descriptions, but got them named anyhow. I will give a proof of my zeal: one day, on tearing off some old bark, I saw two rare beetles, and seized one in each hand; then I saw a third and new kind, which I could not bear to lose, so that I popped the one which I held in my right hand into my mouth. Alas! it ejected some intensely acrid fluid, which burnt my tongue so that I was forced to spit the beetle out, which was lost, as was the third one.

I was very successful in collecting, and invented two new methods; I employed a labourer to scrape, during the winter, moss off old trees and place it in a large bag, and likewise to collect the rubbish at the bottom of the barges in which reeds are brought from the fens, and thus I got some very rare species. No poet ever felt more delighted at seeing his first poem published than I did at seeing, in Stephen's *Illustrations of British Insects*, the magic words, 'captured by C. Darwin, Esq.' I was introduced to entomology by my second cousin, W. Darwin Fox, a clever and most pleasant man, who was then at Christ's College, and with whom I became extremely intimate. Afterwards I became well acquainted, and went out collecting, with Albert Way of Trinity, who in after years became a well-known archæologist; also with H. Thompson, of the same College, afterwards a leading agriculturist, chairman of a great railway, and Member of Parliament. It seems, therefore, that a taste for collecting beetles is some indication of future success in life.

* * * *

I have not yet mentioned a circumstance which influenced my whole career more than any other. This was my friendship with Professor Henslow. Before coming up to Cambridge, I had heard of him from my brother as a man who knew every branch of science, and I was accordingly prepared to reverence him. He kept open house once every week when all undergraduates and some older members of the University, who were attached to science, used to meet in the evening. I soon got, through Fox, an invitation, and went there regularly. Before long I became well acquainted with Henslow, and during the latter half of my time at Cambridge took long walks with him on most days; so that I was called by some of the dons 'the man who walks with Henslow'; and in the evening I was very often asked to join his family dinner. His knowledge was great in botany, entomology, chemistry, mineralogy, and geology. His strongest taste was to draw conclusions from long-continued minute observations. His judgment was excellent, and his whole mind well-balanced; but I do not suppose that any one would say that he possessed much original genius.

He was deeply religious, and so orthodox, that he told me one day he should be grieved if a single word of the Thirty-nine Articles were altered.

His moral qualities were in every way admirable. He was free from every tinge of vanity or other petty feeling; and I never saw a man who thought so little about himself or his own concerns. His temper was imperturbably good, with the most winning and courteous manners; yet, as I have seen, he could be roused by any bad action to the warmest indignation and prompt action.

* * * *

Henslow's benevolence was unbounded, as he proved by his many excellent schemes for his poor parishioners, when in after years he held the living of Hitcham. My intimacy with such a man ought to have been, and I hope was, an inestimable benefit. I cannot resist mentioning a trifling incident, which showed his kind consideration. Whilst examining some pollen-grains on a damp surface, I saw the tubes exserted, and instantly rushed off to communicate my surprising discovery to him. Now I do not suppose any other professor of botany could have helped laughing at my coming in such a hurry to make such a communication. But he agreed how interesting the phenomenon was, and explained its meaning; but made me clearly understand how well it was known; so I left him not in the least mortified, but well pleased at having discovered for myself so remarkable a fact, but determined not to be in such a hurry again to communicate my discoveries.

* * * *

Looking back, I infer that there must have been something in me a little superior to the common run of youths, otherwise the above-mentioned men, so much older than me and higher in academical position, would never have allowed me to associate with them. Certainly I was not aware of any such superiority, and I remember one of my sporting friends, Turner, who saw me at work with my beetles, saying that I should some day be a Fellow of the Royal Society, and the notion seemed to me preposterous.

* * * *

My summer vacations were given up to collecting beetles, to some reading, and short tours. In the autumn my whole time was devoted to shooting, chiefly at Woodhouse and Maer, and sometimes with young Eyton of Eyton. Upon the whole the three years which I spent at Cambridge were the most joyful in my happy life; for I was then in excellent health, and almost always in high spirits.

As I had at first come up to Cambridge at Christmas, I was forced to keep two terms after passing my final examination, at the commencement of 1831; and Henslow then persuaded me to begin the study of geology. Therefore on my return to Shropshire I examined sections, and coloured a map of parts round Shrewsbury. Professor Sedgwick intended to visit North Wales in the beginning of August to pursue his famous geological investigations amongst the older rocks, and Henslow asked him to allow me to accompany him. Accordingly he came and slept at my father's house.

A short conversation with him during this evening produced a strong impression on my mind. Whilst examining an old gravel-pit near Shrewsbury, a labourer told me that he had found in it a large worn tropical Volute shell, such as may be seen on chimney-pieces of cottages; and as he would not sell the shell, I was convinced that he had really found it in the pit. I told Sedgwick of the fact, and he at once said (no doubt truly) that it must have been thrown away by some one into the pit; but then added, if really embedded there it would be the greatest misfortune to geology, as it would overthrow all that we know about the superficial deposits of the Midland Counties. These gravel-beds belong in fact to the glacial period, and in after years I found in them broken arctic shells. But I was then utterly astonished at Sedgwick not being delighted at so wonderful a fact as a tropical shell being found near the surface in the middle of England. Nothing before had ever made me thoroughly realise, though I had read various scientific books, that science consists in grouping facts so that general laws or conclusions may be drawn from them.

Next morning we started for Llangollen, Conway, Bangor, and Capel Curig. This tour was of decided use in teaching me a little how to make out the geology of a country. Sedgwick often sent me on a line parallel to his, telling me to bring back specimens of the rocks and to mark the stratification on a map. I have little doubt that he did this for my good, as I was too ignorant to have aided him. On this tour I had a striking instance how easy it is to overlook phenomena, however conspicuous, before they have been observed by any one. We spent many hours in Cwm Idwal, examining all the rocks with extreme care, as Sedgwick was anxious to find fossils in them; but neither of us saw a trace of the wonderful glacial phenomena all around us; we did not notice the plainly scored rocks, the perched boulders, the lateral and terminal moraines. Yet these phenomena are so conspicuous that, as I declared in a paper published many years afterwards in the *Philosophical Magazine*, a house burnt down by fire did not tell its story more plainly than did this valley. If it had still been filled by a glacier, the phenomena would have been less distinct than they now are.

* * * *

VOYAGE OF THE *Beagle:* FROM DECEMBER 27, 1831, TO OCTOBER 2, 1836

On returning home from my short geological tour in North Wales, I found a letter from Henslow, informing me that Captain Fitz-Roy was willing to give up part of his own cabin to any young man who would volunteer to go with him without pay as naturalist to the Voyage of the *Beagle*. I have given, as I believe, in my MS. Journal an account of all the circumstances which then occurred; I will here only say that I was instantly eager to accept the offer, but my father strongly objected, adding the words, fortunate for me, 'If you can find any man of common-sense who advises you to go I will give my consent.' So I wrote that evening and refused the offer. On the next morning I went to Maer to be ready for September 1st, and whilst out shooting, my uncle sent for me, offering to drive me over to Shrewsbury and talk with my father, as my uncle thought it would be wise in me to accept the offer. My father always maintained that [my uncle] was one of the most sensible men in the world, and he at once consented in the kindest manner. I had been rather extravagant at Cambridge, and to console my father, said, 'that I should be deuced clever to spend more than my allowance whilst on board the *Beagle*'; but he answered with a smile, 'But they tell me you are very clever.'

Next day I started for Cambridge to see Henslow, and thence to London to see Fitz-Roy, and all was soon arranged. Afterwards, on becoming very intimate with Fitz-Roy, I heard that I had run a very narrow risk of being rejected on account of the shape of my nose! He was an ardent disciple of Lavater, and was convinced that he could judge of a man's character by the outline of his features; and he doubted whether any one with my nose could possess sufficient energy and determination for the voyage. But I think he was afterwards well satisfied that my nose had spoken falsely.

Fitz-Roy's character was a singular one, with very many noble features: he was devoted to his duty, generous to a fault, bold, determined, and indomitably energetic, and an ardent friend to all under his sway. He would undertake any sort of trouble to assist those whom he thought deserved assistance. He was a handsome man, strikingly like a gentleman, with highly-courteous manners, which resembled those of his maternal uncle, the famous Lord Castlereagh, as I was told by the Minister at Rio. Nevertheless he must have inherited much in his appearance from Charles II., for Dr. Wallich gave me a collection of photographs which he had made, and I was struck with the resemblance of one to Fitz-Roy; and on looking at the name, I found it Ch. E. Sobieski Stuart, Count d'Albanie, a descendant of the same monarch.

Fitz-Roy's temper was a most unfortunate one. It was usually worst in the early morning, and with his eagle eye he could generally detect something amiss about the ship, and was then unsparing in his blame. He was very kind to me, but was a man very difficult to live with on the intimate terms which necessarily followed from our messing by ourselves in the same cabin, We had several quarrels; for instance, early in the voyage at Bahia, in Brazil, he defended and praised slavery, which I abominated, and told me that he had just visited a great slave-owner, who had called up many of his slaves and asked them whether they were happy, and whether they wished to be free, and all answered 'No'. I then asked him, perhaps with a sneer, whether he thought that the answer of slaves in the presence of their master was worth anything? This made him excessively angry, and he said that as I doubted his word we could not live any longer together. I thought that I should have been compelled to leave the ship; but as soon as the news spread, which it did quickly, as the captain sent for the first lieutenant to assuage his anger by abusing me, I was deeply gratified by receiving an invitation from all the gun-room officers to mess with them. But after a few hours Fitz-Roy showed his usual magnanimity by sending an officer to me with an apology and a request that I would continue to live with him.

His character was in several respects one of the most noble which I have ever known.

The voyage of the *Beagle* has been by far the most important event in my life, and has determined my whole career; yet it depended on so small a circumstance as my uncle offering to drive me thirty miles to Shrewsbury, which few uncles would have done, and on such a trifle as the shape of my nose. I have always felt that I owe to the voyage the first real training or education of my mind; I was led to attend closely to several branches of natural history, and thus my powers of observation were improved, though they were always fairly developed.

The investigation of the geology of all the places visited was far more important, as reasoning here comes into play. On first examining a new district, nothing can appear more hopeless than the chaos of rocks; but by recording the stratification and nature of the rocks and fossils at many points, always reasoning and predicting what will be found elsewhere, light soon begins to dawn on the district, and the structure of the whole becomes more or less intelligible. I had brought with me the first volume of Lyell's *Principles of Geology*, which I studied attentively; and the book was of the highest service to me in many ways. The very first place which I examined, namely, St. Jago, in the Cape de Verde Islands, showed me clearly the wonderful superiority of Lyell's manner of treating geology, compared with that of any other author whose works I had with me or ever afterwards read.

Another of my occupations was collecting animals of all classes, briefly describing and roughly dissecting many of the marine ones; but from not being able to draw, and from not having sufficient anatomical knowledge, a great pile of MS. which I made during the voyage has proved almost useless. I thus lost much time, with the exception of that spent in acquiring some knowledge of the Crustaceans, as this was of service when in after years I undertook a monograph of the Cirripedia.

During some part of the day I wrote my Journal, and took much pains in describing carefully and vividly all that I had seen; and this was good practice. My Journal served also, in part, as letters to my home, and portions were sent to England whenever there was an opportunity.

The above various special studies were, however, of no importance compared with the habit of energetic industry and of concentrated attention to whatever I was engaged in, which I then acquired. Everything about which I thought or read was made to bear directly on what I had seen or was likely to see; and this habit of mind was continued during the five years of the voyage. I feel sure that it was this training which has enabled me to do whatever I have done in science.

Looking backwards, I can now perceive how my love for science gradually preponderated over every other taste. During the first two years my old passion for shooting survived in nearly full force, and I shot myself all the birds and animals for my collection; but gradually I gave up my gun more and more, and finally altogether, to my servant, as shooting interfered with my work, more especially with making out the geological structure of a country. I discovered, though unconsciously and insensibly, that the pleasure of observing and reasoning was a much higher one than that of skill and sport. That my mind became developed through my pursuits during the voyage is rendered probable by a remark made by my father, who was the most acute observer whom I ever saw, of a sceptical disposition, and far from being a believer in phrenology; for on first seeing me after the voyage, he turned round to my sisters, and exclaimed, 'Why, the shape of his head is quite altered.'

To return to the voyage. On September 11th (1831), I paid a flying visit with Fitz-Roy to the *Beagle* at Plymouth. Thence to Shrewsbury to wish my father and sisters a long farewell. On October 24th I took up my residence at Plymouth, and remained there until December 27th, when the *Beagle* finally left the shores of England for her circumnavigation of the world. We made two earlier attempts to sail, but were driven back each time by heavy gales. These two months at Plymouth were the most miserable which I ever spent, though I exerted myself in various ways. I was out of spirits at the thought of leaving all my family and friends for so long a time, and the weather seemed to me inexpressibly gloomy. I was also troubled with palpitation and pain about the heart, and like many a young ignorant man, especially one with a smattering of medical knowledge, was convinced that I had heart disease. I did not consult any doctor, as I fully expected to hear the verdict that I was not fit for the voyage, and I was resolved to go at all hazards.

I need not here refer to the events of the voyage—where we went and what we did—as I have given a sufficiently full account in my published Journal. The glories of the vegetation of the Tropics rise before my mind at the present time more vividly than anything else; though the sense of sublimity, which the great deserts of Patagonia and the forest-clad mountains of Tierra del Fuego excited in me, has left an indelible impression on my mind. The sight of a naked savage in his native land is an event which can never be forgotten. Many of my excursions on horseback through wild countries, or in the boats, some of which lasted several weeks, were deeply interesting; their discomfort and some degree of danger were at that time hardly a drawback, and none at all afterwards. I also reflect with high satisfaction on some of my scientific work, such as solving the problem of coral islands, and making out the geological structure of certain islands, for instance, St. Helena. Nor must I pass over the discovery of the singular relations of the animals and plants inhabiting the several islands of the Galapagos Archipelago, and of all of them to the inhabitants of South America.

As far as I can judge of myself, I worked to the utmost during the voyage from the mere pleasure of investigation, and from my strong desire to add a few facts to the great mass of facts in Natural Science. But I was also ambitious to take a fair place among scientific men,—whether more ambitious or less so than most of my fellow-workers, I can form no opinion.

* * * *

Towards the close of our voyage I received a letter whilst at Ascension, in which my sisters told me that Sedgwick had called on my father, and said that I should take a place among the leading scientific men. I could not at the time understand how he could have learnt anything of my proceedings, but I heard (I believe afterwards) that Henslow had read some of the letters which I wrote to him before the Philosophical Society of

Cambridge, and had printed them for private distribution. My collection of fossil bones, which had been sent to Henslow, also excited considerable attention amongst palæontologists. After reading this letter, I clambered over the mountains of Ascension with a bounding step and made the volcanic rocks resound under my geological hammer. All this shows how ambitious I was; but I think that I can say with truth that in after years, though I cared in the highest degree for the approbation of such men as Lyell and Hooker, who were my friends, I did not care much about the general public. I do not mean to say that a favourable review or a large sale of my books did not please me greatly, but the pleasure was a fleeting one, and I am sure that I have never turned one inch out of my course to gain fame.

* * * *

FROM THE RETURN TO ENGLAND, OCTOBER 2, 1836, TO SETTLING AT DOWN, SEPTEMBER 14, 1842

[On his return to England, Darwin lived first in Cambridge and then in London. He prepared his *Journal* of the voyage of the *Beagle* for publication, and was busy with the various technical reports arising fron the voyage. On January 29, 1839 he married his cousin, Emma Wedgwood, and the couple settled down in London at No. 12, Upper Gower Street.]

During the three years and eight months whilst we resided in London, I did less scientific work, though I worked as hard as I possibly could, than during any other equal length of time in my life. This was owing to frequently recurring unwellness, and to one long and serious illness. The greater part of my time, when I could do anything, was devoted to my work on *Coral Reefs*, which I had begun before my marriage, and of which the last proof-sheet was corrected on May 6th, 1842. This book, though a small one, cost me twenty months of hard work, as I had to read every work on the islands of the Pacific and to consult many charts. It was thought highly of by scientific men, and the theory therein given is, I think, now well established.

No other work of mine was begun in so deductive a spirit as this, for the whole theory was thought out on the west coast of South America, before I had seen a true coral reel. I had therefore only to verify and extend my views by a careful examination of living reefs. But it should be observed that I had during the two previous years been incessantly attending to the effects on the shores of South America of the intermittent elevation of the land, together with denudation and the deposition of sediment. This necessarily led me to reflect much on the effects of subsidence, and it was easy to replace in imagination the continued deposition of sediment by the upward growth of corals. To do this was to form my theory of the formation of barrier-reefs and atolls.

Besides my work on coral-reefs, during my residence in London, I read before the Geological Society papers on the Erratic Boulders of South America, on Earthquakes, and on the Formation by the Agency of Earthworms of Mould. I also continued to superintend the publication of the *Zoology of the Voyage of the Beagle*. Nor did I ever intermit collecting facts bearing on the origin of species; and I could sometimes do this when I could do nothing else from illness.

* * * *

RESIDENCE AT DOWN, FROM SEPTEMBER 14, 1842, TO THE PRESENT TIME, 1876

After several fruitless searches in Surrey and elsewhere, we found this house and purchased it. I was pleased with the diversified appearance of the vegetation proper to a chalk district, and so unlike what I had been accustomed to in the Midland counties; and still more pleased with the extreme quietness and rusticity of the place. It is not, however, quite so retired a place as a writer in a German periodical makes it, who says that my house can be approached only by a mule-track! Our fixing ourselves here has answered admirably in one way which we did not anticipate, namely, by being very convenient for frequent visits from our children.

Few persons can have lived a more retired life than we have done. Besides short visits to the houses of relations, and occasionally to the seaside or elsewhere, we have gone nowhere. During the first part of our residence we went a little into society, and received a few friends here; but my health almost always suffered from the excitement, violent shivering and vomiting attacks being thus brought on. I have therefore been compelled for many years to give up all dinner-parties; and this has been somewhat of a deprivation to me, as such parties always put me into high spirits. From the same cause I have been able to invite here very few scientific acquaintances.

My chief enjoyment and sole employment throughout life has been scientific work, and the excitement from such work makes me for the time forget, or drives quite away, my daily discomfort. I have therefore nothing to record during the rest of my life, except the publication of my several books. Perhaps a few details how they arose may be worth giving.

My several Publications.—In the early part of 1844, my observations on the volcanic islands visited during the voyage of the *Beagle* were published. In 1845, I took much pains in correcting a new edition of my

Journal of Researches, which was originally published in 1839 as part of Fitz-Roy's work. The success of this my first literary child always tickles my vanity more than that of any of my other books. Even to this day it sells steadily in England and the United States, and has been translated for the second time into German, and into French and other languages. This success of a book of travels, especially of a scientific one, so many years after its first publication, is surprising. Ten thousand copies have been sold in England of the second edition. In 1846 my *Geological Observations on South America* were published. I record in a little diary, which I have always kept, that my three geological books (*Coral Reefs* included) consumed four and a half years' steady work; 'and now it is ten years since my return to England. How much time have I lost by illness?' I have nothing to say about these three books except that to my surprise new editions have lately been called for.

In October, 1846, I began to work on 'Cirripedia' (Barnacles). When on the coast of Chile, I found a most curious form, which burrowed into shells of Concholepas, and which differed so much from all other Cirripedes that I had to form a new sub-order for its sole reception. Lately an allied burrowing genus has been found on the shores of Portugal. To understand the structure of my new Cirripede I had to examine and dissect many of the common forms: and this gradually led me on to take up the whole group. I worked steadily on the subject for the next eight years, and ultimately published two thick volumes, describing all the known living species, and two thin quartos on the extinct species. I do not doubt that Sir E. Lytton Bulwer had me in his mind when he introduced in one of his novels a Professor Long, who had written two huge volumes on limpets.

Although I was employed during eight years on this work, yet I record in my diary that about two years out of this time was lost by illness. On this account I went in 1848 for some months to Malvern for hydropathic treatment, which did me much good, so that on my return home I was able to resume work. So much was I out of health that when my dear father died on November 13th, 1848, I was unable to attend his funeral or to act as one of his executors.

My work on the Cirripedia possesses, I think, considerable value, as besides describing several new and remarkable forms, I made out the homologies of the various parts—I discovered the cementing apparatus, though I blundered dreadfully about the cement glands—and lastly I proved the existence in certain genera of minute males complemental to and parasitic on the hermaphrodites. This latter discovery has at last been fully confirmed; though at one time a German writer was pleased to attribute the whole account to my fertile imagination. The Cirripedes form a highly varying and difficult group of species to class; and my work was of considerable use to me, when I had to discuss in the *Origin of Species* the principles of a natural classification. Nevertheless, I doubt whether the work was worth the consumption of so much time.

From September 1854 I devoted my whole time to arranging my huge pile of notes, to observing, and to experimenting in relation to the transmutation of species. During the voyage of the *Beagle* I had been deeply impressed by discovering in the Pampean formation great fossil animals covered with armour like that on the existing armadillos; secondly, by the manner in which closely allied animals replace one another in proceeding southwards over the Continent; and thirdly, by the South American character of most of the productions of the Galapagos Archipelago, and more especially by the manner in which they differ slightly on each island of the group; none of the islands appearing to be very ancient in a geological sense.

It was evident that such facts as these, as well as many others, could only be explained on the supposition that species gradually become modified; and the subject haunted me. But it was equally evident that neither the action of the surrounding conditions, nor the will of the organisms (especially in the case of plants), could account for the innumerable cases in which organisms of every kind are beautifully adapted to their habits of life—for instance, a woodpecker or a tree-frog to climb trees, or a seed for dispersal by hooks or plumes. I had always been much struck by such adaptations, and until these could be explained it seemed to me almost useless to endeavour to prove by indirect evidence that species have been modified.

After my return to England it appeared to me that by following the example of Lyell in Geology, and by collecting all facts which bore in any way on the variation of animals and plants under domestication and nature, some light might perhaps be thrown on the whole subject. My first note-book was opened in July 1837. I worked on true Baconian principles, and without any theory collected facts on a wholesale scale, more especially with respect to domesticated productions, by printed enquiries, by conversation with skilful breeders and gardeners, and by extensive reading. When I see the list of books of all kinds which I read and abstracted, including whole series of Journals and Transactions, I am surprised at my industry. I soon perceived that selection was the keystone of man's success in making useful races of animals and plants. But how selection could be applied to organisms living in a state of nature remained for some time a mystery to me.

In October 1838, that is, fifteen months after I had begun my systematic enquiry, I happened to read for amusement Malthus on *Population*, and being well prepared to appreciate the struggle for existence which everywhere goes on from long-continued observation of the habits of animals and plants, it at once struck me that under these circumstances favourable variations would tend to be preserved, and unfavourable ones to be destroyed. The result of this would be the formation of new species. Here, then, I had at last got a theory by which to work; but I was so anxious to avoid prejudice, that I determined not for some time to write even the briefest sketch of it. In June 1842 I first allowed myself the satisfaction of writing a very brief abstract of my theory in pencil in 35 pages; and this was enlarged during the summer of 1844 into one of 230 pages, which I had fairly copied out and still possess.

But at that time I overlooked one problem of great importance; and it is astonishing to me, except on the principle of Columbus and his egg, how I could have overlooked it and its solution. This problem is the tendency in organic beings descended from the same stock to diverge in character as they become modified. That they have diverged greatly is obvious from the manner in which species of all kinds can be classed under genera, genera under families, families under sub-orders, and so forth; and I can remember the very spot in the road, whilst in my carriage, when to my joy the solution occurred to me; and this was long after I had come to Down. The solution, as I believe, is that the modified offspring of all dominant and increasing forms tend to become adapted to many and highly diversified places in the economy of nature.

Early in 1856 Lyell advised me to write out my views pretty fully, and I began at once to do so on a scale three or four times as extensive as that which was afterwards followed in my *Origin of Species*; yet it was only an abstract of the materials which I had collected, and I got through about half the work on this scale. But my plans were overthrown, for early in the summer of 1858 Mr. Wallace, who was then in the Malay Archipelago, sent me an essay *On the Tendency of Varieties to depart indefinitely from the Original Type*; and this essay contained exactly the same theory as mine. Mr. Wallace expressed the wish that if I thought well of his essay, I should send it to Lyell for perusal.

The circumstances under which I consented at the request of Lyell and Hooker to allow of an abstract from my MS., together with a letter to Asa Gray, dated September 5, 1857, to be published at the same time with Wallace's Essay, are given in the *Journal of the Proceedings of the Linnean Society*, 1858, p. 45. I was at first very unwilling to consent, as

I thought Mr. Wallace might consider my doing so unjustifiable, for I did not then know how generous and noble was his disposition. The extract from my MS. and the letter to Asa Gray had neither been intended for publication, and were badly written. Mr. Wallace's essay, on the other hand, was admirably expressed and quite clear. Nevertheless, our joint productions excited very little attention, and the only published notice of them which I can remember was by Professor Haughton of Dublin, whose verdict was that all that was new in them was false, and what was true was old. This shows how necessary it is that any new view should be explained at considerable length in order to arouse public attention.

In September 1858 I set to work by the strong advice of Lyell and Hooker to prepare a volume on the transmutation of species, but was often interrupted by ill-health, and short visits to Dr. Lane's delightful hydropathic establishment at Moor Park. I abstracted the MS. begun on a much larger scale in 1856, and completed the volume on the same reduced scale. It cost me thirteen months and ten days' hard labour. It was published under the title of the *Origin of Species*, in November 1859. Though considerably added to and corrected in the later editions, it has remained substantially the same book.

It is no doubt the chief work of my life. It was from the first highly successful. The first small edition of 1250 copies was sold on the day of publication, and a second edition of 3000 copies soon afterwards. Sixteen thousand copies have now (1876) been sold in England; and considering how stiff a book it is, this is a large sale. It has been translated into almost every European tongue, even into such languages as Spanish, Bohemian, Polish, and Russian. It has also, according to Miss Bird, been translated into Japanese, and is there much studied. Even an essay in Hebrew has appeared on it, showing that the theory is contained in the Old Testament! The reviews were very numerous; for some time I collected all that appeared on the *Origin* and on my related books, and these amount (excluding newspaper reviews) to 265; but after a time I gave up the attempt in despair. Many separate essays and books on the subject have appeared; and in Germany a catalogue or bibliography on 'Darwinismus' has appeared every year or two.

The success of the *Origin* may, I think, be attributed in large part to my having long before written two condensed sketches, and to my having finally abstracted a much larger manuscript, which was itself an abstract. By this means I was enabled to select the more striking facts and conclusions. I had, also during many years, followed a golden rule, namely, that whenever a published fact, a new observation or thought came across me, which was opposed to my general results, to make a memorandum of it without fail and at once; for I had found by experience that such facts and thoughts were far more apt to escape from the memory than favourable ones. Owing to this habit, very few objections were raised against my views which I had not at least noticed and attempted to answer.

It has sometimes been said that the success of the *Origin* proved 'that the subject was in the air', or 'that men's minds were prepared for it'. I do not think that this is strictly true, for I occasionally sounded not a few naturalists, and never happened to come across a single one who seemed to doubt about the permanence of species. Even Lyell and Hooker, though they would listen with interest to me, never seemed to agree. I tried once or twice to explain to able men what I meant by Natural Selection, but signally failed. What I believe was strictly true is that innumerable well-observed facts were stored in the minds of naturalists ready to take their proper places as soon as any theory which would receive them was sufficiently explained. Another element in the success of the book was its moderate size; and this I owe to the appearance of Mr. Wallace's essay; had I published on the scale in which I began to write in 1856, the book would have been four or five times as large as the *Origin*, and very few would have had the patience to read it.

I gained much by my delay in publishing from about 1839, when the theory was clearly conceived, to 1859; and I lost nothing by it, for I cared very little whether men attributed most originality to me or Wallace; and his essay no doubt aided in the reception of the theory. I was forestalled in only one important point, which my vanity has always made me regret, namely, the explanation by means of the Glacial period of the presence of the same species of plants and of some few animals on distant mountain summits and in the arctic regions. This view pleased me so much that I wrote it out *in extenso*, and I believe that it was read by Hooker some years before E. Forbes published his celebrated memoir on the subject. In the very few points in which we differed, I still think that I was in the right. I have never, of course, alluded in print to my having independently worked out this view.

Hardly any point gave me so much satisfaction when I was at work on the *Origin*, as the explanation of the wide difference in many classes between the embryo and the adult animal, and of the close resemblance of the embryos within the same class. No notice of this point was taken, as far as I remember, in the early reviews of the *Origin*, and I recollect expressing my surprise on this head in a letter to Asa Gray. Within late years several reviewers have given the whole credit to Fritz Müller and Häckel, who undoubtedly have worked it out much more fully, and in some respects more correctly than I did. I had materials for a whole chapter on the subject, and I ought to have made the discussion longer; for it is clear that I failed to impress my readers; and he who succeeds in doing so deserves, in my opinion, all the credit.

This leads me to remark that I have almost always been treated honestly by my reviewers, passing over those without scientific knowledge as not worthy of notice. My views have often been grossly misrepresented, bitterly opposed and ridiculed, but this has been generally done, as I believe, in good faith. On the whole I do not doubt that my works have been over and over again greatly overpraised. I rejoice that I have avoided controversies, and this I owe to Lyell, who many years ago, in reference to my geological works, strongly advised me never to get entangled in a controversy, as it rarely did any good and caused a miserable loss of time and temper.

Whenever I have found out that I have blundered, or that my work has been imperfect, and when I have been contemptuously criticised, and even when I have been overpraised, so that I have felt mortified, it has been my greatest comfort to say hundreds of times to myself that 'I have worked as hard and as well as I could, and no man can do more than this'. I remember when in Good Success Bay, in Tierra del Fuego, thinking (and, I believe, that I wrote home to the effect) that I could not employ my life better than in adding a little to Natural Science. This I have done to the best of my abilities, and critics may say what they like, but they cannot destroy this conviction.

* * * *

My *Descent of Man* was published in February 1871. As soon as I had become, in the year 1837 or 1838, convinced that species were mutable productions, I could not avoid the belief that man must come under the same law. Accordingly I collected notes on the subject for my own satisfaction, and not for a long time with any intention of publishing. Although in the *Origin of Species* the derivation of any particular species is never discussed, yet I thought it best, in order that no honourable man should accuse me of concealing my views, to add that by the work 'light would be thrown on the origin of man and his history'. It would have been useless, and injurious to the success of the book, to have paraded, without giving any evidence, my conviction with respect to his origin.

But when I found that many naturalists fully accepted the doctrine of the evolution of species, it seemed to me advisable to work up such notes as I possessed, and to publish a special treatise on the origin of man. I was the more glad to do so, as it gave me an opportunity of fully discussing sexual selection—a subject which had always greatly interested me. This subject, and that of the variation of our domestic productions, together with the causes and laws of variation, inheritance, and the intercrossing of plants, are the sole subjects which I have been able to write about in full, so as to use all the materials which I have collected. The *Descent of Man* took me three years to write, but then as usual some of this time was lost by ill health, and some was consumed by preparing new editions and other minor works. A second and largely corrected edition of the *Descent* appeared in 1874.

My book on the *Expression of the Emotions in Men and Animals* was published in the autumn of 1872. I had intended to give only a chapter on the subject in the *Descent of Man*, but as soon as I began to put my notes together, I saw that it would require a separate treatise.

My first child was born on December 27th, 1839, and I at once commenced to make notes on the first dawn of the various expressions which he exhibited, for I felt convinced, even at this early period, that the most complex and fine shades of expression must all have had a gradual and natural origin. During the summer of the following year, 1840, I read Sir C. Bell's admirable work on expression, and this greatly increased the interest which I felt in the subject, though I could not at all agree with his belief that various muscles had been specially created for the sake of expression. From this time forward I occasionally attended to the subject, both with respect to man and our domesticated animals. My book sold largely; 5267 copies having been disposed of on the day of publication.

★ ★ ★ ★

I am not conscious of any change in my mind during the last thirty years, excepting in one point presently to be mentioned; nor, indeed, could any change have been expected unless one of general deterioration. But my father lived to his eighty-third year with his mind as lively as ever it was, and all his faculties undimmed; and I hope that I may die before my mind fails to a sensible extent. I think that I have become a little more skilful in guessing right explanations and in devising experimental tests; but this may probably be the result of mere practice, and of a larger store of knowledge. I have as much difficulty as ever in expressing myself clearly and concisely; and this difficulty has caused me a very great loss of time; but it has had the compensating advantage of forcing me to think long and intently about every sentence, and thus I have been led to see errors in reasoning and in my own observations or those of others.

There seems to be a sort of fatality in my mind leading me to put at first my statement or proposition in a wrong or awkward form. Formerly I used to think about my sentences before writing them down; but for several years I have found that it saves time to scribble in a vile hand, whole pages as quickly as I possibly can, contracting half the words; and then correct deliberately. Sentences thus scribbled down are often better ones than I could have written deliberately.

Having said thus much about my manner of writing, I will add that with my large books I spend a good deal of time over the general arrangement of the matter. I first make the rudest outline in two or three pages, and then a larger one in several pages, a few words or one word standing for a whole discussion or series of facts. Each one of these headings is again enlarged and often transferred before I begin to write *in extenso*. As in several of my books facts observed by others have been very extensively used, and as I have always had several quite distinct subjects in hand at the same time, I may mention that I keep from thirty to forty large portfolios, in cabinets with labelled shelves, into which I can at once put a detached reference or memorandum. I have bought many books, and at their ends I make an index of all the facts that concern my work; or, if the book is not my own, write out a separate abstract, and of such abstracts I have a large drawer full. Before beginning on any subject I look to all the short indexes and make a general and classified index, and by taking the one or more proper portfolios I have all the information collected during my life ready for use.

I have said that in one respect my mind has changed during the last twenty or thirty years. Up to the age of thirty, or beyond it, poetry of many kinds, such as the works of Milton, Gray, Byron, Wordsworth, Coleridge, and Shelley, gave me great pleasure, and even as a schoolboy I took intense delight in Shakespeare, especially in the historical plays. I have also said that formerly pictures gave me considerable, and music very great delight. But now for many years I cannot endure to read a line of poetry: I have tried lately to read Shakespeare, and found it so intolerably dull that it nauseated me. I have also almost lost my taste for pictures or music. Music generally sets me thinking too energetically on what I have been at work on, instead of giving me pleasure. I retain some taste for fine scenery, but it does not cause me the exquisite delight which it formerly did. On the other hand, novels, which are works of the imagination, though not of a very high order, have been for years a wonderful relief and pleasure to me, and I often bless all novelists. A surprising number have been read aloud to me, and I like all if moderately good, and if they do not end unhappily—against which a law ought to be passed. A novel, according to my taste, does not come into the first class unless it contains some person whom one can thoroughly love, and if a pretty woman all the better.

This curious and lamentable loss of the higher æsthetic tastes is all the odder, as books on history, biographies, and travels (independently of any scientific facts which they may contain), and essays on all sorts of subjects interest me as much as ever they did. My mind seems to have become a kind of machine for grinding general laws out of large collections of facts, but why this should have caused the atrophy of that part of the brain alone, on which the higher tastes depend, I cannot conceive. A man with a mind more highly organised or better constituted than mine, would not, I suppose, have thus suffered; and if I had to live my life again, I would have made a rule to read some poetry and listen to some music at least once every week; for perhaps the parts of my brain now atrophied would thus have been kept active through use. The loss of these tastes is a loss of happiness, and may possibly be injurious to the intellect, and more probably to the moral character, by enfeebling the emotional part of our nature.

My books have sold largely in England, have been translated into many languages, and passed through several editions in foreign countries. I have heard it said that the success of a work abroad is the best test of its enduring value. I doubt whether this is at all trustworthy; but judged by this standard my name ought to last for a few years. Therefore it may be worth while to try to analyse the mental qualities and the conditions on which my success has depended; though I am aware that no man can do this correctly.

I have no great quickness of apprehension or wit which is so remarkable in some clever men, for instance, Huxley. I am therefore a poor critic: a paper or book, when first read, generally excites my admiration, and it is only after considerable reflection that I perceive the weak points. My power to follow a long and purely abstract train of thought is very limited; and therefore I could never have succeeded with metaphysics or mathematics. My memory is extensive, yet hazy: it suffices to make me cautious by vaguely telling me that I have observed or read something opposed to the conclusion which I am drawing, or on the other hand in favour of it; and after a time I can generally recollect where to search for my authority. So poor in one sense is my memory, that I have never been able to remember for more than a few days a single date or a line of poetry.

Some of my critics have said, 'Oh, he is a good observer, but he has no power of reasoning!' I do not think that this can be true, for the *Origin of Species* is one long argument from the beginning to the end, and it has convinced not a few able men. No one could have written it without having some power of reasoning. I have a fair share of invention, and of common sense or judgment, such as every fairly successful lawyer or doctor must have, but not, I believe, in any higher degree.

On the favourable side of the balance, I think that I am superior to the common run of men in noticing things which easily escape attention, and in observing them carefully. My industry has been nearly as great as it could have been in the observation and collection of facts. What is far more important, my love of natural science has been steady and ardent.

This pure love has, however, been much aided by the ambition to be esteemed by my fellow naturalists. From my early youth I have had the strongest desire to understand or explain whatever I observed,—that is, to group all facts under some general laws. These causes combined have given me the patience to reflect or ponder for any number of years over any unexplained problem. As far as I can judge, I am not apt to follow blindly the lead of other men. I have steadily endeavoured to keep my mind free so as to give up any hypothesis, however much beloved (and I cannot resist forming one on every subject), as soon as facts are shown to be opposed to it. Indeed, I have had no choice but to act in this manner, for with the exception of the Coral Reefs, I cannot remember a single first-formed hypothesis which had not after a time to be given up or greatly modified. This has naturally led me to distrust greatly, deductive reasoning in the mixed sciences. On the other hand, I am not very sceptical,—a frame of mind which I believe to be injurious to the progress of science. A good deal of scepticism in a scientific man is advisable to avoid much loss of time, [but] I have met with not a few men, who, I feel sure, have often thus been deterred from experiment or observations, which would have proved directly or indirectly serviceable.

* * * *

My habits are methodical, and this has been of not a little use for my particular line of work. Lastly, I have had ample leisure from not having to earn my own bread. Even ill-health, though it has annihilated several years of my life, has saved me from the distractions of society and amusement.

Therefore, my success as a man of science, whatever this may have amounted to, has been determined, as far as I can judge, by complex and diversified mental qualities and conditions. Of these, the most important have been—the love of science—unbounded patience in long reflecting over any subject—industry in observing and collecting facts—and a fair share of invention as well as of common-sense. With such moderate abilities as I possess, it is truly surprising that I should have influenced to a considerable extent the belief of scientific men on some important points.

PART TWO

THE VOYAGE OF THE *BEAGLE*

CHAPTER 2

TIERRA DEL FUEGO

[Chapter X of the *Beagle*. The significance for Darwin's life of the five years that he spent on the *Beagle* is well brought out in his *Autobiography*. As he there notes, he spent some time every day writing up his journal, trying to describe carefully everything that he had seen. On his return to England, he set about the task of re-writing and editing this journal for publication. The manuscript was completed in July, 1837, and was published in 1839 as Vol. III of the official *Narrative of the Surveying Voyage of Her Majesty's Ships 'Adventure' and 'Beagle'*, the first two volumes being by Captain King and Captain Fitz-Roy. Darwin's volume was immediately successful and it was reissued the same year with a separate title as *Journal of Researches into the Geology and Natural History of the Various Countries Visited by H.M.S. Beagle*, with another printing in 1840.

In 1844, the well-known publisher, John Murray, asked Darwin to rewrite the *Journal* for a popular series of books called the 'Colonial and Home Library'. Darwin spent several months of hard work on the re-writing, cutting a great deal, but also making large additions which were now possible because his specimens had been identified and because he had had time to reflect on the meaning of his observations. He had already, in 1842, written the first brief abstract of his theory of natural selection, and this idea coloured his re-writing of the *Journal*, though he made no open mention of evolution. This revised *Journal*, published in 1845, is the book we now know as the *Voyage of the Beagle*.

The *Voyage of the Beagle* is a delightful book that should be read in its entirety. The decision on what selections to use for an anthology has not been easy. Regretfully, we have omitted the first half of the book, which deals with the east coast of South America and which contains many vivid descriptions of life in Brazil, Uruguay and Argentina in the year 1832. All we have included of this is part of the section on Tierra del Fuego. We have also omitted the many interesting descriptions of scenery, people and towns on the west coast of South America, leaving only the material on the Galapagos Archipelago because of its great interest in relation to the development of the theory of evolution through natural selection.

There is fascinating material on the Pacific, too, on Tahiti, New Zealand and Australia. Our decision here has been to include only the material on coral formations because this covers one of Darwin's important theories, developed in full in a book entitled *The Structure and Distribution of Coral Reefs* published in 1842. The coral reef book was written in a technical style unlikely to interest the general reader, and Darwin's own summary of his ideas, published in the 1845 edition of the *Beagle*, seems the best way of introducing the reader to this work.]

DECEMBER 17*th*, 1832.—Having now finished with Patagonia and the Falkland Islands, I will describe our first arrival in Tierra del Fuego. A little after noon we doubled Cape St. Diego, and entered the famous strait of Le Maire. We kept close to the Fuegian shore, but the outline of the rugged, inhospitable Staten-land was visible amidst the clouds. In the afternoon we anchored in the Bay of Good Success. While entering we were saluted in a manner becoming the inhabitants of this savage land. A group of Fuegians partly concealed by the entangled forest, were perched on a wild point overhanging the sea; and as we passed by, they sprang up and waving their tattered cloaks sent forth a loud and sonorous shout. The savages followed the ship, and just before dark we saw their fire, and again heard their wild cry. The harbour consists of a fine piece of water half surrounded by low rounded mountains of clay-slate, which are covered to the water's edge by one dense gloomy forest. A single glance at the landscape was sufficient to show me how widely different it was from any thing I had ever beheld. At night it blew a gale of wind, and heavy squalls from the mountains swept past us. It would have been a bad time out at sea, and we, as well as others, may call this Good Success Bay.

In the morning the Captain sent a party to communicate with the Fuegians. When we came within hail, one of the four natives who were present advanced to receive us, and began to shout most vehemently, wishing to direct us where to land. When we were on shore the party looked rather alarmed, but continued talking and making gestures with great rapidity. It was without exception the most curious and interesting spectacle I ever beheld: I could not have believed how wide was the difference between savage and civilized man: it is greater than between a wild and domesticated animal, inasmuch as in man there is a greater power of improvement. The chief spokesman was old, and appeared to be the head of the family; the three others were powerful young men, about six feet high. The women and children had been sent away. These Fuegians are a very different race from the stunted, miserable wretches farther westward; and they seem closely allied to the famous Patagonians of the Strait of Magellan. Their only garment consists of a mantle made of guanaco skin, with the wool outside; this they wear just thrown over their shoulders, leaving their persons as often exposed as covered. Their skin is of a dirty coppery red colour.

The old man had a fillet of white feathers tied round his head, which partly confined his black, coarse, and entangled hair. His face was crossed by two broad transverse bars; one, painted bright red, reached from ear to ear and included the upper lip; the other, white like chalk, extended above and parallel to the first, so that even his eyelids were thus coloured. The other two men were ornamented by streaks of black powder, made of charcoal. The party altogether closely resembled the devils which come on the stage in plays like *Der Freischutz*.

Their very attitudes were abject, and the expression of their countenances distrustful, surprised, and startled. After we had presented them with some scarlet cloth, which they immediately tied round their necks, they became good friends. This was shown by the old man patting our breasts, and making a chuckling kind of noise, as people do when feeding chickens. I walked with the old man, and this demonstration of friendship was repeated several times; it was concluded by three hard slaps, which were given me on the breast and back at the same time. He then bared his bosom for me to return the compliment, which being done, he seemed highly pleased. The language of these people, according to our notions, scarcely deserves to be called articulate. Captain Cook has compared it to a man clearing his throat, but certainly no European ever cleared his throat with so many hoarse, guttural, and clicking sounds.

They are excellent mimics: as often as we coughed or yawned, or made any odd motion, they immediately imitated us. Some of our party began to squint and look awry; but one of the young Fuegians (whose whole face was painted black, excepting a white band across his eyes) succeeded in making far more hideous grimaces. They could repeat with perfect correctness each word in any sentence we addressed them, and they remembered such words for some time. Yet we Europeans all know how difficult it is to distinguish apart the sounds in a foreign language. Which of us, for instance, could follow an American Indian through a sentence of more than three words? All savages appear to possess, to an uncommon degree, this power of mimicry. I was told, almost in the same words, of the same ludicrous habit among the Caffres: the Australians, likewise, have long been notorious for being able to imitate and describe the gait of any man, so that he may be recognised. How can this faculty be explained? is it a consequence of the more practised habits of perception and keener senses, common to all men in a savage state, as compared with those long civilized?

When a song was struck up by our party, I thought the Fuegians would have fallen down with astonishment. With equal surprise they viewed our dancing; but one of the young men, when asked, had no objection to a little waltzing. Little accustomed to Europeans as they appeared to be, yet they knew and dreaded our fire-arms; nothing would tempt them to take a gun in their hands. They begged for knives, calling them by the Spanish word 'cuchilla'. They explained also what they wanted, by acting as if they had a piece of blubber in their mouth, and then pretending to cut instead of tear it.

I have not as yet noticed the Fuegians whom we had on board. During the former voyage of the *Adventure* and *Beagle* in 1826 to 1830, Captain Fitz-Roy seized on a party of natives, as hostages for the loss of a boat, which had been stolen, to the great jeopardy of a party employed on the survey; and some of these natives, as well as a child whom he bought for a pearl-button, he took with him to England, determining to educate them and instruct them in religion at his own expense. To settle these natives in their own country, was one chief inducement to Captain Fitz-Roy to undertake our present voyage; and before the Admiralty had resolved to send out this expedition, Captain Fitz-Roy had generously chartered a vessel, and would himself have taken them back. The natives were accompanied by a missionary, R. Matthews; of whom and of the natives, Captain Fitz-Roy has published a full and excellent account. Two men, one of whom died in England of the small-pox, a boy and a little girl, were originally taken; and we had now on board, York Minster, Jemmy Button (whose name expresses his purchase-money), and Fuegia Basket. York Minster was a full-grown, short, thick, powerful man: his disposition was reserved, taciturn, morose, and when excited violently passionate; his affections were very strong towards a few friends on board; his intellect good. Jemmy Button was a universal favourite, but likewise passionate; the expression of his face at once showed his nice disposition. He was merry and often laughed, and was remarkably sympathetic with any one in pain: when the water was rough, I was often a little sea-sick, and he used to come to me and say in a plaintive voice, 'Poor, poor fellow!' but the notion, after his aquatic life, of a man being sea-sick, was too ludicrous, and he was generally obliged to turn on one side to hide a smile or laugh, and then he would repeat his 'Poor, poor fellow!' He was of a patriotic disposition; and he liked to praise his own tribe and country, in which he truly said there were 'plenty of trees', and he abused all the other tribes: he stoutly declared that there was no Devil in his land. Jemmy was short, thick, and fat, but vain of his personal appearance; he used to wear gloves, his hair was neatly cut, and he was distressed if his well-polished shoes were dirtied. He was fond of admiring himself in a looking-glass; and a merry-faced little Indian boy from the Dio Negro, whom we had for some months on board, soon perceived this, and used to mock him:

Jemmy, who was always rather jealous of the attention paid to this little boy, did not at all like this, and used to say, with rather a contemptuous twist of his head, 'Too much skylark.' It seems yet wonderful to me, when I think over all his many good qualities, that he should have been of the same race, and doubtless partaken of the same character, with the miserable, degraded savages whom we first met here. Lastly, Fuegia Basket was a nice, modest, reserved young girl, with a rather pleasing but sometimes sullen expression, and very quick in learning anything, especially languages. This she showed in picking up some Portuguese and Spanish, when left on shore for only a short time at Rio de Janeiro and Monte Video, and in her knowledge of England. York Minster was very jealous of any attention paid to her; for it was clear he determined to marry her as soon as they were settled on shore.

Although all three could both speak and understand a good deal of English, it was singularly difficult to obtain much information from them, concerning the habits of their countrymen: this was partly owing to their apparent difficulty in understanding the simplest alternative. Every one accustomed to very young children, knows how seldom one can get an answer even to so simple a question as whether a thing is black *or* white; the idea of black or white seems alternately to fill their minds. So it was with these Fuegians, and hence it was generally impossible to find out, by cross-questioning, whether one had rightly understood anything which they had asserted. Their sight was remarkably acute: it is well known that sailors, from long practice, can make out a distant object much better than a landsman; but both York and Jemmy were much superior to any sailor on board: several times they have declared what some distant object has been, and though doubted by every one, they have proved right, when it has been examined through a telescope. They were quite conscious of this power; and Jemmy, when he had any little quarrel with the officer on watch, would say, 'Me see ship, me no tell.'

It was interesting to watch the conduct of the savages, when we landed, towards Jemmy Button: they immediately perceived the difference between him and ourselves, and held much conversation one with another on the subject. The old man addressed a long harangue to Jemmy, which it seems was to invite him to stay with them. But Jemmy understood very little of their language, and was, moreover, thoroughly ashamed of his countrymen. When York Minster afterwards came on shore, they noticed him in the same way, and told him he ought to shave; yet he had not twenty dwarf hairs on his face, whilst we all wore our untrimmed beards. They examined the colour of his skin, and compared it with ours. One of our arms being bared, they expressed the liveliest surprise and admiration at its whiteness, just in the same way in which I have seen the orang-outang do at the Zoological Gardens. We thought that they mistook two or three of the officers, who were rather shorter and fairer, though adorned with large beards, for the ladies of our party. The tallest among the Fuegians was evidently much pleased at his height being noticed. When placed back to back with the tallest of the boat's crew, he tried his best to edge on higher ground, and to stand on tiptoe. He opened his mouth to show his teeth, and turned his face for a side view; and all this was done with such alacrity, that I dare say he thought himself the handsomest man in Tierra del Fuego. After our first feeling of grave astonishment was over, nothing could be more ludicrous than the odd mixture of surprise and imitation which these savages every moment exhibited.

The next day I attempted to penetrate some way into the country. Tierra del Fuego may be described as a mountainous land, partly submerged in the sea, so that deep inlets and bays occupy the place where valleys should exist. The mountain sides, except on the exposed western coast, are covered from the water's edge upwards by one great forest. The trees reach to an elevation of between 1000 and 1500 feet, and are succeeded by a band of peat, with minute alpine plants; and this again is succeeded by the line of perpetual snow, which, according to Captain King, in the Strait of Magellan descends to between 3000 and 4000 feet. To find an acre of level land in any part of the country is most rare. I recollect only one little flat piece near Port Famine, and another of rather larger extent near Goeree Road. In both places, and everywhere else, the surface is covered by a thick bed of swampy peat. Even within the forest, the ground is concealed by a mass of slowly putrefying vegetable matter, which, from being soaked with water, yields to the foot.

Finding it nearly hopeless to push my way through the wood, I followed the course of a mountain torrent. At first, from the waterfalls and number of dead trees, I could hardly crawl along; but the bed of the stream soon became a little more open, from the floods having swept the sides. I continued slowly to advance for an hour along the broken and rocky banks, and was amply repaid by the grandeur of the scene. The gloomy depth of the ravine well accorded with the universal signs of violence. On every side were lying irregular masses of rock and torn-up trees; other trees, though still erect, were decayed to the heart and ready to fall. The entangled mass of the thriving and the fallen reminded me of the forests within the tropics—yet there was a difference: for in these still solitudes, Death, instead of Life, seemed the predominant spirit. I followed the watercourse till I came to a spot, where a great slip had cleared a straight space down the mountain side. By this road I ascended to a considerable elevation, and obtained a good view of the surrounding woods. The trees all belong to one kind, the Fagus betuloides; for the number of the other species of Fagus and of the Winter's Bark, is quite inconsiderable. This beech keeps its leaves throughout the year; but its foliage is of a peculiar brownish-green colour, with a tinge of yellow. As the whole landscape is thus coloured, it has a sombre, dull appearance; nor is it often enlivened by the rays of the sun.

★ ★ ★ ★

The Fuegian wigwam resembles, in size and dimensions, a haycock. It merely consists of a few broken branches stuck in the ground, and very imperfectly thatched on one side with a few tufts of grass and rushes. The whole cannot be the work of an hour, and it is only used for a few days. At Goeree Roads I saw a place where one of these naked men had slept, which absolutely offered no more cover than the form of a hare. The man was evidently living by himself, and York Minster said he was 'very bad man', and that probably he had stolen something. On the west coast, however, the wigwams are rather better, for they are covered with seal-skins. We were detained here several days by the bad weather. The climate is certainly wretched: the summer solstice was now passed, yet every day snow fell on the hills, and in the valleys there was rain, accompanied by sleet. The thermometer generally stood about 45°, but in the night fell to 38° or 40°. From the damp and boisterous state of the atmosphere, not cheered by a gleam of sunshine, one fancied the climate even worse than it really was.

While going one day on shore near Wollaston Island, we pulled alongside a canoe with six Fuegians. These were the most abject and miserable creatures I anywhere beheld. On the east coast the natives, as we have seen, have guanaco cloaks, and on the west, they possess seal-skins. Amongst these central tribes the men generally have an otter-skin, or some small scrap about as large as a pocket-handkerchief, which is barely sufficient to cover their backs as low down as their loins. It is laced across the breast by strings, and according as the wind blows, it is shifted from side to side. But these Fuegians in the canoe were quite naked, and even one full-grown woman was absolutely so. It was raining heavily, and the fresh water, together with the spray, trickled down her body. In another harbour not far distant, a woman, who was suckling a recently-born child, came one day alongside the vessel, and remained there out of mere curiosity, whilst the sleet fell and thawed on her naked bosom, and on the skin of her naked baby! These poor wretches were stunted in their growth, their hideous faces bedaubed with white paint, their skins filthy and greasy, their hair entangled, their voices discordant, and their gestures violent. Viewing such men, one can hardly make oneself believe that they are fellow-creatures, and inhabitants of the same world. It is a common subject of conjecture what pleasure in life some of the lower animals can enjoy: how much more reasonably the same question may be asked with respect to these barbarians! At night, five or six human beings, naked and scarcely protected from the wind and rain of this tempestuous climate, sleep on the wet ground coiled up like animals. Whenever it is low water, winter or summer, night or day, they must rise to pick shell-fish from the rocks; and the women either dive to collect sea-eggs, or sit patiently in their canoes, and with a baited hair-line without any hook, jerk out little fish. If a seal is killed, or the floating carcass of a putrid whale discovered, it is a feast; and such miserable food is assisted by a few tasteless berries and fungi.

They often suffer from famine: I heard Mr. Low, a sealing-master intimately acquainted with the natives of this country, give a curious account of the state of a party of one hundred and fifty natives on the west coast, who were very thin and in great distress. A succession of gales prevented the women from getting shell-fish on the rocks, and they could not go out in their canoes to catch seal. A small party of these men one morning set out, and the other Indians explained to him, that they were going a four days' journey for food: on their return, Low went to meet them, and he found them excessively tired, each man carrying a great square piece of putrid whales-blubber with a hole in the middle, through which they put their heads, like the Gauchos do through their ponchos or cloaks. As soon as the blubber was brought into a wigwam, an old man cut off thin slices, and muttering over them, broiled them for a minute, and distributed them to the famished party, who during this time preserved a profound silence. Mr. Low believes that whenever a whale is cast on shore, the natives bury large pieces of it in the sand, as a resource in time of famine; and a native boy, whom he had on board, once found a stock thus buried. The different tribes when at war are cannibals. From the concurrent, but quite independent evidence of the boy taken by Mr. Low, and of Jemmy Button, it is certainly true, that when pressed in winter by hunger, they kill and devour their old women before they kill their dogs: the boy, being asked by Mr. Low why they did this, answered, 'Doggies catch otters, old women no.' This boy described the manner in which they are killed by being held over smoke and thus choked; he imitated their screams as a joke, and described the parts of their bodies which are considered best to eat. Horrid as such a death by the hands of their friends and relatives must be, the fears of the old women, when hunger begins to press, are more painful to think of; we were told that they then often run away into the mountains, but that they are pursued by the men and brought back to the slaughter-house at their own fire-sides!

Captain Fitz-Roy could never ascertain that the Fuegians have any distinct belief in a future life. They sometimes bury their dead in caves, and sometimes in the mountain forests; we do not know what ceremonies they perform. Jemmy Button would not eat land-birds, because 'eat dead men': they are unwilling even to mention their dead friends. We have no reason to believe that they perform any sort of religious worship; though perhaps the muttering of the old man before he distributed the putrid blubber to his famished party, may be of this nature. Each family or tribe has a wizard or conjuring doctor, whose office we could never clearly ascertain. Jemmy believed in dreams, though not, as I have said, in the devil: I do not think that our Fuegians were much more superstitious than some of the sailors; for an old quarter-master firmly believed that the successive heavy gales, which we encountered off Cape Horn, were caused by our having the Fuegians on board. The nearest approach to a religious feeling which I heard of, was shown by York Minster, who, when Mr. Bynoe shot some very young ducklings as specimens, declared in the most solemn manner, 'Oh Mr. Bynoe, much rain, snow, blow much.' This was evidently a retributive punishment for wasting human food. In a wild and excited manner he also related, that his brother, one day whilst returning to pick up some dead birds which he had left on the coast, observed some feathers blown by the wind. His brother said (York imitating his manner), 'What that?' and crawling onwards, he peeped over the cliff, and saw 'wild man' picking his birds; he crawled a little nearer, and then hurled down a great stone and killed him. York declared for a long time afterwards storms raged, and much rain and snow fell. As far as we could make out, he seemed to consider the elements themselves as the avenging agents: it is evident in this case, how naturally, in a race a little more advanced in culture, the elements would become personified. What the 'bad wild men' were, has always appeared to me most mysterious: from what York said, when we found the place like the form of a hare, where a single man had slept the night before, I should have thought that they were thieves who had been driven from their tribes; but other obscure speeches made me doubt this; I have sometimes imagined that the most probable explanation was that they were insane.

The different tribes have no government or chief; yet each is surrounded by other hostile tribes, speaking different dialects, and separated from each other only by a deserted border or neutral territory: the cause of their warfare appears to be the means of subsistence. Their country is a broken mass of wild rocks, lofty hills, and useless forests: and these are viewed through mists and endless storms. The habitable land is reduced to the stones on the beach; in search of food they are compelled unceasingly to wander from spot to spot, and so steep is the coast, that they can only move about in their wretched canoes. They cannot know the feeling of having a home, and still less that of domestic affection; for the husband is to the wife a brutal master to a laborious slave. Was a more horrid deed ever perpetrated, than that witnessed on the west coast by Byron, who saw a wretched mother pick up her bleeding dying infant-boy, whom her husband had mercilessly dashed on the stones for dropping a basket of sea-eggs! How little can the higher powers of the mind be brought into play: what is there for imagination to picture, for reason to compare, for judgment to decide upon? to knock a limpet from the rock does not require even cunning, that lowest power of the mind. Their skill in some respects may be compared to the instinct of animals; for it is not improved by experience: the canoe, their most ingenious work, poor as it is, has remained the same, as we know from Drake, for the last two hundred and fifty years.

Whilst beholding these savages, one asks, whence have they come? What could have tempted, or what change compelled a tribe of men, to leave the fine regions of the north, to travel down the Cordillera or backbone of America, to invent and build canoes, which are not used by the tribes of Chile, Peru, and Brazil, and then to enter on one of the most inhospitable countries within the limits of the globe? Although such reflections must at first seize on the mind, yet we may feel sure that they are partly erroneous. There is no reason to believe that the Fuegians decrease in number; therefore we must suppose that they enjoy a sufficient share of happiness, of whatever kind it may be, to render life worth having. Nature by making habit omnipotent, and its effects hereditary, has fitted the Fuegian to the climate and the productions of his miserable country.

* * * *

January 15th, 1833.—The *Beagle* anchored in Goeree Roads. Captain Fitz-Roy having resolved to settle the Fuegians, according to their wishes, in Ponsonby Sound, four boats were equipped to carry them there through the Beagle Channel. This channel, which was discovered by Captain Fitz-Roy during the last voyage, is a most remarkable feature in the geography of this, or indeed of any other country: it may be compared to the valley of Lochness in Scotland, with its chain of lakes and friths,

It is about one hundred and twenty miles long, with an average breadth, not subject to any very great variation, of about two miles; and is throughout the great part so perfectly straight, that the view, bounded on each side by a line of mountains, gradually becomes indistinct in the long distance. It crosses the southern part of Tierra del Fuego in an east and west line, and in the middle is joined at right angles on the south side by an irregular channel, which has been called Ponsonby Sound. This is the residence of Jemmy Button's tribe and family.

19th.—Three whale-boats and the yawl, with a party of twenty-eight, started under the command of Captain Fitz-Roy. In the afternoon we entered the eastern mouth of the channel, and shortly afterwards found a snug little cove concealed by some surrounding islets. Here we pitched our tents and lighted our fires. Nothing could look more comfortable than this scene. The glassy water of the little harbour, with the branches of the trees hanging over the rocky beach, the boats at anchor, the tents supported by the crossed oars, and the smoke curling up the wooded valley, formed a picture of quiet retirement. The next day (20th) we smoothly glided onwards in our little fleet, and came to a more inhabited district. Few if any of these natives could ever have seen a white man; certainly nothing could exceed their astonishment at the apparition of the four boats. Fires were lighted on every point (hence the name of Tierra del Fuego, or the land of fire), both to attract our attention and to spread far and wide the news. Some of the men ran for miles along the shore. I shall never forget how wild and savage one group appeared: suddenly four or five men came to the edge of an overhanging cliff; they were absolutely naked, and their long hair streamed about their faces; they held rugged staffs in their hands, and, springing from the ground, they waved their arms round their heads, and sent forth the most hideous yells.

At dinner-time we landed among a party of Fuegians. At first they were not inclined to be friendly; for until the Captain pulled in ahead of the other boats, they kept their slings in their hands. We soon, however, delighted them by trifling presents, such as tying red tape round their heads. They liked our biscuit: but one of the savages touched with his finger some of the meat preserved in tin cases which I was eating, and feeling it soft and cold, showed as much disgust at it, as I should have done at putrid blubber. Jemmy was thoroughly ashamed of his countrymen, and declared his own tribe were quite different, in which he was woefully mistaken. It was as easy to please as it was difficult to satisfy these savages. Young and old, men and children, never ceased repeating the word 'yammerschooner', which means 'give me'. After pointing to almost every object, one after the other, even to the buttons on our coats, and saying their favourite word in as many intonations as possible, they would then use it in a neuter sense, and vacantly repeat 'yammerschooner'. After yammerschoonering for any article very eagerly, they would by a simple artifice point to their young women or little children, as much as to say, 'If you will not give it me, surely you will to such as these.'

At night we endeavoured in vain to find an uninhabited cove; and at last were obliged to bivouac not far from a party of natives. They were very inoffensive as long as they were few in numbers, but in the morning (21st) being joined by others they showed symptoms of hostility, and we thought that we should have come to a skirmish. An European labours under great disadvantages when treating with savages like these, who have not the least idea of the power of fire-arms. In the very act of levelling his musket he appears to the savage far inferior to a man armed with a bow and arrow, a spear, or even a sling. Nor is it easy to teach them our superiority except by striking a fatal blow. Like wild beasts, they do not appear to compare numbers; for each individual, if attacked, instead of retiring, will endeavour to dash your brains out with a stone, as certainly as a tiger under similar circumstances would tear you. Captain Fitz-Roy on one occasion being very anxious, from good reasons, to frighten away a small party, first flourished a cutlass near them, at which they only laughed; he then twice fired his pistol close to a native. The man both times looked astounded, and carefully but quickly rubbed his head; he then stared awhile, and gabbled to his companions, but he never seemed to think of running away. We can hardly put ourselves in the position of these savages, and understand their actions. In the case of this Fuegian, the possibility of such a sound as the report of a gun close to his ear could never have entered his mind. He perhaps literally did not for a second know whether it was a sound or a blow, and therefore very naturally rubbed his head. In a similar manner, when a savage sees a mark struck by a bullet, it may be some time before he is able at all to understand how it is effected; for the fact of a body being invisible from its velocity would perhaps be to him an idea totally inconceivable. Moreover, the extreme force of a bullet, that penetrates a hard substance without tearing it, may convince the savage that it has no force at all. Certainly I believe that many savages of the lowest grade, such as these of Tierra del Fuego, have seen objects struck, and even small animals killed by the musket, without being in the least aware how deadly an instrument it is.

22nd.—After having passed an unmolested night, in what would appear to be neutral territory between Jemmy's tribe and the people whom we saw yesterday, we sailed pleasantly along. I do not know anything which shows more clearly the hostile state of the different tribes, than these wide border or neutral tracts. Although Jemmy Button well knew the force of our party, he was, at first, unwilling to land amidst the hostile tribe nearest to his own. He often told us how the savage Oens men 'when the leaf red', crossed the mountains from the eastern coast of Tierra del Fuego, and made inroads on the natives of this part of the country. It was most curious to watch him when thus talking, and see his eyes gleaming and his whole face assume a new and wild expression. As we proceeded along the Beagle Channel, the scenery assumed a peculiar and very magnificent character; but the effect was much lessened from the lowness of the point of view in a boat, and from looking along the valley, and thus losing all the beauty of a succession of ridges. The mountains were here about three thousand feet high, and terminated in sharp and jagged points. They rose in one unbroken sweep from the water's edge, and were covered to the height of fourteen or fifteen hundred feet by the dusky-coloured forest. It was most curious to observe, as far as the eye could range, how level and truly horizontal the line on the mountain side was, at which trees ceased to grow: it precisely resembled the high-water mark of drift-weed on a sea-beach.

At night we slept close to the junction of Ponsonby Sound with the Beagle Channel. A small family of Fuegians, who were living in the cove, were quiet and inoffensive, and soon joined our party round a blazing fire. We were well clothed, and though sitting close to the fire were far from too warm; yet these naked savages, though further off, were observed, to our great surprise, to be streaming with perspiration at undergoing such a roasting. They seemed, however, very well pleased, and all joined in the chorus of the seamen's songs: but the manner in which they were invariably a little behindhand was quite ludicrous.

During the night the news had spread, and early in the morning (23rd) a fresh party arrived, belonging to the Tekenika, or Jemmy's tribe. Several of them had run so fast that their noses were bleeding, and their mouths frothed from the rapidity with which they talked; and with their naked bodies all bedaubed with black, white, and red, they looked like so many demoniacs who had been fighting. We then proceeded (accompanied by twelve canoes, each holding four or five people) down Ponsonby Sound to the spot where poor Jemmy expected to find his mother and relatives. He had already heard that his father was dead; but as he had had a 'dream in his head' to that effect, he did not seem to care much about it, and repeatedly comforted himself with the very natural reflection—'Me no help it.' He was not able to learn any particulars regarding his father's death, as his relations would not speak about it.

Jemmy was now in a district well known to him, and guided the boats to a quiet pretty cove named Woollya, surrounded by islets, every one of which and every point had its proper native name. We found here a family of Jemmy's tribe, but not his relations: we made friends with them; and in the evening they sent a canoe to inform Jemmy's mother and brothers. The cove was bordered by some acres of good sloping land, not covered (as elsewhere) either by peat or by forest-trees. Captain Fitz-Roy originally intended, as before stated, to have taken York Minster and Fuegia to their own tribe on the west coast; but as they expressed a wish to remain here, and as the spot was singularly favourable, Captain Fitz-Roy determined to settle here the whole party, including Matthews, the missionary. Five days were spent in building for them three large wigwams, in landing their goods, in digging two gardens, and sowing seeds.

The next morning after our arrival (the 24th) the Fuegians began to pour in, and Jemmy's mother and brothers arrived. Jemmy recognized the stentorian voice of one of his brothers at a prodigious distance. The meeting was less interesting than that between a horse, turned out into a field, when he joins an old companion. There was no demonstration of affection; they simply stared for a short time at each other; and the mother immediately went to look after her canoe. We heard, however, through York, that the mother had been inconsolable for the loss of Jemmy, and had searched everywhere for him, thinking that he might have been left after having been taken in the boat. The women took much notice of and were very kind to Fuegia. We had already perceived that Jemmy had almost forgotten his own language. I should think there was scarcely another human being with so small a stock of language, for his English was very imperfect. It was laughable, but almost pitiable, to hear him speak to his wild brother in English, and then ask him in Spanish ('no sabe?') whether he did not understand him.

Everything went on peaceably during the three next days, whilst the gardens were digging and wigwams building. We estimated the number of natives at about one hundred and twenty. The women worked hard, whilst the men lounged about all day long, watching us. They asked for everything they saw, and stole what they could. They were delighted at our dancing and singing, and were particularly interested at seeing us wash in a neighbouring brook; they did not pay much attention to anything else, not even to our boats. Of all the things which York saw, during his absence from his country, nothing seems more to have astonished him than an ostrich, near Maldonado: breathless with astonishment he came running to Mr. Bynoe, with whom he was out walking—'Oh, Mr. Bynoe, oh, bird all same horse!' Much as our white skins surprised the natives, by Mr. Low's account a negro-cook to a sealing vessel did so more effectually; and the poor fellow was so mobbed and shouted at that he would never go on shore again. Everything went on so quietly, that some of the officers and myself took long walks in the surrounding hills and woods. Suddenly, however, on the 27th, every woman and child disappeared. We were all uneasy at this, as neither York nor Jemmy could make out the cause. It was thought by some that they had been frightened by our cleaning and firing off our muskets on the previous evening: by others, that it was owing to offence taken by an old savage, who, when told to keep further off, had coolly spit in the sentry's face, and had then, by gestures acted over a sleeping Fuegian, plainly showed, as it was said, that he should like to cut up and eat our man. Captain Fitz-Roy, to avoid the chance of an encounter, which would have been fatal to so many of the Fuegians, thought it advisable for us to sleep at a cove a few miles distant. Matthews, with his usual quiet fortitude (remarkable in a man apparently possessing little energy of character), determined to stay with the Fuegians, who evinced no alarm for themselves; and so we left them to pass their first awful night.

On our return in the morning (28th) we were delighted to find all quiet, and the men employed in their canoes spearing fish. Captain Fitz-Roy determined to send the yawl and one whale-boat back to the ship; and to proceed with the two other boats, one under his own command (in which he most kindly allowed me to accompany him), and one under Mr. Hammond, to survey the western parts of the Beagle Channel, and afterwards to return and visit the settlement. The day to our astonishment was overpoweringly hot, so that our skins were scorched: with this beautiful weather, the view in the middle of the Beagle Channel was very remarkable. Looking towards either hand, no object intercepted the vanishing points of this long canal between the mountains. The circumstance of its being an arm of the sea was rendered very evident by several huge whales spouting in different directions. On one occasion I saw two of these monsters, probably male and female, slowly swimming one after the other within less than a stone's throw of the shore, over which the beech-tree extended its branches.

We sailed on till it was dark, and then pitched our tents in a quiet creek. The greatest luxury was to find for our beds a beach of pebbles, for they were dry and yielded to the body. Peaty soil is damp; rock is uneven and hard; sand gets into one's meat, when cooked and eaten boat-fashion; but when lying in our blanket-bags, on a good bed of smooth pebbles, we passed most comfortable nights.

It was my watch till one o'clock. There is something very solemn in these scenes. At no time does the consciousness in what a remote corner of the world you are then standing, come so strongly before the mind. Everything tends to this effect; the stillness of the night is interrupted only by the heavy breathing of the seamen beneath the tents, and sometimes by the cry of a night-bird. The occasional barking of a dog, heard in the distance, reminds one that it is the land of the savage.

* * * *

February 6*th*.—We arrived at Woollya. Matthews gave so bad an account of the conduct of the Fuegians, that Captain Fitz-Roy determined to take him back to the *Beagle*; and ultimately he was left at New Zealand, where his brother was a missionary. From the time of our leaving, a regular system of plunder commenced; fresh parties of the natives kept arriving: York and Jemmy lost many things, and Matthews almost everything which had not been concealed underground. Every article seemed to have been torn up and divided by the natives. Matthews described the watch he was obliged always to keep as most harassing; night and day he was surrounded by the natives, who tried to tire him out by making an incessant noise close to his head. One day an old man, whom Matthews asked to leave his wigwam, immediately returned with a large stone in his hand: another day a whole party came armed with stones and stakes, and some of the younger men and Jemmy's brother were crying: Matthews met them with presents. Another party showed by signs that they wished to strip him naked and pluck all the hairs out of his face and body. I think we arrived just in time to save his life. Jemmy's relatives had been so vain and foolish, that they had showed to strangers their plunder, and their manner of obtaining it. It was quite melancholy leaving the three Fuegians with their savage countrymen; but it was a great comfort that they had no personal fears. York, being a powerful resolute man, was pretty sure to get on well, together with his wife Fuegia. Poor Jemmy looked rather disconsolate, and would then, I have little doubt, have been glad to have returned with us. His own brother had stolen many things from him; and as he remarked, 'what fashion call that:' he abused his countrymen, 'all bad men, no sabe (know) nothing,' and, though I never heard him swear before, 'damned fools'. Our three Fuegians, though they had been only three years with civilized men, would, I am sure, have been glad to have retained their new habits; but this was obviously impossible. I fear it is more than doubtful, whether their visit will have been of any use to them.

In the evening, with Matthews on board, we made sail back to the ship, not by the Beagle Channel, but by the southern coast. The boats were heavily laden and the sea rough, and we had a dangerous passage. By the evening of the 7th we were on board the *Beagle* after an absence of twenty days, during which time we had gone three hundred miles in the open boats. On the 11th, Captain Fitz-Roy paid a visit by himself to the Fuegians and found them going on well; and that they had lost very few more things.

On the last day of February in the succeeding year (1834), the *Beagle* anchored in a beautiful little cove at the eastern entrance of the Beagle Channel. Captain Fitz-Roy determined on the bold, and as it proved successful, attempt to beat against the westerly winds by the same route, which we had followed in the boats to the settlement at Woollya. We did not see many natives until we were near Ponsonby Sound, where we were followed by ten or twelve canoes. The natives did not at all understand the reason of our tacking, and, instead of meeting us at each tack, vainly strove to follow us in our zig-zag course. I was amused at finding what a difference the circumstance of being quite superior in force made, in the interest of beholding these savages. While in the boats I got to hate the very sound of their voices, so much trouble did they give us. The first and last word was 'yammerschooner'. When, entering some quiet little cove, we have looked round and thought to pass a quiet night, the odious word 'yammerschooner' has shrilly sounded from some gloomy nook, and then the little signal-smoke has curled up to spread the news far and wide. On leaving some place we have said to each other, 'Thank Heaven, we have at last fairly left these wretches!' when one more faint halloo from an all-powerful voice, heard at a prodigious distance, would reach our ears, and clearly could we distinguish—'yammerschooner'. But now, the more Fuegians the merrier; and very merry work it was. Both parties laughing, wondering, gaping at each other; we pitying them, for giving us good fish and crabs for rags, &c.; they grasping at the chance of finding people so foolish as to exchange such splendid ornaments for a good supper. It was most amusing to see the undisguised smile of satisfaction with which one young woman with her face painted black, tied several bits of scarlet cloth round her head with rushes. Her husband, who enjoyed the very universal privilege in this country of possessing two wives, evidently became jealous of all the attention paid to his young wife; and, after a consultation with his naked beauties, was paddled away by them.

Some of the Fuegians plainly showed that they had a fair notion of barter. I gave one man a large nail (a most valuable present) without making any signs for a return; but he immediately picked out two fish, and handed them up on the point of his spear. If any present was designed for one canoe, and it fell near another, it was invariably given to the right owner. The Fuegian boy, whom Mr. Low had on board, showed, by going into the most violent passion, that he quite understood the reproach of being called a liar, which in truth he was. We were this time, as on all former occasions, much surprised at the little notice, or rather none whatever, which was taken of many things, the use of which must have been evident to the natives. Simple circumstances—such as the beauty of scarlet cloth or blue beads, the absence of women, our care in washing ourselves,—excited their admiration far more than any grand or complicated object, such as our ship. Bougainville has well remarked concerning these people, that they treat the 'chef-d'œuvres de l'industrie humaine, comme ils traitent les loix de la nature et ses phénomènes'.

On the 5th of March, we anchored in the cove at Woollya, but we saw not a soul there. We were alarmed at this, for the natives in Ponsonby Sound showed by gestures, that there had been fighting; and we afterwards heard that the dreaded Oens men had made a descent. Soon a canoe, with a little flag flying, was seen approaching, with one of the men in it washing the paint off his face. This man was poor Jemmy,—now a thin haggard savage, with long disordered hair, and naked, except a bit of a blanket round his waist. We did not recognize him till he was close to us; for he was ashamed of himself, and turned his back to the ship. We had left him plump, fat, clean, and well dressed;—I never saw so complete and grievous a change. As soon however as he was clothed, and the first flurry was over, things wore a good appearance. He dined with Captain Fitz-Roy, and ate his dinner as tidily as formerly. He told us he had 'too much' (meaning enough) to eat, that he was not cold, that his relations were very good people, and that he did not wish to go back to England: in the evening we found out the cause of this great change in Jemmy's feelings, in the arrival of his young and nice-looking wife. With his usual good feeling, he brought two beautiful otter-skins for two of his best friends, and some spear-heads and arrows made with his own hands for the Captain. He said he had built a canoe for himself, and he boasted that he could talk a little of his own language! But it is a most singular fact, that he appears to have taught all his tribe some English: an old man spontaneously announced 'Jemmy Button's wife'. Jemmy had lost all his property. He told us that York Minster had built a large canoe, and with his wife Fuegia, had several months since gone to his own country, and had taken farewell by an act of consummate villainy; he persuaded Jemmy and his mother to come with him, and then on the way deserted them by night, stealing every article of their property.

Jemmy went to sleep on shore, and in the morning returned, and remained on board till the ship got under weigh, which frightened his wife, who continued crying violently till he got into his canoe. He returned loaded with valuable property. Every soul on board was heartily sorry to shake hands with him for the last time. I do not now doubt that he will be as happy as, perhaps happier than, if he had never left his own country. Every one must sincerely hope that Captain Fitz-Roy's noble hope may be fulfilled, of being rewarded for the many generous sacrifices which he made for these Fuegians, by some shipwrecked sailor being protected by the descendants of Jemmy Button and his tribe! When Jemmy reached the shore, he lighted a signal fire, and the smoke curled up, bidding us a last and long farewell, as the ship stood on her course into the open sea.

The perfect equality among the individuals composing the Fuegian tribes, must for a long time retard their civilization. As we see those animals, whose instinct compels them to live in society and obey a chief, are most capable of improvement, so is it with the races of mankind. Whether we look at it as a cause or a consequence, the more civilized always have the most artificial governments. For instance, the inhabitants of Otaheite, who, when first discovered, were governed by hereditary kings, had arrived at a far higher grade than another branch of the same people, the New Zealanders,—who, although benefited by being compelled to turn their attention to agriculture, were republicans in the most absolute sense. In Tierra del Fuego, until some chief shall arise with power sufficient to secure any acquired advantage, such as the domesticated animals, it seems scarcely possible that the political state of the country can be improved. At present, even a piece of cloth given to one is torn into shreds and distributed; and no one individual becomes richer than another. On the other hand, it is difficult to understand how a chief can arise till there is property of some sort by which he might manifest his superiority and increase his power.

I believe, in this extreme part of South America, man exists in a lower state of improvement than in any other part of the world. The South Sea Islanders of the two races inhabiting the Pacific, are comparatively civilized. The Esquimaux, in his subterranean hut, enjoys some of the comforts of life, and in his canoe, when fully equipped, manifests much skill. Some of the tribes of Southern Africa, prowling about in search of roots, and living concealed on the wild and arid plains, are sufficiently wretched. The Australian, in the simplicity of the arts of life, comes nearest the Fuegian: he can, however, boast of his boomerang, his spear and throwing-stick, his method of climbing trees, of tracking animals, and of hunting. Although the Australian may be superior in acquirements, it by no means follows that he is likewise superior in mental capacity: indeed, from what I saw of the Fuegians when on board, and from what I have read of the Australians, I should think the case was exactly the reverse.

CHAPTER 3

GALAPAGOS ARCHIPELAGO

[Chapter XVII of the *Beagle*.]

SEPTEMBER 15*th*.—This archipelago consists of ten principal islands, of which five exceed the others in size. They are situated under the Equator, and between five and six hundred miles westward of the coast of America. They are all formed of volcanic rocks; a few fragments of granite curiously glazed and altered by the heat, can hardly be considered as an exception. Some of the craters, surmounting the larger islands, are of immense size, and they rise to a height of between three and four thousand feet. Their flanks are studded by innumerable smaller orifices. I scarcely hesitate to affirm, that there must be in the whole archipelago at least two thousand craters. These consist either of lava and scoriæ, or of finely-stratified, sandstone-like tuff. Most of the latter are beautifully symmetrical; they owe their origin to eruptions of volcanic mud without any lava: it is a remarkable circumstance that every one of the twenty-eight tuff-craters which were examined, had their southern sides either much lower than the other sides, or quite broken down and removed. As all these craters have apparently been formed when standing in the sea, and as the waves from the trade-wind and the swell from the open Pacific here unite their forces on the southern coasts of all the islands, this singular uniformity in the broken state of the craters, composed of the soft and yielding tuff, is easily explained.

Considering that these islands are placed directly under the Equator, the climate is far from being excessively hot; this seems chiefly caused by the singularly low temperature of the surrounding water, brought here by the great southern Polar current. Excepting during one short season, very little rain falls, and even then it is irregular; but the clouds generally hang low. Hence, whilst the lower parts of the island are very sterile, the upper parts, at a height of a thousand feet and upwards, possess a damp climate and a tolerably luxuriant vegetation. This is especially the case on the windward sides of the islands, which first receive and condense the moisture from the atmosphere.

In the morning (17th) we landed on Chatham Island, which, like the others, rises with a tame and rounded outline, broken here and there by

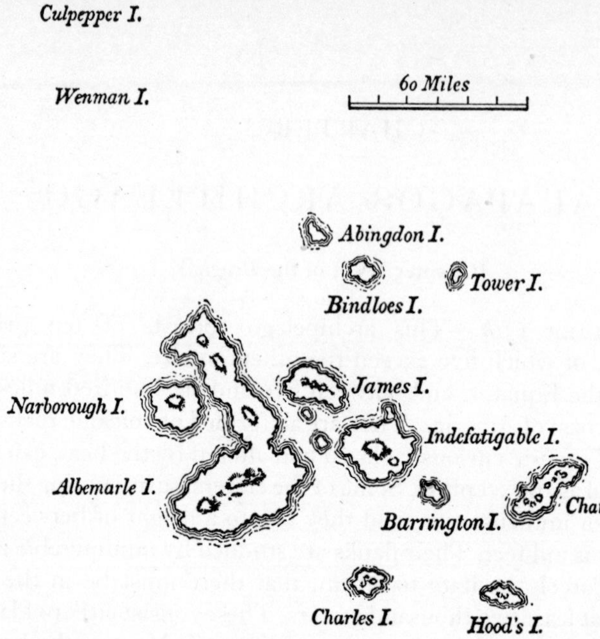

scattered hillocks, the remains of former craters. Nothing could be less inviting than the first appearance. A broken field of black basaltic lava, thrown into the most rugged waves, and crossed by great fissures, is everywhere covered by stunted, sunburnt brushwood, which shows little signs of life. The dry and parched surface, being heated by the noonday sun, gave to the air a close and sultry feeling, like that from a stove: we fancied even that the bushes smelt unpleasantly. Although I diligently tried to collect as many plants as possible, I succeeded in getting very few; and such wretched-looking little weeds would have better become an arctic than an equatorial Flora. The brushwood appears, from a short distance, as leafless as our trees during winter; and it was some time before I discovered that not only almost every plant was now in full leaf, but that the greater number were in flower. The commonest bush is one of the Euphorbiaceæ: an acacia and a great odd-looking cactus are the only trees which afford any shade. After the season of heavy rains, the islands are said to appear for a short time partially green. The volcanic island of Fernando Noronha, placed in many respects under nearly similar conditions, is the only other country where I have seen a vegetation at all like this of the Galapagos Islands.

The *Beagle* sailed round Chatham Island, and anchored in several bays.

One night I slept on shore on a part of the island, where black truncated cones were extraordinarily numerous: from one small eminence I counted sixty of them, all surmounted by craters more or less perfect. The greater number consisted merely of a ring of red scoriæ or slags, cemented together: and their height above the plane of lava was not more than from fifty to a hundred feet: none had been very lately active. The entire surface of this part of the island seems to have been permeated, like a sieve, by the subterranean vapours: here and there the lava, whilst soft, has been blown into great bubbles; and in other parts, the tops of caverns similarly formed have fallen in, leaving circular pits with steep sides. From the regular form of the many craters, they gave to the country an artificial appearance, which vividly reminded me of those parts of Staffordshire, where the great iron-foundries are most numerous. The day was glowing hot, and the scrambling over the rough surface and through the intricate thickets, was very fatiguing; but I was well repaid by the strange Cyclopean scene. As I was walking along I met two large tortoises, each of which must have weighed at least two hundred pounds: one was eating a piece of cactus, and as I approached, it stared at me and slowly stalked away; the other gave a deep hiss, and drew in its head. These huge reptiles, surrounded by the black lava, the leafless shrubs, and large cacti, seemed to my fancy like some antediluvian animals. The few dull-coloured birds cared no more for me, than they did for the great tortoises.

23rd.—The *Beagle* proceeded to Charles Island. This archipelago has long been frequented, first by the Bucaniers, and latterly by whalers, but it is only within the last six years, that a small colony has been established here. The inhabitants are between two and three hundred in number: they are nearly all people of colour, who have been banished for political crimes from the Republic of the Equator, of which Quito is the capital. The settlement is placed about four and a half miles inland, and at a height probably of a thousand feet. In the first part of the road we passed through leafless thickets, as in Chatham Island. Higher up, the woods gradually became greener: and as soon as we crossed the ridge of the island, we were cooled by a fine southerly breeze, and our sight refreshed by a green and thriving vegetation. In this upper region coarse grasses and ferns abound; but there are no tree-ferns: I saw nowhere any member of the Palm family, which is the more singular, as 360 miles northward, Cocos Island takes its name from the number of cocoa-nuts. The houses are irregularly scattered over a flat space of ground, which is cultivated with sweet potatoes and bananas. It will not easily be imagined how pleasant the sight of black mud was to us, after having been so long accustomed to the parched soil of Peru and northern Chile. The inhabitants, although complaining of poverty, obtain, without much trouble, the means of subsistence. In the woods there are many wild pigs and goats; but the staple article of animal food is supplied by the tortoises. Their numbers have of course been greatly reduced in this island, but the people yet count on two days' hunting giving them food for the rest of the week. It is said that formerly single vessels have taken away as many as seven hundred, and that the ship's company of a frigate some years since brought down in one day two hundred tortoises to the beach.

September 29th.—We doubled the south-west extremity of Albemarle Island, and the next day were nearly becalmed between it and Narborough Island. Both are covered with immense deluges of black naked lava, which have flowed either over the rims of the great caldrons, like pitch over the rim of a pot in which it has been boiled, or have burst forth from smaller orifices on the flanks; in their descent they have spread over miles of the sea-coast. On both of these islands, eruptions are known to have taken place; and in Albemarle, we saw a small jet of smoke curling from the summit of one of the great craters. In the evening we anchored in Banks' Cove, in Albemarle Island. The next morning I went out walking. To the south of the broken tuff-crater, in which the *Beagle* was anchored, there was another beautifully symmetrical one of an elliptic form; its longer axis was a little less than a mile, and its depth about 500 feet. At its bottom there was a shallow lake, in the middle of which a tiny crater formed an islet. The day was overpoweringly hot, and the lake looked clear and blue: I hurried down the cindery slope, and choked with dust eagerly tasted the water—but, to my sorrow, I found it salt as brine.

The rocks on the coast abounded with great black lizards, between three and four feet long; and on the hills, an ugly yellowish-brown species was equally common. We saw many of this latter kind, some clumsily running out of our way, and others shuffling into their burrows. I shall presently describe in more detail the habits of both these reptiles. The whole of this northern part of Albemarle Island is miserably sterile.

October 8th.—We arrived at James Island; this island, as well as Charles Island, were long since thus named after our kings of the Stuart line. Mr. Bynoe, myself, and our servants were left here for a week, with provisions and a tent, whilst the *Beagle* went for water. We found here a party of Spaniards, who had been sent from Charles Island to dry fish, and to salt tortoise-meat. About six miles inland, and at the height of nearly 2000 feet, a hovel had been built in which two men lived, who were employed in catching tortoises, whilst the others were fishing on the coast. I paid this party two visits, and slept there one night. As in the other islands, the lower region was covered by nearly leafless bushes, but the trees were here of a larger growth than elsewhere, several being two feet and some even two feet nine inches in diameter. The upper region being kept damp by the clouds, supports a green and flourishing vegetation. So damp was the ground, that there were large beds of a coarse cyperus, in which great numbers of a very small water-rail lived and bred. While staying in this upper region, we lived entirely upon tortoise-meat: the breast-plate roasted (as the Gauchos do *carne con cuero*), with the flesh on it, is very good; and the young tortoises make excellent soup; but otherwise the meat to my taste is indifferent.

One day we accompanied a party of the Spaniards in their whale-boat to a salina, or lake from which salt is procured. After landing, we had a very rough walk over a rugged field of recent lava, which has almost surrounded a tuff-crater, at the bottom of which the salt-lake lies. The water is only three or four inches deep, and rests on a layer of beautifully crystallized, white salt. The lake is quite circular, and is fringed with a border of bright green succulent plants; the almost precipitous walls of the crater are clothed with wood, so that the scene was altogether both picturesque and curious. A few years since, the sailors belonging to a sealing-vessel murdered their captain in this quiet spot; and we saw his skull lying among the bushes.

During the greater part of our stay of a week, the sky was cloudless, and if the trade-wind failed for an hour, the heat became very oppressive. On two days, the thermometer within the tent stood for some hours at 93°; but in the open air, in the wind and sun, at only 85°. The sand was extremely hot; the thermometer placed in some of a brown colour immediately rose to 137°, and how much above that it would have risen, I do not know, for it was not graduated any higher. The black sand felt much hotter, so that even in thick boots it was quite disagreeable to walk over it.

The natural history of these islands is eminently curious, and well deserves attention. Most of the organic productions are aboriginal creations, found nowhere else; there is even a difference between the inhabitants of the different islands; yet all show a marked relationship with those of America, though separated from that continent by an open space of ocean, between 500 and 600 miles in width. The archipelago is a little world within itself, or rather a satellite attached to America, whence it has derived a few stray colonists, and has received the general character of its indigenous productions. Considering the small size of these islands, we feel the more astonished at the number of their aboriginal beings, and at their confined range. Seeing every height crowned with its crater, and the boundaries of most of the lava-streams still distinct, we are led to believe that within a period, geologically recent, the unbroken ocean was here spread out. Hence, both in space and time, we seem to be brought somewhat near to that great fact—that mystery of mysteries—the first appearance of new beings on this earth.

Of terrestrial mammals, there is only one which must be considered as indigenous, namely, a mouse (Mus Galapagoensis), and this is confined, as far as I could ascertain, to Chatham Island, the most easterly island of the group. It belongs, as I am informed by Mr. Waterhouse, to a division of the family of mice characteristic of America. At James Island, there is a rat sufficiently distinct from the common kind to have been named and described by Mr. Waterhouse; but as it belongs to the old-world division of the family, and as this island has been frequented by ships for the last hundred and fifty years, I can hardly doubt that this rat is merely a variety, produced by the new and peculiar climate, food, and soil, to which it has been subjected. Although no one has a right to speculate without distinct facts, yet even with respect to the Chatham Island mouse, it should be borne in mind, that it may possibly be an American species imported here; for I have seen, in a most unfrequented part of the Pampas, a native mouse living in the roof of a newly-built hovel, and therefore its transportation in a vessel is not improbable: analogous facts have been observed by Dr. Richardson in North America.

Of land-birds I obtained twenty-six kinds, all peculiar to the group and found nowhere else, with the exception of one lark-like finch from North America (Dolichonyx oryzivorus), which ranges on that continent as far north as 54°, and generally frequents marshes. The other twenty-five birds consist, firstly, of a hawk, curiously intermediate in structure between a Buzzard and the American group of carrion-feeding Polybori; and with these latter birds it agrees most closely in every habit and even tone of voice. Secondly, there are two owls, representing the short-eared and white barn-owls of Europe. Thirdly, a wren, three tyrant fly-catchers (two of them species of Pyrocephalus, one or both of which would be ranked by some ornithologists as only varieties), and a dove—all analogous to, but distinct from, American species. Fourthly, a swallow, which though differing from the Progne purpurea of both Americas, only in being rather duller coloured, smaller, and slenderer, is considered by Mr. Gould as specifically distinct. Fifthly, there are three species of mocking-thrush—a form highly characteristic of America. The remaining land-birds form a most singular group of finches, related to each other in the structure of their beaks, short tails, form of body, and plumage: there are thirteen species, which Mr. Gould has divided into four sub-groups. All these species are peculiar to this archipelago; and so is the whole group, with the exception of one species of the sub-group Cactornis, lately brought from Bow Island, in the Low Archipelago. Of Cactornis, the two species may be often seen climbing about the flowers of the great cactus-trees; but all the other species of this group of finches, mingled together in flocks, feed on the dry and sterile ground of the lower districts. The males of all, or certainly of the greater number, are jet black; and the females (with perhaps one or two exceptions) are brown. The most curious fact is

1. Geospiza magnirostris. 2. Geospiza fortis.
3. Geospiza parvula. 4. Certhidea olivacea.

the perfect gradation in the size of the beaks in the different species of Geospiza, from one as large as that of a hawfinch to that of a chaffinch, and (if Mr. Gould is right in including his sub-group, Certhidea, in the main group), even to that of a warbler. The largest beak in the genus Geospiza is shown in Fig. 1, and the smallest in Fig. 3; but instead of there being only one intermediate species, with a beak of the size shown in Fig. 2, there are no less than six species with insensibly graduated beaks. The beak of the sub-group Certhidea, is shown in Fig. 4. The beak of Cactornis is somewhat like that of a starling; and that of the fourth sub-group, Camarhynchus, is slightly parrot-shaped. Seeing this gradation and diversity of structure in one small, intimately related group of birds, one might really fancy that from an original paucity of birds in this archipelago, one species had been taken and modified for different ends. In a like manner it might be fancied that a bird originally a buzzard, had been induced here to undertake the office of the carrion-feeding Polybori of the American continent.

Of waders and water-birds I was able to get only eleven kinds, and of these only three (including a rail confined to the damp summits of the islands) are new species. Considering the wandering habits of the gulls, I was surprised to find that the species inhabiting these islands is peculiar, but allied to one from the southern parts of South America. The far greater peculiarity of the land-birds, namely, twenty-five out of twenty-six being new species or at least new races, compared with the waders and web-footed birds, is in accordance with the greater range which these latter orders have in all parts of the world. We shall hereafter see this law of aquatic forms, whether marine or fresh-water, being less peculiar at any given point of the earth's surface than the terrestrial forms of the same classes, strikingly illustrated in the shells, and in a lesser degree in the insects of this archipelago.

Two of the waders are rather smaller than the same species brought from other places: the swallow is also smaller, though it is doubtful whether or not it is distinct from its analogue. The two owls, the two tyrant fly-catchers (Pyrocephalus) and the dove, are also smaller than the analogous but distinct species, to which they are most nearly related; on the other hand, the gull is rather larger. The two owls, the swallow, all three species of mocking-thrush, the dove in its separate colours though not in its whole plumage, the Totanus, and the gull, are likewise duskier coloured than their analogous species; and in the case of the mocking-thrush and Totanus, than any other species of the two genera. With the exception of a wren with a fine yellow breast, and of a tyrant fly-catcher with a scarlet tuft and breast, none of the birds are brilliantly coloured, as might have been expected in an equatorial district. Hence it would appear probable, that the same causes which here make the immigrants of some species smaller, make most of the peculiar Galapageian species also smaller, as well as very generally more dusky coloured. All the plants have a wretched, weedy appearance, and I did not see one beautiful flower. The insects, again, are small sized and dull coloured, and, as Mr. Waterhouse informs me, there is nothing in their general appearance which would have led him to imagine that they had come from under the equator. The birds, plants, and insects have a desert character, and are not more brilliantly coloured than those from southern Patagonia; we may, therefore, conclude that the usual gaudy colouring of the inter-tropical productions, is not related either to the heat or light of those zones, but to some other cause, perhaps to the conditions of existence being generally favourable to life.

We will now turn to the order of reptiles, which gives the most striking character to the zoology of these islands. The species are not numerous, but the numbers of individuals of each species are extraordinarily great. There is one small lizard belonging to a South American genus, and two species (and probably more) of the Amblyrhynchus—a genus confined to the Galapagos Islands. There is one snake which is numerous; it is identical, as I am informed by M. Bibron, with the Psammophis Temminckii from Chile. Of sea-turtle I believe there is more than one species; and of tortoises there are, as we shall presently show, two or three species or races. Of toads and frogs there are none: I was surprised at this, considering how well suited for them the temperate and damp upper woods appeared to be. It recalled to my mind the remark made by Bory St. Vincent, namely, that none of this family are found on any of the volcanic islands in the great oceans. As far as I can ascertain from various works, this seems to hold good throughout the Pacific, and even in the large islands of the Sandwich Archipelago. Mauritius offers an apparent exception, where I saw the Rana Mascariensis in abundance: this frog is said now to inhabit the Seychelles, Madagascar, and Bourbon; but on the other hand, Du Bois, in his voyage of 1669, states that there were no reptiles in Bourbon except tortoises; and the Officier du Roi asserts that before 1768 it had been attempted, without success, to introduce frogs into Mauritius—I presume, for the purpose of eating: hence it may be well doubted whether this frog is an aboriginal of these islands. The absence of the frog family in the oceanic islands is the more remarkable, when contrasted with the case of lizards, which swarm on most of the smallest islands. May this difference not be caused, by the greater facility with which the eggs of lizards, protected by calcareous shells, might be transported through salt-water, than could the slimy spawn of frogs?

I will first describe the habits of the tortoise (Testudo nigra, formerly called Indica), which has been so frequently alluded to. These animals are found, I believe, on all the islands of the archipelago; certainly on the greater number. They frequent in preference the high damp parts, but they likewise live in the lower and arid districts. I have already shown, from the numbers which have been caught in a single day, how very numerous they must be. Some grow to an immense size: Mr. Lawson, an Englishman, and vice-governor of the colony, told us that he had seen several so large, that it required six or eight men to lift them from the ground; and that some had afforded as much as two hundred pounds of meat. The old males are the largest, the females rarely growing to so great a size: the male can readily be distinguished from the female by the greater length of its tail. The tortoises which live on those islands where there is no water, or in the lower and arid parts of the others, feed chiefly on the succulent cactus. Those which frequent the higher and damp regions, eat the leaves of various trees, a kind of berry (called guayavita) which is acid and austere, and likewise a pale green filamentous lichen (Usnera plicata), that hangs in tresses from the boughs of the trees.

The tortoise is very fond of water, drinking large quantities, and wallowing in the mud. The larger islands alone possess springs, and these are always situated towards the central parts, and at a considerable height. The tortoises, therefore, which frequent the lower districts, when thirsty, are obliged to travel from a long distance. Hence broad and well-beaten paths branch off in every direction from the wells down to the sea-coast; and the Spaniards by following them up, first discovered the watering-places. When I landed at Chatham Island, I could not imagine what animal travelled so methodically along well-chosen tracks. Near the springs it was a curious spectacle to behold many of these huge creatures, one set eagerly travelling onwards with outstretched necks, and another set returning, after having drunk their fill. When the tortoise arrives at the spring, quite regardless of any spectator, he buries his head in the water above his eyes, and greedily swallows great mouthfuls, at the rate of about ten in a minute. The inhabitants say each animal stays three or four days in the neighbourhood of the water, and then returns to the lower country; but they differed respecting the frequency of these visits. The animal probably regulates them according to the nature of the food on which it has lived. It is however, certain, that tortoises can subsist even on those islands, where there is no other water than what falls during a few rainy days in the year.

I believe it is well ascertained, that the bladder of the frog acts as a reservoir for the moisture necessary to its existence: such seems to be the case with the tortoise. For some time after a visit to the springs, their urinary bladders are distended with fluid, which is said gradually to decrease in volume, and to become less pure. The inhabitants, when walking in the lower district, and overcome with thirst, often take advantage of this circumstance, and drink the contents of the bladder if full: in one I saw killed, the fluid was quite limpid, and had only a very slightly bitter taste. The inhabitants, however, always first drink the water in the pericardium, which is described as being best.

The tortoises, when purposely moving towards any point, travel by night and day, and arrive at their journey's end much sooner than would be expected. The inhabitants, from observing marked individuals, consider that they travel a distance of about eight miles in two or three days. One large tortoise, which I watched, walked at the rate of sixty yards in ten minutes, that is 360 yards in the hour, or four miles a day,—allowing a little time for it to eat on the road. During the breeding season, when the male and female are together, the male utters a hoarse roar or bellowing, which, it is said, can be heard at the distance of more than a hundred yards. The female never uses her voice, and the male only at these times; so that when the people hear this noise, they know that the two are together. They were at this time (October) laying their eggs. The female, where the soil is sandy, deposits them together, and covers them up with sand; but where the ground is rocky she drops them indiscriminately in any hole: Mr. Bynoe found seven placed in a fissure. The egg is white and spherical; one which I measured was seven inches and three-eighths in circumference, and therefore larger than a hen's egg. The young tortoises, as soon as they are hatched, fall a prey in great numbers to the carrion-feeding buzzard. The old ones seem generally to die from accidents, as from falling down precipices: at least, several of the inhabitants told me, that they had never found one dead without some evident cause.

The inhabitants believe that these animals are absolutely deaf; certainly they do not overhear a person walking close behind them. I was always amused when overtaking one of these great monsters, as it was quietly pacing along, to see how suddenly, the instant I passed, it would draw in its head and legs, and uttering a deep hiss fall to the ground with a heavy sound, as if struck dead. I frequently got on their backs, and then giving a few raps on the hinder part of their shells, they would rise up and walk away;—but I found it very difficult to keep my balance. The flesh of this animal is largely employed, both fresh and salted; and a beautifully clear oil is prepared from the fat. When a tortoise is caught, the man makes a slit in the skin near its tail, so as to see inside its body, whether the fat under the dorsal plate is thick. If it is not, the animal is liberated; and it is said to recover soon from this strange operation. In order to secure the tortoises, it is not sufficient to turn them like turtle, for they are often able to get on their legs again.

There can be little doubt that this tortoise is an aboriginal inhabitant of the Galapagos; for it is found on all, or nearly all, the islands, even on some of the smaller ones where there is no water; had it been an imported species, this would hardly have been the case in a group which has been so little frequented. Moreover, the old Bucaniers found this tortoise in greater numbers even than at present: Wood and Rogers also, in 1708, say that it is the opinion of the Spaniards, that it is found nowhere else in this quarter of the world. It is now widely distributed; but it may be questioned whether it is in any other place an aboriginal. The bones of a tortoise at Mauritius, associated with those of the extinct Dodo, have generally been considered as belonging to this tortoise: if this had been so, undoubtedly it must have been there indigenous; but M. Bibron informs me that he believes that it was distinct, as the species now living there certainly is.

The Amblyrhynchus, a remarkable genus of lizards, is confined to this archipelago: there are two species, resembling each other in general form, one being terrestrial and the other aquatic. This latter species (A. cristatus) was first characterized by Mr. Bell, who well foresaw, from its short, broad head, and strong claws of equal length, that its habits of life would turn out very peculiar, and different from those of its nearest ally, the Iguana. It is extremely common on all the islands throughout the group, and lives exclusively on the rocky sea-beaches, being never found, at least

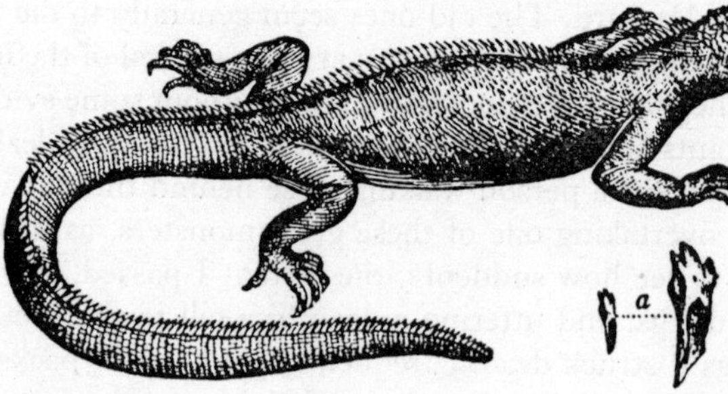

Amblyrhynchus cristatus. *a*. Tooth of natural size, and likewise magnified.

I never saw one, even ten yards in-shore. It is a hideous-looking creature, of a dirty black colour, stupid, and sluggish in its movements. The usual length of a full-grown one is about a yard, but there are some even four feet long; a large one weighed twenty pounds: on the island of Albemarle they seem to grow to a greater size than elsewhere. Their tails are flattened sideways, and all four feet partially webbed. They are occasionally seen some hundred yards from the shore, swimming about; and Captain Collinett, in his *Voyage*, says, 'They go to sea in herds a-fishing, and sun themselves on the rocks; and may be called alligators in miniature.' It must not, however, be supposed that they live on fish. When in the water this lizard swims with perfect ease and quickness, by a serpentine movement of its body and flattened tail—the legs being motionless and closely collapsed on its sides. A seaman on board sank one, with a heavy weight attached to it, thinking thus to kill it directly; but when, an hour afterwards, he drew up the line, it was quite active. Their limbs and strong claws are admirably adapted for crawling over the rugged and fissured masses of lava, which everywhere form the coast. In such situations, a group of six or seven of these hideous reptiles may oftentimes be seen on the black rocks, a few feet above the surf, basking in the sun with outstretched legs.

I opened the stomachs of several, and found them largely distended with minced sea-weed (Ulvæ), which grows in thin foliaceous expansions of a bright green or a dull red colour. I do not recollect having observed this sea-weed in any quantity on the tidal rocks; and I have reason to believe it grows at the bottom of the sea, at some little distance from the coast. If such be the case, the object of these animals occasionally going out to sea is explained. The stomach contained nothing but the sea-weed. Mr. Bynoe, however, found a piece of a crab in one; but this might have got in accidentally, in the same manner as I have seen a caterpillar, in the midst of some lichen, in the paunch of a tortoise. The intestines were large, as in other herbivorous animals. The nature of this lizard's food, as well as the structure of its tail and feet, and the fact of its having been seen voluntarily swimming out at sea, absolutely prove its aquatic habits; yet there is in this respect one strange anomaly, namely, that when frightened it will not enter the water. Hence it is easy to drive these lizards down to any little point overhanging the sea, where they will sooner allow a person to catch hold of their tails than jump into the water. They do not seem to have any notion of biting; but when much frightened they squirt a drop of fluid from each nostril. I threw one several times as far as I could, into a deep pool left by the retiring tide; but it invariably returned in a direct line to the spot where I stood. It swam near the bottom, with a very graceful and rapid movement, and occasionally aided itself over the uneven ground with its feet. As soon as it arrived near the edge, but still being under water, it tried to conceal itself in the tufts of sea-weed, or it entered some crevice. As soon as it thought the danger was past, it crawled out on the dry rocks, and shuffled away as quickly as it could. I several times caught this same lizard, by driving it down to a point, and though possessed of such perfect powers of diving and swimming, nothing would induce it to enter the water; and as often as I threw it in, it returned in the manner above described. Perhaps this singular piece of apparent stupidity may be accounted for by the circumstance, that this reptile has no enemy whatever on shore, whereas at sea it must often fall a prey to the numerous sharks. Hence, probably, urged by a fixed and hereditary instinct that the shore is its place of safety, whatever the emergency may be, it there takes refuge.

During our visit (in October), I saw extremely few small individuals of this species, and none I should think under a year old. From this circumstance it seems probable that the breeding season had not then commenced. I asked several of the inhabitants if they knew where it laid its eggs: they said that they knew nothing of its propagation, although well acquainted with the eggs of the land kind—a fact, considering how very common this lizard is, not a little extraordinary.

We will now turn to the terrestrial species (A. Demarlii), with a round tail, and toes without webs. This lizard, instead of being found like the other on all the islands, is confined to the central part of the archipelago, namely to Albemarle, James, Barrington, and Indefatigable Islands. To the southward, in Charles, Hood, and Chatham Islands, and to the northward, in Towers, Bindloes, and Abingdon, I neither saw nor heard of any. It would appear as if it had been created in the centre of the archipelago, and thence had been dispersed only to a certain distance. Some of these lizards inhabit the high and damp parts of the islands, but they are much more numerous in the lower and sterile districts near the coast. I cannot give a more forcible proof of their numbers, than by stating that when we were left at James Island, we could not for some time find a spot free from their burrows on which to pitch our single tent. Like their brothers the sea-kind, they are ugly animals, of a yellowish orange beneath, and of a brownish red colour above: from their low facial angle they have a singularly stupid appearance. They are, perhaps, of a rather less size than the marine species; but several of them weighed between ten and fifteen pounds. In their movements they are lazy and half torpid. When not frightened, they slowly crawl along with their tails and bellies dragging on the ground. They often stop, and doze for a minute or two, with closed eyes and hind legs spread out on the parched soil.

They inhabit burrows, which they sometimes make between fragments of lava, but more generally on level patches of the soft sandstone-like tuff. The holes do not appear to be very deep, and they enter the ground at a small angle; so that when walking over these lizard-warrens, the soil is constantly giving way, much to the annoyance of the tired walker. This animal, when making its burrow, works alternately the opposite sides of its body. One front leg for a short time scratches up the soil, and throws it towards the hind foot, which is well placed so as to heave it beyond the mouth of the hole. That side of the body being tired, the other takes up the task, and so on alternately. I watched one for a long time, till half its body was buried; I then walked up and pulled it by the tail; at this it was greatly astonished, and soon shuffled up to see what was the matter; and then stared me in the face, as much as to say, 'What made you pull my tail?'

They feed by day, and do not wander far from their burrows; if frightened, they rush to them with a most awkward gait. Except when running down hill, they cannot move very fast, apparently from the lateral position of their legs. They are not at all timorous: when attentively watching any one, they curl their tails, and, raising themselves on their front legs, nod their heads vertically, with a quick movement, and try to look very fierce: but in reality they are not at all so; if one just stamps on the ground, down go their tails, and off they shuffle as quickly as they can. I have frequently observed small fly-eating lizards, when watching anything, nod their heads in precisely the same manner; but I do not at all know for what purpose. If this Amblyrhynchus is held and plagued with a stick, it will bite it very severely; but I caught many by the tail, and they never tried to bite me. If two are placed on the ground and held together, they will fight, and bite each other till blood is drawn.

The individuals, and they are the greater number, which inhabit the lower country, can scarcely taste a drop of water throughout the year; but they consume much of the succulent cactus, the branches of which are occasionally broken off by the wind. I several times threw a piece to two or three of them when together; and it was amusing enough to see them trying to seize and carry it away in their mouths, like so many hungry dogs with a bone. They eat very deliberately, but do not chew their food. The little birds are aware how harmless these creatures are: I have seen one of the thick-billed finches picking at one end of a piece of cactus (which is much relished by all the animals of the lower region), whilst a lizard was eating at the other end; and afterwards the little bird with the utmost indifference hopped on the back of the reptile.

I opened the stomachs of several, and found them full of vegetable fibres and leaves of different trees, especially of an acacia. In the upper region they live chiefly on the acid and astringent berries of the guayavita, under which trees I have seen these lizards and huge tortoises feeding together. To obtain the acacia-leaves they crawl up the low stunted trees; and it is not uncommon to see a pair quietly browsing, whilst seated on a branch several feet above the ground. These lizards, when cooked, yield a white meat, which is liked by those whose stomachs soar above all prejudices. Humboldt has remarked that in intertropical South America, all lizards which inhabit dry regions are esteemed delicacies for the table. The inhabitants state that those which inhabit the upper damp parts drink water, but that the others do not, like the tortoises, travel up for it from the lower sterile country. At the time of our visit, the females had within their bodies numerous large, elongated eggs, which they lay in their burrows: the inhabitants seek them for food.

These two species of Amblyrhynchus agree, as I have already stated, in their general structure, and in many of their habits. Neither have that rapid movement, so characteristic of the genera Lacerta and Iguana. They are both herbivorous, although the kind of vegetation on which they feed is so very different. Mr. Bell has given the name to the genus from the shortness of the snout; indeed, the form of the mouth may almost be compared to that of the tortoise: one is led to suppose that this is an adaptation to their herbivorous appetites. It is very interesting thus to find a well-characterized genus, having its marine and terrestrial species, belonging to so confined a portion of the world. The aquatic species is by far the most remarkable, because it is the only existing lizard which lives on marine vegetable productions. As I at first observed, these islands are not so remarkable for the number of the species of reptiles, as for that of the individuals; when we remember the well-beaten paths made by the thousands of huge tortoises—the many turtles—the great warrens of the terrestrial Amblyrhynchus—and the groups of the marine species basking on the coast-rocks of every island—we must admit that there is no other quarter of the world where this Order replaces the herbivorous mammalia in so extraordinary a manner. The geologist on hearing this will probably refer back in his mind to the Secondary epochs, when lizards, some herbivorous, some carnivorous, and of dimensions comparable only with our existing whales, swarmed on the land and in the sea. It is, therefore, worthy of his observation, that this archipelago, instead of possessing a humid climate and rank vegetation, cannot be considered otherwise than extremely arid, and, for an equatorial region, remarkably temperate.

* * * *

The botany of this group is fully as interesting as the zoology. Dr. J. Hooker will soon publish in the '*Linnean Transactions*' a full account of the Flora, and I am much indebted to him for the following details. Of flowering plants there are, as far as at present is known, 185 species, and 40 cryptogamic species, making together 225; of this number I was fortunate enough to bring home 193. Of the flowering plants, 100 are new species, and are probably confined to this archipelago. Dr. Hooker conceives that, of the plants not so confined, at least 10 species found near the cultivated ground at Charles Island, have been imported. It is, I think, surprising that more American species have not been introduced naturally, considering that the distance is only between 500 and 600 miles from the continent; and that (according to Collnett, p. 58) drift-wood, bamboos, canes, and the nuts of a palm, are often washed on the south-eastern shores. The proportion of 100 flowering plants out of 185 (or

175 excluding the imported weeds) being new, is sufficient, I conceive, to make the Galapagos Archipelago a distinct botanical province; but this Flora is not nearly so peculiar as that of St. Helena, nor, as I am informed by Dr. Hooker, of Juan Fernandez. The peculiarity of the Galapageian Flora is best shown in certain families;—thus there are 21 species of Compositæ, of which 20 are peculiar to this archipelago; these belong to twelve genera, and of these genera no less than ten are confined to the archipelago! Dr. Hooker informs me that the Flora has an undoubted Western American character; nor can he detect in it any affinity with that of the Pacific. If, therefore, we except the eighteen marine, the one fresh-water, and one land-shell, which have apparently come here as colonists from the central islands of the Pacific, and likewise the one distinct Pacific species of the Galapageian group of finches, we see that this archipelago, though standing in the Pacific Ocean, is zoologically part of America.

If this character were owing merely to immigrants from America, there would be little remarkable in it; but we see that a vast majority of all the land animals, and that more than half of the flowering plants, are aboriginal productions. It was most striking to be surrounded by new birds, new reptiles, new shells, new insects, new plants, and yet by innumerable trifling details of structure, and even by the tones of voice and plumage of the birds, to have the temperate plains of Patagonia, or the hot dry deserts of Northern Chile, vividly brought before my eyes. Why, on these small points of land, which within a late geological period must have been covered by the ocean, which are formed of basaltic lava, and therefore differ in geological character from the American continent, and which are placed under a peculiar climate,—why were their aboriginal inhabitants, associated, I may add, in different proportions both in kind and number from those on the continent, and therefore acting on each other in a different manner—why were they created on American types of organization? It is probable that the islands of the Cape de Verd group resemble, in all their physical conditions, far more closely the Galapagos Islands than these latter physically resemble the coast of America; yet the aboriginal inhabitants of the two groups are totally unlike; those of the Cape de Verd Islands bearing the impress of Africa, as the inhabitants of the Galapagos Archipelago are stamped with that of America.

I have not as yet noticed by far the most remarkable feature in the natural history of this archipelago; it is, that the different islands to a considerable extent are inhabited by a different set of beings. My attention was first called to this fact by the Vice-Governor, Mr. Lawson, declaring that the tortoises differed from the different islands, and that he could with certainty tell from which island any one was brought. I did not for some time pay sufficient attention to this statement, and I had already partially mingled together the collections from two of the islands. I never dreamed that islands, about fifty or sixty miles apart, and most of them in sight of each other, formed of precisely the same rocks, placed under a quite similar climate, rising to a nearly equal height, would have been differently tenanted; but we shall soon see that this is the case. It is the fate of most voyagers, no sooner to discover what is most interesting in any locality, than they are hurried from it; but I ought, perhaps, to be thankful that I obtained sufficient material to establish this most remarkable fact in the distribution of organic beings.

The inhabitants, as I have said, state that they can distinguish the tortoises from the different islands; and that they differ not only in size, but in other characters. Captain Porter has described those from Charles and from the nearest island to it, namely, Hood Island, as having their shells in front thick and turned up like a Spanish saddle, whilst the tortoises from James Island are rounder, blacker, and have a better taste when cooked. M. Bibron, moreover, informs me that he has seen what he considers two distinct species of tortoise from the Galapagos, but he does not know from which islands. The specimens that I brought from three islands were young ones; and probably owing to this cause, neither Mr. Gray nor myself could find in them any specific differences. I have remarked that the marine Amblyrhynchus was larger at Albemarle Island than elsewhere; and M. Bibron informs me that he has seen two distinct aquatic species of this genus; so that the different islands probably have their representative species or races of the Amblyrhynchus, as well as of the tortoise. My attention was first thoroughly aroused, by comparing together the numerous specimens, shot by myself and several other parties on board, of the mocking-thrushes, when, to my astonishment, I discovered that all those from Charles Island belonged to one species (Mimus trifasciatus); all from Albemarle Island to M. parvulus; and all from James and Chatham Islands (between which two other islands are situated, as connecting links) belonged to M. melanotis. These two latter species are closely allied, and would by some ornithologists be considered as only well-marked races or varieties; but the Mimus trifasciatus is very distinct. Unfortunately most of the specimens of the finch tribe were mingled together; but I have strong reasons to suspect that some of the species of the sub-group Geospiza are confined to separate islands. If the different islands have their representatives of Geospiza, it may help to explain the singularly large number of the species of this sub-group in this one small archipelago, and as a probable consequence of their numbers, the perfectly graduated series in the size of their beaks. Two species of the sub-group Cactornis, and two of Camarhynchus, were procured in the archipelago; and of the numerous specimens of these two sub-groups shot by four collectors at James Island, all were found to belong to one species of each; whereas the numerous specimens shot either on Chatham or Charles Island (for the two sets were mingled together) all belonged to the two other species: hence we may feel almost sure that these islands possess their representative species of these two sub-groups. In land-shells this law of distribution does not appear to hold good. In my very small collection of insects, Mr. Waterhouse remarks, that of those which were ticketed with their locality, not one was common to any two of the islands.

If we now turn to the Flora, we shall find the aboriginal plants of the different islands wonderfully different. I give all the following results on the high authority of my friend Dr. J. Hooker. I may premise that I indiscriminately collected everything in flower on the different islands, and fortunately kept my collections separate. Too much confidence, however, must not be placed in the proportional results, as the small collections brought home by some other naturalists, though in some respects confirming the results, plainly show that much remains to be done in the botany of this group: the Leguminosæ, moreover, have as yet been only approximately worked out:

Name of Island	*Total No. of Species*	*No. of Species found in other parts of the world*	*No. of Species confined to the Galapagos Archipelago*	*No. confined to the one Island*	*No. of species confined to the Galapagos Archipelago, but found on more than the one Island*
James Island	71	33	38	30	8
Albemarle Island	46	18	26	22	4
Chatham Island	32	16	16	12	4
Charles Island	68	39 (or 29, if the probably imported plants be subtracted)	29	21	8

Hence we have the truly wonderful fact, that in James Island, of the thirty-eight Galapageian plants, or those found in no other part of the world, thirty are exclusively confined to this one island; and in Albemarle Island, of the twenty-six aboriginal Galapageian plants, twenty-two are confined to this one island, that is, only four are at present known to grow in the other islands of the archipelago; and so on, as shown in the above table, with the plants from Chatham and Charles Islands. This fact will, perhaps, be rendered even more striking, by giving a few illustrations: thus, Scalesia, a remarkable arborescent genus of the Compositæ, is confined to the archipelago: it has six species; one from Chatham, one from Albemarle, one from Charles Island, two from James Island, and the sixth from one of the three latter islands, but it is not known from which: not one of these six species grows on any two islands. Again, Euphorbia, a mundane or widely distributed genus, has here eight species, of which seven are confined to the archipelago, and not one found on any two islands: Acalypha and Borreria, both mundane genera, have respectively six and seven species, none of which have the same species on two islands, with the exception of one Borreria, which does occur on two islands. The species of the Compositæ are particularly local; and Dr. Hooker has furnished me with several other most striking illustrations of the difference of the species on the different islands. He remarks that this law of distribution holds good both with those genera confined to the archipelago, and those distributed in other quarters of the world: in like manner we have seen that the different islands have their proper species of the mundane genus of tortoise, and of the widely distributed American genus of the mocking-thrush, as well as of two of the Galapageian subgroups of finches, and almost certainly of the Galapageian genus Amblyrhynchus.

The distribution of the tenants of this archipelago would not be nearly so wonderful, if, for instance, one island had a mocking-thrush, and a second island some other quite distinct genus;—if one island had its genus of lizard, and a second island another distinct genus, or none whatever;—or if the different islands were inhabited, not by representative species of the same genera of plants, but by totally different genera, as does to a certain extent hold good; for, to give one instance, a large berry-bearing tree at James Island has no representative species in Charles Island. But it is the circumstance, that several of the islands possess their own species of the tortoise, mocking-thrush, finches, and numerous plants, these species having the same general habits, occupying analogous situations, and obviously filling the same place in the natural economy of this archipelago, that strikes me with wonder. It may be suspected that some of these representative species, at least in the case of the tortoise and of some of the birds, may hereafter prove to be only well-marked races; but this would be of equally great interest to the philosophical naturalist. I have said that most of the islands are in sight of each other: I may specify that Charles Island is fifty miles from the nearest part of Chatham Island, and thirty-three miles from the nearest part of Albemarle Island. Chatham Island is sixty miles from the nearest part of James Island, but there are two intermediate islands between them which were not visited by me. James Island is only ten miles from the nearest part of Albemarle Island, but the two points where the collections were made are thirty-two miles apart. I must repeat, that neither the nature of the soil, nor height of the land, nor the climate, nor the general character of the associated beings, and therefore their action one on another, can differ much in the different islands. If there be any sensible difference in their climates, it must be between the windward group (namely Charles and Chatham Islands), and that to leeward; but there seems to be no corresponding difference in the productions of these two halves of the archipelago.

The only light which I can throw on this remarkable difference in the inhabitants of the different islands, is, that very strong currents of the sea running in a westerly and W.N.W. direction must separate, as far as transportal by the sea is concerned, the southern islands from the northern ones; and between these northern islands a strong N.W. current was observed, which must effectually separate James and Albemarle Islands. As the archipelago is free to a most remarkable degree from gales of wind, neither the birds, insects, nor lighter seeds, would be blown from island to island. And lastly, the profound depth of the ocean between the islands, and their apparently recent (in a geological sense) volcanic origin, render it highly unlikely that they were ever united; and this, probably, is a far more important consideration than any other, with respect to the geographical distribution of their inhabitants. Reviewing the facts here given, one is astonished at the amount of creative force, if such an expression may be used, displayed on these small, barren, and rocky islands; and still more so, at its diverse yet analogous action on points so near each other. I have said that the Galapagos Archipelago might be called a satellite attached to America, but it should rather be called a group of satellites, physically similar, organically distinct, yet intimately related to each other, and all related in a marked, though much lesser degree, to the great American continent.

I will conclude my description of the natural history of these islands, by giving an account of the extreme tameness of the birds.

This disposition is common to all the terrestrial species; namely, to the mocking-thrushes, the finches, wrens, tyrant-flycatchers, the dove, and carrion-buzzard. All of them often approached sufficiently near to be killed with a switch, and sometimes, as I myself tried, with a cap or hat. A gun is here almost superfluous; for with the muzzle I pushed a hawk off the branch of a tree. One day, whilst lying down, a mocking-thrush alighted on the edge of a pitcher, made of the shell of a tortoise, which I held in my hand, and began very quietly to sip the water; it allowed me to lift it from the ground whilst seated on the vessel: I often tried, and very nearly succeeded, in catching these birds by their legs. Formerly the birds appear to have been even tamer than at present. Cowley (in the year 1684) says that the 'Turtle-doves were so tame, that they would often alight upon our hats and arms, so as that we could take them alive: they not fearing man, until such time as some of our company did fire at them, whereby they were rendered more shy.' Dampier also, in the same year, says that a man in a morning's walk might kill six or seven dozen of these doves. At present, although certainly very tame, they do not alight on people's arms, nor do they suffer themselves to be killed in such large numbers. It is surprising that they have not become wilder; for these islands during the last hundred and fifty years have been frequently visited by bucaniers and whalers; and the sailors, wandering through the woods in search of tortoises, always take cruel delight in knocking down the little birds.

These birds, although now still more persecuted, do not readily become wild: in Charles Island, which had then been colonized about six years, I saw a boy sitting by a well with a switch in his hand, with which he killed the doves and finches as they came to drink. He had already procured a little heap of them for his dinner; and he said that he had constantly been in the habit of waiting by this well for the same purpose. It would appear that the birds of this archipelago, not having as yet learnt that man is a more dangerous animal than the tortoise or the Amblyrhynchus, disregard him, in the same manner as in England shy birds, such as magpies, disregard the cows and horses grazing in our fields.

CHAPTER 4

CORAL FORMATIONS

[The second half of Chapter XX of the *Beagle*.]

I WILL NOW give a very brief account of the three great classes of coral-reefs; namely, Atolls, Barrier, and Fringing-reefs, and will explain my views on their formation. Almost every voyager who has crossed the Pacific has expressed his unbounded astonishment at the lagoon-islands, or as I shall for the future call them by their Indian name of atolls, and has attempted some explanation. Even as long ago as the year 1605, Pyrard de Laval well exclaimed, 'C'est une merveille de voir chacun de ces atollons, environné d'un grand banc de pierre tout autour, n'y ayant point d'artifice humain.' The accompanying sketch of Whitsunday Island in the Pacific, copied from Capt. Beechey's admirable *Voyage*, gives but a faint idea of the singular aspect of an atoll: it is one of the smallest size, and has its narrow islets united together in a ring. The immensity of the ocean, the fury of the breakers, contrasted with the lowness of the land and the smoothness of the bright green water within the lagoon, can hardly be imagined without having been seen.

The earlier voyagers fancied that the coral-building animals instinctively built up their great circles to afford themselves protection in the inner parts; but so far is this from the truth, that those massive kinds, to whose growth on the exposed outer shores the very existence of the reef depends, cannot live within the lagoon, where other delicately-branching kinds flourish. Moreover, on this view, many species of distinct genera and families are supposed to combine for one end; and of such a combination, not a single instance can be found in the whole of nature. The theory that has been most generally received is, that atolls are based on submarine craters; but when we consider the form and size of some, the number, proximity, and relative positions of others, this idea loses its plausible character: thus, Suadiva Atoll is 44 geographical miles in diameter in one line, by 34 miles in another line; Rimsky is 54 by 20 miles across, and it has a strangely sinuous margin; Bow Atoll is 30 miles long, and on an average only 6 in width; Menchicoff Atoll consists of three atolls united or tied together. This theory, moreover, is totally inapplicable to the northern Maldiva Atolls in the Indian Ocean (one of which is

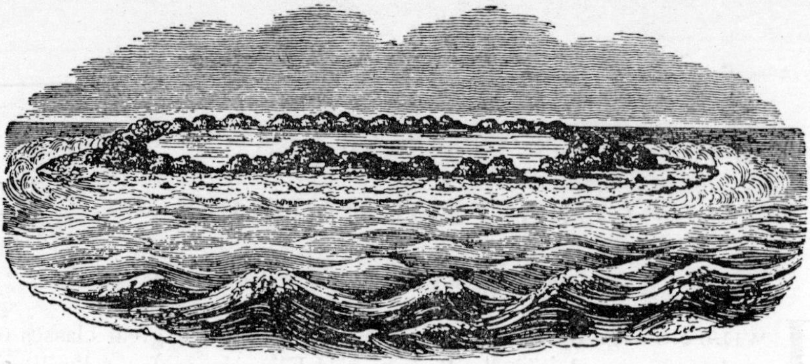

88 miles in length, and between 10 and 20 in breadth), for they are not bounded like ordinary atolls by narrow reefs, but by a vast number of separate little atolls; other little atolls rising out of the great central lagoon-like spaces. A third and better theory was advanced by Chamisso, who thought that from the corals growing more vigorously where exposed to the open sea, as undoubtedly is the case, the outer edges would grow up from the general foundation before any other part, and that this would account for the ring or cup-shaped structure. But we shall immediately see, that in this, as well as in the crater-theory, a most important consideration has been overlooked, namely, on what have the reef-building corals, which cannot live at a great depth, based their massive structures?

Numerous soundings were carefully taken by Captain Fitz-Roy on the steep outside of Keeling Atoll, and it was found that within ten fathoms, the prepared tallow at the bottom of the lead, invariably came up marked with the impressions of living corals, but as perfectly clean as if it had been dropped on a carpet of turf; as the depth increased, the impressions became less numerous, but the adhering particles of sand more and more numerous, until at last it was evident that the bottom consisted of a smooth sandy layer: to carry on the analogy of the turf, the blades of grass grew thinner and thinner, till at last the soil was so sterile, that nothing sprang from it. From these observations, confirmed by many others, it may be safely inferred that the utmost depth at which corals can construct reefs is between 20 and 30 fathoms. Now there are enormous areas in the Pacific and Indian Oceans, in which every single island is of coral formation, and is raised only to that height to which the waves can throw up fragments, and the winds pile up sand. Thus the Radack group of atolls is an irregular square, 520 miles long and 240 broad; the Low Archipelago is elliptic-formed, 840 miles in its longer, and 420 in its shorter axis: there are other small groups and single low islands between these two archipelagoes, making a linear space of ocean actually more than 4000 miles in length, in which not one single island rises above the specified height. Again, in the Indian Ocean there is a space of ocean 1500 miles in length, including three archipelagoes, in which every island is low and of coral formation. From the fact of the reef-building corals not living at great depths, it is absolutely certain that throughout these vast areas, wherever there is now an atoll, a foundation must have originally existed within a depth of from 20 to 30 fathoms from the surface. It is improbable in the highest degree that broad, lofty, isolated, steep-sided banks of sediment, arranged in groups and lines hundreds of leagues in length, could have been deposited in the central and profoundest parts of the Pacific and Indian Oceans, at an immense distance from any continent, and where the water is perfectly limpid. It is equally improbable that the elevatory forces should have uplifted throughout the above vast areas, innumerable great rocky banks within 20 to 30 fathoms, or 120 to 180 feet, of the surface of the sea, and not one single point above that level; for where on the whole face of the globe can we find a single chain of mountains, even a few hundred miles in length, with their many summits rising within a few feet of a given level, and not one pinnacle above it? If then the foundations, whence the atoll-building corals sprang, were not formed of sediment, and if they were not lifted up to the required level, they must of necessity have subsided into it; and this at once solves the difficulty. For as mountain after mountain, and island after island, slowly sank beneath the water, fresh bases would be successively afforded for the growth of the corals. It is impossible here to enter into all the necessary details, but I venture to defy any one to explain in any other manner, how it is possible that numerous islands should be distributed throughout vast areas—all the islands being low—all being built of corals, absolutely requiring a foundation within a limited depth from the surface.

Before explaining how atoll-formed reefs acquire their peculiar structure, we must turn to the second great class, namely, barrier-reefs. These either extend in straight lines in front of the shores of a continent or of a large island, or they encircle smaller islands; in both cases, being separated from the land by a broad and rather deep channel of water, analogous to the lagoon within an atoll. It is remarkable how little attention has been paid to encircling barrier-reefs; yet they are truly wonderful structures. The following sketch represents part of the barrier encircling the island of Bolabola in the Pacific, as seen from one of the central peaks. In this instance the whole line of reef has been converted into land; but usually a snow-white line of great breakers, with only here and there a single low islet crowned with cocoa-nut trees, divides the dark heaving waters of the ocean from the light-green expanse of the lagoon-channel. And the quiet waters of this channel generally bathe a fringe of low alluvial soil, loaded with the most beautiful productions of the tropics, and lying at the foot of the wild, abrupt, central mountains.

Encircling barrier-reefs are of all sizes, from three miles to no less than forty-four miles in diameter; and that which fronts one side, and encircles both ends, of New Caledonia, is 400 miles long. Each reef includes one, two, or several rocky islands of various heights; and in one instance, even

Bolabola

as many as twelve separate islands. The reef runs at a greater or less distance from the included land; in the Society Archipelago generally from one to three or four miles; but at Hogoleu the reef is 20 miles on the southern side, and 14 miles on the opposite or northern side, from the included islands. The depth within the lagoon-channel also varies much; from 10 to 30 fathoms may be taken as an average; but at Vanikoro there are spaces no less than 56 fathoms or 336 feet deep. Internally the reef either slopes gently into the lagoon-channel, or ends in a perpendicular wall sometimes between two and three hundred feet under water in height: externally the reef rises, like an atoll, with extreme abruptness out of the profound depths of the ocean. What can be more singular than these structures? We see an island, which may be compared to a castle situated on the summit of a lofty submarine mountain, protected by a great wall of coral-rock, always steep externally and sometimes internally, with a broad level summit, here and there breached by narrow gateways, through which the largest ships can enter the wide and deep encircling moat.

As far as the actual reef of coral is concerned, there is not the smallest difference, in general size, outline, grouping, and even in quite trifling details of structure, between a barrier and an atoll. The geographer Balbi has well remarked, that an encircled island is an atoll with high land rising out of its lagoon; remove the land from within, and a perfect atoll is left.

But what has caused these reefs to spring up at such great distances from the shores of the included islands? It cannot be that the corals will not grow close to the land; for the shores within the lagoon-channel, when not surrounded by alluvial soil, are often fringed by living reefs; and we shall presently see that there is a whole class, which I have called

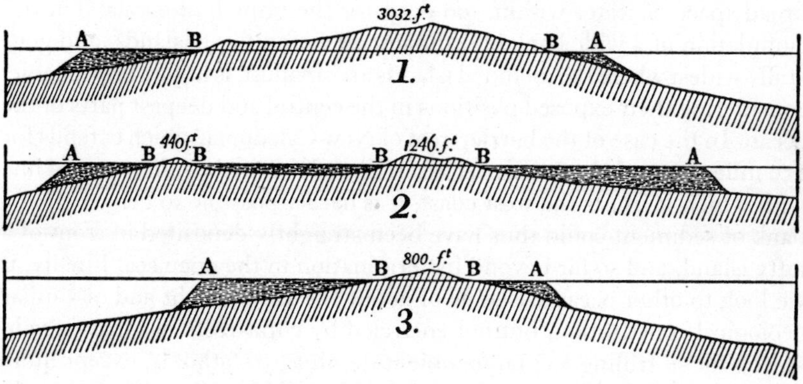

1. Vanikoro. 2. Gambier Islands. 3. Maurua.

The horizontal shading shows the barrier-reefs and lagoon-channels. The inclined shading above the level of the sea (AA), shows the actual form of the land; the inclined shading below this line, shows its probable prolongation under water.

Fringing-reefs from their close attachment to the shores both of continents and of islands. Again, on what have the reef-building corals, which cannot live at great depths, based their encircling structures? This is a great apparent difficulty, analogous to that in the case of atolls, which has generally been overlooked. It will be perceived more clearly by inspecting the following sections, which are real ones, taken in north and south lines, through the islands with their barrier-reefs, of Vanikoro, Gambier, and Maurua; and they are laid down, both vertically and horizontally, on the same scale of a quarter of an inch to a mile.

It should be observed that the sections might have been taken in any direction through these islands, or through many other encircled islands, and the general features would have been the same. Now bearing in mind that reef-building coral cannot live at a greater depth than from 20 to 30 fathoms, and that the scale is so small that the plummets on the right hand show a depth of 200 fathoms, on what are these barrier-reefs based? Are we to suppose that each island is surrounded by a collar-like submarine ledge of rock, or by a great bank of sediment, ending abruptly where the reef ends? If the sea had formerly eaten deeply into the islands, before they were protected by the reefs, thus having left a shallow ledge round them under water, the present shores would have been invariably bounded by great precipices; but this is most rarely the case. Moreover, on this notion, it is not possible to explain why the corals should have sprung up, like a wall, from the extreme outer margin of the ledge, often leaving a broad space of water within, too deep for the growth of corals. The accumulation of a wide bank of sediment all round these islands, and generally widest where the included islands are smallest, is highly improbable, considering their exposed positions in the central and deepest parts of the ocean. In the case of the barrier-reef of New Caledonia, which extends for 150 miles beyond the northern point of the island, in the same straight line with which it fronts the west coast, it is hardly possible to believe, that a bank of sediment could thus have been straightly deposited in front of a lofty island, and so far beyond its termination in the open sea. Finally, if we look to other oceanic islands of about the same height and of similar geological constitution, but not encircled by coral-reefs, we may in vain search for so trifling a circumambient depth as 30 fathoms, except quite near to their shores; for usually land that rises abruptly out of water, as do most of the encircled and non-encircled oceanic islands, plunges abruptly under it. On what then, I repeat, are these barrier-reefs based? Why, with their wide and deep moat-like channels, do they stand so far from the included land? We shall soon see how easily these difficulties disappear.

We come now to our third class of Fringing-reefs, which will require a very short notice. Where the land slopes abruptly under water, these reefs are only a few yards in width, forming a mere ribbon or fringe round the shores: where the land slopes gently under the water the reef extends further, sometimes even as much as a mile from the land; but in such cases the soundings outside the reef always show that the submarine prolongation of the land is gently inclined. In fact the reefs extend only to that distance from the shore, at which a foundation within the requisite depth from 20 to 30 fathoms is found. As far as the actual reef is concerned, there is no essential difference between it and that forming a barrier or an atoll: it is, however, generally of less width, and consequently few islets have been formed on it. From the corals growing more vigorously on the outside, and from the noxious effect of the sediment washed inwards, the outer edge of the reef is the highest part, and between it and the land there is generally a shallow sandy channel a few feet in depth. Where banks of sediment have accumulated near to the surface, as in parts of the West Indies, they sometimes become fringed with corals, and hence in some degree resemble lagoon-islands or atolls; in the same manner as fringing-reefs, surrounding gently-sloping islands, in some degree resemble barrier-reefs.

No theory on the formation of coral-reefs can be considered satisfactory which does not include the three great classes. We have seen that we are driven to believe in the subsidence of these vast areas, interspersed with low islands, of which not one rises above the height to which the wind and

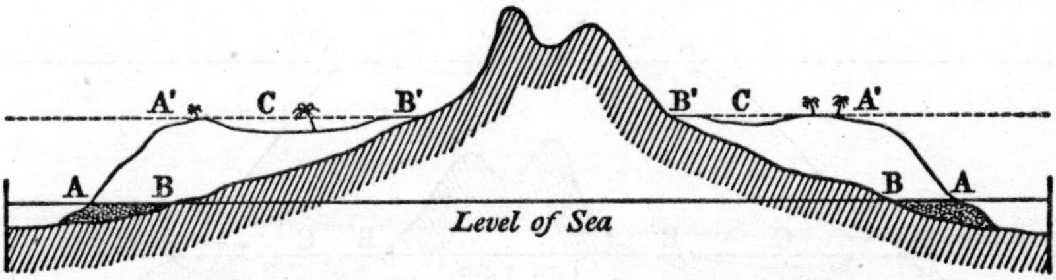

AA. Outer edges of the fringing-reef, at the level of the sea. BB. The shores of the fringed island.

A′A′. Outer edges of the reef, after its upward growth during a period of subsidence, now converted into a barrier, with islets on it. B′B′. The shores of the now encircled island. CC. Lagoon-channel.

N.B. In this and the following woodcut, the subsidence of the land could be represented only by an apparent rise in the level of the sea.

waves can throw up matter, and yet are constructed by animals requiring a foundation, and that foundation to lie at no great depth. Let us then take an island surrounded by fringing-reefs, which offer no difficulty in their structure; and let this island with its reef, represented by the unbroken lines in the woodcut, slowly subside. Now as the island sinks down, either a few feet at a time or quite insensibly, we may safely infer, from what is known of the conditions favourable to the growth of coral, that the living masses, bathed by the surf on the margin of the reef, will soon regain the surface. The water, however, will encroach little by little on the shore, the island becoming lower and smaller, and the space between the inner edge of the reef and the beach proportionally broader. A section of the reef and island in this state, after a subsidence of several hundred feet, is given by the dotted lines. Coral islets are supposed to have been formed on the reef; and a ship is anchored in the lagoon-channel. This channel will be more or less deep, according to the rate of subsidence, to the amount of sediment accumulated in it, and to the growth of the delicately branched corals which can live there. The section in this state resembles in every respect one drawn through an encircled island: in fact, it is a real section (on the scale of .517 of an inch to a mile) through Bolabola in the Pacific. We can now at once see why encircling barrier-reefs stand so far from the shores which they front. We can also perceive, that a line drawn perpendicularly down from the outer edge of the new reef, to the foundation of solid rock beneath the old fringing-reef, will exceed by as many feet as there have been feet of subsidence, that small limit of depth at which the effective corals can live: the little architects having built up their great wall-like mass, as the whole sank down, upon a basis formed of other

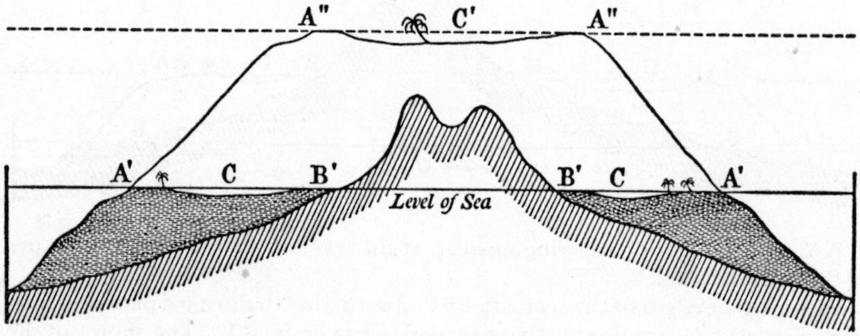

A′A′. Outer edges of the barrier-reef at the level of the sea, with islets on it. B′B′. The shores of the included island. CC. The lagoon-channel.

A″A″. Outer edges of the reef, now converted into an atoll. C′. The lagoon of the new atoll.

N.B. According to the true scale, the depths of the lagoon-channel and lagoon are much exaggerated.

corals and their consolidated fragments. Thus the difficulty on this head, which appeared so great, disappears.

If, instead of an island, we had taken the shore of a continent fringed with reefs, and had imagined it to have subsided, a great straight barrier, like that of Australia or New Caledonia, separated from the land by a wide and deep channel, would evidently have been the result.

Let us take our new encircling barrier-reef, of which the section is now represented by unbroken lines, and which, as I have said, is a real section through Bolabola, and let it go on subsiding. As the barrier-reef slowly sinks down, the corals will go on vigorously growing upwards; but as the island sinks, the water will gain inch by inch on the shore—the separate mountains first forming separate islands within one great reef—and finally, the last and highest pinnacle disappearing. The instant this takes place, a perfect atoll is formed: I have said, remove the high land from within an encircling barrier-reef, and an atoll is left, and the land has been removed. We can now perceive how it comes that atolls, having sprung from encircling barrier-reefs, resemble them in general size, form, in the manner in which they are grouped together, and in their arrangement in single or double lines; for they may be called rude outline charts of the sunken islands over which they stand. We can further see how it arises that the atolls in the Pacific and Indian oceans extend in lines parallel to the generally prevailing strike of the high islands and the great coast-lines of those oceans. I venture, therefore, to affirm, that on the theory of the upward growth of the corals during the sinking of the land, all the leading features in those wonderful structures, the lagoon-islands or atolls, which have so long excited the attention of voyagers, as well as in the no less wonderful barrier-reefs, whether encircling small islands or stretching for hundreds of miles along the shores of a continent, are simply explained.

It may be asked, whether I can offer any direct evidence of the subsidence of barrier-reefs or atolls; but it must be borne in mind how difficult it must ever be to detect a movement, the tendency of which is to hide under water the part affected. Nevertheless, at Keeling Atoll I observed on all sides of the lagoon old cocoa-nut trees undermined and falling; and in one place the foundation-posts of a shed, which the inhabitants asserted had stood seven years before just above high-water mark, but now was daily washed by every tide: on inquiry I found that three earthquakes, one of them severe, had been felt here during the last ten years. At Vanikoro, the lagoon-channel is remarkably deep, scarcely any alluvial soil has accumulated at the foot of the lofty included mountains, and remarkably few islets have been formed by the heaping of fragments and sand on the wall-like barrier-reef; these facts, and some analogous ones, led me to believe that this island must lately have subsided and the reef grown upwards: here again earthquakes are frequent and very severe. In the Society Archipelago, on the other hand, where the lagoon-channels are almost choked up, where much low alluvial land has accumulated, and where in some cases long islets have been formed on the barrier-reefs—facts all showing that the islands have not very lately subsided—only feeble shocks are most rarely felt. In these coral formations, where the land and water seem struggling for mastery, it must be ever difficult to decide between the effects of a change in the set of the tides and of a slight subsidence: that many of these reefs and atolls are subject to changes of some kind is certain; on some atolls the islets appear to have increased greatly within a late period; on others they have been partially or wholly washed away. The inhabitants of parts of the Maldiva Archipelago know the date of the first formation of some islets; in other parts, the corals are now flourishing on water-washed reefs, where holes made for graves attest the former existence of inhabited land. It is difficult to believe in frequent changes in the tidal currents of an open ocean; whereas, we have in the earthquakes recorded by the natives on some atolls, and in the great fissures observed on other atolls, plain evidence of changes and disturbances in progress in the subterranean regions.

It is evident, on our theory, that coasts merely fringed by reefs cannot have subsided to any perceptible amount; and therefore they must, since the growth of their corals, either have remained stationary or have been upheaved. Now it is remarkable how generally it can be shown, by the presence of upraised organic remains, that the fringed islands have been elevated: and so far, this is indirect evidence in favour of our theory. I was particularly struck with this fact, when I found to my surprise, that the descriptions given by MM. Quoy and Gaimard were applicable, not to reefs in general as implied by them, but only to those of the fringing-class; my surprise, however, ceased when I afterwards found that, by a strange chance, all the several islands visited by these eminent naturalists, could be shown by their own statements to have been elevated within a recent geological era.

Not only the grand features in the structure of barrier-reefs and of atolls, and of their likeness to each other in form, size, and other characters, are explained on the theory of subsidence—which theory we are independently forced to admit in the very areas in question, from the necessity of finding bases for the corals within the requisite depth—but many details in structure and exceptional cases can thus also be simply explained. I will give only a few instances. In barrier-reefs it has long been remarked with surprise, that the passages through the reef exactly face valleys in the included land, even in cases where the reef is separated from the land by a lagoon-channel so wide and so much deeper than the actual passage itself, that it seems hardly possible that the very small quantity of water or sediment brought down could injure the corals on the reef. Now, every reef of the fringing-class is breached by a narrow gateway in front of the smallest rivulet, even if dry during the greater part of the year, for the mud, sand, or gravel, occasionally washed down, kills the corals on which it is deposited. Consequently, when an island thus fringed subsides, though most of the narrow gateways will probably become closed by the outward and upward growth of the corals, yet any that are not closed (and some must always be kept open by the sediment and impure water flowing out of the lagoon-channel) will still continue to front exactly the upper parts of those valleys, at the mouths of which the original basal fringing-reef was breached.

We can easily see how an island fronted only on one side, or on one side with one end or both ends encircled by barrier-reefs, might after long-continued subsidence be converted either into a single wall-like reef, or into an atoll with a great straight spur projecting from it, or into two or three atolls tied together by straight reefs—all of which exceptional cases actually occur. As the reef-building corals require food, are preyed upon by other animals, are killed by sediment, cannot adhere to a loose bottom, and may be easily carried down to a depth whence they cannot spring up again, we need feel no surprise at the reefs both of atolls and barriers becoming in parts imperfect. The great barrier of New Caledonia is thus imperfect and broken in many parts; hence, after long subsidence, this great reef would not produce one great atoll 400 miles in length, but a chain or archipelago of atolls, of very nearly the same dimensions with those in the Maldiva Archipelago. Moreover, in an atoll once breached on opposite sides, from the likelihood of the oceanic and tidal currents passing straight through the breaches, it is extremely improbable that the corals, especially during continued subsidence, would ever be able again to unite the rim; if they did not, as the whole sank downwards, one atoll would be divided into two or more. In the Maldiva Archipelago there are distinct atolls so related to each other in position, and separated by channels either unfathomable or very deep (the channel between Ross and Ari Atolls is 150 fathoms, and that between the north and south Nillandoo Atolls is 200 fathoms in depth), that it is impossible to look at a map of them without believing that they were once more intimately related. And in this same archipelago, Mahlos-Mahdoo Atoll is divided by a bifurcating channel from 100 to 132 fathoms in depth, in such a manner, that it is scarcely possible to say whether it ought strictly to be called three separate atolls, or one great atoll not yet finally divided.

I will not enter on many more details; but I must remark that the curious structure of the northern Maldiva Atolls receives (taking into consideration the free entrance of the sea through their broken margins) a simple explanation in the upward and outward growth of the corals, originally based both on small detached reefs in their lagoons, such as occur in common atolls, and on broken portions of the linear marginal reef, such as bounds every atoll of the ordinary form. I cannot refrain from once again remarking on the singularity of these complex structures—a great sandy and generally concave disk rises abruptly from the unfathomable ocean, with its central expanse studded, and its edge symmetrically bordered with oval basins of coral-rock just lipping the surface of the sea, sometimes clothed with vegetation, and each containing a lake of clear water!

One more point in detail: as in two neighbouring archipelagoes corals flourish in one and not in the other, and as so many conditions before enumerated must affect their existence, it would be an inexplicable fact if, during the changes to which earth, air, and water are subjected, the reef-building corals were to keep alive for perpetuity on any one spot or area. And as by our theory the areas including atolls and barrier-reefs are subsiding, we ought occasionally to find reefs both dead and submerged. In all reefs, owing to the sediment being washed out of the lagoon or lagoon-channel to leeward, that side is least favourable to the long-continued vigorous growth of the corals; hence dead portions of reef not unfrequently occur on the leeward side; and these, though still retaining their proper wall-like form, are now in several instances sunk several fathoms beneath the surface. The Chagos group appears from some cause, possibly from the subsidence having been too rapid, at present to be much less favourably circumstanced for the growth of reefs than formerly: one atoll has a portion of its marginal reef, nine miles in length, dead and submerged; a second has only a few quite small living points which rise to the surface; a third and fourth are entirely dead and submerged; a fifth is a mere wreck, with its structure almost obliterated. It is remarkable that in all these cases, the dead reefs and portions of reef lie at nearly the same depth, namely, from six to eight fathoms beneath the surface, as if they had been carried down by one uniform movement. One of these 'half-drowned atolls', so called by Capt. Moresby (to whom I am indebted for much invaluable information), is of vast size, namely, ninety nautical miles across in one direction, and seventy miles in another line; and is in many respects eminently curious. As by our theory it follows that new atolls will generally be formed in each new area of subsidence, two weighty objections might have been raised, namely, that atolls must be increasing indefinitely in number; and secondly, that in old areas of subsidence each separate atoll must be increasing indefinitely in thickness, if proofs of their occasional destruction could not have been adduced. Thus have we traced the history of these great rings of coral-rock, from their first origin through their normal changes, and through the occasional accidents of their existence, to their death and final obliteration.

In my volume on '*Coral Formations*' I have published a map, in which I have coloured all the atolls dark-blue, the barrier-reefs pale-blue, and the fringing-reefs red. These latter reefs have been formed whilst the land has been stationary, or, as appears from the frequent presence of upraised organic remains, whilst it has been slowly rising: atolls and barrier-reefs, on the other hand, have grown up during the directly opposite movement of subsidence, which movement must have been very gradual, and in the case of atolls so vast in amount as to have buried every mountain-summit over wide ocean-spaces. Now in this map we see that the reefs tinted pale and dark blue, which have been produced by the same order of movement, as a general rule manifestly stand near each other. Again we see, that the areas with the two blue tints are of wide extent; and that they lie separate from extensive lines of coast coloured red, both of which circumstances might naturally have been inferred, on the theory of the nature of the reefs having been governed by the nature of the earth's movement. It deserves notice, that in more than one instance where single red and blue circles approach near each other, I can show that there have been oscillations of level; for in such cases the red or fringed circles consist of atolls, originally by our theory formed during subsidence, but subsequently upheaved; and on the other hand, some of the pale-blue or encircled islands are composed of coral-rock, which must have been uplifted to its present height before that subsidence took place, during which the existing barrier-reefs grew upwards.

Authors have noticed with surprise, that although atolls are the commonest coral-structures throughout some enormous oceanic tracts, they are entirely absent in other seas, as in the West Indies: we can now at once perceive the cause, for where there has not been subsidence, atolls cannot have been formed; and in the case of the West Indies and parts of the East Indies, these tracts are known to have been rising within the recent period. The larger areas, coloured red and blue, are all elongated; and between the two colours there is a degree of rude alternation, as if the rising of one had balanced the sinking of the other. Taking into consideration the proofs of recent elevation both on the fringed coasts and on some others (for instance, in South America) where there are no reefs, we are led to conclude that the great continents are for the most part rising areas; and from the nature of the coral-reefs, that the central parts of the great oceans are sinking areas. The East Indian Archipelago, the most broken land in the world, is in most parts an area of elevation, but surrounded and penetrated, probably in more lines than one, by narrow areas of subsidence.

I have marked with vermilion spots all the many known active volcanoes within the limits of this same map. Their entire absence from every one of the great subsiding areas, coloured either pale or dark blue, is most striking; and not less so is the coincidence of the chief volcanic chains with the parts coloured red, which we are led to conclude have either long remained stationary, or more generally have been recently upraised. Although a few of the vermilion spots occur within no great distance of single circles tinted blue, yet not one single active volcano is situated within several hundred miles of an archipelago, or even small group of atolls. It is, therefore, a striking fact that in the Friendly Archipelago, which consists of a group of atolls upheaved and since partially worn down, two volcanoes, and perhaps more, are historically known to have been in action. On the other hand, although most of the islands in the Pacific which are encircled by barrier-reefs, are of volcanic origin, often with the remnants of craters still distinguishable, not one of them is known to have ever been in eruption. Hence in these cases it would appear, that volcanoes burst forth into action and become extinguished on the same spots, according as elevatory or subsiding movements prevail there. Numberless facts could be adduced to prove that upraised organic remains are common wherever there are active volcanoes; but until it could be shown that in areas of subsidence, volcanoes were either absent or inactive, the inference, however probable in itself, that their distribution depended on the rising or falling of the earth's surface, would have been hazardous. But now, I think, we may freely admit this important deduction.

Taking a final view of the map, and bearing in mind the statement made with respect to the upraised organic remains, we must feel astonished at the vastness of the areas, which have suffered changes in level either downwards or upwards, within a period not geologically remote. It would appear, also, that the elevatory and subsiding movements follow nearly the same laws. Throughout the spaces interspersed with atolls, where not a single peak of high land has been left above the level of the sea, the sinking must have been immense in amount. The sinking, moreover, whether continuous, or recurrent with intervals sufficiently long for the corals again to bring up their living edifices to the surface, must necessarily have been extremely slow. This conclusion is probably the most important one which can be deduced from the study of coral formations;—and it is one which it is difficult to imagine, how otherwise could ever have been arrived at. Nor can I quite pass over the probability of the former existence of large archipelagoes of lofty islands, where now only rings of coral-rock scarcely break the open expanse of the sea, throwing some light on the distribution of the inhabitants of the other high islands, now left standing so immensely remote from each other in the midst of the great oceans. The reef-constructing corals have indeed reared and preserved wonderful memorials of the subterranean oscillations of level; we see in each barrier-reef a proof that the land has there subsided, and in each atoll a monument over an island now lost. We may thus, like unto a geologist who had lived his ten thousand years and kept a record of the passing changes, gain some insight into the great system by which the surface of this globe has been broken up, and land and water interchanged.

CHAPTER 5

REFLECTIONS ON THE VOYAGE

[The last part of Chapter XXI of the *Beagle*, entitled 'Mauritius to England'.]

On the 19th of August we finally left the shores of Brazil. I thank God, I shall never again visit a slave-country. To this day, if I hear a distant scream, it recalls with painful vividness my feelings, when passing a house near Pernambuco, I heard the most pitiable moans, and could not but suspect that some poor slave was being tortured, yet knew that I was as powerless as a child even to remonstrate. I suspected that these moans were from a tortured slave, for I was told that this was the case in another instance. Near Rio de Janeiro I lived opposite to an old lady, who kept screws to crush the fingers of her female slaves. I have stayed in a house where a young household mulatto, daily and hourly, was reviled, beaten, and persecuted enough to break the spirit of the lowest animal. I have seen a little boy, six or seven years old, struck thrice with a horse-whip (before I could interfere) on his naked head, for having handed me a glass of water not quite clean; I saw his father tremble at a mere glance from his master's eye. These latter cruelties were witnessed by me in a Spanish colony, in which it has always been said, that slaves are better treated than by the Portuguese, English, or other European nations. I have seen at Rio de Janeiro a powerful negro afraid to ward off a blow directed, as he thought, at his face. I was present when a kind-hearted man was on the point of separating for ever the men, women, and little children of a large number of families who had long lived together. I will not even allude to the many heart-sickening atrocities which I authentically heard of;—nor would I have mentioned the above revolting details, had I not met with several people, so blinded by the constitutional gaiety of the negro, as to speak of slavery as a tolerable evil. Such people have generally visited at the houses of the upper classes, where the domestic slaves are usually well treated; and they have not, like myself, lived amongst the lower classes. Such enquirers will ask slaves about their condition; they forget that the slave must indeed be dull, who does not calculate on the chance of his answer reaching his master's ears.

It is argued that self-interest will prevent excessive cruelty; as if self-interest protected our domestic animals, which are far less likely than degraded slaves, to stir up the rage of their savage masters. It is an argument long since protested against with noble feeling, and strikingly exemplified, by the ever illustrious Humboldt. It is often attempted to palliate slavery by comparing the state of slaves with our poorer countrymen: if the misery of our poor be caused not by the laws of nature, but by our institutions, great is our sin; but how this bears on slavery, I cannot see; as well might the use of the thumbscrew be defended in one land, by showing that men in another land suffered from some dreadful disease. Those who look tenderly at the slave-owner, and with a cold heart at the slave, never seem to put themselves into the position of the latter;—what a cheerless prospect, with not even a hope of change! picture to yourself the chance, ever hanging over you, of your wife and your little children—those objects which nature urges even the slave to call his own—being torn from you and sold like beasts to the first bidder! And these deeds are done and palliated by men, who profess to love their neighbours as themselves, who believe in God, and pray that his Will be done on earth! It makes one's blood boil, yet heart tremble, to think that we Englishmen and our American descendants, with their boastful cry of liberty, have been and are so guilty: but it is a consolation to reflect, that we at least have made a greater sacrifice, than ever made by any nation, to expiate our sin.

⋆ ⋆ ⋆ ⋆

Our Voyage having come to an end, I will take a short retrospect of the advantages and disadvantages, the pains and pleasures, of our circumnavigation of the world. If a person asked my advice, before undertaking a long voyage, my answer would depend upon his possessing a decided taste for some branch of knowledge, which could by this means be advanced. No doubt it is a high satisfaction to behold various countries and the many races of mankind, but the pleasures gained at the time do not counter-balance the evils. It is necessary to look forward to a harvest, however distant that may be, when some fruit will be reaped, some good effected.

Many of the losses which must be experienced are obvious; such as that of the society of every old friend, and of the sight of those places with which every dearest remembrance is so intimately connected. These losses, however, are at the time partly relieved by the exhaustless delight of anticipating the long wished-for day of return. If, as poets say, life is a dream, I am sure in a voyage these are the visions which best serve to pass away the long night. Other losses, although not at first felt, tell heavily after a period: these are the want of room, of seclusion, of rest; the jading feeling of constant hurry; the privation of small luxuries, the loss of domestic society, and even of music and the other pleasures of imagination. When such trifles are mentioned, it is evident that the real grievances, excepting from accidents, of a sea-life are at an end. The short space of sixty years has made an astonishing difference in the facility of distant navigation. Even in the time of Cook, a man who left his fireside for such expeditions underwent severe privations. A yacht now, with every luxury of life, can circumnavigate the globe. Besides the vast improvements in ships and naval resources, the whole western shores of America are thrown open, and Australia has become the capital of a rising continent. How different are the circumstances to a man shipwrecked at the present day in the Pacific, to what they were in the time of Cook! Since his voyage a hemisphere has been added to the civilized world.

If a person suffer much from sea-sickness, let him weigh it heavily in the balance. I speak from experience: it is no trifling evil, cured in a week. If, on the other hand, he take pleasure in naval tactics, he will assuredly have full scope for his taste. But it must be borne in mind, how large a proportion of the time, during a long voyage, is spent on the water, as compared with the days in harbour. And what are the boasted glories of the illimitable ocean? A tedious waste, a desert of water, as the Arabian calls it. No doubt there are some delightful scenes. A moonlight night, with the clear heavens and the dark glittering sea, and the white sails filled by the soft air of a gently-blowing trade-wind; a dead calm, with the heaving surface polished like a mirror, and all still except the occasional flapping of the canvas. It is well once to behold a squall with its rising arch and coming fury, or the heavy gale of wind and mountainous waves. I confess, however, my imagination had painted something more grand, more terrific in the full-grown storm. It is an incomparably finer spectacle when beheld on shore, where the waving trees, the wild flight of the birds, the dark shadows and bright lights, the rushing of the torrents, all proclaim the strife of the unloosed elements. At sea the albatross and little petrel fly as if the storm were their proper sphere, the water rises and sinks as if fulfilling its usual task, the ship alone and its inhabitants seem the objects of wrath. On a forlorn and weather-beaten coast, the scene is indeed different, but the feelings partake more of horror than of wild delight.

Let us now look at the brighter side of the past time. The pleasure derived from beholding the scenery and the general aspect of the various countries we have visited, has decidedly been the most constant and highest source of enjoyment. It is probable that the picturesque beauty of many parts of Europe exceeds anything which we beheld. But there is a growing pleasure in comparing the character of the scenery in different countries, which to a certain degree is distinct from merely admiring its beauty. It depends chiefly on an acquaintance with the individual parts of each view: I am strongly induced to believe that, as in music, the person who understands every note will, if he also possesses a proper taste, more thoroughly enjoy the whole, so he who examines each part of a fine view, may also thoroughly comprehend the full and combined effect. Hence, a traveller should be a botanist, for in all views plants form the chief embellishment. Group masses of naked rock even in the wildest forms, and they may for a time afford a sublime spectacle, but they will soon grow monotonous. Paint them with bright and varied colours, as in Northern Chile, they will become fantastic; clothe them with vegetation, they must form a decent, if not a beautiful picture.

* * * *

Among the scenes which are deeply impressed on my mind, none exceed in sublimity the primeval forests undefaced by the hand of man; whether those of Brazil, where the powers of Life are predominant, or those of Tierra del Fuego, where Death and Decay prevail. Both are temples filled with the varied productions of the God of Nature:—no one can stand in these solitudes unmoved, and not feel that there is more in man than the mere breath of his body. In calling up images of the past, I find that the plains of Patagonia frequently cross before my eyes; yet these plains are pronounced by all wretched and useless. They can be described only by negative characters; without habitations, without water, without trees, without mountains, they support merely a few dwarf plants. Why then, and the case is not peculiar to myself, have these arid wastes taken so firm a hold on my memory? Why have not the still more level, the greener and more fertile Pampas, which are serviceable to mankind, produced an equal impression? I can scarcely analyse these feelings: but it must be partly owing to the free scope given to the imagination. The plains of Patagonia are boundless, for they are scarcely passable, and hence unknown: they bear the stamp of having lasted, as they are now, for ages, and there appears no limit to their duration through future time. If, as the ancients supposed, the flat earth was surrounded by an impassable breadth of water or by deserts heated to an intolerable excess, who would not look at these last boundaries to man's knowledge with deep but ill-defined sensations?

* * * *

Of individual objects, perhaps nothing is more certain to create astonishment than the first sight in his native haunt of a barbarian,—of man in his lowest and most savage state. One's mind hurries back over past centuries, and then asks, could our progenitors have been men like these?—men, whose very signs and expressions are less intelligible to us than those of the domesticated animals; men, who do not possess the instinct of those animals, nor yet appear to boast of human reason, or at least of arts consequent on that reason. I do not believe it is possible to describe or paint the difference between savage and civilized man. It is the difference between a wild and tame animal: and part of the interest in beholding a savage, is the same which would lead every one to desire to see the lion in his desert, the tiger tearing his prey in the jungle, or the rhinoceros wandering over the wild plains of Africa.

* * * *

There are several other sources of enjoyment in a long voyage, which are of a more reasonable nature. The map of the world ceases to be a blank; it becomes a picture full of the most varied and animated figures. Each part assumes its proper dimensions; continents are not looked at in the light of islands, or islands considered as mere specks, which are, in truth, larger than many kingdoms of Europe. Africa, or North and South America, are well-sounding names, and easily pronounced; but it is not until having sailed for weeks along small portions of their shore, that one is thoroughly convinced what vast spaces on our immense world these names imply.

From seeing the present state, it is impossible not to look forward with high expectations to the future progress of nearly an entire hemisphere. The march of improvement, consequent on the introduction of Christianity throughout the South Sea, probably stands by itself in the records of history. It is the more striking when we remember that only sixty years since, Cook, whose excellent judgment none will dispute, could foresee no prospect of a change. Yet these changes have now been effected by the philanthropic spirit of the British nation.

In the same quarter of the globe Australia is rising, or indeed may be said to have risen, into a grand centre of civilization, which, at some not very remote period, will rule as empress over the southern hemisphere. It is impossible for an Englishman to behold these distant colonies, without a high pride and satisfaction. To hoist the British flag, seems to draw with it as a certain consequence, wealth, prosperity, and civilization.

In conclusion, it appears to me that nothing can be more improving to a young naturalist, than a journey in distant countries. It both sharpens, and partly allays that want and craving, which, as Sir J. Herschel remarks, a man experiences although every corporeal sense be fully satisfied. The excitement from the novelty of objects, and the chance of success, stimulate him to increased activity. Moreover, as a number of isolated facts soon become uninteresting, the habit of comparison leads to generalization. On the other hand, as the traveller stays but a short time in each place, his descriptions must generally consist of mere sketches, instead of detailed observations. Hence arises, as I have found to my cost, a constant tendency to fill up the wide gaps of knowledge, by inaccurate and superficial hypotheses.

But I have too deeply enjoyed the voyage, not to recommend any naturalist, although he must not expect to be so fortunate in his companions as I have been, to take all chances, and to start, on travels by land if possible, if otherwise on a long voyage. He may feel assured, he will meet with no difficulties or dangers, excepting in rare cases, nearly so bad as he beforehand anticipates. In a moral point of view, the effect ought to be, to teach him good-humoured patience, freedom from selfishness, the habit of acting for himself, and of making the best of every occurrence. In short, he ought to partake of the characteristic qualities of most sailors. Travelling ought also to teach him distrust; but at the same time he will discover, how many truly kind-hearted people there are, with whom he never before had, or ever again will have any further communication, who yet are ready to offer him the most disinterested assistance.

PART THREE

THE ORIGIN OF SPECIES

CHAPTER 6

THE DARWIN-WALLACE ESSAYS OF 1858

[Darwin has sketched the history of the publication of the *Origin* in his *Autobiography*—how he was finally brought to put his theory of natural selection into print by the receipt of a short essay from Alfred Russel Wallace, then living in Ternate, outlining an identical conception. The two essays, by Darwin and Wallace, published in the *Journal of the Proceedings of the Linnean Society*, make a sort of capsule statement of the theory and thus, even apart from their historic interest, make an appropriate introduction to the *Origin of Species* itself, which was published late in the following year.]

London, *June 30th*, 1858

MY DEAR SIR,—The accompanying papers, which we have the honour of communicating to the Linnean Society, and which all relate to the same subject, viz. the Laws which affect the Production of Varieties, Races, and Species, contain the results of the investigations of two indefatigable naturalists, Mr. Charles Darwin and Mr. Alfred Wallace.

These gentlemen having, independently and unknown to one another, conceived the same very ingenious theory to account for the appearance and perpetuation of varieties and of specific forms on our planet, may both fairly claim the merit of being original thinkers in this important line of inquiry; but neither of them having published his views, though Mr. Darwin has for many years past been repeatedly urged by us to do so, and both authors having now unreservedly placed their papers in our hands, we think it would best promote the interests of science that a selection from them should be laid before the Linnean Society.

Taken in the order of their dates, they consist of:

1. Extracts from a MS. work on Species, by Mr. Darwin, which was sketched in 1839, and copied in 1844, when the copy was read by Dr. Hooker, and its contents afterwards communicated to Sir Charles Lyell. The first Part is devoted to 'The Variation of Organic Beings under Domestication and in their Natural State', and the second chapter of that

Part, from which we propose to read to the Society the extracts referred to, is headed, 'On the Variation of Organic Beings in a state of Nature; on the Natural Means of Selection; on the Comparison of Domestic Races and true Species.'

2. An abstract of a private letter addressed to Professor Asa Gray, of Boston, U.S., in October 1857, by Mr. Darwin, in which he repeats his views, and which shows that these remained unaltered from 1839 to 1857.

3. An Essay by Mr. Wallace, entitled 'On the Tendency of Varieties to depart indefinitely from the Original Type'. This was written at Ternate in February 1858, for the perusal of his friend and correspondent Mr. Darwin, and sent to him with the expressed wish that it should be forwarded to Sir Charles Lyell, if Mr. Darwin thought it sufficiently novel and interesting. So highly did Mr. Darwin appreciate the value of the views therein set forth, that he proposed, in a letter to Sir Charles Lyell, to obtain Mr. Wallace's consent to allow the Essay to be published as soon as possible. Of this step we highly approved, provided Mr. Darwin did not withhold from the public, as he was strongly inclined to do (in favour of Mr. Wallace), the memoir which he had himself written on the same subject, and which, as before stated, one of us had perused in 1844, and the contents of which we had both of us been privy to for many years. On representing this to Mr. Darwin, he gave us permission to make what use we thought proper of his memoir, &c.; and in adopting our present course, of presenting it to the Linnean Society, we have explained to him that we are not solely considering the relative claims to priority of himself and his friend, but the interests of science generally; for we feel it to be desirable that views founded on a wide deduction from facts, and matured by years of reflection, should constitute at once a goal from which others may start, and that, while the scientific world is waiting for the appearance of Mr. Darwin's complete work, some of the leading results of his labours, as well as those of his able correspondent, should together be laid before the public.

We have the honour to be yours very obediently,

Charles Lyell
Jos. D. Hooker

J. J. Bennett, Esq.,
Secretary of the Linnean Society.

I. EXTRACT FROM AN UNPUBLISHED WORK ON SPECIES, BY C. DARWIN, ESQ., CONSISTING OF A PORTION OF A CHAPTER ENTITLED, 'ON THE VARIATION OF ORGANIC BEINGS IN A STATE OF NATURE; ON THE NATURAL MEANS OF SELECTION; ON THE COMPARISON OF DOMESTIC RACES AND TRUE SPECIES'

De Candolle, in an eloquent passage, has declared that all nature is at war, one organism with another, or with external nature. Seeing the contented face of nature, this may at first well be doubted; but reflection will inevitably prove it to be true. The war, however, is not constant, but recurrent in a slight degree at short periods, and more severely at occasional more distant periods; and hence its effects are easily overlooked. It is the doctrine of Malthus applied in most cases with tenfold force. As in every climate there are seasons, for each of its inhabitants, of greater and less abundance, so all annually breed; and the moral restraint which in some small degree checks the increase of mankind is entirely lost. Even slow-breeding mankind has doubled in twenty-five years; and if he could increase his food with greater ease, he would double in less time. But for animals without artificial means, the amount of food for each species must, *on an average*, be constant, whereas the increase of all organisms tends to be geometrical, and in a vast majority of cases at an enormous ratio. Suppose in a certain spot there are eight pairs of birds, and that *only* four pairs of them annually (including double hatches) rear only four young, and that these go on rearing their young at the same rate, then at the end of seven years (a short life, excluding violent deaths, for any bird) there will be 2048 birds, instead of the original sixteen. As this increase is quite impossible, we must conclude either that birds do not rear nearly half their young, or that the average life of a bird is, from accident, not nearly seven years. Both checks probably concur. The same kind of calculation applied to all plants and animals affords results more or less striking, but in very few instances more striking than in man.

Many practical illustrations of this rapid tendency to increase are on record, among which, during peculiar seasons, are the extraordinary numbers of certain animals; for instance, during the years 1826 to 1828, in La Plata, when from drought some millions of cattle perished, the whole country actually swarmed with mice. Now I think it cannot be doubted that during the breeding-season all the mice (with the exception of a few males or females in excess) ordinarily pair, and therefore that this astounding increase during three years must be attributed to a greater number than usual surviving the first year, and then breeding, and so on till the third year, when their numbers were brought down to their usual limits on the return of wet weather. Where man has introduced plants and animals into a new and favourable country, there are many accounts in how surprisingly few years the whole country has become stocked with them. This increase would necessarily stop as soon as the country was fully stocked; and yet we have every reason to believe, from what is known of wild animals, that *all* would pair in the spring. In the majority of cases it is most difficult to imagine where the checks fall—though generally, no doubt, on the seeds, eggs, and young; but when we remember how impossible, even in mankind (so much better known than any other animal), it is to infer from repeated casual observations what the average duration of life is, or to discover the different percentage of deaths to births in different countries, we ought to feel no surprise at our being unable to discover where the check falls in any animal or plant. It should always be remembered, that in most cases the checks are recurrent yearly in a small, regular degree, and in an extreme degree during unusually cold, hot, dry, or wet years, according to the constitution of the being in question. Lighten any check in the least degree, and the geometrical powers of increase in every organism will almost instantly increase the average number of the favoured species. Nature may be compared to a surface on which rest ten thousand sharp wedges touching each other and driven inwards by incessant blows. Fully to realize these views much reflection is requisite. Malthus on man should be studied; and all such cases as those of the mice in La Plata, of the cattle and horses when first turned out in South America, of the birds by our calculation, &c., should be well considered. Reflect on the enormous multiplying power *inherent and annually in action* in all animals; reflect on the countless seeds scattered by a hundred ingenious contrivances, year after year, over the whole face of the land; and yet we have every reason to suppose that the average percentage of each of the inhabitants of a country usually remains constant. Finally, let it be borne in mind that this average number of individuals (the external conditions remaining the same) in each country is kept up by recurrent struggles against other species or against external nature (as on the borders of the Arctic regions, where the cold checks life), and that ordinarily each individual of every species holds its place, either by its own struggle and capacity of acquiring nourishment in some period of its life, from the egg upwards; or by the struggle of its parents (in short-lived organisms, when the main check occurs at longer intervals) with other individuals of the *same* or *different* species.

But let the external condition of a country alter. If in a small degree, the relative proportions of the inhabitants will in most cases simply be slightly changed; but let the number of inhabitants be small, as on an island, and free access to it from other countries be circumscribed, and let the change of conditions continue progressing (forming new stations), in such a case the original inhabitants must cease to be as perfectly adapted to the changed conditions as they were originally. It has been shown in a former part of this work, that such changes of external conditions would, from their acting on the reproductive system, probably cause the organization of those beings which were most affected to become, as under domestication, plastic. Now, can it be doubted, from the struggle each individual has to obtain subsistence, that any minute variation in structure, habits, or instincts, adapting that individual better to the new conditions, would tell upon its vigour and health? In the struggle it would have a better *chance* of surviving; and those of its offspring which inherited the variation, be it ever so slight, would also have a better *chance*. Yearly more are bred than can survive; the smallest grain in the balance, in the long run, must tell on which death shall fall, and which shall survive. Let this work of selection on the one hand, and death on the other, go on for a thousand generations, who will pretend to affirm that it would produce no effect, when we remember what, in a few years, Bakewell effected in cattle, and Western in sheep, by this identical principle of selection?

To give an imaginary example from changes in progress on an island: —let the organization of a canine animal which preyed chiefly on rabbits, but sometimes on hares, become slightly plastic; let these same changes cause the number of rabbits very slowly to decrease, and the number of hares to increase; the effect of this would be that the fox or dog would be driven to try to catch more hares; his organization, however, being slightly plastic, those individuals with the lightest forms, longest limbs, and best eyesight, let the difference be ever so small, would be slightly favoured, and would tend to live longer, and to survive during that time of the year when food was scarcest; they would also rear more young, which would tend to inherit these slight peculiarities. The less fleet ones would be rigidly destroyed. I can see no more reason to doubt that these causes in a thousand generations would produce a marked effect, and adapt the form of the fox or dog to the catching of hares instead of rabbits, than that greyhounds can be improved by selection and careful breeding. So would it be with plants under similar circumstances. If the number of individuals of a species with plumed seeds could be increased by greater powers of dissemination within its own area (that is, if the check to increase fell chiefly on the seeds), those seeds which were provided with ever so little more down, would in the long run be most disseminated; hence a greater number of seeds thus formed would germinate, and would tend to produce plants inheriting the slightly better-adapted down.

Besides this natural means of selection, by which those individuals are preserved, whether in their egg, or larval, or mature state, which are best adapted to the place they fill in nature, there is a second agency at work in most unisexual animals, tending to produce the same effect, namely, the struggle of the males for the females. These struggles are generally decided by the law of battle, but in the case of birds, apparently, by the charms of their song, by their beauty or their power of courtship, as in the dancing rock-thrush of Guiana. The most vigorous and healthy males, implying perfect adaptation, must generally gain the victory in their contests. This kind of selection, however, is less rigorous than the other; it does not require the death of the less successful, but gives to them fewer descendants. The struggle falls, moreover, at a time of year when food is generally abundant, and perhaps the effect chiefly produced would be the modification of the secondary sexual characters, which are not related to the power of obtaining food, or to defence from enemies, but to fighting with or rivalling other males. The result of this struggle amongst the males may be compared in some respects to that produced by those agriculturists who pay less attention to the careful selection of all their young animals, and more to the occasional use of a choice mate.

II. ABSTRACT OF A LETTER FROM C. DARWIN, ESQ., TO PROF. ASA GRAY, BOSTON, U.S., DATED DOWN, SEPTEMBER 5TH, 1857

1. It is wonderful what the principle of selection by man, that is the picking out of individuals with any desired quality, and breeding from them, and again picking out, can do. Even breeders have been astounded at their own results. They can act on differences inappreciable to an uneducated eye. Selection has been *methodically* followed in *Europe* for only the last half century; but it was occasionally, and even in some degree methodically, followed in the most ancient times. There must have been also a kind of unconscious selection from a remote period, namely in the preservation of the individual animals (without any thought of their offspring) most useful to each race of man in his particular circumstances. The 'roguing,' as nurserymen call the destroying of varieties which depart from their type, is a kind of selection. I am convinced that intentional and occasional selection has been the main agent in the production of our domestic races; but however this may be, its great power of modification has been indisputably shown in later times. Selection acts only by the accumulation of slight or greater variations, caused by external condi-

tions, or by the mere fact that in generation the child is not absolutely similar to its parent. Man, by this power of accumulating variations, adapts living beings to his wants—may be said to make the wool of one sheep good for carpets, of another for cloth, &c.

2. Now suppose there were a being who did not judge by mere external appearances, but who could study the whole internal organization, who was never capricious, and should go on selecting for one object during millions of generations; who will say what he might not effect? In nature we have some *slight* variation occasionally in all parts; and I think it can be shown that changed conditions of existence is the main cause of the child not exactly resembling its parents; and in nature geology shows us what changes have taken place, and are taking place. We have almost unlimited time; no one but a practical geologist can fully appreciate this. Think of the Glacial period, during the whole of which the same species at least of shells have existed; there must have been during this period millions on millions of generations.

3. I think it can be shown that there is such an unerring power at work in *Natural Selection* (the title of my book), which selects exclusively for the good of each organic being. The elder De Candolle, W. Herbert, and Lyell have written excellently on the struggle for life; but even they have not written strongly enough. Reflect that every being (even the elephant) breeds at such a rate, that in a few years, or at most a few centuries, the surface of the earth would not hold the progeny of one pair. I have found it hard constantly to bear in mind that the increase of every single species is checked during some part of its life, or during some shortly recurrent generation. Only a few of those annually born can live to propagate their kind. What a trifling difference must often determine which shall survive, and which perish!

4. Now take the case of a country undergoing some change. This will tend to cause some of its inhabitants to vary slightly—not but that I believe most beings vary at all times enough for selection to act on them. Some of its inhabitants will be exterminated; and the remainder will be exposed to the mutual action of a different set of inhabitants, which I believe to be far more important to the life of each being than mere climate. Considering the infinitely various methods which living beings follow to obtain food by struggling with other organisms, to escape danger at various times of life, to have their eggs or seeds disseminated, &c. &c., I cannot doubt that during millions of generations individuals of a species will be occasionally born with some slight variation, profitable to some part of their economy. Such individuals will have a better chance of surviving, and of propagating their new and slightly different structure; and

the modification may be slowly increased by the accumulative action of natural selection to any profitable extent. The variety thus formed will either coexist with, or, more commonly, will exterminate its parent form. An organic being, like the woodpecker or misseltoe, may thus come to be adapted to a score of contingencies—natural selection accumulating those slight variations in all parts of its structure, which are in any way useful to it during any part of its life.

5. Multiform difficulties will occur to every one, with respect to this theory. Many can, I think, be satisfactorily answered. *Natura non facit saltum* answers some of the most obvious. The slowness of the change, and only a very few individuals undergoing change at any one time, answers others. The extreme imperfection of our geological records answers others.

6. Another principle, which may be called the principle of divergence, plays, I believe, an important part in the origin of species. The same spot will support more life if occupied by very diverse forms. We see this in the many generic forms in a square yard of turf, and in the plants or insects on any little uniform islet, belonging almost invariably to as many genera and families as species. We can understand the meaning of this fact amongst the higher animals, whose habits we understand. We know that it has been experimentally shown that a plot of land will yield a greater weight if sown with several species and genera of grasses, than if sown with only two or three species. Now, every organic being, by propagating so rapidly, may be said to be striving its utmost to increase in numbers. So it will be with the offspring of any species after it has become diversified into varieties, or sub-species, or true species. And it follows, I think, from the foregoing facts, that the varying offspring of each species will try (only few will succeed) to seize on as many and as diverse places in the economy of nature as possible. Each new variety or species, when formed, will generally take the place of, and thus exterminate its less well-fitted parent. This I believe to be the origin of the classification and affinities of organic beings at all times; for organic beings always *seem* to branch and sub-branch like the limbs of a tree from a common trunk, the flourishing and diverging twigs destroying the less vigorous—the dead and lost branches rudely representing extinct genera and families.

This sketch is *most* imperfect; but in so short a space I cannot make it better. Your imagination must fill up very wide blanks.

C. Darwin

III. ON THE TENDENCY OF VARIETIES TO DEPART INDEFINITELY FROM THE ORIGINAL TYPE. BY ALFRED RUSSEL WALLACE

One of the strongest arguments which have been adduced to prove the original and permanent distinctness of species is, that *varieties* produced in a state of domesticity are more or less unstable, and often have a tendency, if left to themselves, to return to the normal form of the parent species; and this instability is considered to be a distinctive peculiarity of all varieties, even of those occurring among wild animals in a state of nature, and to constitute a provision for preserving unchanged the originally created distinct species.

In the absence or scarcity of facts and observations as to *varieties* occurring among wild animals, this argument has had great weight with naturalists, and has led to a very general somewhat prejudiced belief in the stability of species. Equally general, however, is the belief in what are called 'permanent or true varieties',—races of animals which continually propagate their like, but which differ so slightly (although constantly) from some other race, that the one is considered to be a variety of the other. Which is the *variety* and which the original *species*, there is generally no means of determining, except in those rare cases in which the one race has been known to produce an offspring unlike itself and resembling the other. This, however, would seem quite incompatible with the 'permanent invariability of species', but the difficulty is overcome by assuming that such varieties have strict limits, and can never again vary further from the original type, although they may return to it, which, from the analogy of the domesticated animals, is considered to be highly probable, if not certainly proved.

It will be observed that this argument rests entirely on the assumption, that *varieties* occurring in a state of nature are in all respects analogous to or even identical with those of domestic animals, and are governed by the same laws as regards their permanence or further variation. But it is the object of the present paper to show that this assumption is altogether false, that there is a general principle in nature which will cause many *varieties* to survive the parent species, and to give rise to successive variations departing further and further from the original type, and which also produces, in domesticated animals, the tendency of varieties to return to the parent form.

The life of wild animals is a struggle for existence. The full exertion of all their faculties and all their energies is required to preserve their own existence and provide for that of their infant offspring. The possibility of procuring food during the least favourable seasons, and of escaping the attacks of their most dangerous enemies, are the primary conditions which determine the existence both of individuals and of entire species. These conditions will also determine the population of a species; and by a careful consideration of all the circumstances we may be enabled to comprehend, and in some degree to explain, what at first sight appears so inexplicable—the excessive abundance of some species, while others closely allied to them are very rare.

The general proportion that must obtain between certain groups of animals is readily seen. Large animals cannot be so abundant as small ones; the carnivora must be less numerous than the herbivora; eagles and lions can never be so plentiful as pigeons and antelopes; the wild asses of the Tartarian deserts cannot equal in numbers the horses of the more luxuriant prairies and pampas of America. The greater or less fecundity of an animal is often considered to be one of the chief causes of its abundance or scarcity; but a consideration of the facts will show us that it really has little or nothing to do with the matter. Even the least prolific of animals would increase rapidly if unchecked, whereas it is evident that the animal population of the globe must be stationary, or perhaps, through the influence of man, decreasing. Fluctuations there may be; but permanent increase, except in restricted localities, is almost impossible. For example, our own observation must convince us that birds do not go on increasing every year in a geometrical ratio, as they would do, were there not some powerful check to their natural increase. Very few birds produce less than two young ones each year, while many have six, eight, or ten; four will certainly be below the average; and if we suppose that each pair produce young only four times in their life, that will also be below the average, supposing them not to die either by violence or want of food. Yet at this rate how tremendous would be the increase in a few years from a single pair! A simple calculation will show that in fifteen years each pair of birds would have increased to nearly ten millions! whereas we have no reason to believe that the number of the birds of any country increases at all in fifteen or in one hundred and fifty years. With such powers of increase the population must have reached its limits, and have become stationary, in a very few years after the origin of each species. It is evident, therefore, that each year an immense number of birds must perish—as many in fact as are born; and as on the lowest calculation the progeny are each year twice as numerous as their parents, it follows that, whatever be the average number of individuals existing in any given country, *twice that number must perish annually*,—a striking result, but one which seems at least highly probable, and is perhaps under rather than over the truth. It would therefore appear that, as far as the continuance of the species and the keeping up the average number of individuals are concerned, large broods are superfluous. On the average all above *one* become food for hawks and kites, wild cats and weasels, or perish of cold and hunger as winter comes on. This is strikingly proved by the case of particular species; for we find that their abundance in individuals bears no relation whatever to their fertility in producing offspring. Perhaps the most remarkable instance of an immense bird population is that of the passenger pigeon of the United States, which lays only one, or at most two eggs, and is said to rear generally but one young one. Why is this bird so extraordinarily abundant, while others producing two or three times as many young are much less plentiful? The explanation is not difficult. The food most congenial to this species, and on which it thrives best, is abundantly distributed over a very extensive region, offering such differences of soil and climate, that in one part or another of the area the supply never fails. The bird is capable of a very rapid and long-continued flight, so that it can pass without fatigue over the whole of the district it inhabits, and as soon as the supply of food begins to fail in one place is able to discover a fresh feeding-ground. This example strikingly shows us that the procuring of a constant supply of wholesome food is almost the sole condition requisite for ensuring the rapid increase of a given species, since neither the limited fecundity, nor the unrestrained attacks of birds of prey and of man are here sufficient to check it. In no other birds are these peculiar circumstances so strikingly combined. Either their food is more liable to failure, or they have not sufficient power of wing to search for it over an extensive area, or during some season of the year it becomes very scarce, and less wholesome substitutes have to be found; and thus, though more fertile in offspring, they can never increase beyond the supply of food in the least favourable seasons. Many birds can only exist by migrating, when their food becomes scarce, to regions possessing a milder, or at least a different climate, though, as these migrating birds are seldom excessively abundant, it is evident that the countries they visit are still deficient in a constant and abundant supply of wholesome food. Those whose organization does not permit them to migrate when their food becomes periodically scarce, can never attain a large population. This is probably the reason why woodpeckers are scarce with us, while in the tropics they are among the most abundant of solitary birds. Thus the house sparrow is more abundant than the redbreast, because its food is more constant and plentiful—seeds of grasses being preserved during the winter, and our farm-yards and stubble-fields furnishing an almost inexhaustible supply. Why, as a general rule, are aquatic, and especially sea birds, very numerous in individuals? Not because they are more prolific than others, generally the contrary; but because their food never fails, the sea-shores and river-banks daily swarming with a fresh supply of small mollusca and crustacea. Exactly the same laws will apply to mammals. Wild cats are prolific and have few enemies; why then are they never as abundant as rabbits? The only intelligible answer is, that their supply of food is more precarious. It appears evident, therefore, that so long as a country remains physically unchanged, the numbers of its animal population cannot materially increase. If one species does so, some others requiring the same kind of food must diminish in proportion. The numbers that die annually must be immense; and as the individual existence of each animal depends upon itself, those that die must be the weakest—the very young, the aged, and the diseased—while those that prolong their existence can only be the most perfect in health and vigour—those who are best able to obtain food regularly, and avoid their numerous enemies. It is, as we commenced by remarking, 'a struggle for existence', in which the weakest and least perfectly organized must always succumb.

Now it is clear that what takes place among the individuals of a species must also occur among the several allied species of a group—viz. that those which are best adapted to obtain a regular supply of food, and to defend themselves against the attacks of their enemies and the vicissitudes of the seasons, must necessarily obtain and preserve a superiority in population; while those species which from some defect of power or organization are the least capable of counteracting the vicissitudes of food supply, &c., must diminish in numbers, and, in extreme cases, become altogether extinct. Between these extremes the species will present various degrees of capacity for ensuring the means of preserving life; and it is thus we account for the abundance or rarity of species. Our ignorance will generally prevent us from accurately tracing the effects to their causes; but could we become perfectly acquainted with the organization and habits of the various species of animals, and could we measure the capacity of each for performing the different acts necessary to its safety and existence under all the varying circumstances by which it is surrounded, we might be able even to calculate the proportionate abundance of individuals which is the necessary result.

If now we have succeeded in establishing these two points—1st, *that the animal population of a country is generally stationary, being kept down by a periodical deficiency of food, and other checks;* and 2nd, *that the comparative abundance or scarcity of the individuals of the several species is entirely due to their organization and resulting habits, which, rendering it more difficult to procure a regular supply of food and to provide for their personal safety in some cases than in others, can only be balanced by a difference in the population which have to exist in a given area*—we shall be in a condition to proceed to the consideration of *varieties*, to which the preceding remarks have a direct and very important application.

Most or perhaps all the variations from the typical form of a species must have some definite effect, however slight, on the habits or capacities of the individuals. Even a change of colour might, by rendering them more or less distinguishable, affect their safety; a greater or less development of hair might modify their habits. More important changes, such as an increase in the power or dimensions of the limbs or any of the external organs, would more or less affect their mode of procuring food or the range of country which they inhabit. It is also evident that most changes would affect, either favourably or adversely, the powers of prolonging existence. An antelope with shorter or weaker legs must necessarily suffer more from the attacks of the feline carnivora; the passenger pigeon with less powerful wings would sooner or later be affected in its powers of procuring a regular supply of food; and in both cases the result must necessarily be a diminution of the population of the modified species. If, on the other hand, any species should produce a variety having slightly increased powers of preserving existence, that variety must inevitably in time acquire a superiority in numbers. These results must follow as surely as old age, intemperance, or scarcity of food produce an increased mortality. In both cases there may be many individual exceptions; but on the average the rule will invariably be found to hold good. All varieties will therefore fall into two classes—those which under the same conditions would never reach the population of the parent species, and those which would in time obtain and keep a numerical superiority. Now, let some alteration of physical conditions occur in the district—a long period of drought, a destruction of vegetation by locusts, the irruption of some new carnivorous animal seeking 'pastures new'—any change in fact tending to render existence more difficult to the species in question, and tasking its utmost powers to avoid complete extermination; it is evident that, of all the individuals composing the species, those forming the least numerous and most feebly organized variety would suffer first, and, were the pressure severe, must soon become extinct. The same causes continuing in action, the parent species would next suffer, would gradually diminish in numbers, and with a recurrence of similar unfavourable conditions might also become extinct. The superior variety would then alone remain, and on a return to favourable circumstances would rapidly increase in numbers and occupy the place of the extinct species and variety.

The *variety* would now have replaced the *species*, of which it would be a more perfectly developed and more highly organized form. It would be in all respects better adapted to secure its safety, and to prolong its individual existence and that of the race. Such a variety *could not* return to the original form; for that form is an inferior one, and could never compete with it for existence. Granted, therefore, a 'tendency' to reproduce the original type of the species, still the variety must ever remain preponderant in numbers, and under adverse physical conditions *again alone survive*. But this new, improved, and populous race might itself, in course of time, give rise to new varieties, exhibiting several diverging modifications of form, any of which, tending to increase the facilities for preserving existence, must, by the same general law, in their turn become predominant. Here, then we have *progression and continued divergence* deduced from the general laws which regulate the existence of animals in a state of nature, and from the undisputed fact that varieties do frequently occur. It is not, however, contended that this result would be invariable; a change of physical conditions in the district might at times materially modify it, rendering the race which had been the most capable of supporting existence under the former conditions now the least so, and even causing the extinction of the newer and, for a time, superior race, while the old or parent species and its first inferior varieties continued to flourish. Variations in unimportant parts might also occur, having no perceptible effect on the life-preserving powers; and the varieties so furnished might run a course parallel with the parent species, either giving rise to further variations or returning to the former type. All we argue for is, that certain varieties have a tendency to maintain their existence longer than the original species, and this tendency must make itself felt; for though the doctrine of chances or averages can never be trusted to on a limited scale, yet, if applied to high numbers, the results come nearer to what theory demands, and, as we approach to an infinity of examples, become strictly accurate. Now the scale on which nature works is so fast—the numbers of individuals and periods of time with which she deals approach so near to infinity, that any cause, however slight, and however liable to be veiled and counteracted by accidental circumstances, must in the end produce its full legitimate results.

Let us now turn to domesticated animals, and inquire how varieties produced among them are affected by the principles here enunciated. The essential difference in the condition of wild and domestic animals is this, —that among the former, their well-being and very existence depend upon the full exercise and healthy condition of all their senses and physical powers, whereas, among the latter, these are only partially exercised, and in some cases are absolutely unused. A wild animal has to search, and often to labour, for every mouthful of food—to exercise sight, hearing, and smell in seeking it, and in avoiding dangers, in procuring shelter from the inclemency of the seasons, and in providing for the subsistence and safety of its offspring. There is no muscle of its body that is not called into daily and hourly activity; there is no sense or faculty that is not strengthened by continual exercise. The domestic animal, on the other hand, has food provided for it, is sheltered, and often confined, to guard it against the vicissitudes of the seasons, is carefully secured from the attacks of its natural enemies, and seldom even rears its young without human assistance. Half of its senses and faculties are quite useless; and the other half are but occasionally called into feeble exercise, while even its muscular system is only irregularly called into action.

Now when a variety of such an animal occurs, having increased power or capacity in any organ or sense, such increase is totally useless, is never called into action, and may even exist without the animal ever becoming aware of it. In the wild animal, on the contrary, all its faculties and powers being brought into full action for the necessities of existence, any increase becomes immediately available, is strengthened by exercise, and must even slightly modify the food, the habits, and the whole economy of the race. It creates as it were a new animal, one of superior powers, and which will necessarily increase in numbers and outlive those inferior to it.

Again, in the domesticated animal all variations have an equal chance of continuance; and those which would decidedly render a wild animal unable to compete with its fellows and continue its existence are no disadvantage whatever in a state of domesticity. Our quickly fattening pigs, short-legged sheep, pouter pigeons, and poodle dogs could never have come into existence in a state of nature, because the very first step towards such inferior forms would have led to the rapid extinction of the race; still less could they now exist in competition with their wild allies. The great speed but slight endurance of the race horse, the unwieldy strength of the ploughman's team, would both be useless in a state of nature. If turned wild on the pampas, such animals would probably soon become extinct, or under favourable circumstances might each lose those extreme qualities which would never be called into action, and in a few generations would revert to a common type, which must be that in which the various powers and faculties are so proportioned to each other as to be best adapted to procure food and secure safety,—that in which by the full exercise of every part of his organization the animal can alone continue to live. Domestic varieties, when turned wild, *must* return to something near the type of the original wild stock *or become altogether extinct*.

We see, then, that no inferences as to varieties in a state of nature can be deduced from the observation of those occurring among domestic animals. The two are so much opposed to each other in every circumstance of their existence, that what applies to the one is almost sure not to apply to the other. Domestic animals are abnormal, irregular, artificial; they are subject to varieties which never occur and never can occur in a state of nature: their very existence depends altogether on human care; so far are many of them removed from that just proportion of faculties, that true balance of organization, by means of which alone an animal left to its own resources can preserve its existence and continue its race.

The hypothesis of Lamarck—that progressive changes in species have been produced by the attempts of animals to increase the development of their own organs, and thus modify their structure and habits—has been repeated and easily refuted by all writers on the subject of varieties and species, and it seems to have been considered that when this was done the whole question has been finally settled; but the view here developed renders such an hypothesis quite unnecessary, by showing that similar results must be produced by the action of principles constantly at work in nature. The powerful retractile talons of the falcon- and the cat-tribes have not been produced or increased by the volition of those animals; but among the different varieties which occurred in the earlier and less highly organized forms of these groups, *those always survived longest which had the greatest facilities for seizing their prey*. Neither did the giraffe acquire its long neck by desiring to reach the foliage of the more lofty shrubs, and constantly stretching its neck for the purpose, but because any varieties which occurred among its antitypes with a longer neck than usual *at once secured a fresh range of pasture over the same ground as their shorter-necked companions, and on the first scarcity of food were thereby enabled to outlive them*. Even the peculiar colours of many animals, especially insects, so closely resembling the soil or the leaves or the trunks on which they habitually reside, are explained on the same principle; for though in the course of ages varieties of many tints may have occurred, yet *those races having colours best adapted to concealment from their enemies would inevitably survive the longest*. We have also here an acting cause to account for that balance so often observed in nature,—a deficiency in one set of organs always being compensated by an increased development of some others—powerful wings accompanying weak feet, or great velocity making up for the absence of defensive weapons; for it has been shown that all varieties in which an unbalanced deficiency occurred could not long continue their existence. The action of this principle is exactly like that of the centrifugal governor of the steam engine, which checks and corrects any irregularities almost before they become evident; and in like manner no unbalanced deficiency in the animal kingdom can ever reach any conspicuous magnitude, because it would make itself felt at the very first step, by rendering existence difficult and extinction almost sure soon to follow. An origin such as is here advocated will also agree with the peculiar character of the modifications of form and structure which obtain in organized beings—the many lines of divergence from a central type, the increasing efficiency and power of a particular organ through a succession of allied species, and the remarkable persistence of unimportant parts such as colour, texture of plumage and hair, form of horns or crests, through a series of species differing considerably in more essential characters. It also furnishes us with a reason for that 'more specialized structure' which Professor Owen states to be a characteristic of recent compared with extinct forms, and which would evidently be the result of the progressive modification of any organ applied to a special purpose in the animal economy.

We believe we have now shown that there is a tendency in nature to the continued progression of certain classes of *varieties* further and further from the original type—a progression to which there appears no reason to assign any definite limits—and that the same principle which produces this result in a state of nature will also explain why domestic varieties have a tendency to revert to the original type. This progression, by minute steps, in various directions, but always checked and balanced by the necessary conditions, subject to which alone existence can be preserved, may, it is believed, be followed out so as to agree with all the phenomena presented by organized beings, their extinction and succession in past ages, and all the extraordinary modifications of form, instinct, and habits which they exhibit.

Ternate, February, 1858.

CHAPTER 7

THE VARIATION OF ORGANISMS

[Chapters I and II of the *Origin*, from the sixth edition of 1872. Darwin wrote 'an historical sketch of the progress of opinion on the origin of species, previously to the publication of the first edition of this work' which was inserted at the beginning of the second and subsequent editions. This was intended to meet the criticism that he had neglected the historical precedents for his ideas. It is omitted here. The first two sections of Chapter I, dealing with the causes of variability and inheritance have also been omitted, since the progress of genetics has greatly changed ideas on these subjects. Darwin was keenly aware of the deficiencies in information on inheritance available to him, writing that 'the laws governing inheritance are for the most part unknown'.]

CHARACTER OF DOMESTIC VARIETIES; DIFFICULTY OF DISTINGUISHING BETWEEN VARIETIES AND SPECIES; ORIGIN OF DOMESTIC VARIETIES FROM ONE OR MORE SPECIES

When we look to the hereditary varieties or races of our domestic animals and plants, and compare them with closely allied species, we generally perceive in each domestic race . . . less uniformity of character than in true species. Domestic races often have a somewhat monstrous character; by which I mean, that, although differing from each other, and from other species of the same genus, in several trifling respects, they often differ in an extreme degree in some one part, both when compared one with another, and more especially when compared with the species under nature to which they are nearest allied. With these exceptions (and with that of the perfect fertility of varieties when crossed,—a subject hereafter to be discussed), domestic races of the same species differ from each other in the same manner as do the closely-allied species of the same genus in a state of nature, but the differences in most cases are less in degree. This must be admitted as true, for the domestic races of many animals and plants have been ranked by some competent judges as the descendants of aboriginally distinct species, and by other competent judges as mere varieties. If any well marked distinction existed between a domestic race and a species, this source of doubt would not so perpetually recur. It has often been stated that domestic races do not differ from each other in characters of generic value. It can be shown that this statement is not correct; but naturalists differ much in determining what characters are of generic value; all such valuations being at present empirical. When it is explained how genera originate under nature, it will be seen that we have no right to expect often to find a generic amount of difference in our domesticated races.

* * * *

It has often been assumed that man has chosen for domestication animals and plants having an extraordinary inherent tendency to vary, and likewise to withstand diverse climates. I do not dispute that these capacities have added largely to the value of most of our domesticated productions: but how could a savage possibly know, when he first tamed an animal, whether it would vary in succeeding generations, and whether it would endure other climates? Has the little variability of the ass and goose, or the small power of endurance of warmth by the reindeer, or of cold by the common camel, prevented their domestication? I cannot doubt that if other animals and plants, equal in number to our domesticated productions, and belonging to equally diverse classes and countries, were taken from a state of nature, and could be made to breed for an equal number of generations under domestication, they would on an average vary as largely as the parent species of our existing domesticated productions have varied.

In the case of most of our anciently domesticated animals and plants, it is not possible to come to any definite conclusion, whether they are descended from one or several wild species. The argument mainly relied on by those who believe in the multiple origin of our domestic animals is, that we find in the most ancient times, on the monuments of Egypt, and in the lake-habitations of Switzerland, much diversity in the breeds; and that some of these ancient breeds closely resemble, or are even identical with, those still existing. But this only throws far backwards the history of civilisation, and shows that animals were domesticated at a much earlier period than has hitherto been supposed. The lake-inhabitants of Switzerland cultivated several kinds of wheat and barley, the pea, the poppy for oil, and flax; and they possessed several domesticated animals. They also carried on commerce with other nations. All this clearly shows, as Heer has remarked, that they had at this early age progressed considerably in civilisation; and this again implies a long continued previous period of less advanced civilisation, during which the domesticated animals, kept by different tribes in different districts, might have varied and given rise to distinct races. Since the discovery of flint tools in the superficial formations of many parts of the world, all geologists believe that barbarian man existed at an enormously remote period; and we know that at the present day there is hardly a tribe so barbarous, as not to have domesticated at least the dog.

* * * *

PRINCIPLES OF SELECTION ANCIENTLY FOLLOWED, AND THEIR EFFECTS

Let us now briefly consider the steps by which domestic races have been produced, either from one or from several allied species. Some effect may be attributed to the direct and definite action of the external conditions of life, and some to habit; but he would be a bold man who would account by such agencies for the differences between a dray- and race-horse, a greyhound and bloodhound, a carrier and tumbler pigeon. One of the most remarkable features in our domesticated races is that we see in them adaptation, not indeed to the animal's or plant's own good, but to man's use or fancy. Some variations useful to him have probably arisen suddenly, or by one step; many botanists, for instance, believe that the fuller's teasel, with its hooks, which cannot be rivalled by any mechanical contrivance, is only a variety of the wild Dipsacus; and this amount of change may have suddenly arisen in a seedling. . . . But when we compare the dray-horse and race-horse, the dromedary and camel, the various breeds of sheep fitted either for cultivated land or mountain pasture, with the wool of one breed good for one purpose, and that of another breed for another purpose; when we compare the many breeds of dogs, each good for man in different ways; when we compare the game-cock, so pertinacious in battle, with other breeds so little quarrelsome, with 'everlasting layers' which never desire to sit, and with the bantam so small and elegant; when we compare the host of agricultural, culinary, orchard, and flower-garden races of plants, most useful to man at different seasons and for different purposes, or so beautiful in his eyes, we must, I think, look further than to mere variability. We cannot suppose that all the breeds were suddenly produced as perfect and as useful as we now see them; indeed, in many cases, we know that this has not been their history. The key is man's power of accumulative selection: nature gives successive variations; man adds them up in certain directions useful to him. In this sense he may be said to have made for himself useful breeds.

The great power of this principle of selection is not hypothetical. It is certain that several of our eminent breeders have, even within a single lifetime, modified to a large extent their breeds of cattle and sheep. In order fully to realise what they have done, it is almost necessary to read several of the many treatises devoted to this subject, and to inspect the animals. Breeders habitually speak of an animal's organisation as something plastic, which they can model almost as they please. If I had space I could quote numerous passages to this effect from highly competent authorities. Youatt, who was probably better acquainted with the works of agriculturists than almost any other individual, and who was himself a very good judge of animals, speaks of the principle of selection as 'that which enables the agriculturist, not only to modify the character of his flock, but to change it altogether. It is the magician's wand, by means of which he may summon into life whatever form and mould he pleases.' Lord Somerville, speaking of what breeders have done for sheep, says:— 'It would seem as if they had chalked out upon a wall a form perfect in itself, and then had given it existence.' In Saxony the importance of the principle of selection in regard to merino sheep is so fully recognised, that men follow it as a trade: the sheep are placed on a table and are studied, like a picture by a connoisseur; this is done three times at intervals of months, and the sheep are each time marked and classed, so that the very best may ultimately be selected for breeding.

What English breeders have actually effected is proved by the enormous prices given for animals with a good pedigree; and these have been exported to almost every quarter of the world. The improvement is by no means generally due to crossing different breeds; all the best breeders are strongly opposed to this practice, except sometimes amongst closely allied sub-breeds. And when a cross has been made, the closest selection is far more indispensable even than in ordinary cases. If selection consisted merely in separating some very distinct variety, and breeding from it, the principle would be so obvious as hardly to be worth notice; but its importance consists in the great effect produced by the accumulation in one direction, during successive generations, of differences absolutely inappreciable by an uneducated eye—differences which I for one have vainly attempted to appreciate. Not one man in a thousand has accuracy of eye and judgment sufficient to become an eminent breeder. If gifted with these qualities, and he studies his subject for years, and devotes his lifetime to it with indomitable perseverance, he will succeed, and may make great improvements; if he wants any of these qualities, he will assuredly fail. Few would readily believe in the natural capacity and years of practice requisite to become even a skilful pigeon-fancier.

The same principles are followed by horticulturists; but the variations are here often more abrupt. No one supposes that our choicest productions have been produced by a single variation from the aboriginal stock. We have proofs that this has not been so in several cases in which exact records have been kept; thus, to give a very trifling instance, the steadily-increasing size of the common gooseberry may be quoted. We see an astonishing improvement in many florists' flowers, when the flowers of the present day are compared with drawings made only twenty or thirty years ago. When a race of plants is once pretty well established, the seed-raisers do not pick out the best plants, but merely go over their seed-beds, and pull up the 'rogues', as they call the plants that deviate from the proper standard. With animals this kind of selection is, in fact, likewise followed; for hardly any one is so careless as to breed from his worst animals.

In regard to plants, there is another means of observing the accumulated effects of selection—namely, by comparing the diversity of flowers in the different varieties of the same species in the flower-garden; the diversity of leaves, pods, or tubers, or whatever part is valued, in the kitchen garden, in comparison with the flowers of the same varieties; and the diversity of fruit of the same species in the orchard, in comparison with the leaves and flowers of the same set of varieties. See how different the leaves of the cabbage are, and how extremely alike the flowers; how unlike the flowers of the heartsease are, and how alike the leaves; how much the fruit of the different kinds of gooseberries differ in size, colour, shape, and hairiness, and yet the flowers present very slight differences. It is not that the varieties which differ largely in some one point do not differ at all in other points; this is hardly ever,—I speak after careful observation,—perhaps never, the case. The law of correlated variation, the importance of which should never be overlooked, will ensure some differences; but, as a general rule, it cannot be doubted that the continued selection of slight variations, either in the leaves, the flowers, or the fruit, will produce races differing from each other chiefly in these characters.

It may be objected that the principle of selection has been reduced to methodical practice for scarcely more than three-quarters of a century; it has certainly been more attended to of late years, and many treatises have been published on the subject; and the result has been, in a corresponding degree, rapid and important. But it is very far from true that the principle is a modern discovery. I could give several references to works of high antiquity, in which the full importance of the principle is acknowledged. In rude and barbarous periods of English history choice animals were often imported, and laws were passed to prevent their exportation: the destruction of horses under a certain size was ordered, and this may be compared to the 'roguing' of plants by nurserymen. The principle of selection I find distinctly given in an ancient Chinese encyclopædia.

Explicit rules are laid down by some of the Roman classical writers. From passages in Genesis, it is clear that the colour of domestic animals was at that early period attended to. Savages now sometimes cross their dogs with wild canine animals, to improve the breed, and they formerly did so, as is attested by passages in Pliny. The savages in South Africa match their draught cattle by colour, as do some of the Esquimaux their teams of dogs. Livingstone states that good domestic breeds are highly valued by the Negroes in the interior of Africa who have not associated with Europeans. Some of these facts do not show actual selection, but they show that the breeding of domestic animals was carefully attended to in ancient times, and is now attended to by the lowest savages. It would, indeed, have been a strange fact, had attention not been paid to breeding, for the inheritance of good and bad qualities is so obvious.

UNCONSCIOUS SELECTION

At the present time, eminent breeders try by methodical selection, with a distinct object in view, to make a new strain or sub-breed, superior to anything of the kind in the country. But, for our purpose, a form of Selection, which may be called Unconscious, and which results from every one trying to possess and breed from the best individual animals, is more important. Thus, a man who intends keeping pointers naturally tries to get as good dogs as he can, and afterwards breeds from his own best dogs, but he has no wish or expectation of permanently altering the breed. Nevertheless we may infer that this process, continued during centuries, would improve and modify any breed, in the same way as Bakewell, Collins, &c., by this very same process, only carried on more methodically, did greatly modify, even during their lifetimes, the forms and qualities of their cattle. Slow and insensible changes of this kind can never be recognised unless actual measurements or careful drawings of the breeds in question have been made long ago, which may serve for comparison. In some cases, however, unchanged, or but little changed individuals of the same breed exist in less civilised districts, where the breed has been less improved. There is reason to believe that King Charles's spaniel has been unconsciously modified to a large extent since the time of that monarch. Some highly competent authorities are convinced that the setter is directly derived from the spaniel, and has probably been slowly altered from it. It is known that the English pointer has been greatly changed within the last century, and in this case the change has, it is believed, been chiefly effected by crosses with the foxhound; but what concerns us is, that the change has been effected unconsciously and gradually, and yet so effectually, that, though the old Spanish pointer certainly came from Spain, Mr. Borrow has not seen, as I am informed by him, any native dog in Spain like our pointer.

⋆ ⋆ ⋆ ⋆

If there exist savages so barbarous as never to think of the inherited character of the offspring of their domestic animals, yet any one animal particularly useful to them, for any special purpose, would be carefully preserved during famines and other accidents, to which savages are so liable, and such choice animals would thus generally leave more offspring than the inferior ones; so that in this case there would be a kind of unconscious selection going on. We see the value set on animals even by the barbarians of Tierra del Fuego, by their killing and devouring their old women, in times of dearth, as of less value than their dogs.

In plants the same gradual process of improvement, through the occasional preservation of the best individuals, whether or not sufficiently distinct to be ranked at their first appearance, as distinct varieties, and whether or not two or more species or races have become blended together by crossing, may plainly be recognised in the increased size and beauty which we now see in the varieties of the heartsease, rose, pelargonium, dahlia, and other plants, when compared with the older varieties or with their parent-stocks. No one would ever expect to get a first-rate heartsease or dahlia from the seed of a wild plant. No one would expect to raise a first-rate melting pear from the seed of the wild pear, though he might succeed from a poor seedling growing wild, if it had come from a garden-stock. The pear though cultivated in classical times, appears, from Pliny's description, to have been a fruit of very inferior quality. I have seen great surprise expressed in horticultural works at the wonderful skill of gardeners, in having produced such splendid results from such poor materials; but the art has been simple, and, as far as the final result is concerned, has been followed almost unconsciously. It has consisted in always cultivating the best-known variety, sowing its seeds, and, when a slightly better variety chanced to appear, selecting it, and so onwards. But the gardeners of the classical period, who cultivated the best pears which they could procure, never thought what splendid fruit we should eat; though we owe our excellent fruit in some small degree, to their having naturally chosen and preserved the best varieties they could anywhere find.

A large amount of change, thus slowly and unconsciously accumulated, explains, as I believe, the well-known fact, that in a number of cases we cannot recognise, and therefore do not know, the wild parent-stocks of the plants which have been longest cultivated in our flower and kitchen gardens. If it has taken centuries or thousands of years to improve or modify most of our plants up to their present standard of usefulness to man, we can understand how it is that neither Australia, the Cape of Good Hope, nor any other region inhabited by quite uncivilised man, has afforded us a single plant worth culture. It is not that these countries, so rich in species, do not by a strange chance possess the aboriginal stocks of any useful plants, but that the native plants have not been improved by continued selection up to a standard of perfection comparable with that acquired by the plants in countries anciently civilised.

* * * *

On the view here given of the important part which selection by man has played, it becomes at once obvious, how it is that our domestic races show adaptation in their structure or in their habits to man's wants or fancies. We can, I think, further understand the frequently abnormal characters of our domestic races, and likewise their differences being so great in external characters, and relatively so slight in internal parts or organs. Man can hardly select, or only with much difficulty, any deviation of structure excepting such as is externally visible; and indeed he rarely cares for what is internal. He can never act by selection, excepting on variations which are first given to him in some slight degree by nature. No man would ever try to make a fantail till he saw a pigeon with a tail developed in some slight degree in an unusual manner, or a pouter till he saw a pigeon with a crop of somewhat unusual size; and the more abnormal or unusual any character was when it first appeared, the more likely it would be to catch his attention. But to use such an expression as trying to make a fantail, is, I have no doubt, in most cases, utterly incorrect. The man who first selected a pigeon with a slightly larger tail, never dreamed what the descendants of that pigeon would become through long-continued, partly unconscious and partly methodical, selection. Perhaps the parent-bird of all fantails had only fourteen tail-feathers somewhat expanded, like the present Java fantail, or like individuals of other and distinct breeds, in which as many as seventeen tail-feathers have been counted. Perhaps the first pouter-pigeon did not inflate its crop much more than the turbit now does the upper part of its œsophagus,—a habit which is disregarded by all fanciers, as it is not one of the points of the breed.

Nor let it be thought that some great deviation of structure would be necessary to catch the fancier's eye: he perceives extremely small differences, and it is in human nature to value any novelty, however slight, in one's own possession. Nor must the value which would formerly have been set on any slight differences in the individuals of the same species, be judged of by the value which is now set on them, after several breeds have fairly been established. It is known that with pigeons many slight variations now occasionally appear, but these are rejected as faults or deviations from the standard of perfection in each breed. The common goose has not given rise to any marked varieties; hence the Toulouse and the common breed, which differ only in colour, that most fleeting of characters, have lately been exhibited as distinct at our poultry-shows.

These views appear to explain what has sometimes been noticed—namely, that we know hardly anything about the origin or history of any of our domestic breeds. But, in fact, a breed, like a dialect of a language, can hardly be said to have a distinct origin. A man preserves and breeds from an individual with some slight deviation of structure, or takes more care than usual in matching his best animals, and thus improves them, and the improved animals slowly spread in the immediate neighbourhood. But they will as yet hardly have a distinct name, and from being only slightly valued, their history will have been disregarded. When further improved by the same slow and gradual process, they will spread more widely, and will be recognised as something distinct and valuable, and will then probably first receive a provincial name. In semi-civilised countries, with little free communication, the spreading of a new sub-breed would be a slow process. As soon as the points of value are once acknowledged, the principle, as I have called it, of unconscious selection will always tend,—perhaps more at one period than at another, as the breed rises or falls in fashion,—perhaps more in one district than in another, according to the state of civilisation of the inhabitants,—slowly to add to the characteristic features of the breed, whatever they may be. But the chance will be infinitely small of any record having been preserved of such slow, varying, and insensible changes.

* * * *

To sum up on the origin of our domestic races of animals and plants. Changed conditions of life are of the highest importance in causing variability, both by acting directly on the organisation, and indirectly by affecting the reproductive system. It is not probable that variability is an inherent and necessary contingent, under all circumstances. The greater or less force of inheritance and reversion, determine whether variations shall endure. Variability is governed by many unknown laws, of which correlated growth is probably the most important. Something, but how much we do not know, may be attributed to the definite action of the conditions of life. Some, perhaps a great, effect may be attributed to the increased use or disuse of parts. The final result is thus rendered infinitely complex. In some cases the intercrossing of aboriginally distinct species appears to have played an important part in the origin of our breeds. When several breeds have once been formed in any country, their occasional intercrossing, with the aid of selection, has, no doubt, largely aided in the formation of new sub-breeds; but the importance of crossing has been much exaggerated, both in regard to animals and to those plants which are propagated by seed. With plants which are temporarily propagated by cuttings, buds, &c., the importance of crossing is immense; for the cultivator may here disregard the extreme variability both of hybrids and of mongrels, and the sterility of hybrids; but plants not propagated by seed are of little importance to us, for their endurance is only temporary. Over all these causes of Change, the accumulative action of Selection, whether applied methodically and quickly, or unconsciously and slowly but more efficiently seems to have been the predominant Power.

VARIATION UNDER NATURE

Before applying the principles arrived at [above] to organic beings in a state of nature, we must briefly discuss whether these latter are subject to any variation. To treat this subject properly, a long catalogue of dry facts ought to be given; but these I shall reserve for a future work. Nor shall I here discuss the various definitions which have been given of the term species. No one definition has satisfied all naturalists; yet every naturalist knows vaguely what he means when he speaks of a species. Generally the term includes the unknown element of a distant act of creation. The term 'variety' is almost equally difficult to define; but here community of descent is almost universally implied, though it can rarely be proved. We have also what are called monstrosities; but they graduate into varieties. By a monstrosity I presume is meant some considerable deviation of structure, generally injurious, or not useful to the species. Some authors use the term 'variation' in a technical sense, as implying a modification directly due to the physical conditions of life; and 'variations' in this sense are supposed not to be inherited; but who can say that the dwarfed condition of shells in the brackish waters of the Baltic, or dwarfed plants on Alpine summits, or the thicker fur of an animal from far northwards, would not in some cases be inherited for at least a few generations? And in this case I presume that the form would be called a variety.

It may be doubted whether sudden and considerable deviations of structure such as we occasionally see in our domestic productions, more especially with plants, are ever permanently propagated in a state of nature. Almost every part of every organic being is so beautifully related to its complex conditions of life that it seems as improbable that any part should have been suddenly produced perfect, as that a complex machine should have been invented by man in a perfect state. Under domestication monstrosities sometimes occur which resemble normal structures in widely different animals. Thus pigs have occasionally been born with a sort of proboscis, and if any wild species of the same genus had naturally possessed a proboscis, it might have been argued that this had appeared as a monstrosity; but I have as yet failed to find, after diligent search, cases of monstrosities resembling normal structures in nearly allied forms, and these alone bear on the question. If monstrous forms of this kind ever do appear in a state of nature and are capable of reproduction (which is not always the case), as they occur rarely and singularly, their preservation would depend on unusually favourable circumstances. They would, also, during the first and succeeding generations cross with the ordinary form, and thus their abnormal character would almost inevitably be lost. But I shall have to return in a future chapter to the preservation and perpetuation of single or occasional variations.

INDIVIDUAL DIFFERENCES

The many slight differences which appear in the offspring from the same parents, or which it may be presumed have thus arisen, from being observed in the individuals of the same species inhabiting the same confined locality, may be called individual differences. No one supposes that all the individuals of the same species are cast in the same actual mould. These individual differences are of the highest importance for us, for they are often inherited, as must be familiar to every one; and they thus afford materials for natural selection to act on and accumulate, in the same manner as man accumulates in any given direction individual differences in his domesticated productions. These individual differences generally affect what naturalists consider unimportant parts; but I could show by a long catalogue of facts, that parts which must be called important, whether viewed under a physiological or classificatory point of view, sometimes vary in the individuals of the same species. I am convinced that the most experienced naturalist would be surprised at the number of the cases of variability, even in important parts of structure, which he could collect on good authority, as I have collected, during a course of years. It should be remembered that systematists are far from being pleased at finding variability in important characters, and that there are not many men who will laboriously examine internal and important organs, and compare them in many specimens of the same species. It would never have been expected that the branching of the main nerves close to the great central ganglion of an insect would have been variable in the same species; it might have been thought that changes of this nature could have been effected only by slow degrees; yet Sir J. Lubbock has shown a degree of variability in these main nerves in Coccus, which may almost be compared to the irregular branching of a stem of a tree. This philosophical naturalist, I may add, has also shown that the muscles in the larvæ of certain insects are far from uniform. Authors sometimes argue in a circle when they state that important organs never vary; for these same authors practically rank those parts as important (as some few naturalists have honestly confessed) which do not vary; and, under this point of view, no instance will ever be found of an important part varying; but under any other point of view many instances assuredly can be given.

* * * *

Individuals of the same species often present, as is known to every one, great differences of structure, independently of variation, as in the two sexes of various animals, in the two or three castes of sterile females or workers amongst insects, and in the immature and larval states of many of the lower animals. There are, also, cases of dimorphism and trimorphism, both with animals and plants. Thus, Mr. Wallace, who has lately called attention to the subject, has shown that the females of certain species of butterflies, in the Malayan Archipelago, regularly appear under two or even three conspicuously distinct forms, not connected by intermediate varieties. Fritz Müller has described analogous but more extraordinary cases with the males of certain Brazilian Crustaceans: thus, the males of the Tanais regularly occurs under two distinct forms; one of these has strong and differently shaped pincers, and the other has antennæ much more abundantly furnished with smelling-hairs. Although in most of these cases, the two or three forms, both with animals and plants are not now connected by intermediate gradations, it is probable that they were once thus connected. Mr. Wallace, for instance, describes a certain butterfly which presents in the same island a great range of varieties connected by intermediate links, and the extreme links of the chain closely resemble the two forms of an allied dimorphic species inhabiting another part of the Malay Archipelago. Thus also with ants, the several worker-castes are generally quite distinct; but in some cases, as we shall hereafter see, the castes are connected together by finely graduated varieties. So it is, as I myself observed, with some dimorphic plants. It certainly at first appears a highly remarkable fact that the same female butterfly should have the power of producing at the same time three distinct female forms and a male; and that an hermaphrodite plant should produce from the same seed-capsule three distinct hermaphrodite forms, bearing three different kinds of females and three or even six different kinds of males. Nevertheless these cases are only exaggerations of the common fact that the female produces offspring of two sexes which sometimes differ from each other in a wonderful manner.

★ ★ ★ ★

WIDE-RANGING, MUCH DIFFUSED, AND COMMON SPECIES VARY MOST

Guided by theoretical considerations, I thought that some interesting results might be obtained in regard to the nature and relations of the species which vary most, by tabulating all the varieties in several well-worked floras. At first this seemed a simple task; but Mr. H. C. Watson, to whom I am much indebted for valuable advice and assistance on this subject, soon convinced me that there were many difficulties, as did subsequently Dr. Hooker, even in stronger terms. I shall reserve for a future work the discussion of these difficulties, and the tables of the proportional numbers of the varying species. Dr. Hooker permits me to add that after having carefully read my manuscript, and examined the tables, he thinks that the following statements are fairly well established. The whole subject, however, treated as it necessarily here is with much brevity, is rather perplexing, and allusions cannot be avoided to the 'struggle for existence', 'divergence of character', and other questions, hereafter to be discussed.

Alphonse de Candolle and others have shown that plants which have very wide ranges generally present varieties; and this might have been expected, as they are exposed to diverse physical conditions, and as they come into competition (which, as we shall hereafter see, is an equally or more important circumstance) with different sets of organic beings. But my tables further show that, in any limited country, the species which are the most common, that is abound most in individuals, and the species which are most widely diffused within their own country (and this is a different consideration from wide range, and to a certain extent from commonness), oftenest give rise to varieties sufficiently well marked to have been recorded in botanical works. Hence it is the most flourishing, or, as they may be called, the dominant species,—those which range widely, are the most diffused in their own country, and are the most numerous in individuals,—which oftenest produce well-marked varieties, or, as I consider them, incipient species. And this, perhaps, might have been anticipated; for, as varieties, in order to become in any degree permanent, necessarily have to struggle with the other inhabitants of the country, the species which are already dominant will be the most likely to yield offspring, which, though in some slight degree modified, still inherit those advantages that enabled their parents to become dominant over their compatriots. In these remarks on predominance, it should be understood that reference is made only to the forms which come into competition with each other, and more especially to the members of the same genus or class having nearly similar habits of life. With respect to the number of individuals or commonness of species, the comparison of course relates only to the members of the same group. One of the higher plants may be said to be dominant if it be more numerous in individuals and more widely diffused than the other plants of the same country, which live under nearly the same conditions. A plant of this kind is not the less dominant because some conferva inhabiting the water or some parasitic fungus is infinitely more numerous in individuals and more widely diffused. But if the conferva or parasitic fungus exceeds its allies in the above respects, it will then be dominant within its own class.

SPECIES OF THE LARGER GENERA IN EACH COUNTRY VARY MORE FREQUENTLY THAN THE SPECIES OF THE SMALLER GENERA

If the plants inhabiting a country, as described in any Flora, be divided into two equal masses, all those in the larger genera (*i.e.*, those including many species) being placed on one side, and all those in the smaller genera on the other side, the former will be found to include a somewhat larger number of the very common and much diffused or dominant species. This might have been anticipated; for the mere fact of many species of the same genus inhabiting any country, shows that there is something in the organic or inorganic conditions of that country favourable to the genus; and, consequently, we might have expected to have found in the larger genera or those including many species, a larger proportional number of dominant species. But so many causes tend to obscure this result, that I am surprised that my tables show even a small majority on the side of the larger genera. I will here allude to only two causes of obscurity. Fresh-water and salt-loving plants generally have very wide ranges and are much diffused, but this seems to be connected with the nature of the stations inhabited by them, and has little or no relation to the size of the genera to which the species belong. Again, plants low in the scale of organisation are generally much more widely diffused than plants higher in the scale; and here again there is no close relation to the size of the genera. The cause of lowly-organised plants ranging widely will be discussed in our chapter on Geographical Distribution.

From looking at species as only strongly-marked and well-defined varieties, I was led to anticipate that the species of the larger genera in each country would oftener present varieties, than the species of the smaller genera; for wherever many closely related species (*i.e.*, species of the same genus) have been formed, many varieties or incipient species ought, as a general rule, to be now forming. Where many large trees grow, we expect to find saplings. Where many species of a genus have been formed through variation, circumstances have been favourable for variation; and hence we might expect that the circumstances would generally be still favourable to variation. On the other hand, if we look at each species as a special act of creation, there is no apparent reason why more varieties should occur in a group having many species, than in one having few.

To test the truth of this anticipation I have arranged the plants of twelve countries, and the coleopterous insects of two districts, into two nearly equal masses, the species of the larger genera on one side, and those of the smaller genera on the other side, and it has invariably proved to be the case that a larger proportion of the species on the side of the larger genera presented varieties, than on the side of the smaller genera. Moreover, the species of the large genera which present any varieties, invariably present a larger average number of varieties than do the species of the small genera. Both these results follow when another division is made, and when all the least genera, with from only one to four species, are altogether excluded from the tables. These facts are of plain signification on the view that species are only strongly-marked and permanent varieties; for wherever many species of the same genus have been formed, or where, if we may use the expression, the manufactory of species has been active, we ought generally to find the manufactory still in action, more especially as we have every reason to believe the process of manufacturing new species to be a slow one. And this certainly holds true, if varieties be looked at as incipient species; for my tables clearly show as a general rule that, wherever many species of a genus have been formed, the species of that genus present a number of varieties, that is of incipient species, beyond the average. It is not that all large genera are now varying much, and are thus increasing in the number of their species, or that no small genera are now varying and increasing; for if this had been so, it would have been fatal to my theory; inasmuch as geology plainly tells us that small genera have in the lapse of time often increased greatly in size; and that large genera have often come to their maxima, decline, and disappeared. All that we want to show is, that, when many species of a genus have been formed, on an average many are still forming; and this certainly holds good.

* * * *

SUMMARY

Finally, varieties cannot be distinguished from species,—except, first, by the discovery of intermediate linking forms; and, secondly, by a certain indefinite amount of difference between them; for two forms, if differing very little, are generally ranked as varieties, notwithstanding that they cannot be closely connected; but the amount of difference considered necessary to give to any two forms the rank of species cannot be defined. In genera having more than the average number of species in any country, the species of these genera have more than the average number of varieties. In large genera the species are apt to be closely, but unequally, allied together, forming little clusters round other species. Species very closely allied to other species apparently have restricted ranges. In all these respects the species of large genera present a strong analogy with varieties. And we can clearly understand these analogies, if species once existed as varieties, and thus originated; whereas, these analogies are utterly inexplicable if species are independent creations.

We have, also, seen that it is the most flourishing or dominant species of the larger genera within each class which on an average yield the greatest number of varieties; and varieties, as we shall hereafter see, tend to become converted into new and distinct species. Thus the larger genera tend to become larger; and throughout nature the forms of life which are now dominant tend to become still more dominant by leaving many modified and dominant descendants. But by steps hereafter to be explained, the larger genera also tend to break up into smaller genera. And thus, the forms of life throughout the universe become divided into groups subordinate to groups.

CHAPTER 8

NATURAL SELECTION

[From Chapters III and IV of the *Origin*.]

STRUGGLE FOR EXISTENCE

BEFORE ENTERING on the subject of this chapter, I must make a few preliminary remarks, to show how the struggle for existence bears on Natural Selection. It has been seen in the last chapter that amongst organic beings in a state of nature there is some individual variability: indeed I am not aware that this has ever been disputed. It is immaterial for us whether a multitude of doubtful forms be called species or sub-species or varieties; what rank, for instance, the two or three hundred doubtful forms of British plants are entitled to hold, if the existence of any well-marked varieties be admitted. But the mere existence of individual variability and of some few well-marked varieties, though necessary as the foundation for the work, helps us but little in understanding how species arise in nature. How have all those exquisite adaptations of one part of the organisation to another part, and to the conditions of life, and of one organic being to another being, been perfected? We see these beautiful co-adaptations most plainly in the woodpecker and the mistletoe; and only a little less plainly in the humblest parasite which clings to the hairs of a quadruped or feathers of a bird; in the structure of the beetle which dives through the water; in the plumed seed which is wafted by the gentlest breeze; in short, we see beautiful adaptations everywhere and in every part of the organic world.

Again, it may be asked, how is it that varieties, which I have called incipient species, become ultimately converted into good and distinct species which in most cases obviously differ from each other far more than do the varieties of the same species? How do those groups of species, which constitute what are called distinct genera, and which differ from each other more than do the species of the same genus, arise? All these results, as we shall more fully see in the next chapter, follow from the struggle for life. Owing to this struggle, variations, however slight and from whatever cause proceeding, if they be in any degree profitable to the individuals of a species, in their infinitely complex relations to other organic beings and to their physical conditions of life, will tend to the preservation of such individuals, and will generally be inherited by the offspring. The offspring, also, will thus have a better chance of surviving, for, of the many individuals of any species which are periodically born, but a small number can survive. I have called this principle, by which each slight variation, if useful, is preserved, by the term Natural Selection, in order to mark its relation to man's power of selection. But the expression often used by Mr. Herbert Spencer of the Survival of the Fittest is more accurate, and is sometimes equally convenient. We have seen that man by selection can certainly produce great results, and can adapt organic beings to his own uses, through the accumulation of slight but useful variations, given to him by the hand of Nature. But Natural Selection, as we shall hereafter see, is a power incessantly ready for action, and is as immeasurably superior to man's feeble efforts, as the works of Nature are to those of Art.

* * * *

Nothing is easier than to admit in words the truth of the universal struggle for life, or more difficult—at least I have found it so—than constantly to bear this conclusion in mind. Yet unless it be thoroughly engrained in the mind, the whole economy of nature, with every fact on distribution, rarity, abundance, extinction, and variation, will be dimly seen or quite misunderstood. We behold the face of nature bright with gladness, we often see superabundance of food; we do not see or we forget, that the birds which are idly singing round us mostly live on insects or seeds, and are thus constantly destroying life; or we forget how largely these songsters, or their eggs, or their nestlings, are destroyed by birds and beasts of prey; we do not always bear in mind, that, though food may be now superabundant, it is not so at all seasons of each recurring year.

THE TERM, STRUGGLE FOR EXISTENCE, USED IN A LARGE SENSE

I should premise that I use this term in a large and metaphorical sense including dependence of one being on another, and including (which is more important) not only the life of the individual, but success in leaving progeny. Two canine animals, in a time of dearth, may be truly said to struggle with each other which shall get food and live. But a plant on the edge of a desert is said to struggle for life against the drought, though more properly it should be said to be dependent on the moisture. A plant which annually produces a thousand seeds, of which only one of an average comes to maturity, may be more truly said to struggle with the plants of the same and other kinds which already clothe the ground. The mistletoe is dependent on the apple and a few other trees, but can only in a farfetched sense be said to struggle with these trees, for, if too many of these parasites grow on the same tree, it languishes and dies. But several seedling mistletoes, growing close together on the same branch, may more truly be said to struggle with each other. As the mistletoe is disseminated by birds, its existence depends on them; and it may methodically be said to struggle with other fruit-bearing plants, in tempting the birds to devour and thus disseminate its seeds. In these several senses, which pass into each other, I use for convenience' sake the general term of Struggle for Existence.

GEOMETRICAL RATIO OF INCREASE

A struggle for existence inevitably follows from the high rate at which all organic beings tend to increase. Every being, which during its natural lifetime produces several eggs or seeds, must suffer destruction during some period of its life, and during some season or occasional year, otherwise, on the principle of geometrical increase, its numbers would quickly become so inordinately great that no country could support the product. Hence, as more individuals are produced than can possibly survive, there must in every case be a struggle for existence, either one individual with another of the same species, or with the individuals of distinct species, or with the physical conditions of life. It is the doctrine of Malthus applied with manifold force to the whole animal and vegetable kingdoms; for in this case there can be no artificial increase of food, and no prudential restraint from marriage. Although some species may be now increasing, more or less rapidly, in numbers, all cannot do so, for the world would not hold them.

There is no exception to the rule that every organic being naturally increases at so high a rate, that, if not destroyed, the earth would soon be covered by the progeny of a single pair. Even slow-breeding man has doubled in twenty-five years, and at this rate, in less than a thousand years, there would literally not be standing-room for his progeny. Linnæus has calculated that if an annual plant produced only two seeds—and there is no plant so unproductive as this—and their seedlings next year produced two, and so on, then in twenty years there should be a million plants. The elephant is reckoned the slowest breeder of all known animals, and I have taken some pains to estimate its probable minimum rate of natural increase; it will be safest to assume that it begins breeding when thirty years old, and goes on breeding till ninety years old, bringing forth six young in the interval, and surviving till one hundred years old; if this be so, after a period of from 740 to 750 years there would be nearly nineteen million elephants alive, descended from the first pair.

But we have better evidence on this subject than mere theoretical calculations, namely, the numerous recorded cases of the astonishingly rapid increase of various animals in a state of nature, when circumstances have been favourable to them during two or three following seasons. Still more striking is the evidence from our domestic animals of many kinds which have run wild in several parts of the world; if the statements of the rate of increase of slow-breeding cattle and horses in South America, and latterly in Australia, had not been well authenticated, they would have been incredible. So it is with plants; cases could be given of introduced plants which have become common throughout whole islands in a period of less than ten years. Several of the plants, such as the cardoon and a tall thistle, which are now the commonest over the whole plains of La Plata, clothing square leagues of surface almost to the exclusion of every other plant, have been introduced from Europe; and there are plants which now range in India, as I hear from Dr. Falconer, from Cape Comorin to the Himalaya, which have been imported from America since its discovery. In such cases, and endless others could be given, no one supposes, that the fertility of the animals or plants has been suddenly and temporarily increased in any sensible degree. The obvious explanation is that the conditions of life have been highly favourable, and that there has consequently been less destruction of the old and young, and that nearly all the young have been enabled to breed. Their geometrical ratio of increase, the result of which never fails to be surprising, simply explains their extraordinarily rapid increase and wide diffusion in their new homes.

In a state of nature almost every full-grown plant annually produces seed, and amongst animals there are very few which do not annually pair. Hence we may confidently assert, that all plants and animals are tending to increase at a geometrical ratio,—that all would rapidly stock every station in which they could anyhow exist,—and that this geometrical tendency to increase must be checked by destruction at some period of life. Our familiarity with the larger domestic animals tends, I think, to mislead us: we see no great destruction falling on them, but we do not keep in mind that thousands are annually slaughtered for food, and that in a state of nature an equal number would have somehow to be disposed of.

The only difference between organisms which annually produce eggs or seeds by the thousand, and those which produce extremely few, is, that the slow-breeders would require a few more years to people, under favourable conditions, a whole district, let it be ever so large. The condor lays a couple of eggs and the ostrich a score, and yet in the same country the condor may be the more numerous of the two; the Fulmar petrel lays but one egg, yet it is believed to be the most numerous bird in the world. One fly deposits hundreds of eggs, and another, like the hippobosca, a single one; but this difference does not determine how many individuals of the two species can be supported in a district. A large number of eggs is of some importance to those species which depend on a fluctuating amount of food, for it allows them rapidly to increase in number. But the real importance of a large number of eggs or seeds is to make up for much destruction at some period of life; and this period in the great majority of cases is an early one. If an animal can in any way protect its own eggs or young, a small number may be produced, and yet the average stock be fully kept up; but if many eggs or young are destroyed, many must be produced, or the species will become extinct. It would suffice to keep up the full number of a tree, which lived on an average for a thousand years, if a single seed were produced once in a thousand years, supposing that this seed were never destroyed, and could be ensured to germinate in a fitting place. So that, in all cases, the average number of any animal or plant depends only indirectly on the number of its eggs or seeds.

In looking at Nature, it is most necessary to keep the foregoing considerations always in mind—never to forget that every single organic being may be said to be striving to the utmost to increase in numbers; that each lives by a struggle at some period of its life; that heavy destruction inevitably falls either on the young or old, during each generation or at recurrent intervals. Lighten any check, mitigate the destruction ever so little, and the number of the species will almost instantaneously increase to any amount.

NATURE OF THE CHECKS TO INCREASE

The causes which check the natural tendency of each species to increase are most obscure. Look at the most vigorous species; by as much as it swarms in numbers, by so much will it tend to increase still further. We know not exactly what the checks are even in a single instance. Nor will this surprise any one who reflects how ignorant we are on this head, even in regard to mankind, although so incomparably better known than any other animal. . . . Eggs or very young animals seem generally to suffer most, but this is not invariably the case. With plants there is a vast destruction of seeds, but, from some observations which I have made it appears that the seedlings suffer most from germinating in ground already thickly stocked with other plants. Seedlings, also, are destroyed in vast numbers by various enemies, for instance, on a piece of ground three feet long and two wide, dug and cleared, and where there could be no choking from other plants, I marked all the seedlings of our native weeds as they came up, and out of 357 no less than 295 were destroyed, chiefly by slugs and insects. If turf which has long been mown, and the case would be the same with turf closely browsed by quadrupeds, be let to grow, the more vigorous plants gradually kill the less vigorous, though fully grown plants; thus out of twenty species growing on a little plot of mown turf (three feet by four) nine species perished, from the other species being allowed to grow up freely.

The amount of food for each species of course gives the extreme limit to which each can increase; but very frequently it is not the obtaining food, but the serving as prey to other animals, which determines the average number of a species. Thus, there seems to be little doubt that the stock of partridges, grouse, and hares on any large estate depends chiefly on the destruction of vermin. If not one head of game were shot during the next twenty years in England, and, at the same time, if no vermin were destroyed, there would, in all probability, be less game than at present, although hundreds of thousands of game animals are now annually shot. On the other hand, in some cases, as with the elephant, none are destroyed by beasts of prey; for even the tiger in India most rarely dares to attack a young elephant protected by its dam.

Climate plays an important part in determining the average number of a species, and periodical seasons of extreme cold or drought seem to be the most effective of all checks. I estimated (chiefly from the greatly reduced numbers of nests in the spring) that the winter of 1854–5 destroyed four-fifths of the birds in my own grounds; and this is a tremendous destruction, when we remember that ten per cent. is an extraordinarily severe mortality from epidemics with man. The action of climate seems at first sight to be quite independent of the struggle for existence; but in so far as climate chiefly acts in reducing food, it brings on the most severe struggle between the individuals, whether of the same or of distinct species, which subsist on the same kind of food. Even when climate, for instance, extreme cold, acts directly, it will be the least vigorous individuals, or those which have got least food through the advancing winter, which will suffer most. When we travel from south to north, or from a damp region to a dry, we invariably see some species gradually getting rarer and rarer, and finally disappearing; and the change of climate being conspicuous, we are tempted to attribute the whole effect to its direct action. But this is a false view; we forget that each species, even where it most abounds, is constantly suffering enormous destruction at some period of its life, from enemies or from competitors for the same place and food; and if these enemies or competitors be in the least degree favoured by any slight change of climate, they will increase in numbers; and as each area is already fully stocked with inhabitants, the other species must decrease. When we travel southward and see a species decreasing in numbers, we may feel sure that the cause lies quite as much in other species being favoured, as in this one being hurt. So it is when we travel northward, but in a somewhat lesser degree, for the number of species of all kinds, and therefore of competitors, decreases northwards; hence in going northwards, or in ascending a mountain, we far oftener meet with stunted forms, due to the *directly* injurious action of climate, than we do in proceeding southwards or in descending a mountain. When we reach the Arctic regions, or snowcapped summits, or absolute deserts, the struggle for life is almost exclusively with the elements.

That climate acts in main part indirectly by favouring other species, we clearly see in the prodigious number of plants which in our gardens can perfectly well endure our climate, but which never become naturalised, for they cannot compete with our native plants nor resist destruction by our native animals.

When a species, owing to highly favourable circumstances, increases inordinately in numbers in a small tract, epidemics—at least, this seems generally to occur with our game animals—often ensue; and here we have a limiting check independent of the struggle for life. But even some of these so-called epidemics appear to be due to parasitic worms, which have from some cause, possibly in part through facility of diffusion amongst the crowded animals, been disproportionally favoured: and here comes in a sort of struggle between the parasite and its prey.

On the other hand, in many cases, a large stock of individuals of the same species, relatively to the numbers of its enemies, is absolutely necessary for its preservation. Thus we can easily raise plenty of corn and rapeseed, &c., in our fields, because the seeds are in great excess compared with the number of birds which feed on them; nor can the birds, though having a super-abundance of food at this one season, increase in number proportionally to the supply of seeds, as their numbers are checked during the winter; but any one who has tried, knows how troublesome it is to get seed from a few wheat or other such plants in a garden: I have in this case lost every single seed. This view of the necessity of a large stock of the same species for its preservation, explains, I believe, some singular facts in nature such as that of very rare plants being sometimes extremely abundant, in the few spots where they do exist; and that of some social plants being social, that is abounding in individuals, even on the extreme verge of their range. For in such cases, we may believe, that a plant could exist only where the conditions of its life were so favourable that many could exist together, and thus save the species from utter destruction. I should add that the good effects of intercrossing, and the ill effects of close interbreeding, no doubt come into play in many of these cases; but I will not here enlarge on this subject.

COMPLEX RELATIONS OF ALL ANIMALS AND PLANTS TO EACH OTHER IN THE STRUGGLE FOR EXISTENCE

Many cases are on record showing how complex and unexpected are the checks and relations between organic beings, which have to struggle together in the same country. I will give only a single instance, which, though a simple one, interested me. In Staffordshire, on the estate of a relation, where I had ample means of investigation, there was a large and extremely barren heath, which had never been touched by the hand of man; but several hundred acres of exactly the same nature had been enclosed twenty-five years previously and planted with Scotch fir. The change in the native vegetation of the planted part of the heath was most remarkable, more than is generally seen in passing from one quite different soil to another: not only the proportional numbers of the heath-plants were wholly changed, but twelve species of plants (not counting grasses and carices) flourished in the plantations, which could not be found on the heath. The effect on the insects must have been still greater, for six insectivorous birds were very common in the plantations, which were not to be seen on the heath; and the heath was frequented by two or three distinct insectivorous birds. Here we see how potent has been the effect of the introduction of a single tree, nothing whatever else having been done, with the exception of the land having been enclosed, so that cattle could not enter. But how important an element enclosure is, I plainly saw near Farnham, in Surrey. Here there are extensive heaths, with a few clumps of old Scotch firs on the distant hilltops: within the last ten years large spaces have been enclosed, and self-sown firs are now springing up in multitudes, so close together that all cannot live. When I ascertained that these young trees had not been sown or planted, I was so much surprised at their numbers that I went to several points of view, whence I could examine hundreds of acres of the unenclosed heath, and literally I could not see a single Scotch fir, except the old planted clumps. But on looking closely between the stems of the heath, I found a multitude of seedlings and little trees which had been perpetually browsed down by the cattle.

In one square yard, at a point some hundred yards distant from one of the old clumps, I counted thirty-two little trees; and one of them, with twenty-six rings of growth, had, during many years tried to raise its head above the stems of the heath, and had failed. No wonder that, as soon as the land was enclosed, it became thickly clothed with vigorously growing young firs. Yet the heath was so extremely barren and so extensive that no one would ever have imagined that cattle would have so closely and effectually searched it for food.

Here we see that cattle absolutely determine the existence of the Scotch fir; but in several parts of the world insects determine the existence of cattle. Perhaps Paraguay offers the most curious instance of this; for here neither cattle nor horses nor dogs have ever run wild, though they swarm southward and northward in a feral state; and Azara and Rengger have shown that this is caused by the greater number in Paraguay of a certain fly, which lays its eggs in the navels of these animals when first born. The increase of these flies, numerous as they are, must be habitually checked by some means, probably by other parasitic insects. Hence, if certain insectivorous birds were to decrease in Paraguay, the parasitic insects would probably increase; and this would lessen the number of the navel-frequenting flies—then cattle and horses would become feral, and this would certainly greatly alter (as indeed I have observed in parts of South America) the vegetation: this again would largely affect the insects; and this, as we have just seen in Staffordshire, the insectivorous birds, and so onwards in ever-increasing circles of complexity. Not that under nature the relations will ever be as simple as this. Battle within battle must be continually recurring with varying success; and yet in the long-run the forces are so nicely balanced, that the face of nature remains for long periods of time uniform, though assuredly the merest trifle would give the victory to one organic being over another. Nevertheless, so profound is our ignorance, and so high our presumption, that we marvel when we hear of the extinction of an organic being; and as we do not see the cause, we invoke cataclysms to desolate the world, or invent laws on the duration of the forms of life!

I am tempted to give one more instance showing how plants and animals remote in the scale of nature, are bound together by a web of complex relations. . . . I find from experiments that humble-bees are almost indispensable to the fertilisation of the heartsease (Viola tricolor), for other bees do not visit this flower. I have also found that the visits of bees are necessary for the fertilisation of some kinds of clover; for instance, 20 heads of Dutch clover (Trifolium repens) yielded 2,290 seeds, but 20 other heads protected from bees produced not one. Again, 100 heads of red clover (T. pratense) produced 2,700 seeds, but the same number of protected heads produced not a single seed. Humble-bees alone visit red clover, as other bees cannot reach the nectar. It has been suggested that moths may fertilise the clovers; but I doubt whether they could do so in the case of the red clover, from their weight not being sufficient to depress the wing petals. Hence we may infer as highly probable that, if the whole genus of humble-bees became extinct or very rare in England, the hearts-ease and red clover would become very rare, or wholly disappear. The number of humble-bees in any district depends in a great measure upon the number of field-mice, which destroy their combs and nests; and Col. Newman, who has long attended to the habits of humble-bees, believes that 'more than two-thirds of them are thus destroyed all over England'. Now the number of mice is largely dependent, as every one knows, on the number of cats; and Col. Newman says, 'Near villages and small towns I have found the nests of humble-bees more numerous than elsewhere, which I attribute to the number of cats that destroy the mice.' Hence it is quite credible that the presence of a feline animal in large numbers in a district might determine, through the intervention first of mice and then of bees, the frequency of certain flowers in that district!

In the case of every species, many different checks, acting at different periods of life, and during different seasons or years, probably come into play; some one check or some few being generally the most potent; but all will concur in determining the average number or even the existence of the species. In some cases it can be shown that widely-different checks act on the same species in different districts. When we look at the plants and bushes clothing an entangled bank, we are tempted to attribute their proportional numbers and kinds to what we call chance. But how false a view is this! Every one has heard that when an American forest is cut down a very different vegetation springs up; but it has been observed that ancient Indian ruins in the Southern United States, which must formerly have been cleared of trees, now display the same beautiful diversity and proportion of kinds as in the surrounding virgin forest. What a struggle must have gone on during long centuries between the several kinds of trees each annually scattering its seeds by the thousand; what war between insect and insect—between insects, snails, and other animals with birds and beasts of prey—all striving to increase, all feeding on each other, or on the trees, their seeds and seedlings, or on the other plants which first clothed the ground and thus checked the growth of the trees! Throw up a handful of feathers, and all fall to the ground according to definite laws; but how simple is the problem where each shall fall compared to that of the action and reaction of the innumerable plants and animals which have determined, in the course of centuries, the proportional numbers and kinds of trees now growing on the old Indian ruins!

The dependency of one organic being on another, as of a parasite on its prey, lies generally between beings remote in the scale of nature. This is likewise sometimes the case with those which may be strictly said to struggle with each other for existence, as in the case of locusts and grass-feeding quadrupeds. But the struggle will almost invariably be most severe between the individuals of the same species, for they frequent the same districts, require the same food, and are exposed to the same dangers. In the case of varieties of the same species, the struggle will generally be almost equally severe, and we sometimes see the contest soon decided: for instance, if several varieties of wheat be sown together, and the mixed seed be resown, some of the varieties which best suit the soil or climate, or are naturally the most fertile, will beat the others and so yield more seed, and will consequently in a few years supplant the other varieties. To keep up a mixed stock of even such extremely close varieties as the variously-coloured sweet peas, they must be each year harvested separately, and the seed then mixed in due proportion, otherwise the weaker kinds will steadily decrease in number and disappear.

* * * *

STRUGGLE FOR LIFE MOST SEVERE BETWEEN INDIVIDUALS AND VARIETIES OF THE SAME SPECIES

As the species of the same genus usually have, though by no means invariably, much similarity in habits and constitution, and always in structure, the struggle will generally be more severe between them, if they come into competition with each other, than between the species of distinct genera. We see this in the recent extension over parts of the United States of one species of swallow having caused the decrease of another species. The recent increase of the missel-thrush in parts of Scotland has caused the decrease of the song-thrush. How frequently we hear of one species of rat taking the place of another species under the most different climates! In Russia the small Asiatic cockroach has everywhere driven before it its great congener. In Australia the imported hive-bee is rapidly exterminating the small, stingless native bee. . . . We can dimly see why the competition should be most severe between allied forms, which fill nearly the same place in the economy of nature; but probably in no one case could we precisely say why one species has been victorious over another in the great battle of life.

A corollary of the highest importance may be deduced from the foregoing remarks, namely, that the structure of every organic being is related, in the most essential yet often hidden manner, to that of all the other organic beings, with which it comes into competition for food or residence, or from which it has to escape, or on which it preys. This is obvious in the structure of the teeth and talons of the tiger; and in that of the legs and claws of the parasite which clings to the hair on the tiger's body. But in the beautifully plumed seed of the dandelion, and in the flattened and fringed legs of the water-beetle, the relation seems at first confined to the elements of air and water. Yet the advantage of plumed seeds no doubt stands in the closest relation to the land being already thickly clothed with other plants; so that the seeds may be widely distributed and fall on unoccupied ground. In the water-beetle, the structure of its legs, so well adapted for diving, allows it to compete with other aquatic insects, to hunt for its own prey, and to escape serving as prey to other animals.

The store of nutriment laid up within the seeds of many plants seems at first to have no sort of relation to other plants. But from the strong growth of young plants produced from such seeds, as peas and beans, when sown in the midst of long grass, it may be suspected that the chief use of the nutriment in the seed is to favour the growth of the seedlings, whilst struggling with other plants growing vigorously all around.

Look at a plant in the midst of its range, why does it not double or quadruple its numbers? We know that it can perfectly well withstand a little more heat or cold, dampness or dryness, for elsewhere it ranges into slightly hotter or colder, damper or drier districts. In this case we can clearly see that if we wish in imagination to give the plant the power of increasing in number, we should have to give it some advantage over its competitors, or over the animals which prey on it. On the confines of its geographical range, a change of constitution with respect to climate would clearly be an advantage to our plan; but we have reason to believe that only a few plants or animals range so far, that they are destroyed exclusively by the rigour of the climate. Not until we reach the extreme confines of life, in the Arctic regions or on the borders of an utter desert, will competition cease. The land may be extremely cold or dry, yet there will be competition between some few species, or between the individuals of the same species, for the warmest or dampest spots.

Hence we can see that when a plant or animal is placed in a new country amongst new competitors, the conditions of its life will generally be changed in an essential manner, although the climate may be exactly the same as in its former home. If its average numbers are to increase in its new home, we should have to modify it in a different way to what we should have had to do in its native country; for we should have to give it some advantage over a different set of competitors or enemies.

It is good thus to try in imagination to give to any one species an advantage over another. Probably in no single instance should we know what to do. This ought to convince us of our ignorance on the mutual relations of all organic beings; a conviction as necessary, as it is difficult to acquire. All that we can do, is to keep steadily in mind that each organic being is striving to increase in a geometrical ratio; that each at some period of its life, during some season of the year, during each generation or at intervals, has to struggle for life and to suffer great destruction. When we reflect on this struggle, we may console ourselves with the full belief, that the war of nature is not incessant, that no fear is felt, that death is generally prompt, and that the vigorous, the healthy, and the happy survive and multiply.

NATURAL SELECTION; OR THE SURVIVAL OF THE FITTEST

How will the struggle for existence . . . act in regard to variation? Can the principle of selection, which we have seen is so potent in the hands of man, apply under nature? I think we shall see that it can act most efficiently. Let the endless number of slight variations and individual differences occurring in our domestic productions, and, in a lesser degree, in those under nature, be borne in mind; as well as the strength of the hereditary tendency. Under domestication, it may be truly said that the whole organisation becomes in some degree plastic. But the variability, which we almost universally meet with in our domestic productions, is not directly produced, as Hooker and Asa Gray have well remarked, by man; he can neither originate varieties, nor prevent their occurrence; he can preserve and accumulate such as do occur. Unintentionally he exposes organic beings to new and changing conditions of life, and variability ensues; but similar changes of conditions might and do occur under nature. Let it also be borne in mind how infinitely complex and close-fitting are the mutual relations of all organic beings to each other and to their physical conditions of life; and consequently what infinitely varied diversities of structure might be of use to each being under changing conditions of life. Can it, then, be thought improbable, seeing that variations useful to man have undoubtedly occurred, that other variations useful in some way to each being in the great and complex battle of life, should occur in the course of many successive generations. If such do occur, can we doubt (remembering that many more individuals are born than can possibly survive) that individuals having any advantage, however slight, over others, would have the best chance of surviving and of procreating their kind? On the other hand, we may feel sure that any variation in the least degree injurious would be rigidly destroyed. This preservation of favourable individual differences and variations, and the destruction of those which are injurious, I have called Natural Selection, or the Survival of the Fittest. Variations neither useful nor injurious would not be affected by natural selection, and would be left either a fluctuating element, as perhaps we see in certain polymorphic species, or would ultimately become fixed, owing to the nature of the organism and the nature of the conditions.

Several writers have misapprehended or objected to the term Natural Selection. Some have even imagined that natural selection induces variability, whereas it implies only the preservation of such variations as arise and are beneficial to the being under its conditions of life. No one objects to agriculturists speaking of the potent effects of man's selection; and in this case the individual differences given by nature, which man for some object selects, must of necessity first occur. Others have objected that the term selection implies conscious choice in the animals which become modified; and it has even been urged that, as plants have no volition, natural selection is not applicable to them! In the literal sense of the word, no doubt, natural selection is a false term; but who ever objected to chemists speaking of the elective affinities of the various elements?—and yet an acid cannot strictly be said to elect the base with which it in preference combines. It has been said that I speak of natural selection as an active power or Deity; but who objects to an author speaking of the attraction of gravity as ruling the movements of the planets? Every one knows what is meant and is implied by such metaphorical expressions; and they are almost necessary for brevity. So again it is difficult to avoid personifying the word Nature; but I mean by Nature, only the aggregate action and product of many natural laws, and by laws the sequence of events as ascertained by us. With a little familiarity such superficial objections will be forgotten.

We shall best understand the probable course of natural selection by taking the case of a country undergoing some slight physical change, for instance, of climate. The proportional numbers of its inhabitants will almost immediately undergo a change, and some species will probably become extinct. We may conclude, from what we have seen of the intimate and complex manner in which the inhabitants of each country are bound together, that any change in the numerical proportions of the inhabitants, independently of the change of climate itself, would seriously affect the others. If the country were open on its borders, new forms would certainly immigrate, and this would likewise seriously disturb the relations of some of the former inhabitants. Let it be remembered how powerful the influence of a single introduced tree or mammal has been shown to be. But in the case of an island, or of a country partly surrounded by barriers, into which new and better adapted forms could not freely enter, we should then have places in the economy of nature which would assuredly be better filled up, if some of the original inhabitants were in some manner modified; for, had the area been open to immigration, these same places would have been seized on by intruders. In such cases, slight modifications, which in any way favoured the individuals of any species, by better adapting them to their altered conditions, would tend to be preserved; and natural selection would have free scope for the work of improvement.

We have good reason to believe . . . that changes in the conditions of life give a tendency to increased variability; and in the foregoing cases the conditions have changed, and this would manifestly be favourable to natural selection, by affording a better chance of the occurrence of profitable variations. Unless such occur, natural selection can do nothing. Under the term of 'variations', it must never be forgotten that mere individual differences are included. As man can produce a great result with his domestic animals and plants by adding up in any given direction individual differences, so could natural selection, but far more easily from having incomparably longer time for action. Nor do I believe that any great physical change, as of climate, or any unusual degree of isolation to check immigration, is necessary in order that new and unoccupied places should be left, for natural selection to fill up by improving some of the varying inhabitants. For as all the inhabitants of each country are struggling together with nicely balanced forces, extremely slight modifications in the structure or habits of one species would often give it an advantage over others; and still further modifications of the same kind would often still further increase the advantage, as long as the species continued under the same conditions of life and profited by similar means of subsistence and defence. No country can be named in which all the native inhabitants are now so perfectly adapted to each other and to the physical conditions under which they live, that none of them could be still better adapted or improved; for in all countries, the natives have been so far conquered by naturalised productions, that they have allowed some foreigners to take firm possession of the land. And as foreigners have thus in every country beaten some of the natives, we may safely conclude that the natives might have been modified with advantage, so as to have better resisted the intruders.

As man can produce, and certainly has produced, a great result by his methodical and unconscious means of selection, what may not natural selection effect? Man can act only on external and visible characters: Nature, if I may be allowed to personify the natural preservation of survival of the fittest, cares nothing for appearances, except in so far as they are useful to any being. She can act on every internal organ, on every shade of constitutional difference, on the whole machinery of life. Man selects only for his own good: Nature only for that of the being which she tends. Every selected character is fully exercised by her, as is implied by the fact of their selection. Man keeps the natives of many climates in the same country; he seldom exercises each selected character in some peculiar and fitting manner; he feeds a long and a short beaked pigeon on the same food; he does not exercise a long-backed or long-legged quadruped in any peculiar manner; he exposes sheep with long and short wool to the same climate. He does not allow the most vigorous males to struggle for the females. He does not rigidly destroy all inferior animals, but protects during each varying season, as far as lies in his power, all his productions. He often begins his selection by some half-monstrous form; or at least by some modification prominent enough to catch the eye or to be plainly useful to him. Under nature, the slightest differences of structure or constitution may well turn the nicely balanced scale in the struggle for life, and so be preserved. How fleeting are the wishes and efforts of man! how short his time! and consequently how poor will be his results, compared with those accumulated by Nature during whole geological periods! Can we wonder, then, that Nature's productions should be far 'truer' in character than man's productions; that they should be infinitely better adapted to the most complex conditions of life, and should plainly bear the stamp of far higher workmanship?

It may metaphorically be said that natural selection is daily and hourly scrutinising, throughout the world, the slightest variations; rejecting those that are bad, preserving and adding up all that are good; silently and insensibly working, *whenever and wherever opportunity offers*, at the improvement of each organic being in relation to its organic and inorganic conditions of life. We see nothing of these slow changes in progress, until the hand of time has marked the lapse of ages, and then so imperfect is our view into long-past geological ages, that we see only that the forms of life are now different from what they formerly were.

* * * *

Natural selection will modify the structure of the young in relation to the parent, and of the parent in relation to the young. In social animals it will adapt the structure of each individual for the benefit of the whole community; if the community profits by the selected change. What natural selection cannot do, is to modify the structure of one species, without giving it any advantage, for the good of another species; and though statements to this effect may be found in works of natural history, I cannot find one case which will bear investigation. A structure used only once in an animal's life, if of high importance to it, might be modified to any extent by natural selection; for instance, the great jaws possessed by certain insects, used exclusively for opening the cocoon—or the hard tip to the beak of unhatched birds, used for breaking the egg. It has been asserted, that of the best short-beaked tumbler-pigeons a greater number perish in the egg than are able to get out of it; so that fanciers assist in the act of hatching. Now if nature had to make the beak of a full-grown pigeon very short for the bird's own advantage, the process of modification would be very slow, and there would be simultaneously the most rigorous selection of all the young birds within the egg, which had the most powerful and hardest beaks, for all with weak beaks would inevitably perish; or, more delicate and more easily broken shells might be selected, the thickness of the shell being known to vary like every other structure.

It may be well here to remark that with all beings there must be much fortuitous destruction, which can have little or no influence on the course of natural selection. For instance a vast number of eggs or seeds are annually devoured, and these could be modified through natural selection only if they varied in some manner which protected them from their enemies. Yet many of these eggs or seeds would perhaps, if not destroyed, have yielded individuals better adapted to their conditions of life than any of those which happened to survive. So again a vast number of mature animals and plants, whether or not they be the best adapted to their conditions, must be annually destroyed by accidental causes, which would not be in the least degree mitigated by certain changes of structure or constitution which would in other ways be beneficial to the species. But let the destruction of the adults be ever so heavy, if the number which can exist in any district be not wholly kept down by such causes,—or again let the destruction of eggs or seeds be so great that only a hundredth or a thousandth part are developed,—yet of those which do survive, the best adapted individuals, supposing that there is any variability in a favourable direction, will tend to propagate their kind in larger numbers than the less well adapted. If the numbers be wholly kept down by the causes just indicated, as will often have been the case, natural selection will be powerless in certain beneficial directions; but this is no valid objection to its efficiency at other times and in other ways for we are far from having any reason to suppose that many species ever undergo modification and improvement at the same time in the same area.

[Darwin introduces a brief discussion of sexual selection at this point. It has been omitted because the subject is treated in detail in *The Descent of Man*.]

ILLUSTRATIONS OF THE ACTION OF NATURAL SELECTION, OR THE SURVIVAL OF THE FITTEST

In order to make it clear how, as I believe, natural selection acts, I must beg permission to give one or two imaginary illustrations. Let us take the case of a wolf, which preys on various animals, securing some by craft, some by strength, and some by fleetness; and let us suppose that the fleetest prey, a deer for instance, had from any change in the country increased in numbers, or that other prey had decreased in numbers, during that season of the year when the wolf was hardest pressed for food. Under such circumstances the swiftest and slimmest wolves would have the best chance of surviving and so be preserved or selected,—provided always that they retained strength to master their prey at this or some other period of the year, when they were compelled to prey on other animals. I can see no more reason to doubt that this would be the result, than that man should be able to improve the fleetness of his greyhounds by careful and methodical selection, or by that kind of unconscious selection which follows from each man trying to keep the best dogs without any thought of modifying the breed. I may add, that, according to Mr. Pierce, there are two varieties of the wolf inhabiting the Catskill Mountains, in the United States, one with a light greyhound-like form, which pursues deer, and the other more bulky, with shorter legs, which more frequently attacks the shepherd's flocks.

* * * *

It may be worth while to give another and more complex illustration of the action of natural selection. Certain plants excrete sweet juice, apparently for the sake of eliminating something injurious from the sap: this is effected, for instance, by glands at the base of the stipules in some Leguminosæ, and at the backs of the leaves of the common laurel. This juice, though small in quantity, is greedily sought by insects; but their visits do not in any way benefit the plant. Now, let us suppose that the juice or nectar was excreted from the inside of the flowers of a certain number of plants of any species. Insects in seeking the nectar would get dusted with pollen, and would often transport it from one flower to another. The flowers of two distinct individuals of the same species would thus get crossed; and the act of crossing, as can be fully proved, gives rise to vigorous seedlings which consequently would have the best chance of flourishing and surviving. The plants which produced flowers with the largest glands or nectaries, excreting most nectar, would oftenest be visited by insects, and would oftenest be crossed; and so in the long-run would gain the upper hand and form a local variety. The flowers, also, which had their stamens and pistils placed, in relation to the size and habits of the particular insects which visited them, so as to favour in any degree the transportal of the pollen, would likewise be favoured. We might have taken the case of insects visiting flowers for the sake of collecting pollen instead of nectar; and as pollen is formed for the sole purpose of fertilisation, its destruction appears to be a simple loss to the plant; yet if a little pollen were carried, at first occasionally and then habitually, by the pollen-devouring insects from flower to flower, and a cross thus effected, although nine-tenths of the pollen were destroyed it might still be a great gain to the plant to be thus robbed; and the individuals which produced more and more pollen, and had larger anthers, would be selected.

When our plant, by the above process long continued, had been rendered highly attractive to insects, they would, unintentionally on their part, regularly carry pollen from flower to flower; and that they do this effectually, I could easily show by many striking facts. I will give only one, as likewise illustrating one step in the separation of the sexes of plants. Some holly-trees bear only male flowers, which have four stamens producing a rather small quantity of pollen, and a rudimentary pistil; other holly-trees bear only female flowers; these have a full-sized pistil, and four stamens with shrivelled anthers, in which not a grain of pollen can be detected. Having found a female tree exactly sixty yards from a male tree, I put the stigmas of twenty flowers, taken from different branches, under the microscope, and on all, without exception, there were a few pollen-grains, and on some a profusion. As the wind had set for several days from the female to the male tree, the pollen could not thus have been carried. The weather had been cold and boisterous, and therefore not favourable to bees, nevertheless every female flower which I examined had been effectually fertilised by the bees, which had flown from tree to tree in search of nectar. But to return to our imaginary case: as soon as the plant had been rendered so highly attractive to insects that pollen was regularly carried from flower to flower, another process might commence. No naturalist doubts the advantage of what has been called the 'physiological division of labour', hence we may believe that it would be advantageous to a plant to produce stamens alone in one flower or on one whole plant, and pistils alone in another flower or on another plant. In plants under culture and placed under new conditions of life, sometimes the male organs and sometimes the female organs become more or less impotent; now if we suppose this to occur in ever so slight a degree under nature, then, as pollen is already carried regularly from flower to flower, and as a more complete separation of the sexes of our plant would be advantageous on the principle of the division of labour, individuals with this tendency more and more increased, would be continually favoured or selected, until at last a complete separation of the sexes might be effected. It would take up too much space to show the various steps, through dimorphism and other means, by which the separation of the sexes in plants of various kinds is apparently now in progress; but I may add that some of the species of holly in North America, are, according to Asa Gray, in an exactly intermediate condition, or, as he expresses it, are more or less diœciously polygamous.

Let us now turn to the nectar-feeding insects; we may suppose the plant, of which we have been slowly increasing the nectar by continued selection, to be a common plant; and that certain insects depended in main part on its nectar for food. I could give many facts showing how anxious bees are to save time: for instance, their habit of cutting holes and sucking the nectar at the bases of certain flowers, which, with a very little more trouble, they can enter by the mouth. Bearing such facts in mind, it may be believed that under certain circumstances individual differences in the curvature or length of the proboscis, &c., too slight to be appreciated by us, might profit a bee or other insect, so that certain individuals would be able to obtain their food more quickly than others; and thus the communities to which they belonged would flourish and throw off many swarms inheriting the same peculiarities. The tubes of the corolla of the common and red and incarnate clovers (Trifolium pratense and incarnatum) do not on a hasty glance appear to differ in length; yet the hive-bee can easily suck the nectar out of the incarnate clover, but not out of the common red clover, which is visited by humble-bees alone; so that whole fields of red clover offer in vain an abundant supply of precious nectar to the hive-bee. That this nectar is much liked by the hive-bee is certain; for I have repeatedly seen, but only in the autumn, many hive-bees sucking the flowers through holes bitten in the base of the tube by humble-bees. The difference in the length of the corolla in the two kinds of clover, which determines the visits of the hive-bee, must be very trifling; for I have been assured that when red clover has been mown, the flowers of the second crop are somewhat smaller, and that these are visited by many hive-bees. I do not know whether this statement is accurate; nor whether another published statement can be trusted, namely, that the Ligurian bee which is generally considered a mere variety of the common hive-bee, and which freely crosses with it, is able to reach and suck the nectar of the red clover. Thus, in a country where this kind of clover abounded, it might be a great advantage to the hive-bee to have a slightly longer or differently constructed proboscis. On the other hand, as the fertility of this clover absolutely depends on bees visiting the flowers, if humble-bees were to become rare in any country, it might be a great advantage to the plant to have a shorter or more deeply divided corolla, so that the hive-bees should be enabled to suck its flowers. Thus I can understand how a flower and a bee might slowly become, either simultaneously or one after the other, modified and adapted to each other in the most perfect manner, by the continued preservation of all the individuals which presented slight deviations of structure mutually favourable to each other.

I am well aware that this doctrine of natural selection, exemplified in the above imaginary instances, is open to the same objections which were first urged against Sir Charles Lyell's noble views on 'the modern changes of the earth, as illustrative of geology'; but we now seldom hear the agencies which we see still at work, spoken of as trifling or insignificant, when used in explaining the excavation of the deepest valleys or the formation of long lines of inland cliffs. Natural selection acts only by the preservation and accumulation of small inherited modifications, each profitable to the preserved being; and as modern geology has almost banished such views as the excavation of a great valley by a single diluvial wave, so will natural selection banish the belief of the continued creation of new organic beings, or of any great and sudden modification in their structure.

★ ★ ★ ★

CIRCUMSTANCES FAVOURABLE FOR THE PRODUCTION OF NEW FORMS THROUGH NATURAL SELECTION

★ ★ ★ ★

To sum up, as far as the extreme intricacy of the subject permits, the circumstances favourable and unfavourable for the production of new species through natural selection. I conclude that for terrestrial productions a large continental area, which has undergone many oscillations of level, will have been the most favourable for the production of many new forms of life, fitted to endure for a long time and to spread widely. Whilst the area existed as a continent, the inhabitants will have been numerous in individuals and kinds, and will have been subjected to severe competition. When converted by subsidence into large separate islands, there will still have existed many individuals of the same species on each island: intercrossing on the confines of the range of each new species will have been checked: after physical changes of any kind, immigration will have been prevented, so that new places in the polity of each island will have had to be filled up by the modification of the old inhabitants; and time will have been allowed for the varieties in each to become well modified and perfected. When, by renewed elevation, the islands were reconverted into a continental area, there will again have been very severe competition: the most favoured or improved varieties will have been enabled to spread: there will have been much extinction of the less improved forms, and the relative proportional numbers of the various inhabitants of the reunited continent will again have been changed; and again there will have been a fair field for natural selection to improve still further the inhabitants, and thus to produce new species.

That natural selection generally acts with extreme slowness I fully admit. It can act only when there are places in the natural polity of a district which can be better occupied by the modification of some of its existing inhabitants. The occurrence of such places will often depend on physical changes, which generally take place very slowly, and on the immigration of better adapted forms being prevented. As some few of the old inhabitants become modified, the mutual relations of others will often be disturbed; and this will create new places, ready to be filled up by better adapted forms, but all this will take place very slowly. Although all the individuals of the same species differ in some slight degree from each other, it would often be long before differences of the right nature in various parts of the organisation might occur. The result would often be greatly retarded by free intercrossing. Many will exclaim that these several causes are amply sufficient to neutralise the power of natural selection. I do not believe so. But I do believe that natural selection will generally act very slowly, only at long intervals of time, and only on a few of the inhabitants of the same region. I further believe that these slow, intermittent results accord well with what geology tells us of the rate and manner at which the inhabitants of the world have changed.

Slow though the process of selection may be, if feeble man can do much by artificial selection, I can see no limit to the amount of change, to the beauty and complexity of the coadaptations between all organic beings, one with another and with their physical conditions of life, which may have been effected in the long course of time through nature's power of selection, that is by the survival of the fittest.

* * * *

DIVERGENCE OF CHARACTER

The principle, which I have designated by this term, is of high importance, and explains, as I believe, several important facts. In the first place, varieties, even strongly-marked ones, though having somewhat of the character of species—as is shown by the hopeless doubts in many cases how to rank them—yet certainly differ far less from each other than do good and distinct species. Nevertheless, according to my view, varieties are species in the process of formation, or are, as I have called them, incipient species. How, then, does the lesser difference between varieties become augmented into the greater difference between species? That this does habitually happen, we must infer from most of the innumerable species throughout nature presenting well-marked differences; whereas varieties, the supposed prototypes and parents of future well-marked species, present slight and ill-defined differences. Mere chance, as we may call it, might cause one variety to differ in some character from its parents, and the offspring of this variety again to differ from its parent in the very same character and in a greater degree; but this alone would never account for so habitual and large a degree of difference as that between the species of the same genus.

As has always been my practice, I have sought light on this head from our domestic productions. We shall here find something analogous. It will be admitted that the production of races so different as short-horn and Hereford cattle, race and cart horses, the several breeds of pigeons, &c., could never have been effected by the mere chance accumulation of similar variations during many successive generations. In practice, a fancier is, for instance, struck by a pigeon having a slightly shorter beak; another fancier is struck by a pigeon having a rather longer beak; and on the acknowledged principle that 'fanciers do not and will not admire a medium standard, but like extremes', they both go on (as has actually occurred with the sub-breeds of the tumbler-pigeon) choosing and breeding from birds with longer and longer beaks, or with shorter and shorter beaks. Again, we may suppose that at an early period of history, the men of one nation or district required swifter horses, whilst those of another required stronger and bulkier horses. The early differences would be very slight; but, in the course of time, from the continued selection of swifter horses in the one case, and of stronger ones in the other, the differences would become greater, and would be noted as forming two sub-breeds. Ultimately, after the lapse of centuries, these sub-breeds would become converted into two well-established and distinct breeds. As the differences became greater, the inferior animals with intermediate characters, being neither swift nor very strong, would not have been used for breeding, and will thus have tended to disappear. Here, then, we see in man's productions the action of what may be called the principle of divergence, causing differences, at first barely appreciable, steadily to increase, and the breeds to diverge in character, both from each other and from their common parent.

But how, it may be asked, can any analogous principle apply in nature? I believe it can and does apply most efficiently (though it was a long time before I saw how), from the simple circumstance that the more diversified the descendants from any one species become in structure, constitution, and habits, by so much will they be better enabled to seize on many and widely diversified places in the polity of nature, and so be enabled to increase in numbers.

We can clearly discern this in the case of animals with simple habits. Take the case of a carnivorous quadruped, of which the number that can be supported in any country has long ago arrived at its full average. If its natural power of increase be allowed to act, it can succeed in increasing (the country not undergoing any change in conditions) only by its varying descendants seizing on places at present occupied by other animals: some of them, for instance, being enabled to feed on new kinds of prey, either dead or alive; some inhabiting new stations, climbing trees, frequenting water, and some perhaps becoming less carnivorous. The more diversified in habits and structure the descendants of our carnivorous animals become, the more places they will be enabled to occupy. What applies to one animal will apply throughout all time to all animals—that is, if they vary—for otherwise natural selection can effect nothing. So it will be with plants. It has been experimentally proved, that if a plot of ground be sown with one species of grass, and a similar plot be sown with several distinct genera of grasses, a greater number of plants and a greater weight of dry herbage can be raised in the latter than in the former case. The same has been found to hold good when one variety and several mixed varieties of wheat have been sown on equal spaces of ground. Hence, if any one species of grass were to go on varying, and the varieties were continually selected which differed from each other in the same manner, though in a very slight degree, as do the distinct species and genera of grasses, a greater number of individual plants of this species, including its modified descendants, would succeed in living on the same piece of ground. And we know that each species and each variety of grass is annually sowing almost countless seeds; and is thus striving, as it may be said, to the utmost to increase in number. Consequently, in the course of many thousand generations, the most distinct varieties of any one species of grass would have the best chance of succeeding and of increasing in numbers, and thus of supplanting the less distinct varieties; and varieties, when rendered very distinct from each other, take the rank of species.

The truth of the principle that the greatest amount of life can be supported by great diversification of structure, is seen under many natural circumstances. In an extremely small area, especially if freely open to immigration, and where the contest between individual and individual must be very severe, we always find great diversity in its inhabitants. For instance, I found that a piece of turf, three feet by four in size, which had been exposed for many years to exactly the same conditions, supported twenty species of plants, and these belonged to eighteen genera and to eight orders, which shows how much these plants differed from each other. So it is with the plants and insects on small and uniform islets: also in small ponds of fresh water. Farmers find that they can raise most food by a rotation of plants belonging to the most different orders: nature follows what may be called a simultaneous rotation. Most of the animals and plants which live close round any small piece of ground, could live on it (supposing its nature not to be in any way peculiar), and may be said to be striving to the utmost to live there; but, it is seen, that where they come into the closest competition, the advantages of diversification of structure, with the accompanying differences of habit and constitution, determine that the inhabitants, which thus jostle each other most closely, shall, as a general rule, belong to what we call different genera and orders.

The same principle is seen in the naturalisation of plants through man's agency in foreign lands. It might have been expected that the plants which would succeed in becoming naturalised in any land would generally have been closely allied to the indigenes; for these are commonly looked at as specially created and adapted for their own country. It might also, perhaps, have been expected that naturalised plants would have belonged to a few groups more especially adapted to certain stations in their new homes. But the case is very different; and Alphonse de Candolle has well remarked, in his great and admirable work, that floras gain by naturalisation, proportionally with the number of the native genera and species far more in new genera than in new species. To give a single instance: in the last edition of Dr. Asa Gray's '*Manual of the Flora of the Northern United States*', 260 naturalised plants are enumerated, and these belong to 162 genera. We thus see that these naturalised plants are of a highly diversified nature. They differ, moreover, to a large extent, from the indigenes, for out of the 162 naturalised genera, no less than 100 genera are not there indigenous, and thus a large proportional addition is made to the genera now living in the United States.

By considering the nature of the plants or animals which have in any country struggled successfully with the indigenes and have there become naturalised, we may gain some crude idea in what manner some of the natives would have to be modified, in order to gain an advantage over their compatriots; and we may at least infer that diversification of structure, amounting to new generic differences, would be profitable to them.

The advantage of diversification of structure in the inhabitants of the same regions is, in fact, the same as that of the physiological division of labour in the organs of the same individual body—a subject so well elucidated by Milne Edwards. No physiologist doubts that a stomach adapted to digest vegetable matter alone, or flesh alone, draws most nutriment from these substances. So in the general economy of any land, the more widely and perfectly the animals and plants are diversified for different habits of life, so will a greater number of individuals be capable of there supporting themselves. A set of animals, with their organisation but little diversified, could hardly compete with a set more perfectly diversified in structure. It may be doubted, for instance, whether the Australian marsupials, which are divided into groups differing but little from each other, and feebly representing, as Mr. Waterhouse and others have remarked, our carnivorous, ruminant, and rodent mammals, could successfully compete with these well-developed orders. In the Australian mammals, we see the process of diversification in an early and incomplete stage of development.

⋆ ⋆ ⋆ ⋆

SUMMARY

If under changing conditions of life organic beings present individual differences in almost every part of their structure, and this cannot be disputed; if there be, owing to their geometrical rate of increase, a severe struggle for life at some age, season, or year, and this certainly cannot be disputed; then, considering the infinite complexity of the relations of all organic beings to each other and to their conditions of life, causing an infinite diversity in structure, constitution, and habits, to be advantageous to them, it would be a most extraordinary fact if no variations had ever occurred useful to each being's own welfare, in the same manner as so many variations have occurred useful to man. But if variations useful to any organic being ever do occur, assuredly individuals thus characterised will have the best chance of being preserved in the struggle for life; and from the strong principle of inheritance, these will tend to produce offspring similarly characterised. This principle of preservation, or the survival of the fittest, I have called Natural Selection. It leads to the improvement of each creature in relation to its organic and inorganic conditions of life; and consequently, in most cases, to what must be regarded as an advance in organisation. Nevertheless, low and simple forms will long endure if well fitted for their simple conditions of life.

Natural selection, on the principle of qualities being inherited at corresponding ages, can modify the egg, seed, or young, as easily as the adult. Amongst many animals, sexual selection will have given its aid to ordinary selection, by assuring to the most vigorous and best adapted males the greatest number of offspring. Sexual selection will also give characters useful to the males alone, in their struggles or rivalry with other males; and these characters will be transmitted to one sex or to both sexes, according to the form of inheritance which prevails.

Whether natural selection has really thus acted in adapting the various forms of life to their several conditions and stations, must be judged by the general tenor and balance of evidence given in the following chapters. But we have already seen how it entails extinction; and how largely extinction has acted in the world's history, geology plainly declares. Natural selection, also leads to divergence of character; for the more organic beings diverge in structure, habits, and constitution, by so much the more can a large number be supported on the area,—of which we see proof by looking to the inhabitants of any small spot, and to the productions naturalised in foreign lands. Therefore, during the modification of the descendants of any one species, and during the incessant struggle of all species to increase in numbers, the more diversified the descendants become, the better will be their chance of success in the battle for life. Thus the small differences distinguishing varieties of the same species, steadily tend to increase, till they equal the greater differences between species of the same genus, or even of distinct genera.

We have seen that it is the common, the widely-diffused and widely-ranging species, belonging to the larger genera within each class, which vary most; and these tend to transmit to their modified offspring that superiority which now makes them dominant in their own countries. Natural selection, as has just been remarked, leads to divergence of character and to much extinction of the less improved and intermediate forms of life. On these principles, the nature of the affinities, and the generally well-defined distinctions between the innumerable organic beings in each class throughout the world, may be explained. It is a truly wonderful fact—the wonder of which we are apt to overlook from familiarity—that all animals and all plants throughout all time and space should be related to each other in groups, subordinate to groups, in the manner which we everywhere behold—namely, varieties of the same species most closely related, species of the same genus less closely and unequally related, forming sections and sub-genera, species of distinct genera much less closely related, and genera related in different degrees, forming sub-families, families, orders, sub-classes and classes. The several subordinate groups in any class cannot be ranked in a single file, but seem clustered round points, and these round other points, and so on in almost endless cycles. If species had been independently created, no explanation would have been possible of this kind of classification; but it is explained through inheritance and the complex action of natural selection, entailing extinction and divergence of character. . . .

The affinities of all the beings of the same class have sometimes been represented by a great tree. I believe this simile largely speaks the truth. The green and budding twigs may represent existing species; and those produced during former years may represent the long succession of extinct species. At each period of growth all the growing twigs have tried to branch out on all sides, and to overtop and kill the surrounding twigs and branches, in the same manner as species and groups of species have at all times overmastered other species in the great battle for life. The limbs divided into great branches, and these into lesser and lesser branches, were themselves once, when the tree was young, budding twigs, and this connection of the former and present buds by ramifying branches may well represent the classification of all extinct and living species in groups subordinate to groups. Of the many twigs which flourished when the tree was a mere bush, only two or three, now grown into great branches, yet survive and bear the other branches; so with the species which lived during long-past geological periods, very few have left living and modified descendants. From the first growth of the tree, many a limb and branch has decayed and dropped off; and these fallen branches of various sizes may represent those whole orders, families, and genera which have now no living representatives, and which are known to us only in a fossil state. As we here and there see a thin straggling branch springing from a fork low down in a tree, and which by some chance has been favoured and is still alive on its summit, so we occasionally see an animal like the Ornithorhynchus or Lepidosiren, which in some small degree connects by its affinities two large branches of life, and which has apparently been saved from fatal competition by

CHAPTER 9

DIFFICULTIES OF THE THEORY

[From Chapters VI, VII and VIII of the *Origin*. Chapter V of the *Origin*, dealing with the 'Laws of Variation', has been omitted entirely because the development of the science of genetics puts this subject in a quite different perspective from the one it had in Darwin's day. Darwin was keenly aware of the deficiencies of contemporary knowledge and repeatedly made statements like 'our ignorance of the laws of variation is profound'. It is interesting that a precise knowledge of the mechanism of inheritance and of the causes of variation was not necessary to build up the theory of evolution through natural selection. One had only to know that variation did occur and that it was inherited.]

LONG before the reader has arrived at this part of my work, a crowd of difficulties will have occurred to him. Some of them are so serious that to this day I can hardly reflect on them without being in some degree staggered; but, to the best of my judgment, the greater number are only apparent, and those that are real are not, I think, fatal to the theory.

These difficulties and objections may be classed under the following heads: First, why, if species have descended from other species by fine gradations, do we not everywhere see innumerable transitional forms? Why is not all nature in confusion, instead of the species being, as we see them, well defined?

Secondly, is it possible that an animal having, for instance, the structure and habits of a bat, could have been formed by the modification of some other animal with widely different habits and structure? Can we believe that natural selection could produce, on the one hand, an organ of trifling importance, such as the tail of a giraffe, which serves as a fly-flapper, and, on the other hand, an organ so wonderful as the eye?

Thirdly, can instincts be acquired and modified through natural selection? What shall we say to the instinct which leads the bee to make cells, and which has practically anticipated the discoveries of profound mathematicians?

Fourthly, how can we account for species, when crossed, being sterile and producing sterile offspring, whereas, when varieties are crossed, their fertility is unimpaired?

* * * *

ON THE ABSENCE OR RARITY OF TRANSITIONAL VARIETIES

As natural selection acts solely by the preservation of profitable modifications, each new form will tend in a fully-stocked country to take the place of, and finally to exterminate, its own less improved parent-form and other less favoured forms with which it comes into competition. Thus extinction and natural selection go hand in hand. Hence, if we look at each species as descended from some unknown form, both the parent and all the transitional varieties will generally have been exterminated by the very process of the formation and perfection of the new form.

But, as by this theory innumerable transitional forms must have existed, why do we not find them embedded in countless numbers in the crust of the earth? It will be more convenient to discuss this question in the chapter on the Imperfection of the Geological Record; and I will here only state that I believe the answer mainly lies in the record being incomparably less perfect than is generally supposed. The crust of the earth is a vast museum; but the natural collections have been imperfectly made, and only at long intervals of time.

But it may be urged that when several closely-allied species inhabit the same territory, we surely ought to find at the present time many transitional forms. Let us take a simple case: in travelling from north to south over a continent, we generally meet at successive intervals with closely allied or representative species, evidently filling nearly the same place in the natural economy of the land. These representative species often meet and interlock; and as the one becomes rarer and rarer, the other becomes more and more frequent, till the one replaces the other. But if we compare these species where they intermingle, they are generally as absolutely distinct from each other in every detail of structure as are specimens taken from the metropolis inhabited by each. By my theory these allied species are descended from a common parent; and during the process of modification, each has become adapted to the conditions of life of its own region, and has supplanted and exterminated its original parent-form and all the transitional varieties between its past and present states. Hence we ought not to expect at the present time to meet with numerous transitional varieties in each region, though they must have existed there, and may be embedded there in a fossil condition. But in the intermediate region, having intermediate conditions of life, why do we not now find closely-linking intermediate varieties? This difficulty for a long time quite confounded me. But I think it can be in large part explained.

In the first place we should be extremely cautious in inferring, because an area is now continuous, that it has been continuous during a long period. Geology would lead us to believe that most continents have been broken up into islands even during the later tertiary periods; and in such islands distinct species might have been separately formed without the possibility of intermediate varieties existing in the intermediate zones. By changes in the form of the land and of climate, marine areas now continuous must often have existed within recent times in a far less continuous and uniform condition than at present. But I will pass over this way of escaping from the difficulty; for I believe that many perfectly defined species have been formed on strictly continuous areas; though I do not doubt that the formerly broken condition of areas now continuous, has played an important part in the formation of new species, more especially with freely-crossing and wandering animals.

In looking at species as they are now distributed over a wide area, we generally find them tolerably numerous over a large territory, then becoming somewhat abruptly rarer and rarer on the confines, and finally disappearing. Hence the neutral territory, between two representative species is generally narrow in comparison with the territory proper to each. We see the same fact in ascending mountains, and sometimes it is quite remarkable how abruptly, as Alphonse de Candolle has observed, a common alpine species disappears. The same fact has been noticed by E. Forbes in sounding the depths of the sea with the dredge. To those who look at climate and the physical conditions of life as the all-important elements of distribution, these facts ought to cause surprise, as climate and height or depth graduate away insensibly. But when we bear in mind that almost every species, even in its metropolis, would increase immensely in numbers, were it not for other competing species; that nearly all either prey on or serve as prey for others; in short, that each organic being is either directly or indirectly related in the most important manner to other organic beings,—we see that the range of the inhabitants of any country by no means exclusively depends on insensibly changing physical conditions, but in a large part on the presence of other species, on which it lives, or by which it is destroyed, or with which it comes into competition; and as these species are already defined objects, not blending one into another by insensible gradations, the range of any one species, depending as it does on the range of others, will tend to be sharply defined. Moreover, each species on the confines of its range, where it exists in lessened numbers, will, during fluctuations in the number of its enemies or of its prey, or in the nature of the seasons, be extremely liable to utter extermination; and thus its geographical range will come to be still more sharply defined.

* * * *

To sum up, I believe that species come to be tolerably well-defined objects, and do not at any one period present an inextricable chaos of varying and intermediate links; first, because new varieties are very slowly formed, for variation is a slow process, and natural selection can do nothing until favourable individual differences or variations occur, and until a place in the natural polity of the country can be better filled by some modification of some one or more of its inhabitants. And such new places will depend on slow changes of climate, or on the occasional immigration of new inhabitants, and, probably, in a still more important degree, on some of the old inhabitants becoming slowly modified, with the new forms thus produced, and the old ones acting and reacting on each other. So that, in any one region and at any one time, we ought to see only a few species presenting slight modifications of structure in some degree permanent; and this assuredly we do see.

Secondly, areas now continuous must often have existed within the recent period as isolated portions, in which many forms, more especially amongst the classes which unite for each birth and wander much, may have separately been rendered sufficiently distinct to rank as representative species. In this case, intermediate varieties between the several representative species and their common parent, must formerly have existed within each isolated portion of the land, but these links during the process of natural selection will have been supplanted and exterminated, so that they will no longer be found in a living state.

Thirdly, when two or more varieties have been formed in different portions of a strictly continuous area, intermediate varieties will, it is probable, at first have been formed in the intermediate zones, but they will generally have had a short duration. For these intermediate varieties will, from reasons already assigned (namely from what we know of the actual distribution of closely allied or representative species, and likewise of acknowledged varieties), exist in the intermediate zones in lesser numbers than the varieties which they tend to connect. From this cause alone the intermediate varieties will be liable to accidental extermination; and during the process of further modification through natural selection, they will almost certainly be beaten and supplanted by the forms which they connect; for these from existing in greater numbers will, in the aggregate, present more varieties, and thus be further improved through natural selection and gain further advantages.

Lastly, looking not to any one time, but to all time, if my theory be true, numberless intermediate varieties, linking closely together all the species of the same group, must assuredly have existed; but the very process of natural selection constantly tends, as has been so often remarked, to exterminate the parent-forms and the intermediate links. Consequently evidence of their former existence could be found only amongst fossil remains, which are preserved, as we shall attempt to show in a future chapter, in an extremely imperfect and intermittent record.

ON THE ORIGIN AND TRANSITIONS OF ORGANIC BEINGS WITH PECULIAR HABITS AND STRUCTURE

It has been asked by the opponents of such views as I hold, how, for instance, could a land carnivorous animal have been converted into one with aquatic habits; for how could the animal in its transitional state have subsisted? It would be easy to show that there now exist carnivorous animals presenting close intermediate grades from stictly terrestrial to aquatic habits; and as each exists by a struggle for life, it is clear that each must be well adapted to its place in nature. Look at the Mustela vison of North America, which has webbed feet, and which resembles an otter in its fur, short legs, and form of tail. During the summer this animal dives for and preys on fish, but during the long winter it leaves the frozen waters, and preys, like other pole-cats, on mice and land animals. If a different case had been taken, and it had been asked how an insectivorous quadruped could possibly have been converted into a flying bat, the question would have been far more difficult to answer. Yet I think such difficulties have little weight.

Here, as on other occasions, I lie under a heavy disadvantage, for, out of the many striking cases which I have collected, I can only give one or two instances of transitional habits and structures in allied species; and of diversified habits, either constant or occasional, in the same species. And it seems to me that nothing less than a long list of such cases is sufficient to lessen the difficulty in any particular case like that of the bat.

Look at the family of squirrels; here we have the finest gradation from animals with their tails only slightly flattened, and from others, as Sir J. Richardson has remarked, with the posterior part of their bodies rather wide and with the skin on their flanks rather full, to the so-called flying squirrels; and flying squirrels have their limbs and even the base of the tail united by a broad expanse of skin, which serves as a parachute and allows them to glide through the air to an astonishing distance from tree to tree. We cannot doubt that each structure is of use to each kind of squirrel in its own country, by enabling it to escape birds or beasts of prey, to collect food more quickly, or, as there is reason to believe, to lessen the danger from occasional falls. But it does not follow from this fact that the structure of each squirrel is the best that it is possible to conceive under all possible conditions. Let the climate and vegetation change, let other competing rodents or new beasts of prey immigrate, or old ones become modified, and all analogy would lead us to believe that some at least of the squirrels would decrease in numbers or become exterminated, unless they also become modified and improved in structure in a corresponding manner. Therefore, I can see no difficulty, more especially under changing conditions of life, in the continued preservation of individuals with fuller and fuller flank-membranes, each modification being useful, each being propagated, until, by the accumulated effects of this process of natural selection, a perfect so-called flying squirrel was produced.

Now look at the Galeopithecus or so-called flying lemur, which formerly was ranked amongst bats, but is now believed to belong to the Insectivora. An extremely wide flank-membrane stretches from the corners of the jaw to the tail, and includes the limbs with the elongated fingers. This flank-membrane is furnished with an extensor muscle. Although no graduated links of structure, fitted for gliding through the air, now connect the Galeopithecus with the other Insectivora, yet there is no difficulty in supposing that such links formerly existed, and that each was developed in the same manner as with the less perfectly gliding squirrels; each grade of structure having been useful to its possessor. Nor can I see any insuperable difficulty in further believing that the membrane connected fingers and fore-arm of the Galeopithecus might have been greatly lengthened by natural selection; and this, as far as the organs of flight are concerned, would have converted the animal into a bat. In certain bats in which the wing-membrane extends from the top of the shoulder to the tail and includes the hind-legs, we perhaps see traces of an apparatus originally fitted for gliding through the air rather than for flight.

If about a dozen genera of birds were to become extinct, who would have ventured to surmise that birds might have existed which used their wings solely as flappers, like the logger-headed duck (Micropterus of Eyton); as fins in the water and as front-legs on the land, like the penguin; as sails, like the ostrich; and functionally for no purpose, like the Apteryx? Yet the structure of each of these birds is good for it, under the conditions of life to which it is exposed, for each has to live by a struggle; but it is not necessarily the best possible under all possible conditions. It must not be inferred from these remarks that any of the grades of wing-structure here alluded to, which perhaps may all be the result of disuse, indicate the steps by which birds actually acquired their perfect power of flight; but they serve to show what diversified means of transition are at least possible.

Seeing that a few members of such water-breathing classes as the Crustacea and Mollusca are adapted to live on the land; and seeing that we have flying birds and mammals, flying insects of the most diversified types, and formerly had flying reptiles, it is conceivable that flying-fish, which now glide far through the air, slightly rising and turning by the aid of their fluttering fins, might have been modified into perfectly winged animals. If this had been effected, who would have ever imagined that in an early transitional state they had been the inhabitants of the open ocean, and had used their incipient organs of flight exclusively, as far as we know, to escape being devoured by other fish?

When we see any structure highly perfected for any particular habit, as the wings of a bird for flight, we should bear in mind that animals displaying early transitional grades of the structure will seldom have survived to the present day, for they will have been supplanted by their successors, which were gradually rendered more perfect through natural selection. Furthermore, we may conclude that transitional states between structures fitted for very different habits of life will rarely have been developed at an early period in great numbers and under many subordinate forms. Thus, to return to our imaginary illustration of the flying-fish, it does not seem probable that fishes capable of true flight would have been developed under many subordinate forms, for taking prey of many kinds in many ways, on the land and in the water, until their organs of flight had come to a high stage of perfection, so as to have given them a decided advantage over other animals in the battle for life. Hence the chance of discovering species with transitional grades of structure in a fossil condition will always be less, from their having existed in lesser numbers, than in the case of species with fully developed structures.

* * * *

He who believes that each being has been created as we now see it, must occasionally have felt surprise when he has met with an animal having habits and structure not in agreement. What can be plainer than that the webbed feet of ducks and geese are formed for swimming? Yet there are upland geese with webbed feet which rarely go near the water; and no one except Audubon has seen the frigate-bird, which has all its four toes webbed, alight on the surface of the ocean. On the other hand, grebes and coots are eminently aquatic, although their toes are only bordered by membrane. What seems plainer than that the long toes, not furnished with membrane of the Grallatores are formed for walking over swamps and floating plants?—the water-hen and landrail are members of this order, yet the first is nearly as aquatic as the coot, and the second nearly as terrestrial as the quail or partridge. In such cases, and many others could be given, habits have changed without a corresponding change of structure. The webbed feet of the upland goose may be said to have become almost rudimentary in function, though not in structure. In the frigate-bird, the deeply scooped membrane between the toes shows that structure has begun to change.

He who believes in separate and innumerable acts of creation may say, that in these cases it has pleased the Creator to cause a being of one type to take the place of one belonging to another type; but this seems to me only re-stating the fact in dignified language. He who believes in the struggle for existence and in the principle of natural selection, will acknowledge that every organic being is constantly endeavouring to increase in numbers; and that if any one being varies ever so little, either in habits or structure, and thus gains an advantage over some other inhabitant of the same country, it will seize on the place of that inhabitant, however different that may be from its own place. Hence it will cause him no surprise that there should be geese and frigate-birds with webbed feet, living on the dry land and rarely alighting on the water, that there should be long-toed corncrakes, living in meadows instead of in swamps; that there should be woodpeckers where hardly a tree grows; that there should be diving thrushes and diving Hymenoptera, and petrels with the habits of auks.

ORGANS OF EXTREME PERFECTION AND COMPLICATION

To suppose that the eye with all its inimitable contrivances for adjusting the focus to different distances, for admiting different amounts of light, and for the correction of spherical and chromatic aberration, could have been formed by natural selection, seems, I freely confess, absurd in the highest degree. When it was first said that the sun stood still and the world turned round, the common sense of mankind declared the doctrine false; but the old saying of *Vox populi, vox Dei*, as every philosopher knows, cannot be trusted in science. Reason tells me, that if numerous gradations from a simple and imperfect eye to one complex and perfect can be shown to exist, each grade being useful to its possessor, as is certainly the case; if further, the eye ever varies and the variations be inherited, as is likewise certainly the case; and if such variations should be useful to any animal under changing conditions of life, then the difficulty of believing that a perfect and complex eye could be formed by natural selection, though insuperable by our imagination, should not be considered as subversive of the theory. How a nerve comes to be sensitive to light, hardly concerns us more than how life itself originated; but I may remark that, as some of the lowest organisms, in which nerves cannot be detected, are capable of perceiving light, it does not seem impossible that certain sensitive elements in their sarcode should become aggregated and developed into nerves, endowed with this special sensibility.

In searching for the gradations through which an organ in any species has been perfected, we ought to look exclusively to its lineal progenitors; but this is scarcely ever possible, and we are forced to look to other species and genera of the same group, that is to the collateral descendants from the same parent-form, in order to see what gradations are possible, and for the chance of some gradations having been transmitted in an unaltered or little altered condition. But the state of the same organ in distinct classes may incidentally throw light on the steps by which it has been perfected.

The simplest organ which can be called an eye consists of an optic nerve, surrounded by pigment-cells and covered by translucent skin, but without any lens or other refractive body. We may, however, according to M. Jourdain, descend even a step lower and find aggregates of pigment-cells, apparently serving as organs of vision, without any nerves, and resting merely on sarcodic tissue. Eyes of the above simple nature are not capable of distinct vision, and serve only to distinguish light from darkness. In certain star-fishes, small depressions in the layer of pigment which surrounds the nerve are filled, as described by the author just quoted, with transparent gelatinous matter, projecting with a convex surface, like the cornea in the higher animals. He suggests that this serves not to form an image, but only to concentrate the luminous rays and render their perception more easy. In this concentration of the rays we gain the first and by far the most important step towards the formation of a true, picture-forming eye; for we have only to place the naked extremity of the optic nerve, which in some of the lower animals lies deeply buried in the body, and in some near the surface, at the right distance from the concentrating apparatus, and an image will be formed on it.

In the great class of the Articulata, we may start from an optic nerve simply coated with pigment, the latter sometimes forming a sort of pupil, but destitute of a lens or other optical contrivance. With insects it is now known that the numerous facets on the cornea of their great compound eyes form true lenses, and that the cones include curiously modified nervous filaments. But these organs in the Articulata are so much diversified that Müller formerly made three main classes with seven subdivisions, besides a fourth main class of aggregated simple eyes.

When we reflect on these facts, here given much too briefly, with respect to the wide, diversified, and graduated range of structure in the eyes of the lower animals; and when we bear in mind how small the number of all living forms must be in comparison with those which have become extinct, the difficulty ceases to be very great in believing that natural selection may have converted the simple apparatus of an optic nerve, coated with pigment and invested by transparent membrane, into an optical instrument as perfect as is possessed by any member of the Articulate Class.

He who will go thus far, ought not to hesitate to go one step further, if he finds on finishing this volume that large bodies of facts, otherwise inexplicable, can be explained by the theory of modification through natural selection; he ought to admit that a structure even as perfect as an eagle's eye might thus be formed, although in this case he does not know the transitional states. It has been objected that in order to modify the eye and still preserve it as a perfect instrument, many changes would have to be effected simultaneously, which, it is assumed, could not be done through natural selection; but as I have attempted to show in my work on the variation of domestic animals, it is not necessary to suppose that the modifications were all simultaneous, if they were extremely slight and gradual. Different kinds of modification would, also, serve for the same general purpose: as Mr. Wallace has remarked, 'if a lens has too short or too long a focus, it may be amended either by an alteration of curvature, or an alteration of density; if the curvature be irregular, and the rays do not converge to a point, then any increased regularity of curvature will be an improvement. So the contraction of the iris and the muscular movements of the eye are neither of them essential to vision, but only improvements which might have been added and perfected at any stage of the construction of the instrument.' Within the highest division of the animal kingdom, namely, the Vertebrata, we can start from an eye so simple, that it consists, as in the lancelet, of a little sack of transparent skin, furnished with a nerve and lined with pigment, but destitute of any other apparatus. In fishes and reptiles, as Owen has remarked, 'the range of gradations of dioptric structures is very great.' It is a significant fact that even in man, according to the high authority of Virchow, the beautiful crystalline lens is formed in the embryo by an accumulation of epidermic cells, lying in a sack-like fold of the skin; and the vitreous body is formed from embryonic sub-cutaneous tissue. To arrive, however, at a just conclusion regarding the formation of the eye, with all its marvellous yet not absolutely perfect characters, it is indispensable that the reason should conquer the imagination; but I have felt the difficulty far too keenly to be surprised at others hesitating to extend the principle of natural selection to so startling a length.

It is scarcely possible to avoid comparing the eye with a telescope. We know that this instrument has been perfected by the long-continued efforts of the highest human intellects; and we naturally infer that the eye has been formed by a somewhat analogous process. But may not this inference be presumptuous? Have we any right to assume that the Creator works by intellectual powers like those of man? If we must compare the eye to an optical instrument, we ought in imagination to take a thick layer of transparent tissue, with spaces filled with fluid, and with a nerve sensitive to light beneath, and then suppose every part of this layer to be continually changing slowly in density, so as to separate into layers of different densities and thicknesses, placed at different distances from each other, and with the surfaces of each layer slowly changing in form. Further we must suppose that there is a power, represented by natural selection or the survival of the fittest, always intently watching each slight alteration in the transparent layers; and carefully preserving each which, under varied circumstances, in any way or in any degree, tends to produce a distincter image. We must suppose each new state of the instrument to be multiplied by the million; each to be preserved until a better one is produced, and then the old ones to be all destroyed. In living bodies, variation will cause the slight alterations, generation will multiply them almost infinitely, and natural selection will pick out with unerring skill each improvement. Let this process go on for millions of years; and during each year on millions of individuals of many kinds; and may we not believe that a living optical instrument might thus be formed as superior to one of glass, as the works of the Creator are to those of man?

MODES OF TRANSITION

If it could be demonstrated that any complex organ existed, which could not possibly have been formed by numerous, successive, slight modifications, my theory would absolutely break down. But I can find out no such case. No doubt many organs exist of which we do not know the transitional grades, more especially if we look to much-isolated species, round which, according to the theory, there has been much extinction. Or again, if we take an organ common to all the members of a class, for in this latter case the organ must have been originally formed at a remote period, since which all the many members of the class have been developed; and in order to discover the early transitional grades through which the organ has passed, we should have to look to very ancient ancestral forms, long since become extinct.

* * * *

Again, two distinct organs, or the same organ under two very different forms, may simultaneously perform in the same individual the same function, and this is an extremely important means of transition: to give one instance,—there are fish with gills or branchiæ that breathe the air dissolved in the water, at the same time that they breathe free air in their swimbladders, this latter organ being divided by highly vascular partitions and having a ductus pneumaticus for the supply of air. To give another instance from the vegetable kingdom: plants climb by three distinct means, by spirally twining, by clasping a support with their sensitive tendrils, and by the emission of aërial rootlets; these three means are usually found in distinct groups, but some few species exhibit two of the means, or even all three, combined in the same individual. In all such cases one of the two organs might readily be modified and perfected so as to perform all the work, being aided during the progress of modification by the other organ; and then this other organ might be modified for some other and quite distinct purpose, or be wholly obliterated.

The illustration of the swimbladder in fishes is a good one, because it shows us clearly the highly important fact that an organ originally constructed for one purpose, namely, flotation, may be converted into one for a widely different purpose, namely, respiration. The swimbladder has, also, been worked in as an accessory to the auditory organs of certain fishes. All physiologists admit that the swimbladder is homologous, or 'ideally similar' in position and structure with the lungs of the higher vertebrate animals: hence there is no reason to doubt that the swimbladder has actually been converted into lungs, or an organ used exclusively for respiration.

According to this view it may be inferred that all vertebrate animals with true lungs are descended by ordinary generation from an ancient and unknown prototype, which was furnished with a floating apparatus or swimbladder. We can thus, as I infer from Owen's interesting description of these parts, understand the strange fact that every particle of food and drink which we swallow has to pass over the orifice of the trachea, with some risk of falling into the lungs, notwithstanding the beautiful contrivance by which the glottis is closed. In the higher Vertebrate the branchiæ have wholly disappeared—but in the embryo the slits on the sides of the neck and the loop-like course of the arteries still mark their former position. But it is conceivable that the now utterly lost branchiæ might have been gradually worked in by natural selection for some distinct purpose: for instance, Landois has shown that the wings of insects are developed from the tracheæ; it is therefore highly probable that in this great class organs which once served for respiration have been actually converted into organs for flight.

SPECIAL DIFFICULTIES OF THE THEORY OF NATURAL SELECTION

Although we must be extremely cautious in concluding that any organ could not have been produced by successive, small, transitional gradations, yet undoubtedly serious cases of difficulty occur.

One of the most serious is that of neuter insects, which are often differently constructed from either the males or fertile females; but this case will be treated of in the next chapter. The electric organs of fishes offer another case of special difficulty; for it is impossible to conceive by what steps these wondrous organs have been produced. But this is not surprising, for we do not even know of what use they are. In the Gymnotus and Torpedo they no doubt serve as powerful means of defence, and perhaps for securing prey; yet in the Ray, as observed by Matteucci, an analogous organ in the tail manifests but little electricity, even when the animal is greatly irritated; so little, that it can hardly be of any use for the above purposes. Moreover, in the Ray, besides the organ just referred to, there is, as Dr. R. M'Donnell has shown, another organ near the head, not known to be electrical, but which appears to be the real homologue of the electric battery in the Torpedo. It is generally admitted that there exists between these organs and ordinary muscle a close analogy, in intimate structure, in the distribution of the nerves, and in the manner in which they are acted on by various reagents. It should, also, be especially observed that muscular contraction is accompanied by an electrical discharge; and, as Dr. Radcliffe insists, 'in the electrical apparatus of the torpedo during rest, there would seem to be a charge in every respect like that which is met with in muscle and nerve during rest, and the discharge of the torpedo, instead of being peculiar, may be only another form of the discharge which depends upon the action of muscle and motor nerve.' Beyond this we cannot at present go in the way of explanation; but as we know so little about the uses of these organs, and as we know nothing about the habits and structure of the progenitors of the existing electric fishes, it would be extremely bold to maintain that no serviceable transitions are possible by which these organs might have been gradually developed.

These organs appear at first to offer another and far more serious difficulty; for they occur in about a dozen kinds of fish, of which several are widely remote in their affinities. When the same organ is found in several members of the same class, especially if in members having very different habits of life, we may generally attribute its presence to inheritance from a common ancestor; and its absence in some of the members to loss through disuse or natural selection. So that, if the electric organs had been inherited from some one ancient progenitor, we might have expected that all electric fishes would have been specially related to each other; but this is far from the case. Nor does geology at all lead to the belief that most fishes formerly possessed electric organs, which their modified descendants have now lost. But when we look at the subject more closely, we find in the several fishes provided with electric organs, that these are situated in different parts of the body,—that they differ in construction, as in the arrangement of the plates, and, according to Pacini, in the process or means by which the electricity is excited—and lastly, in being supplied with nerves proceeding from different sources, and this is perhaps the most important of all the differences. Hence in the several fishes furnished with electric organs, these cannot be considered as homologous, but only as analogous in function. Consequently there is no reason to suppose that they have been inherited from a common progenitor; for had this been the case they would have closely resembled each other in all respects. Thus the difficulty of an organ, apparently the same, arising in several remotely allied species, disappears, leaving only the lesser yet still great difficulty; namely, by what graduated steps these organs have been developed in each separate group of fishes.

The luminous organs which occur in a few insects, belonging to widely different families, and which are situated in different parts of the body, offer, under our present state of ignorance, a difficulty almost exactly parallel with that of the electric organs. Other similar cases could be given; for instance in plants, the very curious contrivance of a mass of pollen-grains, borne on a foot-stalk with an adhesive gland, is apparently the same in Orchis and Asclepias,—genera almost as remote as is possible amongst flowering plants; but here again the parts are not homologous. In all cases of beings, far removed from each other in the scale of organisation, which are furnished with similar and peculiar organs, it will be found that although the general appearance and function of the organs may be the same, yet fundamental differences between them can always be detected. For instance, the eyes of cephalopods or cuttle-fish and of vertebrate animals appear wonderfully alike; and in such widely sundered groups no part of this resemblance can be due to inheritance from a common progenitor. Mr. Mivart has advanced this case as one of special difficulty, but I am unable to see the force of his argument. An organ for vision must be formed of transparent tissue, and must include some sort of lens for throwing an image at the back of a darkened chamber. Beyond this superficial resemblance, there is hardly any real similarity between the eyes of cuttle-fish and vertebrates, as may be seen by consulting Hensen's admirable memoir on these organs in the Cephalopoda. It is impossible for me here to enter on details, but I may specify a few of the points of difference. The crystalline lens in the higher cuttle-fish consists of two parts, placed one behind the other like two lenses, both having a very different structure and disposition to what occurs in the vertebrata. The retina is wholly different, with an actual inversion of the elemental parts, and with a large nervous ganglion included within the membranes of the eye. The relations of the muscles are as different as it is possible to conceive, and so in other points. Hence it is not a little difficult to decide how far even the same terms ought to be employed in describing the eyes of the Cephalopoda and Vertebrata. It is, of course, open to any one to deny that the eye in either case could have been developed through the natural selection of successive slight variations; but if this be admitted in the one case, it is clearly possible in the other; and fundamental differences of structure in the visual organs of two groups might have been anticipated, in accordance with this view of their manner of formation. As two men have sometimes independently hit on the same invention, so in the several foregoing cases it appears that natural selection, working for the good of each being, and taking advantage of all favourable variations, has produced similar organs, as far as function is concerned, in distinct organic beings, which owe none of their structure in common to inheritance from a common progenitor.

* * * *

UTILITARIAN DOCTRINE, HOW FAR TRUE: BEAUTY, HOW ACQUIRED

The foregoing remarks lead me to say a few words on the protest lately made by some naturalists, against the utilitarian doctrine that every detail of structure has been produced for the good of its possessor. They believe that many structures have been created for the sake of beauty, to delight man or the Creator (but this latter point is beyond the scope of scientific discussion), or for the sake of mere variety, a view already discussed. Such doctrines, if true, would be absolutely fatal to my theory. I fully admit that many structures are now of no direct use to their possessors, and may never have been of any use to their progenitors; but this does not prove that they were formed solely for beauty or variety. No doubt the definite action of changed conditions, and the various causes of modifications, lately specified, have all produced an effect, probably a great effect, independently of any advantage thus gained. But a still more important consideration is that the chief part of the organisation of every living creature is due to inheritance; and consequently, though each being assuredly is well fitted for its place in nature, many structures have now no very close and direct relation to present habits of life. Thus, we can hardly believe that the webbed feet of the upland goose or of the frigate-bird are of special use to these birds; we cannot believe that the similar bones in the arm of the monkey, in the fore-leg of the horse, in the wing of the bat, and in the flipper of the seal, are of special use to these animals. We may safely attribute these structures to inheritance. But webbed feet no doubt were as useful to the progenitor of the upland goose and of the frigate-bird, as they now are to the most aquatic of living birds. So we may believe that the progenitor of the seal did not possess a flipper, but a foot with five toes fitted for walking or grasping; but we may further venture to believe that the several bones in the limbs of the monkey, horse, and bat, were originally developed, on the principle of utility, probably through the reduction of more numerous bones in the fin of some ancient fish-like progenitor of the whole class. It is scarcely possible to decide how much allowance ought to be made for such causes of change, as the definite action of external conditions, so-called spontaneous variations, and the complex laws of growth; but with these important exceptions, we may conclude that the structure of every living creature either now is, or was formerly, of some direct or indirect use to its possessor.

With respect to the belief that organic beings have been created beautiful for the delight of man,—a belief which it has been pronounced is subversive of my whole theory,—I may first remark that the sense of beauty obviously depends on the nature of the mind, irrespective of any real quality in the admired object; and that the idea of what is beautiful, is not innate or unalterable. We see this, for instance, in the men of different races admiring an entirely different standard of beauty in their women. If beautiful objects had been created solely for man's gratification, it ought to be shown that before man appeared, there was less beauty on the face of the earth than since he came on the stage. Were the beautiful volute and cone shells of the Eocene epoch, and the gracefully sculptured ammonites of the Secondary period, created that man might ages afterwards admire them in his cabinet? Few objects are more beautiful than the minute siliceous cases of the diatomaceæ: were these created that they might be examined and admired under the higher powers of the microscope? The beauty in this latter case, and in many others, is apparently wholly due to symmetry of growth. Flowers rank amongst the most beautiful productions of nature; but they have been rendered conspicuous in contrast with the green leaves, and in consequence at the same time beautiful, so that they may be easily observed by insects. I have come to this conclusion from finding it an invariable rule that when a flower is fertilised by the wind it never has a gaily-coloured corolla. Several plants habitually produce two kinds of flowers; one kind open and coloured so as to attract insects; the other closed, not coloured, destitute of nectar, and never visited by insects. Hence we may conclude that, if insects had not been developed on the face of the earth, our plants would not have been decked with beautiful flowers, but would have produced only such poor flowers as we see on our fir, oak, nut and ash trees, on grasses, spinach, docks, and nettles, which are all fertilised through the agency of the wind. A similar line of argument holds good with fruits; that a ripe strawberry or cherry is as pleasing to the eye as to the palate, —that the gaily-coloured fruit of the spindle-wood tree and the scarlet berries of the holly are beautiful objects,—will be admitted by every one. But this beauty serves merely as a guide to birds and beasts, in order that the fruit may be devoured and the matured seeds disseminated: I infer that this is the case from having as yet found no exception to the rule that seeds are always thus disseminated when embedded within a fruit of any kind (that is within a fleshy or pulpy envelope), if it be coloured of any brilliant tint, or rendered conspicuous by being white or black.

On the other hand, I willingly admit that a great number of male animals, as all our most gorgeous birds, some fishes, reptiles, and mammals, and a host of magnificently coloured butterflies, have been rendered beautiful for beauty's sake; but this has been effected through sexual selection, that is, by the more beautiful males having been continually preferred by the females, and not for the delight of man. So it is with the music of birds. We may infer from all this that a nearly similar taste for beautiful colours and for musical sounds runs through a large part of the animal kingdom. When the female is as beautifully coloured as the male, which is not rarely the case with birds and butterflies, the cause apparently lies in the colours acquired through sexual selection having been transmitted to both sexes, instead of to the males alone. How the sense of beauty in its simplest form—that is, the reception of a peculiar kind of pleasure from certain colours, forms, and sounds—was first developed in the mind of man and of the lower animals, is a very obscure subject. The same sort of difficulty is presented, if we enquire how it is that certain flavours and odours give pleasure, and others displeasure. Habit in all these cases appears to have come to a certain extent into play; but there must be some fundamental cause in the constitution of the nervous system in each species.

* * *

SUMMARY: THE LAW OF UNITY OF TYPE AND OF THE CONDITIONS OF EXISTENCE EMBRACED BY THE THEORY OF NATURAL SELECTION

We have . . . discussed some of the difficulties and objections which may be urged against the theory. Many of them are serious; but I think that in the discussion light has been thrown on several facts, which on the belief of independent acts of creation are utterly obscure. We have seen that species at any one period are not indefinitely variable, and are not linked together by a multitude of intermediate gradations, partly because the process of natural selection is always very slow, and at any one time acts only on a few forms; and partly because the very process of natural selection implies the continual supplanting and extinction of preceding and intermediate gradations. Closely allied species, now living on a continuous area, must often have been formed when the area was not continuous, and when the conditions of life did not insensibly graduate away from one part to another. When two varieties are formed in two districts of a continuous area, an intermediate variety will often be formed, fitted for an intermediate zone; but from reasons assigned, the intermediate variety will usually exist in lesser numbers than the two forms which it connects; consequently the two latter, during the course of further modification, from existing in greater numbers, will have a great advantage over the less numerous intermediate variety, and will thus generally succeed in supplanting and exterminating it.

We have seen . . . how cautious we should be in concluding that the most different habits of life could not graduate into each other; that a bat, for instance, could not have been formed by natural selection from an animal which at first only glided through the air.

We have seen that a species under new conditions of life may change its habits; or it may have diversified habits, with some very unlike those of its nearest congeners. Hence we can understand, bearing in mind that each organic being is trying to live wherever it can live, how it has arisen that there are upland geese with webbed feet, ground woodpeckers, diving thrushes, and petrels with the habits of auks.

Although the belief that an organ so perfect as the eye could have been formed by natural selection, is enough to stagger any one; yet in the case of any organ, if we know of a long series of gradations in complexity, each good for its possessor, then, under changing conditions of life, there is no logical impossibility in the acquirement of any conceivable degree of perfection through natural selection. In the cases in which we know of no intermediate or transitional states, we should be extremely cautious in concluding that none can have existed, for the metamorphoses of many organs show what wonderful changes in function are at least possible. For instance, a swimbladder has apparently been converted into an air-breathing lung. The same organ having performed simultaneously very different functions, and then having been in part or in whole specialised for one function; and two distinct organs having performed at the same time the same function, the one having been perfected whilst aided by the other, must often have largely facilitated transitions.

We have seen that in two beings widely remote from each other in the natural scale, organs serving for the same purpose and in external appearance closely similar may have been separately and independently formed; but when such organs are closely examined, essential differences in their structure can almost always be detected; and this naturally follows from the principle of natural selection. On the other hand, the common rule throughout nature is infinite diversity of structure for gaining the same end; and this again naturally follows from the same great principle.

In many cases we are far too ignorant to be enabled to assert that a part or organ is so unimportant for the welfare of a species, that modifications in its structure could not have been slowly accumulated by means of natural selection. In many other cases, modifications are probably the direct result of the laws of variation or of growth, independently of any good having been thus gained. But even such structures have often, as we may feel assured, been subsequently taken advantage of, and still further modified, for the good of species under new conditions of life. We may, also, believe that a part formerly of high importance has frequently been retained (as the tail of an aquatic animal by its terrestrial descendants), though it has become of such small importance that it could not, in its present state, have been acquired by means of natural selection.

Natural selection can produce nothing in one species for the exclusive good or injury of another; though it may well produce parts, organs, and excretions highly useful or even indispensable, or again highly injurious to another species, but in all cases at the same time useful to the possessor. In each well-stocked country natural selection acts through the competition of the inhabitants, and consequently leads to success in the battle for life, only in accordance with the standard of that particular country. Hence the inhabitants of one country, generally the smaller one, often yield to the inhabitants of another and generally the larger country. For in the larger country there will have existed more individuals and more diversified forms, and the competition will have been severer, and thus the standard of perfection will have been rendered higher. Natural selection will not necessarily lead to absolute perfection; nor, as far as we can judge by our limited faculties, can absolute perfection be everywhere predicated.

On the theory of natural selection we can clearly understand the full meaning of that old canon in natural history, *Natura non facit saltum.* This canon, if we look to the present inhabitants alone of the world, is not strictly correct; but if we include all those of past times, whether known or unknown, it must on this theory be strictly true.

It is generally acknowledged that all organic beings have been formed on two great laws—Unity of Type, and the Conditions of Existence. By unity of type is meant that fundamental agreement in structure which we see in organic beings of the same class, and which is quite independent of their habits of life. On my theory, unity of type is explained by unity of descent. The expression of conditions of existence, so often insisted on by the illustrious Cuvier, is fully embraced by the principle of natural selection. For natural selection acts by either now adapting the varying parts of each being to its organic and inorganic conditions of life; or by having adapted them during past periods of time: the adaptations being aided in many cases by the increased use or disuse of parts, being affected by the direct action of the external conditions of life, and subjected in all cases to the several laws of growth and variation. Hence, in fact, the law of the Conditions of Existence is the higher law; as it includes, through the inheritance of former variations and adaptations, that of Unity of Type.

* * * *

INSTINCT

Many instincts are so wonderful that their development will probably appear to the reader a difficulty sufficient to overthrow my whole theory. I may here premise that I have nothing to do with the origin of the mental powers, any more than I have with that of life itself. We are concerned only with the diversities of instinct and of the other mental faculties in animals of the same class.

I will not attempt any definition of instinct. It would be easy to show that several distinct mental actions are commonly embraced by this term; but every one understands what is meant, when it is said that instinct impels the cuckoo to migrate and to lay her eggs in other birds' nests. An action, which we ourselves require experience to enable us to perform, when performed by an animal, more especially by a very young one, without experience, and when performed by many individuals in the same way, without their knowing for what purpose it is performed, is usually said to be instinctive. But I could show that none of these characters are universal. A little dose of judgment or reason, as Pierre Huber expresses it, often comes into play, even with animals low in the scale of nature.

Frederick Cuvier and several of the older metaphysicians have compared instinct with habit. This comparison gives, I think, an accurate notion of the frame of mind under which an instinctive action is performed, but not necessarily of its origin. How unconsciously many habitual actions are performed, indeed not rarely in direct opposition to our conscious will! yet they may be modified by the will or reason. Habits easily become associated with other habits, with certain periods of time, and states of the body. When once acquired, they often remain constant throughout life. Several other points of resemblance between instincts and habits could be pointed out. As in repeating a well-known song, so in instincts, one action follows another by a sort of rhythm; if a person be interrupted in a song, or in repeating anything by note, he is generally forced to go back to recover the habitual train of thought; so P. Huber found it was with a caterpillar, which makes a very complicated hammock; for if he took a caterpillar which had completed its hammock up to, say, the sixth stage of construction, and put it into a hammock completed up only to the third stage, the caterpillar simply re-performed the fourth, fifth, and sixth stages of construction. If, however, a caterpillar were taken out of a hammock made up, for instance, to the third stage, and were put into one finished up to the sixth stage, so that much of its work was already done for it, far from deriving any benefit from this, it was much embarrassed, and in order to complete its hammock, seemed forced to start from the third stage, where it had left off, and thus tried to complete the already finished work.

If we suppose any habitual action to become inherited—and it can be shown that this does sometimes happen—then the resemblance between what originally was a habit and an instinct becomes so close as not to be distinguished. If Mozart, instead of playing the pianoforte at three years old with wonderfully little practice, had played a tune with no practice at all, he might truly be said to have done so instinctively. But it would be a serious error to suppose that the greater number of instincts have been acquired by habit in one generation, and then transmitted by inheritance to succeeding generations. It can be clearly shown that the most wonderful instincts with which we are acquainted, namely, those of the hive-bee and of many ants, could not possibly have been acquired by habit.

It will be universally admitted that instincts are as important as corporeal structures for the welfare of each species, under its present conditions of life. Under changed conditions of life, it is at least possible that slight modifications of instinct might be profitable to a species; and if it can be shown that instincts do vary ever so little, then I can see no difficulty in natural selection preserving and continually accumulating variations of instinct to any extent that was profitable. It is thus, as I believe, that all the most complex and wonderful instincts have originated. As modifications of corporeal structure arise from, and are increased by, use or habit, and are diminished or lost by disuse, so I do not doubt it has been with instincts. But I believe that the effects of habit are in many cases of subordinate importance to the effects of the natural selection of what may be called spontaneous variations of instincts;—that is of variations produced by the same unknown causes which produce slight deviations of bodily structure.

No complex instinct can possibly be produced through natural selection, except by the slow and gradual accumulation of numerous slight, yet profitable, variations. Hence, as in the case of corporeal structures, we ought to find in nature, not the actual transitional gradations by which each complex instinct has been acquired—for these could be found only in the lineal ancestors of each species—but we ought to find in the collateral lines of descent some evidence of such gradations; or we ought at least to be able to show that gradations of some kind are possible; and this we certainly can do. I have been surprised to find, making allowance for the instincts of animals having been but little observed except in Europe and North America, and for no instinct being known among extinct species, how very generally gradations, leading to the most complex instincts, can be discovered. Changes of instinct may sometimes be facilitated by the same species having different instincts at different periods of life, or at different seasons of the year, or when placed under different circumstances, &c.; in which case either the one or the other instinct might be preserved by natural selection. And such instances of diversity of instinct in the same species can be shown to occur in nature.

Again, as in the case of corporeal structure, and conformably to my theory, the instinct of each species is good for itself, but has never, as far as we can judge, been produced for the exclusive good of others. One of the strongest instances of an animal apparently performing an action for the sole good of another, with which I am acquainted, is that of aphides voluntarily yielding, as was first observed by Huber, their sweet excretion to ants: that they do so voluntarily, the following facts show. I removed all the ants from a group of about a dozen aphides on a dock-plant, and prevented their attendance during several hours. After this interval, I felt sure that the aphides would want to excrete. I watched them for some time through a lens, but not one excreted; I then tickled and stroked them with a hair in the same manner, as well as I could, as the ants do with their antennæ; but not one excreted. Afterwards I allowed an ant to visit them, and it immediately seemed, by its eager way of running about, to be well aware what a rich flock it had discovered; it then began to play with its antennæ on the abdomen first of one aphis and then of another; and each, as soon as it felt the antennæ, immediately lifted up its abdomen and excreted a limpid drop of sweet juice, which was eagerly devoured by the ant. Even the quite young aphides behaved in this manner, showing that the action was instinctive, and not the result of experience. It is certain, from the observations of Huber, that the aphides show no dislike to the ants: if the latter be not present they are at last compelled to eject their excretion. But as the excretion is extremely viscid, it is no doubt a convenience to the aphides to have it removed; therefore probably they do not excrete solely for the good of the ants. Although there is no evidence that any animal performs an action for the exclusive good of another species, yet each tries to take advantage of the instincts of others, as each takes advantage of the weaker bodily structure of other species. So again certain instincts cannot be considered as absolutely perfect; but as details on this and other such points are not indispensable, they may be here passed over.

As some degree of variation in instincts under a state of nature, and the inheritance of such variations, are indispensable for the action of natural selection, as many instances as possible ought to be given; but want of space prevents me. I can only assert that instincts certainly do vary—for instance, the migratory instinct, both in extent and direction, and in its total loss. So it is with the nests of birds, which vary partly in dependence on the situations chosen, and on the nature and temperature of the country inhabited, but often from causes wholly unknown to us: Audubon has given several remarkable cases of differences in the nests of the same species in the northern and southern United States. Why, it has been asked, if instinct be variable, has it not granted to the bee 'the ability to use some other material when wax was deficient'? But what other natural material could bees use? They will work, as I have seen, with wax hardened with vermilion or softened with lard. Andrew Knight observed that his bees, instead of laboriously collecting propolis, used a cement of wax and turpentine, with which he had covered decorticated trees. It has lately been shown that bees, instead of searching for pollen, will gladly use a very different substance, namely oatmeal. Fear of any particular enemy is certainly an instinctive quality, as may be seen in nestling birds, though it is strengthened by experience, and by the sight of fear of the same enemy in other animals. The fear of man is slowly acquired, as I have elsewhere shown, by the various animals which inhabit desert islands; and we see an instance of this even in England, in the greater wildness of all our large birds in comparison with our small birds; for the large birds have been most persecuted by man. We may safely attribute the greater wildness of our large birds to this cause; for in uninhabited islands large birds are not more fearful than small; and the magpie, so wary in England, is tame in Norway, as is the hooded crow in Egypt.

That the mental qualities of animals of the same kind, born in a state of nature, vary much, could be shown by many facts. Several cases could also be adduced of occasional and strange habits in wild animals, which, if advantageous to the species, might have given rise, through natural selection, to new instincts. But I am well aware that these general statements, without the facts in detail, will produce but a feeble effect on the reader's mind. I can only repeat my assurance, that I do not speak without good evidence.

INHERITED CHANGES OF HABIT OR INSTINCT IN DOMESTICATED ANIMALS

The possibility, or even probability, of inherited variations of instinct in a state of nature will be strengthened by briefly considering a few cases under domestication. We shall thus be enabled to see the part which habit and the selection of so-called spontaneous variations have played in modifying the mental qualities of our domestic animals. It is notorious how much domestic animals vary in their mental qualities. With cats, for instance, one naturally takes to catching rats, and another mice, and these tendencies are known to be inherited. One cat, according to Mr. St. John, always brought home game-birds, another hares or rabbits, and another hunted on marshy ground and almost nightly caught woodcocks or snipes. A number of curious and authentic instances could be given of various shades of disposition and of taste, and likewise of the oddest tricks, associated with certain frames of mind or periods of time, being inherited. But let us look to the familiar case of the breeds of the dogs: it cannot be doubted that young pointers (I have myself seen a striking instance) will sometimes point and even back other dogs the very first time that they are taken out; retrieving is certainly in some degree inherited by retrievers; and a tendency to run round, instead of at, a flock of sheep, by shepherd dogs. I cannot see that these actions, performed without experience by the young, and in nearly the same manner by each individual, performed with eager delight by each breed, and without the end being known—for the young pointer can no more know that he points to aid his master, than the white butterfly knows why she lays her eggs on the leaf of the cabbage—I cannot see that these actions differ essentially from true instincts. If we were to behold one kind of wolf, when young and without any training, as soon as it scented its prey, stand motionless like a statue, and then slowly crawl forward with a peculiar gait; and another kind of wolf rushing round, instead of at, a herd of deer, and driving them to a distant point, we should assuredly call these actions instinctive. Domestic instincts, as they may be called, are certainly far less fixed than natural instincts; but they have been acted on by far less rigorous selection, and have been transmitted for an incomparably shorter period, under less fixed conditions of life.

How strongly these domestic instincts, habits, and dispositions are inherited, and how curiously they become mingled, is well shown when different breeds of dogs are crossed. Thus it is known that a cross with a bull-dog has affected for many generations the courage and obstinacy of greyhounds; and a cross with a greyhound has given to a whole family of shepherd-dogs a tendency to hunt hares. These domestic instincts, when thus tested by crossing, resemble natural instincts, which in a like manner become curiously blended together, and for a long period exhibit traces of the instincts of either parent: for example, Le Roy describes a dog, whose great-grandfather was a wolf, and this dog showed a trace of its wild parentage only in one way, by not coming in a straight line to his master, when called.

Domestic instincts are sometimes spoken of as actions which have become inherited solely from long-continued and compulsory habit; but this is not true. No one would ever have thought of teaching, or probably could have taught, the tumbler-pigeon to tumble,—an action which, as I have witnessed, is performed by young birds, that have never seen a pigeon tumble. We may believe that some one pigeon showed a slight tendency to this strange habit, and that the long-continued selection of the best individuals in successive generations made tumblers what they now are; and near Glasgow there are house-tumblers, as I hear from Mr. Brent, which cannot fly eighteen inches high without going head over heels. It may be doubted whether any one would have thought of training a dog to point, had not some one dog naturally shown a tendency in this line; and this is known occasionally to happen, as I once saw, in a pure terrier: the act of pointing is probably, as many have thought, only the exaggerated pause of an animal preparing to spring on its prey. When the first tendency to point was once displayed, methodical selection and the inherited effects of compulsory training in each successive generation would soon complete the work; and unconscious selection is still in progress, as each man tries to procure, without intending to improve the breed, dogs which stand and hunt best. On the other hand, habit alone in some cases has sufficed; hardly any animal is more difficult to tame than the young of the wild rabbit; scarcely any animal is tamer than the young of the tame rabbit; but I can hardly suppose that domestic rabbits have often been selected for tameness alone; so that we must attribute at least the greater part of the inherited change from extreme wildness to extreme tameness, to habit and long-continued close confinement.

Natural instincts are lost under domestication: a remarkable instance of this is seen in those breeds of fowls which very rarely or never become 'broody', that is, never wish to sit on their eggs. Familiarity alone prevents our seeing how largely and how permanently the minds of our domestic animals have been modified. It is scarcely possible to doubt that the love of man has become instinctive in the dog. All wolves, foxes, jackals, and species of the cat genus, when kept tame, are most eager to attack poultry, sheep, and pigs; and this tendency has been found incurable in dogs which have been brought home as puppies from countries such as Tierra del Fuego and Australia, where the savages do not keep these domestic animals. How rarely, on the other hand, do our civilised dogs, even when quite young, require to be taught not to attack poultry, sheep, and pigs! No doubt they occasionally do make an attack, and are then beaten; and if not cured, they are destroyed; so that habit and some degree of selection have probably concurred in civilising by inheritance our dogs. On the other hand, young chickens have lost, wholly by habit, that fear of the dog and cat which no doubt was originally instinctive in them; for I am informed by Captain Hutton that the young chickens of the parent-stock, the Gallus bankiva, when reared in India under a hen, are at first excessively wild. So it is with young pheasants reared in England under a hen. It is not that chickens have lost all fear, but fear only of dogs and cats, for if the hen gives the danger-chuckle, they will run (more especially young turkeys) from under her, and conceal themselves in the surrounding grass or thickets; and this is evidently done for the instinctive purpose of allowing as we see in wild ground-birds, their mother to fly away. But this instinct retained by our chickens has become useless under domestication, for the mother-hen has almost lost by disuse the power of flight.

Hence, we may conclude, that under domestication instincts have been acquired, and natural instincts have been lost, partly by habit, and partly by man selecting and accumulating, during successive generations, peculiar mental habits and actions, which at first appeared from what we must in our ignorance call an accident. In some cases compulsory habit alone has sufficed to produce inherited mental changes; in other cases, compulsory habit has done nothing, and all has been the result of selection, pursued both methodically and unconsciously: but in most cases habit and selection have probably concurred.

* * * *

OBJECTIONS TO THE THEORY OF NATURAL SELECTION AS APPLIED TO INSTINCTS: NEUTER AND STERILE INSECTS

It has been objected to the foregoing view of the origin of instincts that 'the variations of structure and of instinct must have been simultaneous and accurately adjusted to each other, as a modification in the one without an immediate corresponding change in the other would have been fatal.' The force of this objection rests entirely on the assumption that the changes in the instincts and structure are abrupt. To take as an illustration the case of the larger titmouse (Parus major) alluded to in a previous chapter; this bird often holds the seeds of the yew between its feet on a branch, and hammers with its beak till it gets at the kernel. Now what special difficulty would there be in natural selection preserving all the slight individual variations in the shape of the beak, which were better and better adapted to break open the seeds, until a beak was formed, as well constructed for this purpose as that of the nuthatch, at the same time that habit, or compulsion, or spontaneous variations of taste, led the bird to become more and more of a seed-eater? In this case the beak is supposed to be slowly modified by natural selection, subsequently to, but in accordance with, slowly changing habits or taste; but let the feet of the titmouse vary and grow larger from correlation with the beak, or from any other unknown cause, and it is not improbable that such larger feet would lead the bird to climb more and more until it acquired the remarkable climbing instinct and power of the nuthatch. In this case a gradual change of structure is supposed to lead to changed instinctive habits. To take one more case: few instincts are more remarkable than that which leads the swift of the Eastern Islands to make its nest wholly of inspissated saliva. Some birds build their nests of mud, believed to be moistened with saliva; and one of the swifts of North America makes its nest (as I have seen) of sticks agglutinated with saliva, and even with flakes of this substance. Is it then very improbable that the natural selection of individual swifts, which secreted more and more saliva, should at last produce a species with instincts leading it to neglect other materials, and to make its nest exclusively of inspissated saliva? And so in other cases. It must, however, be admitted that in many instances we cannot conjecture whether it was instinct or structure which first varied.

No doubt many instincts of very difficult explanation could be opposed to the theory of natural selection—cases, in which we cannot see how an instinct could have originated; cases, in which no intermediate gradations are known to exist; cases of instincts of such trifling importance, that they could hardly have been acted on by natural selection; cases of instincts almost identically the same in animals so remote in the scale of nature, that we cannot account for their similarity by inheritance from a common progenitor, and consequently must believe that they were independently acquired through natural selection. I will not here enter on these several cases, but will confine myself to one special difficulty, which at first appeared to me insuperable, and actually fatal to the whole theory. I allude to the neuters or sterile females in insect-communities; for these neuters often differ widely in instinct and in structure from both the males and fertile females, and yet, from being sterile, they cannot propagate their kind.

The subject well deserves to be discussed at great length, but I will here take only a single case, that of working or sterile ants. How the workers have been rendered sterile is a difficulty; but not much greater than that of any other striking modification of structure; for it can be shown that some insects and other articulate animals in a state of nature occasionally become sterile; and if such insects had been social, and it had been profitable to the community that a number should have been annually born capable of work, but incapable of procreation, I can see no especial difficulty in this having been effected through natural selection. But I must pass over this preliminary difficulty. The great difficulty lies in the working ants differing widely from both the males and the fertile females in structure, as in the shape of the thorax, and in being destitute of wings and sometimes of eyes, and in instinct. As far as instinct alone is concerned, the wonderful difference in this respect between the workers and the perfect females, would have been better exemplified by the hive-bee. If a working ant or other neuter insect had been an ordinary animal, I should have unhesitatingly assumed that all its characters had been slowly acquired through natural selection; namely, by individuals having been born with slight profitable modifications, which were inherited by the offspring; and that these again varied and again were selected, and so onwards. But with the working ant we have an insect differing greatly from its parents, yet absolutely sterile; so that it could never have transmitted successively acquired modifications of structure or instinct to its progeny. It may well be asked how is it possible to reconcile this case with the theory of natural selection?

First, let it be remembered that we have innumerable instances, both in our domestic productions and in those in a state of nature, of all sorts of differences of inherited structure which are correlated with certain ages, and with either sex. We have differences correlated not only with one sex, but with that short period when the reproductive system is active, as in the nuptial plumage of many birds, and in the hooked jaws of the male salmon. We have even slight differences in the horns of different breeds of cattle in relation to an artificially imperfect state of the male sex; for oxen of certain breeds have longer horns than the oxen of other breeds, relatively to the length of the horns in both the bulls and cows of these same breeds. Hence I can see no great difficulty in any character becoming correlated with the sterile condition of certain members of insect-communities: the difficulty lies in understanding how such correlated modifications of structure could have been slowly accumulated by natural selection.

This difficulty, though appearing insuperable, is lessened, or, as I believe, disappears, when it is remembered that selection may be applied to the family, as well as to the individual, and may thus gain the desired end. Breeders of cattle wish the flesh and fat to be well marbled together: an animal thus characterised has been slaughtered, but the breeder has gone with confidence to the same stock and has succeeded. Such faith may be placed in the power of selection, that a breed of cattle, always yielding oxen with extraordinarily long horns, could, it is probable, be formed by carefully watching which individual bulls and cows, when matched, produced oxen with the longest horns; and yet no ox would ever have propagated its kind. Here is a better and real illustration: according to M. Verlot, some varieties of the double annual Stock from having been long and carefully selected to the right degree, always produce a large proportion of seedlings bearing double and quite sterile flowers; but they likewise yield some single and fertile plants. These latter, by which alone the variety can be propagated, may be compared with the fertile male and female ants, and the double sterile plants with the neuters of the same community. As with the varieties of the stock, so with social insects, selection has been applied to the family, and not to the individual, for the sake of gaining a serviceable end. Hence we may conclude that slight modifications of structure or of instinct, correlated with the sterile condition of certain members of the community, have proved advantageous: consequently the fertile males and females have flourished, and transmitted to their fertile offspring a tendency to produce sterile members with the same modifications. This process must have been repeated many times, until that prodigious amount of difference between the fertile and sterile females of the same species has been produced, which we see in many social insects.

But we have not as yet touched on the acme of the difficulty; namely, the fact that the neuters of several ants differ, not only from the fertile females and males, but from each other, sometimes to an almost incredible degree, and are thus divided into two or even three castes. The castes, moreover, do not commonly graduate into each other, but are perfectly well defined; being as distinct from each other as are any two species of the same genus, or rather as any two genera of the same family. Thus in Eciton, there are working and soldier neuters, with jaws and instincts extraordinarily different: in Cryptocerus, the workers of one caste alone carry a wonderful sort of shield on their heads, the use of which is quite unknown: in the Mexican Myrmecocystus, the workers of one caste never leave the nest; they are fed by the workers of another caste, and they have an enormously developed abdomen which secretes a sort of honey, supplying the place of that excreted by the aphides, or the domestic cattle as they may be called, which our European ants guard and imprison.

It will indeed be thought that I have an overweening confidence in the principle of natural selection, when I do not admit that such wonderful and well-established facts at once annihilate the theory. In the simpler case of neuter insects all of one caste, which, as I believe, have been rendered different from the fertile males and females through natural selection we may conclude from the analogy of ordinary variations, that the successive, slight, profitable modifications did not first arise in all the neuters in the same nest, but in some few alone; and that by the survival of the communities with females which produced most neuters having the advantageous modifications, all the neuters ultimately came to be thus characterised. According to this view we ought occasionally to find in the same nest neuter insects, presenting gradations of structure; and this we do find, even not rarely, considering how few neuter insects out of Europe have been carefully examined. Mr. F. Smith has shown that the neuters of several British ants differ surprisingly from each other in size and sometimes in colour; and that the extreme forms can be linked together by individuals taken out of the same nest: I have myself compared perfect gradations of this kind. It sometimes happens that the larger or the smaller sized workers are the most numerous; or that both large and small are numerous, whilst those of an intermediate size are scanty in numbers. Formica flava has larger and smaller workers, with some few of intermediate size; and, in this species, as Mr. F. Smith has observed, the larger workers have simple eyes (ocelli), which though small can be plainly distinguished, whereas the smaller workers have their ocelli rudimentary. Having carefully dissected several specimens of these workers, I can affirm that the eyes are far more rudimentary in the smaller workers than can be accounted for merely by their proportionally lesser size; and I fully believe, though I dare not assert so positively, that the workers of intermediate size have their ocelli in an exactly intermediate condition. So that here we have two bodies of sterile workers in the same nest, differing not only in size, but in their organs of vision, yet connected by some few members in an intermediate condition. I may digress by adding, that if the smaller workers had been the most useful to the community, and those males and females had been continually selected, which produced more and more of the smaller workers, until all the workers were in this condition; we should then have had a species of ant with neuters in nearly the same condition as those of Myrmica. For the workers of Myrmica have not even rudiments of ocelli, though the male and female ants of this genus have well-developed ocelli.

I may give one other case: so confidently did I expect occasionally to find gradations of important structures between the different castes of neuters in the same species, that I gladly availed myself of Mr. F. Smith's offer of numerous specimens from the same nest of the driver ant (Anomma) of West Africa. The reader will perhaps best appreciate the amount of difference in these workers, by my giving not the actual measurements, but a strictly accurate illustration: the difference was the same as if we were to see a set of workmen building a house, of whom many were five feet four inches high, and many sixteen feet high; but we must in addition suppose that the larger workmen had heads four instead of three times as big as those of the smaller men, and jaws nearly five times as big. The jaws, moreover, of the working ants of the several sizes differed wonderfully in shape, and in the form and number of the teeth. But the important fact for us is, that, though the workers can be grouped into castes of different size, yet they graduate insensibly into each other, as does the widely-different structure of their jaws. I speak confidently on this latter point, as Sir J. Lubbock made drawings for me, with the camera lucida, of the jaws which I dissected from the workers of the several sizes. Mr. Bates, in his interesting *Naturalist on the Amazons*, has described analogous cases.

With these facts before me, I believe that natural selection, by acting on the fertile ants or parents, could form a species which should regularly produce neuters, all of large size with one form of jaw, or all of small size with widely different jaws; or lastly, and this is the greatest difficulty, one set of workers of one size and structure, and simultaneously another set of workers of a different size and structure;—a graduated series having first been formed, as in the case of the driver ant, and then the extreme forms having been produced in greater and greater numbers, through the survival of the parents which generated them, until none with an intermediate structure were produced.

An analogous explanation has been given by Mr. Wallace, of the equally complex case, of certain Malayan Butterflies regularly appearing under two or even three distinct female forms; and by Fritz Müller, of certain Brazilian crustaceans likewise appearing under two widely distinct male forms. But this subject need not here be discussed.

I have now explained how, as I believe, the wonderful fact of two distinctly defined castes of sterile workers existing in the same nest, both widely different from each other and from their parents, has originated. We can see how useful their production may have been to a social community of ants, on the same principle that the division of labour is useful to civilised man. Ants, however, work by inherited instincts and by inherited organs or tools, whilst man works by acquired knowledge and manufactured instruments. But I must confess, that, with all my faith in natural selection, I should never have anticipated that this principle could have been efficient in so high a degree, had not the case of these neuter insects led me to this conclusion. I have, therefore, discussed this case, at some little but wholly insufficient length, in order to show the power of natural selection, and likewise because this is by far the most serious special difficulty which my theory has encountered. The case, also, is very interesting, as it proves that with animals, as with plants, any amount of modification may be effected by the accumulation of numerous, slight, spontaneous variations, which are in any way profitable, without exercise or habit having been brought into play. For peculiar habits confined to the workers or sterile females, however long they might be followed, could not possibly affect the males and fertile females, which alone leave descendants. I am surprised that no one has hitherto advanced this demonstrative case of neuter insects, against the well-known doctrine of inherited habit, as advanced by Lamarck.

SUMMARY ON INSTINCT

I have endeavoured . . . briefly to show that the mental qualities of our domestic animals vary, and that the variations are inherited. Still more briefly I have attempted to show that instincts vary slightly in a state of nature. No one will dispute that instincts are of the highest importance to each animal. Therefore there is no real difficulty, under changing conditions of life, in natural selection accumulating to any extent slight modifications of instinct which are in any way useful. In many cases habit or use and disuse have probably come into play. I do not pretend that the facts given in this chapter strengthen in any great degree my theory; but none of the cases of difficulty, to the best of my judgment, annihilate it. On the other hand, the fact that instincts are not always absolutely perfect and are liable to mistakes:—that no instinct can be shown to have been produced for the good of other animals, though animals take advantage of the instincts of others;—that the canon in natural history, of *Natura non facit saltum*, is applicable to instincts as well as to corporeal structure, and is plainly explicable on the foregoing views, but is otherwise inexplicable,—all tend to corroborate the theory of natural selection.

This theory is also strengthened by some few other facts in regard to instincts; as by that common case of closely allied, but distinct species, when inhabiting distant parts of the world and living under considerably different conditions of life, yet often retaining nearly the same instincts. For instance, we can understand, on the principle of inheritance, how it is that the thrush of tropical South America lines its nest with mud, in the same peculiar manner as does our British thrush; how it is that the Hornbills of Africa and India have the same extraordinary instinct of plastering up and imprisoning the females in a hole in a tree, with only a small hole left in the plaster through which the males feed them and their young when hatched; how it is that the male wrens (Troglodytes) of North America build 'cock-nests', to roost in, like the males of our Kitty-wrens,—a habit wholly unlike that of any other known bird. Finally, it may not be a logical deduction, but to my imagination it is far more satisfactory to look at such instincts as the young cuckoo ejecting its foster-brother,—ants making slaves,—the larvæ of ichneumonidæ feeding within the live bodies of caterpillars,—not as specially endowed or created instincts, but as small consequences of one general law leading to the advancement of all organic beings,—namely, multiply, vary, let the strongest live and the weakest die.

HYBRIDISM

[Chapter IX of the *Origin* is devoted to a discussion of hybridism as a special sort of difficulty with the theory of natural selection. Only the summary of this chapter is included here, to show the tenor of the argument.]

First crosses between forms, sufficiently distinct to be ranked as species, and their hybrids, are very generally, but not universally, sterile. The sterility is of all degrees, and is often so slight that the most careful experimentalists have arrived at diametrically opposite conclusions in ranking forms by this test. The sterility is innately variable in individuals of the same species, and is eminently susceptible to the action of favourable and unfavourable conditions. The degree of sterility does not strictly follow systematic affinity, but is governed by several curious and complex laws. It is generally different, and sometimes widely different in reciprocal crosses between the same two species. It is not always equal in degree in a first cross and in the hybrids produced from this cross.

In the same manner as in grafting trees, the capacity in one species or variety to take on another, is incidental on differences, generally of an unknown nature, in their vegetative systems, so in crossing, the greater or less facility of one species to unite with another is incidental on unknown differences in their reproductive systems. There is no more reason to think that species have been specially endowed with various degrees of sterility to prevent their crossing and blending in nature, than to think that trees have been specially endowed with various and somewhat analogous degrees of difficulty in being grafted together in order to prevent their inarching in our forests.

The sterility of first crosses and of their hybrid progeny has not been acquired through natural selection. In the case of first crosses it seems to depend on several circumstances; in some instances in chief part on the early death of the embryo. In the case of hybrids, it apparently depends on their whole organisation having been disturbed by being compounded from two distinct forms; the sterility being closely allied to that which so frequently affects pure species, when exposed to new and unnatural conditions of life. He who will explain these latter cases will be able to explain the sterility of hybrids. This view is strongly supported by a parallelism of another kind: namely, that, firstly, slight changes in the conditions of life add to the vigour and fertility of all organic beings; and secondly, that the crossing of forms, which have been exposed to slightly different conditions of life or which have varied, favours the size, vigour, and fertility of their offspring. The facts given on the sterility of the illegitimate unions of dimorphic and trimorphic plants and of their illegitimate progeny, perhaps render it probable that some unknown bond in all cases connects the degree of fertility of first unions with that of their offspring. The consideration of these facts on dimorphism, as well as of the results of reciprocal crosses, clearly leads to the conclusion that the primary cause of the sterility of crossed species is confined to differences in their sexual elements. But why, in the case of distinct species, the sexual elements should so generally have become more or less modified, leading to their mutual infertility, we do not know; but it seems to stand in some close relation to species having been exposed for long periods of time to nearly uniform conditions of life.

It is not surprising that the difficulty in crossing any two species, and the sterility of their hybrid offspring, should in most cases correspond, even if due to distinct causes: for both depend on the amount of difference between the species which are crossed. Nor is it surprising that the facility of effecting a first cross, and the fertility of the hybrids thus produced, and the capacity of being grafted together—though this latter capacity evidently depends on widely different circumstances—should all run, to a certain extent, parallel with the systematic affinity of the forms subjected to experiment; for systematic affinity includes resemblances of all kinds.

First crosses between forms known to be varieties, or sufficiently alike to be considered as varieties, and their mongrel offspring, are very generally, but not, as is so often stated, invariably fertile. Nor is this almost universal and perfect fertility surprising, when it is remembered how liable we are to argue in a circle with respect to varieties in a state of nature; and when we remember that the greater number of varieties have been produced under domestication by the selection of mere external differences, and that they have not been long exposed to uniform conditions of life. It should also be especially kept in mind, that long-continued domestication tends to eliminate sterility, and is therefore little likely to induce this same quality. Independently of the question of fertility, in all other respects there is the closest general resemblance between hybrids and mongrels,—in their variability, in their power of absorbing each other by repeated crosses, and in their inheritance of characters from both parent-forms. Finally, then, although we are as ignorant of the precise cause of the sterility of first crosses and of hybrids as we are why animals and plants removed from their natural conditions become sterile, yet the facts given in this chapter do not seem to me opposed to the belief that species aboriginally existed as varieties.

CHAPTER 10

GEOLOGY AND GEOGRAPHY

[From Chapters X–XIII of the *Origin*.]

IN THE sixth chapter I enumerated the chief objections which might be justly urged against the views maintained in this volume. Most of them have now been discussed. One, namely the distinctness of specific forms, and their not being blended together by innumerable transitional links, is a very obvious difficulty. I assigned reasons why such links do not commonly occur at the present day under the circumstances apparently most favourable for their presence, namely, on an extensive and continuous area with graduated physical conditions. I endeavoured to show, that the life of each species depends in a more important manner on the presence of other already defined organic forms, than on climate, and, therefore, that the really governing conditions of life do not graduate away quite insensibly like heat or moisture. I endeavoured, also, to show that intermediate varieties, from existing in lesser numbers than the forms which they connect, will generally be beaten out and exterminated during the course of further modification and improvement. The main cause, however, of innumerable intermediate links not now occurring everywhere throughout nature, depends on the very process of natural selection, through which new varieties continually take the places of and supplant their parent-forms. But just in proportion as this process of extermination has acted on an enormous scale, so must the number of intermediate varieties, which have formerly existed, be truly enormous. Why then is not every geological formation and every stratum full of such intermediate links? Geology assuredly does not reveal any such finely-graduated organic chain; and this, perhaps, is the most obvious and serious objection which can be urged against the theory. The explanation lies, as I believe, in the extreme imperfection of the geological record.

In the first place, it should always be borne in mind what sort of intermediate forms must, on the theory, have formerly existed. I have found it difficult, when looking at any two species, to avoid picturing to myself forms *directly* intermediate between them. But this is a wholly false view; we should always look for forms intermediate between each species and a common but unknown progenitor; and the progenitor will generally have differed in some respects from all its modified descendants. To give a simple illustration: the fantail and pouter pigeons are both descended from the rock-pigeon; if we possessed all the intermediate varieties which have ever existed, we should have an extremely close series between both and the rock-pigeon; but we should have no varieties directly intermediate between the fantail and pouter; none, for instance, combining a tail somewhat expanded with a crop somewhat enlarged, the characteristic features of these two breeds. These two breeds, moreover, have become so much modified, that, if we had no historical or indirect evidence regarding their origin, it would not have been possible to have determined, from a mere comparison of their structure with that of the rock-pigeon, C. livia, whether they had descended from this species or from some allied form, such as C. œnas.

So, with natural species, if we look to forms very distinct, for instance to the horse and tapir, we have no reason to suppose that links directly intermediate between them ever existed, but between each and an unknown common parent. The common parent will have had in its whole organisation much general resemblance to the tapir and to the horse; but in some points of structure may have differed considerably from both, even perhaps more than they differ from each other. Hence, in all such cases, we should be unable to recognise the parent-form of any two or more species, even if we closely compared the structure of the parent with that of its modified descendants, unless at the same time we had a nearly perfect chain of the intermediate links.

It is just possible by the theory, that one of two living forms might have descended from the other; for instance, a horse from a tapir; and in this case *direct* intermediate links will have existed between them. But such a case would imply that one form had remained for a very long period unaltered, whilst its descendants had undergone a vast amount of change; and the principle of competition between organism and organism, between child and parent, will render this a very rare event; for in all cases the new and improved forms of life tend to supplant the old and unimproved forms.

By the theory of natural selection all living species have been connected with the parent-species of each genus, by differences not greater than we see between the natural and domestic varieties of the same species at the present day; and these parent-species, now generally extinct, have in their turn been similarly connected with more ancient forms; and so on backwards, always converging to the common ancestor of each great class. So that the number of intermediate and transitional links, between all living and extinct species, must have been inconceivably great. But assuredly, if this theory be true, such have lived upon the earth.

ON THE LAPSE OF TIME, AS INFERRED FROM THE RATE OF DEPOSITION AND EXTENT OF DENUDATION

Independently of our not finding fossil remains of such infinitely numerous connecting links, it may be objected that time cannot have sufficed for so great an amount of organic change, all changes having been effected slowly. It is hardly possible for me to recall to the reader who is not a practical geologist, the facts leading the mind feebly to comprehend the lapse of time. He who can read Sir Charles Lyell's grand work on the *Principles of Geology*, which the future historian will recognise as having produced a revolution in natural science, and yet does not admit how vast have been the past periods of time, may at once close this volume. Not that it suffices to study the *Principles of Geology*, or to read special treatises by different observers on separate formations, and to mark how each author attempts to give an inadequate idea of the duration of each formation, or even of each stratum. We can best gain some idea of past time by knowing the agencies at work, and learning how deeply the surface of the land has been denuded, and how much sediment has been deposited. As Lyell has well remarked, the extent and thickness of our sedimentary formations are the result and the measure of the denudation which the earth's crust has elsewhere undergone. Therefore a man should examine for himself the great piles of superimposed strata, and watch the rivulets bringing down mud, and the waves wearing away the sea-cliffs, in order to comprehend something about the duration of past time, the monuments of which we see all around us.

It is good to wander along the coast, when formed of moderately hard rocks, and mark the process of degradation. The tides in most cases reach the cliffs only for a short time twice a day, and the waves eat into them only when they are charged with sand or pebbles; for there is good evidence that pure water effects nothing in wearing away rock. At last the base of the cliff is undermined, huge fragments fall down, and these, remaining fixed, have to be worn away atom by atom, until after being reduced in size they can be rolled about by the waves, and then they are more quickly ground into pebbles, sand, or mud. But how often do we see along the bases of retreating cliffs rounded boulders, all thickly clothed by marine productions, showing how little they are abraded and how seldom they are rolled about! Moreover, if we follow for a few miles any line of rocky cliff, which is undergoing degradation, we find that it is only here and there, along a short length or round a promontory, that the cliffs are at the present time suffering. The appearance of the surface and the vegetation show that elsewhere years have elapsed since the waters washed their base.

We have, however, recently learnt from the observations of Ramsay, in the van of many excellent observers—of Jukes, Geikie, Croll, and others, that subaerial degradation is a much more important agency than coast-action, or the power of the waves. The whole surface of the land is exposed to the chemical action of the air and of the rain-water with its dissolved carbonic acid, and in colder countries to frost; the disintegrated matter is carried down even gentle slopes during heavy rain, and to a greater extent than might be supposed, especially in arid districts, by the wind; it is then transported by the streams and rivers, which when rapid deepen their channels, and triturate the fragments. On a rainy day, even in a gently undulating country, we see the effects of subaerial degradation in the muddy rills which flow down every slope. Messrs. Ramsay and Whitaker have shown, and the observation is a most striking one, that the great lines of escarpment in the Wealden district and those ranging across England, which formerly were looked at as ancient sea-coasts, cannot have been thus formed, for each line is composed of one and the same formation, whilst our sea-cliffs are everywhere formed by the intersection of various formations. This being the case, we are compelled to admit that the escarpments owe their origin in chief part to the rocks of which they are composed having resisted subaerial denudation better than the surrounding surface; this surface consequently has been gradually lowered, with the lines of harder rock left projecting. Nothing impressed the mind with the vast duration of time, according to our ideas of time, more forcibly than the conviction thus gained that subaerial agencies which apparently have so little power, and which seem to work so slowly, have produced great results.

When thus impressed with the slow rate at which the land is worn away through subaerial and littoral action, it is good, in order to appreciate the past duration of time, to consider, on the one hand, the masses of rock which have been removed over many extensive areas, and on the other hand the thickness of our sedimentary formations. I remember having been much struck when viewing volcanic islands, which have been worn by the waves and pared all round into perpendicular cliffs of one or two thousand feet in height; for the gentle slope of the lava-streams, due to their formerly liquid state, showed at a glance how far the hard, rocky beds had once extended into the open ocean. The same story is told still more plainly by faults,—those great cracks along which the strata have been upheaved on one side, or thrown down on the other, to the height or depth of thousands of feet; for since the crust cracked, and it makes no great difference whether the upheaval was sudden, or, as most geologists now believe, was slow and effected by many starts, the surface of the land has been so completely planed down that no trace of these vast dislocations is externally visible. The Craven fault, for instance, extends for upwards of 30 miles, and along this line the vertical displacement of the strata varies from 600 to 3000 feet. Professor Ramsay has published an account of a downthrow in Anglesea of 2300 feet; and he informs me that he fully believes that there is one in Merionethshire of 12,000 feet; yet in these cases there is nothing on the surface of the land to show such prodigious movements; the pile of rocks on either side of the crack having been smoothly swept away.

On the other hand, in all parts of the world the piles of sedimentary strata are of wonderful thickness. In the Cordillera I estimated one mass of conglomerate at ten thousand feet; and although conglomerates have probably been accumulated at a quicker rate than finer sediments, yet from being formed of worn and rounded pebbles, each of which bears the stamp of time, they are good to show how slowly the mass must have been heaped together. Professor Ramsay has given me the maximum thickness, from actual measurement in most cases, of the successive formations in *different* parts of Great Britain; and this is the result:

	Feet
Palæozoic strata (not including igneous beds) - -	57,154
Secondary strata - - - - - - - -	13,190
Tertiary strata - - - - - - - -	2,240

—making altogether 72,584 feet; that is, very nearly thirteen and three-quarters British miles. Some of the formations, which are represented in England by thin beds, are thousands of feet in thickness on the Continent. Moreover, between each successive formation, we have, in the opinion of most geologists, blank periods of enormous length. So that the lofty pile of sedimentary rocks in Britain gives but an inadequate idea of the time which has elapsed during their accumulation. The consideration of these various facts impresses the mind almost in the same manner as does the vain endeavour to grapple with the idea of eternity.

Nevertheless this impression is partly false. Mr. Croll, in an interesting paper, remarks that we do not err 'in forming too great a conception of the length of geological periods', but in estimating them by years. When geologists look at large and complicated phenomena, and then at the figures representing several million years, the two produce a totally different effect on the mind, and the figures are at once pronounced too small. In regard to subaerial denudation, Mr. Croll shows, by calculating the known amount of sediment annually brought down by certain rivers, relatively to their areas of drainage, that 1000 feet of solid rock, as it became gradually disintegrated, would thus be removed from the mean level of the whole area in the course of six million years. This seems an astonishing result, and some considerations lead to the suspicion that it may be too large, but even if halved or quartered it is still very surprising. Few of us, however, know what a million really means: Mr. Croll gives the following illustration: take a narrow strip of paper, 83 feet 4 inches in length, and stretch it along the wall of a large hall; then mark off at one end the tenth of an inch. This tenth of an inch will represent one hundred years, and the entire strip a million years. But let it be borne in mind, in relation to the subject of this work, what a hundred years implies, represented as it is by a measure utterly insignificant in a hall of the above dimensions. Several eminent breeders, during a single lifetime, have so largely modified some of the higher animals which propagate their kind much more slowly than most of the lower animals, that they have formed what well deserves to be called a new sub-breed. Few men have attended with due care to any one strain for more than half a century, so that a hundred years represents the work of two breeders in succession. It is not to be supposed that species in a state of nature ever change so quickly as domestic animals under the guidance of methodical selection. The comparison would be in every way fairer with the effects which follow from unconscious selection, that is the preservation of the most useful or beautiful animals, with no intention of modifying the breed; but by this process of unconscious selection, various breeds have been sensibly changed in the course of two or three centuries.

Species, however, probably change much more slowly, and within the same country only a few change at the same time. This slowness follows from all the inhabitants of the same country being already so well adapted to each other, that new places in the polity of nature do not occur until after long intervals, due to the occurrence of physical changes of some kind, or through the immigration of new forms. Moreover variations or individual differences of the right nature, by which some of the inhabitants might be better fitted to their new places under the altered circumstances, would not always occur at once. Unfortunately we have no means of determining, according to the standards of years, how long a period it takes to modify a species; but to the subject of time we must return.

ON THE POORNESS OF PALÆONTOLOGICAL COLLECTIONS

Now let us turn to our richest geological museums, and what a paltry display we behold! That our collections are imperfect is admitted by everyone. The remark of that admirable palæontologist, Edward Forbes, should never be forgotten, namely, that very many fossil species are known and named from single and often broken specimens, or from a few specimens collected on some one spot. Only a small portion of the surface of the earth has been geologically explored, and no part with sufficient care, as the important discoveries made every year in Europe prove. No organism wholly soft can be preserved. Shells and bones decay and disappear when left on the bottom of the sea, where sediment is not accumulating. We probably take a quite erroneous view, when we assume that sediment is being deposited over nearly the whole bed of the sea, at a rate sufficiently quick to embed and preserve fossil remains. Throughout an enormously large proportion of the ocean, the bright blue tint of the water bespeaks its purity. The many cases on record of a formation conformably covered, after an immense interval of time, by another and later formation, without the underlying bed having suffered in the interval any wear and tear, seem explicable only on the view of the bottom of the sea not rarely lying for ages in an unaltered condition. The remains which do become embedded, if in sand or gravel, will, when the beds are upraised, generally be dissolved by the percolation of rain-water charged with carbonic acid. Some of the many kinds of animals which live on the beach between high and low water mark seem to be rarely preserved. For instance, the several species of the Chthamalinæ (a sub-family of sessile cirripedes) coat the rocks all over the world in infinite numbers: they are all strictly littoral, with the exception of a single Mediterranean species, which inhabits deep water, and this has been found fossil in Sicily, whereas not one other species has hitherto been found in any tertiary formation: yet it is known that the genus Chthamalus existed during the Chalk period. Lastly, many great deposits requiring a vast length of time for their accumulation, are entirely destitute of organic remains, without our being able to assign any reason: one of the most striking instances is that of the Flysch formation, which consists of shale and sandstone, several thousand, occasionally even six thousand feet in thickness, and extending for at least 300 miles from Vienna to Switzerland; and although this great mass has been most carefully searched, no fossils, except a few vegetable remains, have been found.

With respect to the terrestrial productions which lived during the Secondary and Palæozoic periods, it is superfluous to state that our evidence is fragmentary in an extreme degree. For instance, until recently not a land-shell was known belonging to either of these vast periods, with the exception of one species discovered by Sir C. Lyell and Dr. Dawson in the carboniferous strata of North America; but now land-shells have been found in the lias. In regard to mammiferous remains, a glance at the historical table published in Lyell's *Manual* will bring home the truth, how accidental and rare is their preservation, far better than pages of detail. Nor is their rarity surprising, when we remember how large a proportion of the bones of tertiary mammals have been discovered either in caves or in lacustrine deposits; and that not a cave or true lacustrine bed is known belonging to the age of our secondary or palæozoic formations.

But the imperfection in the geological record largely results from another and more important cause than any of the foregoing; namely, from the several formations being separated from each other by wide intervals of time. This doctrine has been emphatically admitted by many geologists and palæontologists, who, like E. Forbes, entirely disbelieve in the change of species. When we see the formations tabulated in written works, or when we follow them in nature, it is difficult to avoid believing that they are closely consecutive. But we know, for instance, from Sir R. Murchison's great work on Russia, what wide gaps there are in that country between the superimposed formations; so it is in North America, and in many other parts of the world. The most skilful geologist if his attention had been confined exclusively to these large territories, would never have suspected that, during the periods which were blank and barren in his own country, great piles of sediment, charged with new and peculiar forms of life, had elsewhere been accumulated. And if, in each separate territory, hardly any idea can be formed of the length of time which has elapsed between the consecutive formations, we may infer that this could nowhere be ascertained. The frequent and great changes in the mineralogical composition of consecutive formations, generally implying great changes in the geography of the surrounding lands, whence the sediment was derived, accord with the belief of vast intervals of time having elapsed between each formation.

We can, I think, see why the geological formations of each region are almost invariably intermittent; that is, have not followed each other in close sequence. Scarcely any fact struck me more when examining many hundred miles of the South American coasts, which have been upraised several hundred feet within the recent period, than the absence of any recent deposits sufficiently extensive to last for even a short geological period. Along the whole west coast, which is inhabited by a peculiar marine fauna, tertiary beds are so poorly developed, that no record of several successive and peculiar marine faunas will probably be preserved to a distant age. A little reflection will explain why, along the rising coast of the western side of South America, no extensive formations with recent or tertiary remains can anywhere be found, though the supply of sediment must for ages have been great, from the enormous degradation of the coast-rocks and from muddy streams entering the sea. The explanation, no doubt, is, that the littoral and sub-littoral deposits are continually worn away, as soon as they are brought up by the slow and gradual rising of the land within the grinding action of the coast-waves.

We may, I think, conclude that sediment must be accumulated in extremely thick, solid, or extensive masses, in order to withstand the incessant action of the waves, when first upraised and during successive oscillations of level as well as the subsequent subaerial degradation. Such thick and extensive accumulations of sediment may be formed in two ways; either in profound depths of the sea, in which case the bottom will not be inhabited by so many and such varied forms of life, as the more shallow seas; and the mass when upraised will give an imperfect record of the organisms which existed in the neighbourhood during the period of its accumulation. Or, sediment may be deposited to any thickness and extent over a shallow bottom, if it continue slowly to subside. In this latter case, as long as the rate of subsidence and the supply of sediment nearly balance each other, the sea will remain shallow and favourable for many and varied forms, and thus a rich fossiliferous formation, thick enough, when upraised, to resist a large amount of denudation, may be formed.

I am convinced that nearly all our ancient formations, which are throughout the greater part of their thickness *rich in fossils*, have thus been formed during subsidence. Since publishing my views on this subject in 1845, I have watched the progress of Geology, and have been surprised to note how author after author, in treating of this or that great formation, has come to the conclusion that it was accumulated during subsidence. I may add, that the only ancient tertiary formation on the west coast of South America, which has been bulky enough to resist such degradation as it has as yet suffered, but which will hardly last to a distant geological age, was deposited during a downward oscillation of level, and thus gained considerable thickness.

All geological facts tell us plainly that each area has undergone slow oscillations of level, and apparently these oscillations have affected wide spaces. Consequently, formations rich in fossils and sufficiently thick and extensive to resist subsequent degradation, will have been formed over wide spaces during periods of subsidence, but only where the supply of sediment was sufficient to keep the sea shallow and to embed and preserve the remains before they had time to decay. On the other hand, as long as the bed of the sea remains stationary, *thick* deposits cannot have been accumulated in the shallow parts, which are the most favourable to life. Still less can this have happened during the alternate periods of elevation; or, to speak more accurately, the beds which were then accumulated will generally have been destroyed by being upraised and brought within the limits of the coast-action.

* * * *

ON THE GEOLOGICAL SUCCESSION OF ORGANIC BEINGS

Let us now see whether the several facts and laws relating to the geological succession of organic beings accord best with the common view of the immutability of species, or with that of their slow and gradual modification, through variation and natural selection.

New species have appeared very slowly, one after another, both on the land and in the waters. Lyell has shown that it is hardly possible to resist the evidence on this head in the case of the several tertiary stages; and every year tends to fill up the blanks between the stages, and to make the proportion between the lost and existing forms more gradual. In some of the most recent beds, though undoubtedly of high antiquity if measured by years, only one or two species are extinct, and only one or two are new, having appeared there for the first time, either locally, or, as far as we know, on the face of the earth. The secondary formations are more broken; but, as Bronn has remarked, neither the appearance nor disappearance of the many species embedded in each formation has been simultaneous.

Species belonging to different genera and classes have not changed at the same rate, or in the same degree. In the older tertiary beds a few living shells may still be found in the midst of a multitude of extinct forms. Falconer has given a striking instance of a similar fact, for an existing crocodile is associated with many lost mammals and reptiles in the sub-Himalayan deposits. The Silurian Lingula differs but little from the living species of this genus; whereas most of the other Silurian Molluscs and all the Crustaceans have changed greatly. The productions of the land seem to have changed at a quicker rate than those of the sea, of which a striking instance has been observed in Switzerland. There is some reason to believe that organisms high in the scale, change more quickly than those that are low: though there are exceptions to this rule. The amount of organic change, as Pictet has remarked, is not the same in each successive so-called formation. Yet if we compare any but the most closely related formations, all the species will be found to have undergone some change. When a species has once disappeared from the face of the earth, we have no reason to believe that the same identical form ever reappears. The strongest apparent exception to this latter rule is that of the so-called 'colonies' of M. Barrande, which intrude for a period in the midst of an older formation, and then allow the pre-existing fauna to reappear; but Lyell's explanation, namely, that it is a case of temporary migration from a distinct geographical province, seems satisfactory.

These several facts accord well with our theory, which includes no fixed law of development, causing all the inhabitants of an area to change abruptly, or simultaneously, or to an equal degree. The process of modification must be slow, and will generally effect only a few species at the same time; for the variability of each species is independent of that of all others. Whether such variations or individual differences as may arise will be accumulated through natural selection in a greater or less degree, thus causing a greater or less amount of permanent modification, will depend on many complex contingencies—on the variations being of a beneficial nature, on the freedom of intercrossing, on the slowly changing physical conditions of the country, on the immigration of new colonists, and on the nature of the other inhabitants with which the varying species come into competition. Hence it is by no means surprising that one species should retain the same identical form much longer than others; or, if changing, should change in a less degree. We find similar relations between the existing inhabitants of distinct countries; for instance, the land-shells and coleopterous insects of Madeira have come to differ considerably from their nearest allies on the continent of Europe, whereas the marine shells and birds have remained unaltered. We can perhaps understand the apparently quicker rate of change in terrestrial and in more highly organised productions compared with marine and lower productions, by the more complex relations of the higher beings to their organic and inorganic conditions of life, as explained in a former chapter. When many of the inhabitants of any area have become modified and improved, we can understand, on the principle of competition, and from the all-important relations of organism to organism in the struggle for life, that any form which did not become in some degree modified and improved, would be liable to extermination. Hence we see why all the species in the same region do at last, if we look to long enough intervals of time, become modified, for otherwise they would become extinct.

In members of the same class the average amount of change, during long and equal periods of time, may, perhaps, be nearly the same; but as the accumulation of enduring formations, rich in fossils, depends on great masses of sediment being deposited on subsiding areas, our formations have been almost necessarily accumulated at wide and irregularly intermittent intervals of time; consequently the amount of organic change exhibited by the fossils embedded in consecutive formations is not equal. Each formation, on this view, does not mark a new and complete act of creation, but only an occasional scene, taken almost at hazard, in an ever slowly changing drama.

We can clearly understand why a species when once lost should never reappear, even if the very same conditions of life, organic and inorganic, should recur. For though the offspring of one species might be adapted (and no doubt this has occurred in innumerable instances) to fill the place of another species in the economy of nature, and thus supplant it; yet the two forms—the old and the new—would not be identically the same; for both would almost certainly inherit different characters from their distinct progenitors; and organisms already differing would vary in a different manner. For instance, it is possible, if all our fantail pigeons were destroyed, that fanciers might make a new breed hardly distinguishable from the present breed; but if the parent rock-pigeon were likewise destroyed, and under nature we have every reason to believe that parent-forms are generally supplanted and exterminated by their improved offspring, it is incredible that a fantail, identical with the existing breed, could be raised from any other species of pigeon, or even from any other well-established race of the domestic pigeon, for the successive variations would almost certainly be in some degree different, and the newly-formed variety would probably inherit from its progenitor some characteristic differences.

Groups of species, that is, genera and families, follow the same general rules in their appearance and disappearance as do single species, changing more or less quickly, and in a greater or lesser degree. A group, when it has once disappeared, never reappears; that is, its existence, as long as it lasts, is continuous. I am aware that there are some apparent exceptions to this rule, but the exceptions are surprisingly few, so few that E. Forbes, Pictet, and Woodward (though all strongly opposed to such views as I maintain) admit its truth; and the rule strictly accords with the theory. For all the species of the same group, however long it may have lasted, are the modified descendants one from the other, and all from a common progenitor. In the genus Lingula, for instance, the species which have successively appeared at all ages must have been connected by an unbroken series of generations, from the lowest Silurian stratum to the present day.

We have seen in the last chapter that whole groups of species sometimes falsely appear to have been abruptly developed; and I have attempted to give an explanation of this fact, which if true would be fatal to my views. But such cases are certainly exceptional; the general rule being a gradual increase in number, until the group reaches its maximum, and then, sooner or later, a gradual decrease. If the number of the species included within a genus, or the number of the genera within a family, be represented by a vertical line of varying thickness, ascending through the successive geological formations, in which the species are found, the line will sometimes falsely appear to begin at its lower end, not in a sharp point, but abruptly; it then gradually thickens upwards, often keeping of equal thickness for a space, and ultimately thins out in the upper beds, marking the decrease and final extinction of the species. This gradual increase in number of the species of a group is strictly conformable with the theory, for the species of the same genus, and the genera of the same family, can increase only slowly and progressively; the process of modification and the production of a number of allied forms necessarily being a slow and gradual process,—one species first giving rise to two or three varieties, these being slowly converted into species, which in their turn produce by equally slow steps other varieties and species, and so on, like the branching of a great tree from a single stem, till the group becomes large.

ON EXTINCTION

We have as yet only spoken incidentally of the disappearance of species and of groups of species. On the theory of natural selection, the extinction of old forms and the production of new and improved forms are intimately connected together. The old notion of all the inhabitants of the earth having been swept away by catastrophes at successive periods is very generally given up, even by those geologists, as Elie de Beaumont, Murchison, Barrande, &c., whose general views would naturally lead them to this conclusion. On the contrary, we have every reason to believe, from the study of the tertiary formations, that species and groups of species gradually disappear, one after another, first from one spot, then from another, and finally from the world. In some few cases however, as by the breaking of an isthmus and the consequent irruption of a multitude of new inhabitants into an adjoining sea, or by the final subsidence of an island, the process of extinction may have been rapid. Both single species and whole groups of species last for very unequal periods; some groups, as we have seen, have endured from the earliest known dawn of life to the present day; some have disappeared before the close of the palæozoic period. No fixed law seems to determine the length of time during which any single species or any single genus endures. There is reason to believe that the extinction of a whole group of species is generally a slower process than their production: if their appearance and disappearance be represented, as before, by a vertical line of varying thickness the line is found to taper more gradually at its upper end, which marks the progress of extermination, than at its lower end, which marks the first appearance and the early increase in number of the species. In some cases, however, the extermination of whole groups, as of ammonites, towards the close of the secondary period, has been wonderfully sudden.

The extinction of species has been involved in the most gratuitous mystery. Some authors have even supposed that, as the individual has a definite length of life, so have species a definite duration. No one can have marvelled more than I have done at the extinction of species. When I found in La Plata the tooth of a horse embedded with the remains of Mastodon, Megatherium, Toxodon, and other extinct monsters, which all co-existed with still living shells at a very late geological period, I was filled with astonishment; for, seeing that the horse, since its introduction by the Spaniards into South America, has run wild over the whole country and has increased in numbers at an unparalleled rate, I asked myself what could so recently have exterminated the former horse under conditions of life apparently so favourable. But my astonishment was groundless. Professor Owen soon perceived that the tooth, though so like that of the existing horse, belonged to an extinct species. Had this horse been still living, but in some degree rare, no naturalist would have felt the least surprise at its rarity; for rarity is the attribute of a vast number of species of all classes, in all countries. If we ask ourselves why this or that species is rare, we answer that something is unfavourable in its conditions of life; but what that something is we can hardly ever tell. On the supposition of the fossil horse still existing as a rare species, we might have felt certain, from the analogy of all other mammals, even of the slow-breeding elephant, and from the history of the naturalisation of the domestic horse in South America, that under more favourable conditions it would in a very few years have stocked the whole continent. But we could not have told what the unfavourable conditions were which checked its increase, whether some one or several contingencies, and at what period of the horse's life, and in what degree they severally acted. If the conditions had gone on, however slowly, becoming less and less favourable, we assuredly should not have perceived the fact, yet the fossil horse would certainly have become rarer and rarer, and finally extinct;—its place being seized on by some more successful competitor.

It is most difficult always to remember that the increase of every creature is constantly being checked by unperceived hostile agencies; and that these same unperceived agencies are amply sufficient to cause rarity, and finally extinction. So little is this subject understood, that I have heard surprise repeatedly expressed at such great monsters as the Mastodon and the more ancient Dinosaurians having become extinct; as if mere bodily strength gave victory in the battle of life. Mere size, on the contrary, would in some cases determine, as has been remarked by Owen, quicker extermination from the greater amount of requisite food. Before man inhabited India or Africa, some cause must have checked the continued increase of the existing elephant. A highly capable judge, Dr. Falconer, believes that it is chiefly insects which, from incessantly harassing and weakening the elephant in India, check its increase; and this was Bruce's conclusion with respect to the African elephant in Abyssinia. It is certain that insects and blood-sucking bats determine the existence of the larger naturalized quadrupeds in several parts of S. America.

We see in many cases in the more recent tertiary formations, that rarity precedes extinction; and we know that this has been the progress of events with those animals which have been exterminated, either locally or wholly, through man's agency. I may repeat what I published in 1845, namely, that to admit that species generally become rare before they become extinct—to feel no surprise at the rarity of a species, and yet to marvel greatly when the species ceases to exist, is much the same as to admit that sickness in the individual is the forerunner of death—to feel no surprise at sickness, but, when the sick man dies, to wonder and to suspect that he died by some deed of violence.

The theory of natural selection is grounded on the belief that each new variety and ultimately each new species, is produced and maintained by having some advantage over those with which it comes into competition; and the consequent extinction of the less-favoured forms almost inevitably follows. It is the same with our domestic productions; when a new and slightly improved variety has been raised, it at first supplants the less improved varieties in the same neighbourhood; when much improved it is transported far and near, like our short-horn cattle, and takes the place of other breeds in other countries. Thus the appearance of new forms and the disappearance of old forms, both those naturally and those artificially produced, are bound together. In flourishing groups, the number of new specific forms which have been produced within a given time has at some periods probably been greater than the number of the old specific forms which have been exterminated; but we know that species have not gone on indefinitely increasing, at least during the later geological epochs, so that, looking to later times, we may believe that the production of new forms has caused the extinction of about the same number of old forms.

The competition will generally be most severe, as formerly explained and illustrated by examples, between the forms which are most like each other in all respects. Hence the improved and modified descendants of a species will generally cause the extermination of the parent-species; and if many new forms have been developed from any one species, the nearest allies of that species, *i.e.* the species of the same genus, will be the most liable to extermination. Thus, as I believe, a number of new species descended from one species, that is a new genus, comes to supplant an old genus, belonging to the same family. But it must often have happened that a new species belonging to some one group has seized on the place occupied by a species belong to a distinct group, and thus have caused its extermination. If many allied forms be developed from the successful intruder, many will have to yield their places; and it will generally be the allied forms, which will suffer from some inherited inferiority in common. But whether it be species belonging to the same or to a distinct class, which have yielded their places to other modified and improved species, a few of the sufferers may often be preserved for a long time, from being fitted to some peculiar line of life, or from inhabiting some distant and isolated station, where they will have escaped severe competition. For instance, some species of Trigonia, a great genus of shells in the secondary formations, survive in the Australian seas; and a few members of the great and almost extinct group of Ganoid fishes still inhabit our fresh waters. Therefore the utter extinction of a group is generally, as we have seen, a slower process than its production.

With respect to the apparently sudden extermination of whole families or orders, as of Trilobites at the close of the palæozoic period and of Ammonites at the close of the secondary period, we must remember what has been already said on the probable wide intervals of time between our consecutive formations; and in these intervals there may have been much slow extermination. Moreover, when, by sudden immigration or by unusually rapid development, many species of a new group have taken possession of an area, many of the older species will have been exterminated in a correspondingly rapid manner; and the forms which thus yield their places will commonly be allied, for they will partake of the same inferiority in common.

Thus, as it seems to me, the manner in which single species and whole groups of species become extinct accords well with the theory of natural selection. We need not marvel at extinction; if we must marvel, let it be at our own presumption in imagining for a moment that we understand the many complex contingencies on which the existence of each species depends. If we forget for an instant that each species tends to increase inordinately, and that some check is always in action, yet seldom perceived by us, the whole economy of nature will be utterly obscured.

Whenever we can precisely say why this species is more abundant in individuals than that; why this species and not another can be naturalised in a given country; then, and not until then, we may justly feel surprise why we cannot account for the extinction of any particular species or group of species.

* * * *

SUMMARY ON GEOLOGICAL RECORD

I have attempted to show that the geological record is extremely imperfect; that only a small portion of the globe has been geologically explored with care; that only certain classes of organic beings have been largely preserved in a fossil state; that the number both of specimens and of species, preserved in our museums, is absolutely as nothing compared with the number of generations which must have passed away even during a single formation; that, owing to subsidence being almost necessary for the accumulation of deposits rich in fossil species of many kinds, and thick enough to outlast future degradation, great intervals of time must have elapsed between most of our successive formations; that there has probably been more extinction during the periods of subsidence, and more variation during the periods of elevation, and during the latter the record will have been less perfectly kept; that each single formation has not been continuously deposited; that the duration of each formation is probably short compared with the average duration of specific forms; that migration has played an important part in the first appearance of new forms in any one area and formation; that widely ranging species are those which have varied most frequently, and have oftenest given rise to new species; that varieties have at first been local; and lastly, although each species must have passed through numerous transitional stages, it is probable that the periods, during which each underwent modification, though many and long as measured by years, have been short in comparison with the periods during which each remained in an unchanged condition. These causes, taken conjointly, will to a large extent explain why—though we do find many links—we do not find interminable varieties, connecting together all extinct and existing forms by the finest graduated steps. It should also be constantly borne in mind that any linking variety between two forms, which might be found, would be ranked, unless the whole chain could be perfectly restored, as a new and distinct species; for it is not pretended that we have any sure criterion by which species and varieties can be discriminated.

He who rejects this view of the imperfection of the geological record, will rightly reject the whole theory. For he may ask in vain where are the numberless transitional links which must formerly have connected the closely allied or representative species, found in the successive stages of the same great formation? He may disbelieve in the immense intervals of time which must have elapsed between our consecutive formations; he may overlook how important a part migration has played, when the formations of any one great region, as those of Europe, are considered; he may urge the apparent, but often falsely apparent, sudden coming in of whole groups of species. He may ask where are the remains of those infinitely numerous organisms which must have existed long before the Cambrian system was deposited? We now know that at least one animal did then exist; but I can answer this last question only by supposing that where our oceans now extend they have extended for an enormous period, and where our oscillating continents now stand they have stood since the commencement of the Cambrian system; but that, long before that epoch, the world presented a widely different aspect; and that the older continents formed of formations older than any known to us, exist now only as remnants in a metamorphosed condition, or lie still buried under the ocean.

Passing from these difficulties, the other great leading facts in palæontology agree admirably with the theory of descent with modification through variation and natural selection. We can thus understand how it is that new species come in slowly and successively; how species of different classes do not necessarily change together, or at the same rate, or in the same degree; yet in the long run that all undergo modification to some extent. The extinction of old forms is the most inevitable consequence of the productions of new forms. We can understand why, when a species has once disappeared, it never reappears. Groups of species increase in numbers slowly, and endure for unequal periods of time; for the process of modification is necessarily slow, and depends on many complex contingencies. The dominant species belonging to large and dominant groups tend to leave many modified descendants, which form new sub-groups and groups. As these are formed, the species of the less vigorous groups, from their inferiority inherited from a common progenitor, tend to become extinct together, and to leave no modified offspring on the face of the earth. But the utter extinction of a whole group of species has sometimes been a slow process, from the survival of a few descendants, lingering in protected and isolated situations. When a group has once wholly disappeared, it does not reappear; for the link of generation has been broken.

We can understand how it is that dominant forms which spread widely and yield the greatest number of varieties tend to people the world with allied, but modified, descendants; and these will generally succeed in displacing the groups which are their inferiors in the struggle for existence. Hence, after long intervals of time, the productions of the world appear to have changed simultaneously.

We can understand how it is that all the forms of life, ancient and recent, make together a few grand classes. We can understand, from the continued tendency to divergence of character, why the more ancient a form is, the more it generally differs from those now living; why ancient and extinct forms often tend to fill up gaps between existing forms, sometimes blending two groups, previously classed as distinct, into one; but more commonly bringing them only a little closer together. The more ancient a form is, the more often it stands in some degree intermediate between groups now distinct; for the more ancient a form is, the more nearly it will be related to, and consequently resemble, the common progenitor of groups, since become widely divergent. Extinct forms are seldom directly intermediate between existing forms; but are intermediate only by a long and circuitous course through other extinct and different forms. We can clearly see why the organic remains of closely consecutive formations are closely allied; for they are closely linked together by generation. We can clearly see why the remains of an intermediate formation are intermediate in character.

The inhabitants of the world at each successive period in its history have beaten their predecessors in the race for life, and are, in so far, higher in the scale, and their structure has generally become more specialised; and this may account for the common belief held by so many palæontologists, that organisation on the whole has progressed. Extinct and ancient animals resemble to a certain extent the embryos of the more recent animals belonging to the same classes, and this wonderful fact receives a simple explanation according to our views. The succession of the same types of structure within the same areas during the later geological periods ceases to be mysterious, and is intelligible on the principle of inheritance.

If then the geological record be as imperfect as many believe, and it may at least be asserted that the record cannot be proved to be much more perfect, the main objections to the theory of natural selection are greatly diminished or disappear. On the other hand, all the chief laws of palæontology plainly proclaim, as it seems to me, that species have been produced by ordinary generation: old forms having been supplanted by new and improved forms of life, the products of Variation and the Survival of the Fittest.

GEOGRAPHICAL DISTRIBUTION

In considering the distribution of organic beings over the face of the globe, the first great fact which strikes us is, that neither the similarity nor the dissimilarity of the inhabitants of various regions can be wholly accounted for by climatal and other physical conditions. Of late, almost every author who has studied the subject has come to this conclusion. The case of America alone would almost suffice to prove its truth; for if we exclude the arctic and northern temperate parts, all authors agree that one of the most fundamental divisions in geographical distribution is that between the New and Old Worlds; yet if we travel over the vast American continent, from the central parts of the United States to its extreme southern point, we meet with the most diversified conditions; humid districts, arid deserts, lofty mountains, grassy plains, forests, marshes, lakes, and great rivers, under almost every temperature. There is hardly a climate or condition in the Old World which cannot be paralleled in the New—at least as closely as the same species generally require. No doubt small areas can be pointed out in the Old World hotter than any in the New World; but these are not inhabited by a fauna different from that of the surrounding districts; for it is rare to find a group of organisms confined to a small area, of which the conditions are peculiar in only a slight degree. Notwithstanding this general parallelism in the conditions of the Old and New Worlds, how widely different are their living productions!

In the southern hemisphere, if we compare large tracts of land in Australia, South Africa, and western South America, between latitudes 25° and 35°, we shall find parts extremely similar in all their conditions, yet it would not be possible to point out three faunas and floras more utterly dissimilar. Or, again, we may compare the productions of South America south of lat. 35° with those north of 25°, which consequently are separated by a space of ten degrees of latitude, and are exposed to considerably different conditions; yet they are incomparably more closely related to each other than they are to the productions of Australia or Africa under nearly the same climate. Analogous facts could be given with respect to the inhabitants of the sea.

A second great fact which strikes us in our general review is, that barriers of any kind, or obstacles to free migration, are related in a close and important manner to the differences between the productions of various regions. We see this in the great difference in nearly all the terrestrial productions of the New and Old Worlds, excepting in the northern parts, where the land almost joins, and where, under a slightly different climate, there might have been free migration for the northern temperate forms, as there now is for the strictly arctic productions. We see the same fact in the great difference between the inhabitants of Australia, Africa, and South America under the same latitude; for these countries are almost as much isolated from each other as is possible. On each continent, also, we see the same fact; for on the opposite sides of lofty and continuous mountain-ranges, of great deserts and even of large rivers, we find different productions; though as mountain-chains, deserts, &c., are not as impassable, or likely to have endured so long, as the oceans separating continents, the differences are very inferior in degree to those characteristic of distinct continents.

Turning to the sea, we find the same law. The marine inhabitants of the eastern and western shores of South America are very distinct, with extremely few shells, crustacea, or echinodermata in common; but Dr. Günther has recently shown that about thirty per cent. of the fishes are the same on the opposite sides of the isthmus of Panama; and this fact has led naturalists to believe that the isthmus was formerly open. Westward of the shores of America, a wide space of open ocean extends, with not an island as a halting-place for emigrants; here we have a barrier of another kind, and as soon as this is passed we meet in the eastern islands of the Pacific with another and totally distinct fauna. So that three marine faunas range far northward and southward in parallel lines not far from each other, under corresponding climates; but from being separated from each other by impassable barriers, either of land or open sea, they are almost wholly distinct. On the other hand, proceeding still farther westward from the eastern islands of the tropical parts of the Pacific, we encounter no impassable barriers, and we have innumerable islands as halting-places, or continuous coasts, until, after travelling over a hemisphere, we come to the shores of Africa; and over this vast space we meet with no well-defined and distinct marine faunas. Although so few marine animals are common to the above-named three approximate faunas of Eastern and Western America and the Eastern Pacific islands, yet many fishes range from the Pacific into the Indian Ocean, and many shells are common to the eastern islands of the Pacific and the eastern shores of Africa on almost exactly opposite meridians of longitude.

A third great fact, partly included in the foregoing statement, is the affinity of the productions of the same continent or of the same sea, though the species themselves are distinct at different points and stations. It is a law of the widest generality, and every continent offers innumerable instances. Nevertheless the naturalist, in travelling, for instance, from north to south, never fails to be struck by the manner in which successive groups of beings, specifically distinct, though nearly related, replace each other. He hears from closely allied, yet distinct kinds of birds, notes nearly similar, and sees their nests similarly constructed, but not quite alike, with eggs coloured in nearly the same manner. The plains near the Straits of Magellan are inhabited by one species of Rhea (American ostrich) and northward the plains of La Plata by another species of the same genus; and not by a true ostrich or emu, like those inhabiting Africa and Australia under the same latitude. On these same plains of La Plata we see the agouti and bizcacha, animals having nearly the same habits as our hares and rabbits, and belonging to the same order of Rodents, but they plainly display an American type of structure. We ascend the lofty peaks of the Cordillera, and we find an alpine species of bizcacha; we look to the waters, and we do not find the beaver or musk-rat, but the coypu and capybara, rodents of the S. American type. Innumerable other instances could be given. If we look to the islands off the American shore, however much they may differ in geological structure, the inhabitants are essentially American, though they may be all peculiar species. We may look back to past ages, as shown in the last chapter, and we find American types then prevailing on the American continent and in the American seas. We see in these facts some deep organic bond, throughout space and time, over the same areas of land and water, independently of physical conditions. The naturalist must be dull who is not led to enquire what this bond is.

The bond is simply inheritance, that cause which alone, as far as we positively know, produces organisms quite like each other, or, as we see in the case of varieties, nearly alike. The dissimilarity of the inhabitants of different regions may be attributed to modification through variation and natural selection, and probably in a subordinate degree to the definite influence of different physical conditions. The degrees of dissimilarity will depend on the migration of the more dominant forms of life from one region into another having been more or less effectually prevented, at periods more or less remote;—on the nature and number of the former immigrants;—and on the action of the inhabitants on each other in leading to the preservation of different modifications; the relation of organism to organism in the struggle for life being, as I have already often remarked, the most important of all relations. Thus the high importance of barriers comes into play by checking migration; as does time for the slow process of modification through natural selection. Widely-ranging species, abounding in individuals, which have already triumphed over many competitors in their own widely-extended homes, will have the best chance of seizing on new places, when they spread into new countries. In their new homes they will be exposed to new conditions, and will frequently undergo further modification and improvement; and thus they will become still further victorious, and will produce groups of modified descendants. On this principle of inheritance with modification we can understand how it is that sections of genera, whole genera, and even families, are confined to the same areas, as is so commonly and notoriously the case.

* * * *

According to these views, it is obvious that the several species of the same genus, though inhabiting the most distant quarters of the world, must originally have proceeded from the same source, as they are descended from the same progenitor. In the case of those species which have undergone during the whole geological periods little modification, there is not much difficulty in believing that they have migrated from the same region; for during the vast geographical and climatal changes which have supervened since ancient times, almost any amount of migration is possible. But in many other cases, in which we have reason to believe that the species of a genus have been produced within comparatively recent times, there is great difficulty on this head. It is also obvious that the individuals of the same species, though now inhabiting distant and isolated regions, must have proceeded from one spot, where their parents were first produced: for, as has been explained, it is incredible that individuals identically the same should have been produced from parents specifically distinct.

* * * *

MEANS OF DISPERSAL

Sir C. Lyell and other authors have ably treated this subject. I can give here only the briefest abstract of the more important facts. Change of climate must have had a powerful influence on migration. A region now impassable to certain organisms from the nature of its climate, might have been a high road for migration, when the climate was different. I shall, however, presently have to discuss this branch of the subject in some detail. Changes of level in the land must also have been highly influential: a narrow isthmus now separates two marine faunas; submerge it, or let it formerly have been submerged, and the two faunas will now blend together, or may formerly have blended. Where the sea now extends, land may at a former period have connected islands or possibly even continents together, and thus have allowed terrestrial productions to pass from one to the other. No geologist disputes that great mutations of level have occurred within the period of existing organisms. Edward Forbes insisted that all the islands in the Atlantic must have been recently connected with Europe or Africa, and Europe likewise with America. Other authors have thus hypothetically bridged over every ocean, and united almost every island with some mainland. If indeed the arguments used by Forbes are to be trusted, it must be admitted that scarcely a single island exists which has not recently been united to some continent. This view cuts the Gordian knot of the dispersal of the same species to the more distant points, and removes many a difficulty; but to the best of my judgment we are not authorised in admitting such enormous geographical changes within the period of existing species. It seems to me that we have abundant evidence of great oscillations in the level of the land or sea; but not of such vast change in the position and extension of our continents, as to have united them within the recent period to each other and to the several intervening oceanic islands. I freely admit the former existence of many islands, now buried beneath the sea, which may have served as halting-places for plants and for many animals during their migration. In the coral-producing oceans such sunken islands are now marked by rings of coral or atolls standing over them. Whenever it is fully admitted, as it will some day be, that each species has proceeded from a single birthplace, and when in the course of time we know something definite about the means of distribution, we shall be enabled to speculate with security on the former extension of the land. But I do not believe that it will ever be proved that within the recent period most of our continents which now stand quite separate have been continuously, or almost continuously united with each other, and with the many existing oceanic islands. Several facts in distribution,—such as the great difference in the marine faunas on the opposite sides of almost every continent,—the close relation of the tertiary inhabitants of several lands and even seas to their present inhabitants,—the degree of affinity between the mammals inhabiting islands with those of the nearest continent, being in part determined (as we shall hereafter see) by the depth of the intervening ocean,—these and other such facts are opposed to the admission of such prodigious geographical revolutions within the recent period, as are necessary on the view advanced by Forbes and admitted by his followers. The nature and relative proportions of the inhabitants of ocean islands are likewise opposed to the belief of their former continuity with continents. Nor does the almost universally volcanic composition of such islands favour the admission that they are the wrecks of sunken continents;—if they had originally existed as continental mountain ranges, some at least of the islands would have been formed, like other mountain summits, of granite, metamorphic schists, old fossiliferous and other rocks, instead of consisting of mere piles of volcanic matter.

I must now say a few words on what are called accidental means, but which more properly should be called occasional means of distribution. I shall here confine myself to plants. In botanical works, this or that plant is often stated to be ill adapted for wide dissemination; but the greater or less facilities for transport across the sea may be said to be almost wholly unknown. Until I tried, with Mr. Berkeley's aid, a few experiments, it was not even known how far seeds could resist the injurious action of sea-water. To my surprise I found that out of 87 kinds, 64 germinated after an immersion of 28 days, and a few survived an immersion of 137 days. It deserves notice that certain orders were far more injured than others: nine Leguminosæ were tried, and, with one exception, they resisted the salt-water badly; seven species of the allied order, Hydrophyllaceæ and Polemoniaceæ, were all killed by a month's immersion. For convenience' sake I chiefly tried small seeds without the capsule or fruit; and as all of these sank in a few days they could not have been floated across wide spaces of the sea, whether or not they were injured by the salt-water. Afterwards I tried some larger fruits, capsules, &c., and some of these floated for a long time. It is well known what a difference there is in the buoyancy of green and seasoned timber; and it occurred to me that floods would often wash into the sea dried plants or branches with seed-capsules or fruit attached to them. Hence I was led to dry the stems and branches of 94 plants with ripe fruit, and to place them on sea-water. The majority sank rapidly, but some which, whilst green, floated for a short time, when dried floated much longer; for instance, ripe hazel-nuts sank immediately, but when dried they floated for 90 days, and afterwards when planted germinated; an asparagus-plant with ripe berries floated for 23 days, when dried it floated for 85 days, and the seeds afterwards germinated; the ripe seeds of Helosciadium sank in two days, when they dried they floated for above 90 days, and afterwards germinated. Altogether, out of the 94 dried plants, 18 floated for above 28 days; and some of the 18 floated for a very much longer period. So that as $\frac{64}{87}$ kinds of seeds germinated after an immersion of 28 days; and as $\frac{18}{94}$ distinct species with ripe fruit (but not all the same species as in the foregoing experiment) floated, after being dried, for above 28 days, we may conclude, as far as anything can be inferred from these scanty facts, that the seeds of $\frac{14}{100}$ kinds of plants of any country might be floated by sea-currents during 28 days, and would retain their power of germination. In Johnston's *Physical Atlas*, the average rate of the several Atlantic currents is 33 miles per diem (some currents running at the rate of 60 miles per diem); on this average, the seeds of $\frac{14}{100}$ plants belonging to one country might be floated across 924 miles of sea to another country, and when stranded, if blown by an inland gale to a favourable spot, would germinate.

Subsequently to my experiments, M. Martens tried similar ones, but in a much better manner, for he placed the seeds in a box in the actual sea, so that they were alternately wet and exposed to the air like really floating plants. He tried 98 seeds, mostly different from mine; but he chose many large fruits and likewise seeds from plants which live near the sea; and this would have favoured both the average length of their flotation and their resistance to the injurious action of the salt-water. On the other hand, he did not previously dry the plants or branches with the fruit; and this, as we have seen, would have caused some of them to have floated much longer. The result was that $\frac{18}{98}$ of his seeds of different kinds floated for 42 days, and were then capable of germination. But I do not doubt that plants exposed to the waves would float for a less time than those protected from violent movement as in our experiments. Therefore it would perhaps be safer to assume that the seeds of about $\frac{10}{100}$ plants of a flora, after having been dried, could be floated across a space of sea 900 miles in width, and would then germinate. The fact of the larger fruits often floating longer than the small, is interesting; as plants with large seeds or fruit which, as Alphonse de Candolle has shown, generally have restricted ranges, could hardly be transported by any other means.

Seeds may be occasionally transported in another manner. Drift timber is thrown up on most islands, even on those in the midst of the widest oceans; and the natives of the coral-islands in the Pacific procure stones for their tools, solely from the roots of drifted trees, these stones being a valuable royal tax. I find that when irregularly shaped stones are embedded in the roots of trees, small parcels of earth are frequently enclosed in their interstices and behind them,—so perfectly that not a particle could be washed away during the longest transport: out of one small portion of earth thus *completely* enclosed by the roots of an oak about 50 years old, three dicotyledonous plants germinated: I am certain of the accuracy of this observation. Again, I can show that the carcases of birds, when floating on the sea, sometimes escape being immediately devoured: and many kinds of seeds in the crops of floating birds long retain their vitality: peas and vetches, for instance, are killed by even a few days' immersion in sea-water; but some taken out of the crop of a pigeon, which had floated on artificial sea-water for 30 days, to my surprise nearly all germinated.

Living birds can hardly fail to be highly effective agents in the transportation of seeds. I could give many facts showing how frequently birds of many kinds are blown by gales to vast distances across the ocean. We may safely assume that under such circumstances their rate of flight would often be 35 miles an hour, and some authors have given a far higher estimate. I have never seen an instance of nutritious seeds passing through the intestines of a bird; but hard seeds of fruit pass uninjured through even the digestive organs of a turkey. In the course of two months, I picked up in my garden 12 kinds of seeds, out of the excrement of small birds, and these seemed perfect, and some of them, which were tried, germinated. But the following fact is more important: the crops of birds do not secrete gastric juice, and do not, as I know by trial, injure in the least the germination of seeds; now, after a bird has found and devoured a large supply of food, it is positively asserted that all the grains do not pass into the gizzard for twelve or even eighteen hours. A bird in this interval might easily be blown to the distance of 500 miles, and hawks are known to look out for tired birds, and the contents of their torn crops might thus readily get scattered. Some hawks and owls bolt their prey whole, and, after an interval of from twelve to twenty hours, disgorge pellets, which, as I know from experiments made in the Zoological Gardens, include seeds capable of germination. Some seeds of the oat, wheat, millet, canary, hemp, clover, and beet germinated after having been from twelve to twenty-one hours in the stomachs of different birds of prey; and two seeds of beet grew after having been thus retained for two days and fourteen hours. Fresh-water fish, I find, eat seeds of many land and water plants; fish are frequently devoured by birds, and thus the seeds might be transported from place to place. I forced many kinds of seeds into the stomachs of dead fish, and then gave their bodies to fishing-eagles, storks, and pelicans; these birds, after an interval of many hours, either rejected the seeds in pellets or passed them in their excrement; and several of these seeds retained the power of germination. Certain seeds, however, were always killed by this process.

Locusts are sometimes blown to great distances from the land; I myself caught one 370 miles from the coast of Africa, and have heard of others caught at greater distances. The Rev. R. T. Lowe informed Sir C. Lyell that in November, 1844, swarms of locusts visited the island of Madeira. They were in countless numbers, as thick as the flakes of snow in the heaviest snowstorm, and extended upwards as far as could be seen with a telescope. During two or three days they slowly careered round and round in an immense ellipse, at least five or six miles in diameter, and at night alighted on the taller trees, which were completely coated with them. They then disappeared over the sea, as suddenly as they had appeared, and have not since visited the island. Now, in parts of Natal it is believed by some farmers, though on insufficient evidence, that injurious seeds are introduced into their grass-land in the dung left by the great flights of locusts which often visit that country. In consequence of this belief Mr. Weale sent me in a letter a small packet of the dried pellets, out of which I extracted under the microscope several seeds, and raised from them seven grass plants, belonging to two species, of two genera. Hence a swarm of locusts, such as that which visited Madeira, might readily be the means of introducing several kinds of plants into an island lying far from the mainland.

Although the beaks and feet of birds are generally clean, earth sometimes adheres to them: in one case I removed sixty-one grains, and in another case twenty-two grains of dry argillaceous earth from the foot of a partridge, and in the earth there was a pebble as large as the seed of a vetch. Here is a better case: the leg of a woodcock was sent to me by a friend, with a little cake of dry earth attached to the shank, weighing only nine grains; and this contained a seed of the toad-rush (Juncus bufonius) which germinated and flowered. Mr. Swaysland, of Brighton, who during the last forty years has paid close attention to our migratory birds, informs me that he has often shot wagtails (Motacillæ), wheat-ears, and whinchats (Saxicolæ), on their first arrival on our shores, before they had alighted; and he has several times noticed little cakes of earth attached to their feet. Many facts could be given showing how generally soil is charged with seeds. For instance, Prof. Newton sent me the leg of a red-legged partridge (Caccabis rufa) which had been wounded and could not fly, with a ball of hard earth adhering to it, and weighing six and a half ounces. The earth had been kept for three years, but when broken, watered and placed under a bell glass, no less than 82 plants sprung from it: these consisted of 12 monocotyledons, including the common oat, and at least one kind of grass, and of 70 dicotyledons, which consisted, judging from the young leaves, of at least three distinct species. With such facts before us, can we doubt that the many birds which are annually blown by gales across great spaces of ocean, and which annually migrate —for instance, the millions of quails across the Mediterranean—must occasionally transport a few seeds embedded in dirt adhering to their feet or beaks? But I shall have to recur to this subject.

As icebergs are known to be sometimes loaded with earth and stones, and have even carried brushwood, bones, and the nest of a land-bird, it can hardly be doubted that they must occasionally, as suggested by Lyell have transported seeds from one part to another of the arctic and antarctic regions; and during the Glacial period from one part of the now temperate regions to another. In the Azores, from the large number of plants common to Europe, in comparison with the species on the other islands of the Atlantic, which stand nearer to the mainland, and (as remarked by Mr. H. C. Watson) from their somewhat northern character in comparison with the latitude, I suspected that these islands had been partly stocked by ice-borne seeds, during the Glacial epoch. At my request Sir C. Lyell wrote to Mr. Hartung to inquire whether he had observed erratic boulders on these islands, and he answered that he had found large fragments of granite and other rocks, which do not occur in the archipelago. Hence we may safely infer that icebergs formerly landed their rocky burthens on the shores of these mid-ocean islands, and it is at least possible that they may have brought thither some few seeds of northern plants.

Considering that these several means of transport, and that other means, which without doubt remain to be discovered, have been in action year after year for tens of thousands of years, it would, I think, be a marvellous fact if many plants had not thus become widely transported. These means of transport are sometimes called accidental, but this is not strictly correct: the currents of the sea are not accidental, nor is the direction of prevalent gales of wind. It should be observed that scarcely any means of transport would carry seeds for very great distances: for seeds do not retain their vitality when exposed for a great length of time to the action of sea-water; nor could they be long carried in the crops or intestines of birds. These means, however, would suffice for occasional transport across tracts of sea some hundred miles in breadth, or from island to island, or from a continent to a neighbouring island, but not from one distant continent to another. The floras of distant continents would not by such means become mingled; but would remain as distinct as they now are. The currents, from their course, would never bring seeds from North America to Britain, though they might and do bring seeds from the West Indies to our western shores, where, if not killed by their very long immersion in salt water, they could not endure our climate. Almost every year, one or two land-birds are blown across the whole Atlantic Ocean, from North America to the western shores of Ireland and England; but seeds could be transported by these rare wanderers only by one means, namely, by dirt adhering to their feet or beaks, which is in itself a rare accident. Even in this case, how small would be the chance of a seed falling on favourable soil, and coming to maturity! But it would be a great error to argue that because a well-stocked island, like Great Britain, has not, as far as is known (and it would be very difficult to prove this), received within the last few centuries, through occasional means of transport, immigrants from Europe or any other continent, that a poorly-stocked island, though standing more remote from the mainland, would not receive colonists by similar means. Out of a hundred kinds of seeds or animals transported to an island, even if far less well-stocked than Britain, perhaps not more than one would be so well fitted to its new home, as to become naturalised. But this is no valid argument against what would be effected by occasional means of transport, during the long lapse of geological time, whilst the island was being upheaved, and before it had become fully stocked with inhabitants. On almost bare land, with few or no destructive insects or birds living there, nearly every seed which chanced to arrive, if fitted for the climate, would germinate and survive.

* * * *

ON THE INHABITANTS OF OCEANIC ISLANDS

We now come to the last of the three classes of facts, which I have selected as presenting the greatest amount of difficulty with respect to distribution, on the view that not only all the individuals of the same species have migrated from some one area, but that allied species, although now inhabiting the most distant points, have proceeded from a single area,—the birthplace of their early progenitors. I have already given my reasons for disbelieving in continental extensions within the period of existing species, on so enormous a scale that all the many islands of the several oceans were thus stocked with their present terrestrial inhabitants. This view removes many difficulties, but it does not accord with all the facts in regard to the productions of islands. In the following remarks I shall not confine myself to the mere question of dispersal, but shall consider some other cases bearing on the truth of the two theories of independent creation and of descent with modification.

The species of all kinds which inhabit oceanic islands are few in number compared with those on equal continental areas: Alphonse de Candolle admits this for plants, and Wollaston for insects. New Zealand, for instance, with its lofty mountains and diversified stations, extending over 780 miles of latitude, together with the outlying islands of Auckland, Campbell and Chatham, contain altogether only 960 kinds of flowering plants; if we compare this moderate number with the species which swarm over equal areas in South-Western Australia or at the Cape of Good Hope, we must admit that some cause, independently of different physical conditions, has given rise to so great a difference in number. Even the uniform county of Cambridge has 847 plants, and the little island of Anglesea 764, but a few ferns and a few introduced plants are included in these numbers, and the comparison in some other respects is not quite fair. We have evidence that the barren island of Ascension aboriginally possessed less than half-a-dozen flowering plants; yet many species have now become naturalised on it, as they have in New Zealand and on every other oceanic island which can be named. In St. Helena there is reason to believe that the naturalised plants and animals have nearly or quite exterminated many native productions. He who admits the doctrine of the creation of each separate species, will have to admit that a sufficient number of the best adapted plants and animals were not created for oceanic islands; for man has unintentionally stocked them far more fully and perfectly than did nature.

Although in oceanic islands the species are few in number, the proportion of endemic kinds (*i.e.*, those found nowhere else in the world) is often extremely large. If we compare, for instance, the number of endemic land-shells in Madeira, or of endemic birds in the Galapagos Archipelago, with the number found on any continent, and then compare the area of the island with that of the continent, we shall see that this is true. This fact might have been theoretically expected, for, as already explained, species occasionally arriving after long intervals of time in the new and isolated district, and having to compete with new associates, would be eminently liable to modification, and would often produce groups of modified descendants. But it by no means follows that, because in an island nearly all the species of one class are peculiar, those of another class, or of another section of the same class, are peculiar; and this difference seems to depend partly on the species which are not modified having immigrated in a body, so that their mutual relations have not been much disturbed; and partly on the frequent arrival of unmodified immigrants from the mother-country, with which the insular forms have intercrossed. It should be borne in mind that the offspring of such crosses would certainly gain in vigour; so that even an occasional cross would produce more effect than might have been anticipated. I will give a few illustrations of the foregoing remarks: in the Galapagos Islands there are 26 land-birds; of these 21 (or perhaps 23) are peculiar, whereas of the 11 marine birds only 2 are peculiar; and it is obvious that marine birds could arrive at these islands much more easily and frequently than land-birds. Bermuda, on the other hand, which lies at about the same distance from North America as the Galapagos Islands do from South America, and which has a very peculiar soil, does not possess a single endemic land-bird, and we know from Mr. J. M. Jones's admirable account of Bermuda, that very many North American birds occasionally or even frequently visit this island. Almost every year, as I am informed by Mr. E. V. Harcourt, many European and African birds are blown to Madeira;

this island is inhabited by 99 kinds of which one alone is peculiar, though very closely related to a European form; and three or four other species are confined to this island and to the Canaries. So that the islands of Bermuda and Madeira have been stocked from the neighbouring continents with birds, which for long ages have there struggled together, and have become mutually co-adapted. Hence when settled in their new homes, each kind will have been kept by the others to its proper place and habits, and will consequently have been but little liable to modification. Any tendency to modification will also have been checked by intercrossing with the unmodified immigrants, often arriving from the mother-country. Madeira again is inhabited by a wonderful number of peculiar land-shells, whereas not one species of sea-shell is peculiar to its shores: now, though we do not know how sea-shells are dispersed, yet we can see that their eggs or larvæ, perhaps attached to seaweed or floating timber, or to the feet of wading-birds, might be transported across three or four hundred miles of open sea far more easily than land-shells. The different orders of insects inhabiting Madeira present nearly parallel cases.

Oceanic islands are sometimes deficient in animals of certain whole classes, and their places are occupied by other classes; thus in the Galapagos Islands reptiles, and in New Zealand gigantic wingless birds, take, or recently took, the place of mammals. Although New Zealand is here spoken of as an oceanic island, it is in some degree doubtful whether it should be so ranked; it is of large size, and is not separated from Australia by a profoundly deep sea; from its geological character and the direction of its mountain-ranges, the Rev. W. B. Clarke has lately maintained that this island, as well as New Caledonia, should be considered as appurtenances of Australia. Turning to plants. Dr. Hooker has shown that in the Galapagos Islands the proportional numbers of the different orders are very different from what they are elsewhere. All such differences in number, and the absence of certain whole groups of animals and plants, are generally accounted for by supposed differences in the physical conditions of the islands; but this explanation is not a little doubtful. Facility of immigration seems to have been fully as important as the nature of the conditions.

Many remarkable little facts could be given with respect to the inhabitants of oceanic islands. For instance, in certain islands not tenanted by a single mammal, some of the endemic plants have beautifully hooked seeds; yet few relations are more manifest than that hooks serve for the transportal of seeds in the wool or fur of quadrupeds. But a hooked seed might be carried to an island by other means; and the plant then becoming modified would form an endemic species, still retaining its hooks, which would form a useless appendage like the shrivelled wings under the soldered wing-covers of many insular beetles. Again, islands often possess trees or bushes belonging to orders which elsewhere include only herbaceous species; now trees, as Alphonse de Candolle has shown, generally have, whatever the cause may be, confined ranges. Hence trees would be little likely to reach distant oceanic islands; and an herbaceous plant, which had no chance of successfully competing with the many fully developed trees growing on a continent, might, when established on an island, gain an advantage over other herbaceous plants by growing taller and taller and overtopping them. In this case, natural selection would tend to add to the stature of the plant, to whatever order it belonged, and thus first convert it into a bush and then into a tree.

ABSENCE OF BATRACHIANS AND TERRESTRIAL MAMMALS ON OCEANIC ISLANDS

With respect to the absence of whole orders of animals on oceanic islands, Bory St. Vincent long ago remarked that Batrachians (frogs, toads, newts) are never found on any of the many islands with which the great oceans are studded. I have taken pains to verify this assertion, and have found it true, with the exception of New Zealand, New Caledonia, the Andaman Islands, and perhaps the Solomon Islands and the Seychelles. But I have already remarked that it is doubtful whether New Zealand and New Caledonia ought to be classed as oceanic islands; and this is still more doubtful with respect to the Andaman and Solomon groups and the Seychelles. This general absence of frogs, toads, and newts on so many true oceanic islands cannot be accounted for by their physical conditions: indeed it seems that islands are peculiarly fitted for these animals; for frogs have been introduced into Madeira, the Azores, and Mauritius, and have multiplied so as to become a nuisance. But as these animals and their spawn are immediately killed (with the exception, as far as known, of one Indian species) by sea-water, there would be great difficulty in their transportal across the sea, and therefore we can see why they do not exist on strictly oceanic islands. But why, on the theory of creation, they should not have been created there, it would be very difficult to explain.

Mammals offer another and similar case. I have carefully searched the oldest voyages, and have not found a single instance, free from doubt, of a terrestrial mammal (excluding domesticated animals kept by the natives) inhabiting an island situated above 300 miles from a continent or great continental island; and many islands situated at a much less distance are equally barren. The Falkland Islands, which are inhabited by a wolf-like fox, come nearest to an exception; but this group cannot be considered as oceanic, as it lies on a bank in connection with the mainland at the distance of about 280 miles; moreover, icebergs formerly brought boulders to its western shores, and they may have formerly transported foxes, as now frequently happens in the arctic regions. Yet it cannot be said that small islands will not support at least small mammals, for they occur in many parts of the world on very small islands, when lying close to a continent; and hardly an island can be named on which our smaller quadrupeds have not become naturalised and greatly multiplied. It cannot be said, on the ordinary view of creation, that there has not been time for the creation of mammals; many volcanic islands are sufficiently ancient, as shown by the stupendous degradation which they have suffered, and by their tertiary strata: there has also been time for the production of endemic species belonging to other classes; and on continents it is known that new species of mammals appear and disappear at a quicker rate than other and lower animals. Although terrestrial mammals do not occur on oceanic islands, aerial mammals do occur on almost every island. New Zealand possesses two bats found nowhere else in the world: Norfolk Island, the Viti Archipelago, the Bonin Islands, the Caroline and Marianne Archipelagoes, and Mauritius, all possess their peculiar bats. Why, it may be asked, has the supposed creative force produced bats and no other mammals on remote islands? On my view this question can easily be answered; for no terrestrial mammal can be transported across a wide space of sea, but bats can fly across. Bats have been seen wandering by day far over the Atlantic Ocean; and two North American species either regularly or occasionally visit Bermuda, at the distance of 600 miles from the mainland. I hear from Mr. Tomes, who has specially studied this family, that many species have enormous ranges, and are found on continents and on far distant islands. Hence we have only to suppose that such wandering species have been modified in their new homes in relation to their new position, and we can understand the presence of endemic bats on oceanic islands, with the absence of all other terrestrial mammals.

Another interesting relation exists, namely, between the depth of the sea separating islands from each other or from the nearest continent, and the degree of affinity of their mammalian inhabitants. Mr. Windsor Earl has made some striking observations on this head, since greatly extended by Mr. Wallace's admirable researches, in regard to the great Malay Archipelago, which is traversed near Celebes by a space of deep ocean, and this separates two widely distinct mammalian faunas. On either side the islands stand on a moderately shallow submarine bank, and these islands are inhabited by the same or by closely allied quadrupeds. I have not as yet had time to follow up this subject in all quarters of the world; but as far as I have gone, the relation holds good. For instance, Britain is separated by a shallow channel from Europe, and the mammals are the same on both sides; and so it is with all the islands near the shores of Australia. The West Indian Islands, on the other hand, stand on a deeply submerged bank, nearly 1000 fathoms in depth, and here we find American forms, but the species and even the genera are quite distinct. As the amount of modification which animals of all kinds undergo partly depends on the lapse of time, and as the islands which are separated from each other or from the mainland by shallow channels, are more likely to have been continuously united within a recent period than the islands separated by deeper channels, we can understand how it is that a relation exists between the depth of the sea separating two mammalian faunas, and the degree of their affinity,—a relation which is quite inexplicable on the theory of independent acts of creation.

The foregoing statements in regard to the inhabitants of oceanic islands, —namely, the fewness of the species, with a large proportion consisting of endemic forms—the members of certain groups, but not those of other groups in the same class, having been modified—the absence of certain whole orders, as of batrachians and of terrestrial mammals, notwithstanding the presence of aerial bats,—the singular proportions of certain orders of plants,—herbaceous forms having been developed into trees, &c.,—seem to me to accord better with the belief in the efficiency of occasional means of transport, carried on during a long course of time, than with the belief in the former connection of all oceanic islands with the nearest continent; for on this latter view it is probable that the various classes would have immigrated more uniformly, and from the species having entered in a body their mutual relations would not have been much disturbed, and consequently they would either have not been modified, or all the species in a more equable manner.

I do not deny that there are many and serious difficulties in understanding how many of the inhabitants of the more remote islands, whether still retaining the same specific form or subsequently modified, have reached their present homes. But the probability of other islands having once existed as halting-places, of which not a wreck now remains, must not be overlooked. I will specify one difficult case. Almost all oceanic islands, even the most isolated and smallest, are inhabited by land-shells, generally by endemic species, but sometimes by species found elsewhere, —striking instances of which have been given by Dr. A. A. Gould in relation to the Pacific. Now it is notorious that land-shells are easily killed by sea-water; their eggs, at least such as I have tried, sink in it and are killed. Yet there must be some unknown, but occasionally efficient means for their transportal. Would the just-hatched young sometimes adhere to the feet of birds roosting on the ground, and thus get transported? It occurred to me that land-shells, when hibernating and having a membranous diaphragm over the mouth of the shell, might be floated in chinks of drifted timber across moderately wide arms of the sea. And I find that several species in this state withstand uninjured an immersion in sea-water during seven days: one shell, the Helix pomatia, after having been thus treated and again hibernating was put into sea-water for twenty days, and perfectly recovered. During this length of time the shell might have been carried by a marine current of average swiftness, to a distance of 660 geographical miles. As this Helix has a thick calcareous operculum, I removed it, and when it had formed a new membranous one, I again immersed it for fourteen days in sea-water, and again it recovered and crawled away. Baron Aucapitaine has since tried similar experiments: he placed 100 land-shells, belonging to ten species, in a box pierced with holes, and immersed it for a fortnight in the sea. Out of the hundred shells, twenty-seven recovered. The presence of an operculum seems to have been of importance, as out of twelve specimens of Cyclostoma elegans, which is thus furnished, eleven revived. It is remarkable, seeing how well the Helix pomatia resisted with me the salt-water, that not one of the fifty-four specimens belonging to four other species of Helix tried by Aucapitaine, recovered. It is, however, not at all probable that land-shells have often been thus transported; the feet of birds offer a more probable method.

ON THE RELATIONS OF THE INHABITANTS OF ISLANDS TO THOSE OF THE NEAREST MAINLAND

The most striking and important fact for us is the affinity of the species which inhabit islands to those of the nearest mainland, without being actually the same. Numerous instances could be given. The Galapagos Archipelago, situated under the equator, lies at the distance of between 500 and 600 miles from the shores of South America. Here almost every product of the land and of the water bears the unmistakable stamp of the American continent. There are twenty-six land-birds; of these, twenty-one, or perhaps twenty-three are ranked as distinct species, and would commonly be assumed to have been here created; yet the close affinity of most of these birds to American species is manifest in every character, in their habits, gestures, and tones of voice. So it is with the other animals, and with a large proportion of the plants, as shown by Dr. Hooker in his admirable Flora of this archipelago. The naturalist, looking at the inhabitants of these volcanic islands in the Pacific, distant several hundred miles from the continent, feels that he is standing on American land. Why should this be so? why should the species which are supposed to have been created in the Galapagos Archipelago, and nowhere else, bear so plainly the stamp of affinity to those created in America? There is nothing in the conditions of life, in the geological nature of the islands, in their height or climate, or in the proportions in which the several classes are associated together, which closely resembles the conditions of the South American coast: in fact, there is a considerable dissimilarity in all these respects. On the other hand, there is a considerable degree of resemblance in the volcanic nature of the soil, in the climate, height, and size of the islands, between the Galapagos and Cape Verde Archipelagoes: but what an entire and absolute difference in their inhabitants! The inhabitants of the Cape Verde Islands are related to those of Africa, like those of the Galapagos to America. Facts such as these admit of no sort of explanation on the ordinary view of independent creation; whereas on the view here maintained, it is obvious that the Galapagos Islands would be likely to receive colonists from America, whether by occasional means of transport or (though I do not believe in this doctrine) by formerly continuous land, and the Cape Verde Islands from Africa; such colonists would be liable to modification,—the principle of inheritance still betraying their original birthplace.

Many analogous facts could be given: indeed it is an almost universal rule that the endemic productions of islands are related to those of the nearest continent, or of the nearest large island. The exceptions are few, and most of them can be explained. Thus although Kerguelen Land stands nearer to Africa than to America, the plants are related, and that very closely, as we know from Dr. Hooker's account, to those of America: but on the view that this island has been mainly stocked by seeds brought with earth and stones on icebergs, drifted by the prevailing currents, this anomaly disappears. New Zealand in its endemic plants is much more closely related to Australia, the nearest mainland, than to any other region: and this is what might have been expected; but it is also plainly related to South America, which, although the next nearest continent, is so enormously remote, that the fact becomes an anomaly. But this difficulty partially disappears on the view that New Zealand, South America, and the other southern lands have been stocked in part from a nearly intermediate though distant point, namely from the antarctic islands, when they were clothed with vegetation, during a warmer tertiary period, before the commencement of the last Glacial period. The affinity, which though feeble, I am assured by Dr. Hooker is real, between the flora of the south-western corner of Australia and of the Cape of Good Hope, is a far more remarkable case; but this affinity is confined to the plants, and will, no doubt, some day be explained.

The same law which has determined the relationship between the inhabitants of islands and the nearest mainland, is sometimes displayed on a small scale, but in a most interesting manner, within the limits of the same archipelago. Thus each separate island of the Galapagos Archipelago is tenanted, and the fact is a marvellous one, by many different species; but these species are related to each other in a very much closer manner than to the inhabitants of the American continent, or of any other quarter of the world. This is what might have been expected, for islands situated so near to each other would almost necessarily receive immigrants from the same original source, and from each other. But how is it that many of the immigrants have been differently modified, though only in a small degree, in islands situated within sight of each other, having the same geological nature, the same height, climate, &c.? This long appeared to me a great difficulty: but it arises in chief part from the deeply-seated error of considering the physical conditions of a country as the most important; whereas it cannot be disputed that the nature of the other species with which each has to compete, is at least as important, and generally a far more important element of success. Now if we look to the species which inhabit the Galapagos Archipelago, and are likewise found in other parts of the world, we find that they differ considerably in the several islands. This difference might indeed have been expected if the islands had been stocked by occasional means of transport—a seed, for instance, of one plant having been brought to one island, and that of another plant to another island, though all proceeding from the same general source. Hence, when in former times an immigrant first settled on one of the islands, or when it subsequently spread from one to another, it would undoubtedly be exposed to different conditions in the different islands, for it would have to compete with a different set of organisms; a plant, for instance, would find the ground best fitted for it occupied by somewhat different species in the different islands, and would be exposed to the attacks of somewhat different enemies. If then it varied, natural selection would probably favour different varieties in the different islands. Some species, however, might spread and yet retain the same character throughout the group, just as we see some species spreading widely throughout a continent and remaining the same.

The really surprising fact in this case of the Galapagos Archipelago, and in a lesser degree in some analogous cases, is that each new species after being formed in any one island, did not spread quickly to the other islands. But the islands, though in sight of each other, are separated by deep arms of the sea, in most cases wider than the British Channel, and there is no reason to suppose that they have at any former period been continuously united. The currents of the sea are rapid and sweep between the islands, and gales of wind are extraordinarily rare; so that the islands are far more effectually separated from each other than they appear on a map. Nevertheless some of the species, both of those found in other parts of the world and of those confined to the archipelago, are common to the several islands; and we may infer from their present manner of distribution, that they have spread from one island to the others. But we often take, I think, an erroneous view of the probability of closely-allied species invading each other's territory, when put into free intercommunication. Undoubtedly, if one species has any advantage over another, it will in a very brief time wholly or in part supplant it; but if both are equally well fitted for their own places, both will probably hold their separate places for almost any length of time. Being familiar with the fact that many species, naturalised through man's agency, have spread with astonishing rapidity over wide areas, we are apt to infer that most species would thus spread; but we should remember that the species which become naturalised in new countries are not generally closely allied to the aboriginal inhabitants, but are very distinct forms, belonging in a large proportion of cases, as shown by Alphonse de Candolle, to distinct genera. In the Galapagos Archipelago, many even of the birds, though so well adapted for flying from island to island, differ on the different islands; thus there are three closely-allied species of mocking-thrush, each confined to its own island. Now let us suppose the mocking-thrush of Chatham Island to be blown to Charles Island, which has its own mocking-thrush, why should it succeed in establishing itself there? We may safely infer that Charles Island is well stocked with its own species, for annually more eggs are laid and young birds hatched, than can possibly be reared; and we may infer that the mocking-thrush peculiar to Charles Island is at least as well fitted for its home as is the species peculiar to Chatham Island. Sir C. Lyell and Mr. Wollaston have communicated to me a remarkable fact bearing on this subject; namely, that Madeira and the adjoining islet of Porto Santo possess many distinct but representative species of land-shells, some of which live in crevices of stone; and although large quantities of stone are annually transported from Porto Santo to Madeira, yet this latter island has not become colonised by the Porto Santo species; nevertheless both islands have been colonised by European land-shells, which no doubt had some advantage over the indigenous species. From these considerations I think we need not greatly marvel at the endemic species which inhabit the several islands of the Galapagos Archipelago, not having all spread from island to island. On the same continent, also, preoccupation has probably played an important part in checking the commingling of the species which inhabit different districts with nearly the same physical conditions. Thus, the south-east and south-west corners of Australia have nearly the same physical conditions, and are united by continuous land, yet they are inhabited by a vast number of distinct mammals, birds, and plants; so it is, according to Mr. Bates, with the butterflies and other animals inhabiting the great, open, and continuous valley of the Amazons.

The same principle which governs the general character of the inhabitants of oceanic islands, namely, the relation to the source whence colonists could have been most easily derived, together with their subsequent modification, is of the widest application throughout nature. We see this on every mountain-summit, in every lake and marsh. For Alpine species, excepting in as far as the same species have become widely spread during the Glacial epoch, are related to those of the surrounding lowlands; thus we have in South America, Alpine humming-birds, Alpine rodents, Alpine plants, &c., all strictly belonging to American forms; and it is obvious that a mountain, as it became slowly unheaved, would be colonised from the surrounding lowlands. So it is with the inhabitants of lakes and marshes, excepting in so far as great facility of transport has allowed the same forms to prevail throughout large portions of the world. We see this same principle in the character of most of the blind animals inhabiting the caves of America and of Europe. Other analogous facts could be given. It will, I believe, be found universally true, that wherever in two regions, let them be ever so distant, many closely allied or representative species occur, there will likewise be found some identical species; and wherever many closely-allied species occur, there will be found many forms which some naturalists rank as distinct species, and others as mere varieties; these doubtful forms showing us the steps in the progress of modification.

The relation between the power and extent of migration in certain species, either at the present or at some former period, and the existence at remote points of the world of closely-allied species, is shown in another and more general way. Mr. Gould remarked to me long ago, that in those genera of birds which range over the world, many of the species have very wide ranges. I can hardly doubt that this rule is generally true, though difficult of proof. Amongst mammals, we see it strikingly displayed in Bats, and in a lesser degree in the Felidæ and Canidæ. We see the same rule in the distribution of butterflies and beetles. So it is with most of the inhabitants of fresh water, for many of the genera in the most distinct classes range over the world, and many of the species have enormous ranges. It is not meant that all, but that some of the species have very wide ranges in the genera which range very widely. Nor is it meant that the species in such genera have on an average a very wide range; for this will largely depend on how far the process of modification has gone; for instance, two varieties of the same species inhabit America and Europe, and thus the species has an immense range; but, if variation were to be carried a little further, the two varieties would be ranked as distinct species, and their range would be greatly reduced. Still less is it meant, that species which have the capacity of crossing barriers and ranging widely, as in the case of certain powerfully-winged birds, will necessarily range widely; for we should never forget that to range widely implies not only the power of crossing barriers, but the more important power of being victorious in distant lands in the struggle for life with foreign associates. But according to the view that all the species of a genus, though distributed to the most remote points of the world, are descended from a single progenitor, we ought to find, and I believe as a general rule we do find, that some at least of the species range very widely.

We should bear in mind that many genera in all classes are of ancient origin, and the species in this case will have had ample time for dispersal and subsequent modification. There is also reason to believe from geological evidence, that within each great class the lower organisms change at a slower rate than the higher; consequently they will have had a better chance of ranging widely and of still retaining the same specific character. This fact, together with that of the seeds and eggs of most lowly organised forms being very minute and better fitted for distant transportal, probably accounts for a law which has long been observed, and which has lately been discussed by Alphonse de Candolle in regard to plants, namely, that the lower any group of organisms stands the more widely it ranges.

The relations just discussed,—namely, lower organisms ranging more widely than the higher,—some of the species of widely-ranging genera themselves ranging widely,—such facts, as alpine, lacustrine, and marsh productions being generally related to those which live on the surrounding low lands and dry lands,—the striking relationship between the inhabitants of islands and those of the nearest mainland—the still closer relationship of the distinct inhabitants of the islands in the same archipelago—are inexplicable on the ordinary view of the independent creation of each species, but are explicable if we admit colonisation from the nearest or readiest source, together with the subsequent adaptation of the colonists to their new homes.

SUMMARY ON GEOGRAPHICAL DISTRIBUTION

In these chapters I have endeavoured to show, that if we make due allowance for our ignorance of the full effects of changes of climate and of the level of the land, which have certainly occurred within the recent period, and of other changes which have probably occurred,—if we remember how ignorant we are with respect to the many curious means of occasional transport,—if we bear in mind, and this is a very important consideration, how often a species may have ranged continuously over a wide area, and then have become extinct in the intermediate tracts,—the difficulty is not insuperable in believing that all the individuals of the same species, wherever found, are descended from common parents. And we are led to this conclusion, which has been arrived at by many naturalists under the designation of single centres of creation, by various general considerations, more especially from the importance of barriers of all kinds, and from the analogical distribution of sub-genera, genera, and families.

With respect to distinct species belonging to the same genus, which on our theory have spread from one parent-source; if we make the same allowances as before for our ignorance, and remember that some forms of life have changed very slowly, enormous periods of time having been thus granted for their migration, the difficulties are far from insuperable though in this case, as in that of the individuals of the same species, they are often great.

As exemplifying the effects of climatal changes on distribution, I have attempted to show how important a part the last Glacial period has played, which affected even the equatorial regions, and which, during the alternations of the cold in the north and south, allowed the productions of opposite hemispheres to mingle, and left some of them stranded on the mountain-summits in all parts of the world. As showing how diversified are the means of occasional transport, I have discussed at some little length the means of dispersal of fresh-water productions.

If the difficulties be not insuperable in admitting that in the long course of time all the individuals of the same species, and likewise of the several species belonging to the same genus, have proceeded from some one source; then all the grand leading facts of geographical distribution are explicable on the theory of migration, together with subsequent modification and the multiplication of new forms. We can thus understand the high importance of barriers, whether of land or water, in not only separating, but in apparently forming the several zoological and botanical provinces. We can thus understand the concentration of related species within the same areas; and how it is that under different latitudes, for instance in South America, the inhabitants of the plains and mountains, of the forests, marshes, and deserts, and linked together in so mysterious a manner, and are likewise linked to the extinct beings which formerly inhabited the same continent. Bearing in mind that the mutual relation of organism to organism is of the highest importance, we can see why two areas having nearly the same physical conditions should often be inhabited by very different forms of life; for according to the length of time which has elapsed since the colonists entered one of the regions, or both; according to the nature of the communication which allowed certain forms and not others to enter, either in greater or lesser numbers; according or not, as those which entered happened to come into more or less direct competition with each other and with the aborigines; and according as the immigrants were capable of varying more or less rapidly, there would ensue in the two or more regions, independently of their physical conditions, infinitely diversified conditions of life,—there would be an almost endless amount of organic action and reaction,—and we should find some groups of beings greatly, and some only slightly modified,—some developed in great force, some existing in scanty numbers—and this we do find in the several great geographical provinces of the world.

On these same principles we can understand, as I have endeavoured to show, why oceanic islands should have few inhabitants, but that of these, a large proportion should be endemic or peculiar; and why, in relation to the means of migration, one group of beings should have all its species peculiar, and another group, even within the same class, should have all its species the same with those in an adjoining quarter of the world. We can see why whole groups of organisms, as batrachians and terrestrial mammals, should be absent from oceanic islands, whilst the most isolated islands should possess their own peculiar species of aerial mammals or bats. We can see why, in islands, there should be some relation between the presence of mammals, in a more or less modified condition, and the depth of the sea between such islands and the mainland. We can clearly see why all the inhabitants of an archipelago, though specifically distinct on the several islets, should be closely related to each other; and should likewise be related, but less closely, to those of the nearest continent, or other source whence immigrants might have been derived. We can see why, if there exists very closely allied or representative species in two areas, however distant from each other, some identical species will almost always there be found.

As the late Edward Forbes often insisted, there is a striking parallelism in the laws of life throughout time and space; the laws governing the succession of forms in past times being nearly the same with those governing at the present time the differences in different areas. We see this in many facts. The endurance of each species and group of species is continuous in time; for the apparent exceptions to the rule are so few, that they may fairly be attributed to our not having as yet discovered in an intermediate deposit certain forms which are absent in it, but which occur both above and below: so in space, it certainly is the general rule that the area inhabited by a single species, or by a group of species, is continuous, and the exceptions, which are not rare, may, as I have attempted to show, be accounted for by former migrations under different circumstances, or through occasional means of transport, or by the species having become extinct in the intermediate tracts. Both in time and space species and groups of species have their points of maximum development. Groups of species, living during the same period of time, or living within the same area, are often characterised by trifling features in common, as of sculpture or colour. In looking to the long succession of past ages, as in looking to distant provinces throughout the world, we find that species in certain classes differ little from each other, whilst those in another class, or only in a different section of the same order, differ greatly from each other. In both time and space the lowly organised members of each class generally change less than the highly organised; but there are in both cases marked exceptions to the rule. According to our theory, these several relations throughout time and space are intelligible; for whether we look to the allied forms of life which have changed during successive ages, or to those which have changed after having migrated into distant quarters, in both cases they are connected by the same bond of ordinary generation; in both cases the laws of variation have been the same, and modifications have been accumulated by the same means of natural selection.

CHAPTER 11

RECAPITULATION AND CONCLUSION

[Chapter XV of the *Origin*. Chapter XIV, entitled 'Mutual Affinities of Organic Beings: Morphology: Embryology: Rudimentary Organs', has been omitted.]

AS THIS whole volume is one long argument, it may be convenient to the reader to have the leading facts and inferences briefly recapitulated.

That many and serious objections may be advanced against the theory of descent with modification through variation and natural selection, I do not deny. I have endeavoured to give to them their full force. Nothing at first can appear more difficult to believe than that the more complex organs and instincts have been perfected, not by means superior to, though analogous with, human reason, but by the accumulation of innumerable slight variations, each good for the individual possessor. Nevertheless, this difficulty, though appearing to our imagination insuperably great, cannot be considered real if we admit the following propositions, namely, that all parts of the organisation and instincts offer, at least, individual differences—that there is a struggle for existence leading to the preservation of profitable deviations of structure or instinct—and, lastly, that gradations in the state of perfection of each organ may have existed, each good of its kind. The truth of these propositions cannot, I think, be disputed.

It is, no doubt, extremely difficult even to conjecture by what gradations many structures have been perfected, more especially amongst broken and failing groups of organic beings, which have suffered much extinction, but we see so many strange gradations in nature, that we ought to be extremely cautious in saying that any organ or instinct, or any whole structure, could not have arrived at its present state by many graduated steps. There are, it must be admitted, cases of special difficulty opposed to the theory of natural selection; and one of the most curious of these is the existence in the same community of two or three defined castes of workers or sterile female ants; but I have attempted to show how these difficulties can be mastered.

With respect to the almost universal sterility of species when first crossed, which forms so remarkable a contrast with the almost universal fertility of varieties when crossed, I must refer the reader to the recapitulation of the facts given at the end of the ninth chapter, which seem to me conclusively to show that this sterility is no more a special endowment than is the incapacity of two distinct kinds of trees to be grafted together; but that it is incidental on differences confined to the reproductive systems of the intercrossed species. We see the truth of this conclusion in the vast difference in the results of crossing the same two species reciprocally,—that is, when one species is first used as the father and then as the mother. Analogy from the consideration of dimorphic and trimorphic plants clearly leads to the same conclusion, for when the forms are illegitimately united, they yield few or no seed, and their offspring are more or less sterile; and these forms belong to the same undoubted species, and differ from each other in no respect except in their reproductive organs and functions.

Although the fertility of varieties when intercrossed and of their mongrel offspring has been asserted by so many authors to be universal, this cannot be considered as quite correct after the facts given on the high authority of Gärtner and Kölreuter. Most of the varieties which have been experimented on have been produced under domestication; and as domestication (I do not mean mere confinement) almost certainly tends to eliminate that sterility which, judging from analogy, would have affected the parent-species if intercrossed, we ought not to expect that domestication would likewise induce sterility in their modified descendants when crossed. This elimination of sterility apparently follows from the same cause which allows our domestic animals to breed freely under diversified circumstances; and this again apparently follows from their having been gradually accustomed to frequent changes in their conditions of life.

A double and parallel series of facts seems to throw much light on the sterility of species, when first crossed, and of their hybrid offspring. On the one side, there is good reason to believe that slight changes in the conditions of life give vigour and fertility to all organic beings. We know also that a cross between the distinct individuals of the same variety, and between distinct varieties, increases the number of their offspring, and certainly gives to them increased size and vigour. This is chiefly owing to the forms which are crossed having been exposed to somewhat different conditions of life; for I have ascertained by a laborious series of experiments that if all the individuals of the same variety be subjected during several generations to the same conditions, the good derived from crossing is often much diminished or wholly disappears. This is one side of the case. On the other side, we know that species which have long been exposed to nearly uniform conditions, when they are subjected under confinement to new and greatly changed conditions, either perish, or if they survive, are rendered sterile, though retaining perfect health. This does not occur, or only in a very slight degree, with our domesticated productions, which have long been exposed to fluctuating conditions. Hence when we find that hybrids produced by a cross between two distinct species are few in number, owing to their perishing soon after conception or at a very early age, or if surviving that they are rendered more or less sterile, it seems highly probable that this result is due to their having been in fact subjected to a great change in their conditions of life, from being compounded of two distinct organisations. He who will explain in a definite manner why, for instance, an elephant or a fox will not breed under confinement in its native country, whilst the domestic pig or dog will breed freely under the most diversified conditions, will at the same time be able to give a definite answer to the question why two distinct species, when crossed, as well as their hybrid offspring, are generally rendered more or less sterile, whilst two domesticated varieties when crossed and their mongrel offspring are perfectly fertile.

Turning to geographical distribution, the difficulties encountered on the theory of descent with modification are serious enough. All the individuals of the same species, and all the species of the same genus, or even higher group, are descended from common parents; and therefore, in however distant and isolated parts of the world they may now be found, they must in the course of successive generations have travelled from some one point to all the others. We are often wholly unable even to conjecture how this could have been effected. Yet, as we have reason to believe that some species have retained the same specific form for very long periods of time, immensely long as measured by years, too much stress ought not to be laid on the occasional wide diffusion of the same species; for during very long periods there will always have been a good chance for wide migration by many means. A broken or interrupted range may often be accounted for by the extinction of the species in the intermediate regions. It cannot be denied that we are as yet very ignorant as to the full extent of the various climatal and geographical changes which have affected the earth during modern periods; and such changes will often have facilitated migration. As an example, I have attempted to show how potent has been the influence of the Glacial period on the distribution of the same and of allied species throughout the world. We are as yet profoundly ignorant of the many occasional means of transport.

With respect to distinct species of the same genus inhabiting distant and isolated regions, as the process of modification has necessarily been slow, all the means of migration will have been possible during a very long period; and consequently the difficulty of the wide diffusion of the species of the same genus is in some degree lessened.

As according to the theory of natural selection an interminable number of intermediate forms must have existed, linking together all the species in each group by gradations as fine as are our existing varieties, it may be asked: Why do we not see these linking forms all around us? Why are not all organic beings blended together in an inextricable chaos? With respect to existing forms, we should remember that we have no right to expect (excepting in rare cases) to discover *directly* connecting links between them, but only between each and some extinct and supplanted form. Even on a wide area, which has during a long period remained continuous, and of which the climatic and other conditions of life change insensibly in proceeding from a district occupied by one species into another district occupied by a closely allied species, we have no just right to expect often to find intermediate varieties in the intermediate zones. For we have reason to believe that only a few species of a genus ever undergo change; the other species becoming utterly extinct and leaving no modified progeny. Of the species which do change, only a few within the same country change at the same time; and all modifications are slowly effected. I have also shown that the intermediate varieties which probably at first existed in the intermediate zones, would be liable to be supplanted by the allied forms on either hand; for the latter, from existing in greater numbers, would generally be modified and improved at a quicker rate than the intermediate varieties, which existed in lesser numbers; so that the intermediate varieties would, in the long run, be supplanted and exterminated.

On this doctrine of the extermination of an infinitude of connecting links, between the living and extinct inhabitants of the world, and at each successive period between the extinct and still older species, why is not every geological formation charged with such links? Why does not every collection of fossil remains afford plain evidence of the gradation and mutation of the forms of life? Although geological research has undoubtedly revealed the former existence of many links, bringing numerous forms of life much closer together, it does not yield the infinitely many fine gradations between past and present species required on the theory; and this is the most obvious of the many objections which may be urged against it. Why, again, do whole groups of allied species appear, though this appearance is often false, to have come in suddenly on the successive geological stages? Although we now know that organic beings appeared on this globe, at a period incalculably remote, long before the lowest bed of the Cambrian system was deposited, why do we not find beneath this system great piles of strata stored with the remains of the progenitors of the Cambrian fossils? For on the theory, such strata must somewhere have been deposited at these ancient and utterly unknown epochs of the world's history.

I can answer these questions and objections only on the supposition that the geological record is far more imperfect than most geologists believe. The number of specimens in all our museums is absolutely as nothing compared with the countless generations of countless species which have certainly existed. The parent-form of any two or more species would not be in all its characters directly intermediate between its modified offspring, any more than the rock-pigeon is directly intermediate in crop and tail between its descendants, the pouter and fantail pigeons. We should not be able to recognise a species as the parent of another and modified species, if we were to examine the two ever so closely, unless we possessed most of the intermediate links; and owing to the imperfection of the geological record, we have no just right to expect to find so many links. If two or three, or even more linking forms were discovered, they would simply be ranked by many naturalists as so many new species, more especially if found in different geological sub-stages, let their differences be ever so slight. Numerous existing doubtful forms could be named which are probably varieties; but who will pretend that in future ages so many fossil links will be discovered, that naturalists will be able to decide whether or not these doubtful forms ought to be called varieties? Only a small portion of the world has been geologically explored. Only organic beings of certain classes can be preserved in a fossil condition, at least in any great number. Many species when once formed never undergo any further change but become extinct without leaving modified descendants; and the periods, during which species have undergone modification, though long as measured by years, have probably been short in comparison with the periods during which they retain the same form. It is the dominant and widely ranging species which vary most frequently and vary most, and varieties are often at first local—both causes rendering the discovery of intermediate links in any one formation less likely. Local varieties will not spread into other and distant regions until they are considerably modified and improved; and when they have spread, and are discovered in a geological formation, they appear as if suddenly created there, and will be simply classed as new species. Most formations have been intermittent in their accumulation; and their duration has probably been shorter than the average duration of specific forms. Successive formations are in most cases separated from each other by blank intervals of time of great length; for fossiliferous formations thick enough to resist future degradations can as a general rule be accumulated only where much sediment is deposited on the subsiding bed of the sea. During the alternate periods of elevation and of stationary level the record will generally be blank. During these latter periods there will probably be more variability in the forms of life; during periods of subsidence, more extinction.

With respect to the absence of strata rich in fossils beneath the Cambrian formation, I can recur only to the hypothesis given in the tenth chapter; namely, that though our continents and oceans have endured for an enormous period in nearly their present relative positions, we have no reason to assume that this has always been the case; consequently formations much older than any now known may lie buried beneath the great oceans. With respect to the lapse of time not having been sufficient since our planet was consolidated for the assumed amount of organic change, and this objection, as urged by Sir William Thompson, is probably one of the gravest as yet advanced, I can only say, firstly, that we do not know at what rate species change as measured by years, and secondly, that many philosophers are not as yet willing to admit that we know enough of the constitution of the universe and of the interior of our globe to speculate with safety on its past duration.

That the geological record is imperfect all will admit; but that it is imperfect to the degree required by our theory, few will be inclined to admit. If we look to long enough intervals of time, geology plainly declares that species have all changed; and they have changed in the manner required by the theory, for they have changed slowly and in a graduated manner. We clearly see this in the fossil remains from consecutive formations invariably being much more closely related to each other, than are the fossils from widely separated formations.

Such is the sum of the several chief objections and difficulties which may be justly urged against the theory; and I have now briefly recapitulated the answers and explanations which, as far as I can see, may be given. I have felt these difficulties far too heavily during many years to doubt their weight. But it deserves especial notice that the more important objections relate to questions on which we are confessedly ignorant; nor do we know how ignorant we are. We do not know all the possible transitional gradations between the simplest and the most perfect organs; it cannot be pretended that we know all the varied means of Distribution during the long lapse of years, or that we know how imperfect is the Geological Record. Serious as these several objections are, in my judgment they are by no means sufficient to overthrow the theory of descent with subsequent modification.

Now let us turn to the other side of the argument. Under domestication we see much variability, caused, or at least excited, by changed conditions of life; but often in so obscure a manner, that we are tempted to consider the variations as spontaneous. Variability is governed by many complex laws,—by correlated growth, compensation, the increased use and disuse of parts, and the definite action of the surrounding conditions. There is much difficulty in ascertaining how largely our domestic productions have been modified; but we may safely infer that the amount has been large, and that modifications can be inherited for long periods. As long as the conditions of life remain the same, we have reason to believe that a modification, which has already been inherited for many generations, may continue to be inherited for an almost infinite number of generations. On the other hand, we have evidence that variability when it has once come into play, does not cease under domestication for a very long period; nor do we know that it ever ceases, for new varieties are still occasionally produced by our oldest domesticated productions.

Variability is not actually caused by man; he only unintentionally exposes organic being to new conditions of life, and then nature acts on the organisation and causes it to vary. But man can and does select the variations given to him by nature, and thus accumulates them in any desired manner. He thus adapts animals and plants for his own benefit or pleasure. He may do this methodically, or he may do it unconsciously by preserving the individuals most useful or pleasing to him without any intention of altering the breed. It is certain that he can largely influence the character of a breed by selecting, in each successive generation, individual differences so slight as to be inappreciable except by an educated eye. This unconscious process of selection has been the great agency in the formation of the most distinct and useful domestic breeds. That many breeds produced by man have to a large extent the character of natural species, is shown by the inextricable doubts whether many of them are varieties or aboriginally distinct species.

There is no reason why the principles which have acted so efficiently under domestication should not have acted under nature. In the survival of favoured individuals and races, during the constantly-recurrent Struggle for Existence, we see a powerful and ever-acting form of Selection. The struggle for existence inevitably follows from the high geometrical ratio of increase which is common to all organic beings. This high rate of increase is proved by calculation,—by the rapid increase of many animals and plants during a succession of peculiar seasons, and when naturalised in new countries. More individuals are born than can possibly survive. A grain in the balance may determine which individuals shall live and which shall die,—which variety or species shall increase in number, and which shall decrease, or finally become extinct. As the individuals of the same species come in all respects into the closest competition with each other, the struggle will generally be most severe between them; it will be almost equally severe between the varieties of the same species, and next in severity between the species of the same genus. On the other hand the struggle will often be severe between beings remote in the scale of nature. The slightest advantage in certain individuals, at any age or during any season, over those with which they come into competition, or better adaptation in however slight a degree to the surrounding physical conditions, will, in the long run, turn the balance.

With animals having separated sexes, there will be in most cases a struggle between the males for the possession of the females. The most vigorous males, or those which have most successfully struggled with their conditions of life, will generally leave most progeny. But success will often depend on the males having special weapons, or means of defence, or charms; and a slight advantage will lead to victory.

As geology plainly proclaims that each land has undergone great physical changes, we might have expected to find that organic beings have varied under nature, in the same way as they have varied under domestication. And if there has been any variability under nature, it would be an unaccountable fact if natural selection had not come into play. It has often been asserted, but the assertion is incapable of proof, that the amount of variation under nature is a strictly limited quantity. Man, though acting on external characters alone and often capriciously, can produce within a short period a great result by adding up mere individual differences in his domestic productions; and every one admits that species present individual differences. But, besides such differences, all naturalists admit that natural varieties exist, which are considered sufficiently distinct to be worthy of record in systematic works. No one has drawn any clear distinction between individual differences and slight varieties; or between more plainly marked varieties and sub-species, and species. On separate continents, and on different parts of the same continent when divided by barriers of any kind, and on outlying islands, what a multitude of forms exist, which some experienced naturalists rank as varieties, others as geographical races or sub-species, and others as distinct, though closely allied species!

If then, animals and plants do vary, let it be ever so slightly or slowly, why should not variations or individual differences, which are in any way beneficial, be preserved and accumulated through natural selection, or the survival of the fittest? If man can by patience select variations useful to him, why, under changing and complex conditions of life, should not variations useful to nature's living products often arise, and be preserved or selected? What limit can be put to this power, acting during long ages and rigidly scrutinising the whole constitution, structure, and habits of each creature,—favouring the good and rejecting the bad? I can see no limit to this power, in slowly and beautifully adapting each form to the most complex relations of life. The theory of natural selection, even if we look no further than this, seems to be in the highest degree probable. I have already recapitulated, as fairly as I could, the opposed difficulties and objections: now let us turn to the special facts and arguments in favour of the theory.

On the view that species are only strongly marked and permanent varieties, and that each species first existed as a variety, we can see why it is that no line of demarcation can be drawn between species, commonly supposed to have been produced by special acts of creation, and varieties which are acknowledged to have been produced by secondary laws. On this same view we can understand how it is that in a region where many species of a genus have been produced, and where they now flourish, these same species should present many varieties; for where the manufactory of species has been active, we might expect, as a general rule, to find it still in action; and this is the case if varieties be incipient species. Moreover, the species of the larger genera, which afford the greater number of varieties or incipient species, retain to a certain degree the character of varieties; for they differ from each other by a less amount of difference than do the species of smaller genera. The closely allied species also of the larger genera apparently have restricted ranges, and in their affinities they are clustered in little groups round other species—in both respects resembling varieties. These are strange relations on the view that each species was independently created, but are intelligible if each existed first as a variety.

As each species tends by its geometrical rate of reproduction to increase inordinately in number; and as the modified descendants of each species will be enabled to increase by as much as they become more diversified in habits and structure, so as to be able to seize on many and widely different places in the economy of nature, there will be a constant tendency in natural selection to preserve the most divergent offspring of any one species. Hence, during a long-continued course of modification, the slight differences characteristic of varieties of the same species, tend to be augmented into the greater differences characteristic of the species of the same genus. New and improved varieties will inevitably supplant and exterminate the older, less improved, and intermediate varieties; and thus species are rendered to a large extent defined and distinct objects. Dominant species belonging to the larger groups within each class tend to give birth to new and dominant forms; so that each large group tends to become still larger, and at the same time more divergent in character. But as all groups cannot thus go on increasing in size, for the world would not hold them, the more dominant groups beat the less dominant. This tendency in the large groups to go on increasing in size and diverging in character, together with the inevitable contingency of much extinction, explains the arrangement of all the forms of life in groups subordinate to groups, all within a few great classes, which has prevailed throughout all time. This grand fact of the grouping of all organic beings under what is called the Natural System, is utterly inexplicable on the theory of creation.

As natural selection acts solely by accumulating slight, successive, favourable variations, it can produce no great or sudden modifications; it can act only by short and slow steps. Hence, the canon of *Natura non facit saltum*, which every fresh addition to our knowledge tends to confirm, is on this theory intelligible. We can see why throughout nature the same general end is gained by an almost infinite diversity of means, for every peculiarity when once acquired is long inherited, and structures already modified in many different ways have to be adapted for the same general purpose. We can, in short, see why nature is prodigal in variety, though niggard in innovation. But why this should be a law of nature if each species has been independently created no man can explain.

Many other facts are, as it seems to me, explicable on this theory. How strange it is that a bird, under the form of a woodpecker, should prey on insects on the ground; that upland geese which rarely or never swim, should possess webbed feet; that a thrush-like bird should dive and feed on sub-aquatic insects; and that a petrel should have the habits and structure fitting it for the life of an awk! and so in endless other cases. But on the view of each species constantly trying to increase in number, with natural selection always ready to adapt the slowly varying descendants of each to any unoccupied or ill-occupied place in nature, these facts cease to be strange, or might even have been anticipated.

We can to a certain extent understand how it is that there is so much beauty throughout nature; for this may be largely attributed to the agency of selection. That beauty, according to our sense of it, is not universal, must be admitted by every one who will look at some venomous snakes, at some fishes, and at certain hideous bats with a distorted resemblance to the human face. Sexual selection has given the most brilliant colours, elegant patterns, and other ornaments to the males, and sometimes to both sexes of many birds, butterflies, and other animals. With birds it has often rendered the voice of the male musical to the female, as well as to our ears. Flowers and fruit have been rendered conspicuous by brilliant colours in contrast with the green foliage, in order that the flowers may be readily seen, visited and fertilised by insects, and the seeds disseminated by birds. How it comes that certain colours, sounds, and forms should give pleasure to man and the lower animals,—that is, how the sense of beauty in its simplest form was first acquired,—we do not know any more than how certain odours and flavours were first rendered agreeable.

As natural selection acts by competition, it adapts and improves the inhabitants of each country only in relation to their co-inhabitants; so that we need feel no surprise at the species of any one country, although on the ordinary view supposed to have been created and specially adapted for that country, being beaten and supplanted by the naturalised productions from another land. Nor ought we to marvel if all the contrivances in nature be not, as far as we can judge, absolutely perfect, as in the case even of the human eye; or if some of them be abhorrent to our ideas of fitness. We need not marvel at the sting of the bee, when used against an enemy, causing the bee's own death; at drones being produced in such great numbers for one single act, and being then slaughtered by their sterile sisters; at the astonishing waste of pollen by our fir-trees; at the instinctive hatred of the queen-bee for her own fertile daughters; at the ichneumonidæ feeding within the living bodies of caterpillars; or at other such cases. The wonder indeed is, on the theory of natural selection, that more cases of the want of absolute perfection have not been detected.

The complex and little known laws governing the production of varieties are the same, as far as we can judge, with the laws which have governed the production of distinct species. In both cases physical conditions seem to have produced some direct and definite effect, but how much we cannot say. Thus, when varieties enter any new station, they occasionally assume some of the characters proper to the species of that station. With both varieties and species, use and disuse seem to have produced a considerable effect; for it is impossible to resist this conclusion when we look, for instance, at the logger-headed duck, which has wings incapable of flight, in nearly the same condition as in the domestic duck; or when we look at the burrowing tucu-tucu, which is occasionally blind, and then at certain moles, which are habitually blind and have their eyes covered with skin; or when we look at the blind animals inhabiting the dark caves of America and Europe. With varieties and species, correlated variation seems to have played an important part, so that when one part has been modified other parts have been necessarily modified. With both varieties and species, reversions to long-lost characters occasionally occur. How inexplicable on the theory of creation is the occasional appearance of stripes on the shoulders and legs of the several species of the horse-genus and of their hybrids! How simply is this fact explained if we believe that these species are all descended from a striped progenitor, in the same manner as the several domestic breeds of the pigeon are descended from the blue and barred rock-pigeon!

On the ordinary view of each species having been independently created, why should specific characters, or those by which the species of the same genus differ from each other, be more variable than generic characters in which they all agree? Why, for instance, should the colour of a flower be more likely to vary in any one species of a genus, if the other species possess differently coloured flowers, than if all possessed the same coloured flowers? If species are only well-marked varieties, of which the characters have become in a high degree permanent, we can understand this fact; for they have already varied since they branched off from a common progenitor in certain characters, by which they have come to be specifically distinct from each other; therefore these same characters would be more likely again to vary than the generic characters which have been inherited without change for an immense period. It is inexplicable on the theory of creation why a part developed in a very unusual manner in one species alone of a genus, and therefore, as we may naturally infer, of great importance to that species, should be eminently liable to variation; but, on our view, this part has undergone, since the several species branched off from a common progenitor, an unusual amount of variability and modification, and therefore we might expect the part generally to be still variable. But a part may be developed in the most unusual manner, like the wing of a bat, and yet not be more variable than any other structure, if the part be common to many subordinate forms, that is, if it has been inherited for a very long period; for in this case, it will have been rendered constant by long-continued natural selection.

Glancing at instincts, marvellous as some are, they offer no greater difficulty than do corporeal structures on the theory of the natural selection of successive slight, but profitable modifications. We can thus understand why nature moves by graduated steps in endowing different animals of the same class with their several instincts. I have attempted to show how much light the principle of gradation throws on the admirable architectural powers of the hive-bee. Habit no doubt often comes into play in modifying instincts; but it certainly is not indispensable, as we see in the case of neuter insects, which leave no progeny to inherit the effects of long-continued habit. On the view of all the species of the same genus having descended from a common parent, and having inherited much in common, we can understand how it is that allied species, when placed under widely different conditions of life, yet follow nearly the same instincts; why the thrushes of tropical and temperate South America, for instance, line their nests with mud like our British species. On the view of instincts having been slowly acquired through natural selection, we need not marvel at some instincts being not perfect and liable to mistakes, and at many instincts causing other animals to suffer.

If species be only well-marked and permanent varieties, we can at once see why their crossed offspring should follow the same complex laws in their degrees and kinds of resemblance to their parents,—in being absorbed into each other by successive crosses, and in other such points,—as do the crossed offspring of acknowledged varieties. This similarity would be a strange fact, if species had been independently created and varieties had been produced through secondary laws.

If we admit that the geological record is imperfect to an extreme degree, then the facts, which the record does give, strongly support the theory of descent with modification. New species have come on the stage slowly and at successive intervals; and the amount of change, after equal intervals of time, is widely different in different groups. The extinction of species and of whole groups of species which has played so conspicuous a part in the history of the organic world, almost inevitably follows from the principle of natural selection; for old forms are supplanted by new and improved forms. Neither single species nor groups of species reappear when the chain of ordinary generation is once broken. The gradual diffusion of dominant forms, with the slow modification of their descendants, causes the forms of life, after long intervals of time, to appear as if they had changed simultaneously throughout the world. The fact of the fossil remains of each formation being in some degree intermediate in character between the fossils in the formations above and below, is simply explained by their intermediate position in the chain of descent. The grand fact that all extinct beings can be classed with all recent beings, naturally follows from the living and the extinct being the offspring of common parents. As species have generally diverged in character during their long course of descent and modification, we can understand why it is that the more ancient forms, or early progenitors of each group, so often occupy a position in some degree intermediate between existing groups. Recent forms are generally looked upon as being, on the whole, higher in the scale of organisation than ancient forms; and they must be higher, in so far as the later and more improved forms have conquered the older and less improved forms in the struggle for life; they have also generally had their organs more specialised for different functions. This fact is perfectly compatible with numerous beings still retaining simple and but little improved structures, fitted for simple conditions of life; it is likewise compatible with some forms having retrograded in organisation, by having become at each stage of descent better fitted for new and degraded habits of life. Lastly, the wonderful law of the long endurance of allied forms on the same continent,—of marsupials in Australia, of edentata in America, and other such cases,—is intelligible, for within the same country the existing and the extinct will be closely allied by descent.

Looking to geographical distribution, if we admit that there has been during the long course of ages much migration from one part of the world to another, owing to former climatal and geographical changes and to the many occasional and unknown means of dispersal, then we can understand, on the theory of descent with modification, most of the great leading facts in Distribution. We can see why there should be so striking a parallelism in the distribution of organic beings throughout space, and in their geological succession throughout time; for in both cases the beings have been connected by the bond of ordinary generation, and the means of modification have been the same. We see the full meaning of the wonderful fact, which has struck every traveller, namely, that on the same continent, under the most diverse conditions, under heat and cold, on mountain and lowland, on deserts and marshes, most of the inhabitants within each great class are plainly related; for they are the descendants of the same progenitors and early colonists. On this same principle of former migration, combined in most cases with modification, we can understand, by the aid of the Glacial period, the identity of some few plants, and the close alliance of many others, on the most distant mountains, and in the northern and southern temperate zones; and likewise the close alliance of some of the inhabitants of the sea in the northern and southern temperate latitudes, though separated by the whole intertropical ocean. Although two countries may present physical conditions as closely similar as the same species ever require, we need feel no surprise at their inhabitants being widely different, if they have been for a long period completely sundered from each other; for as the relation of organism to organism is the most important of all relations, and as the two countries will have received colonists at various periods and in different proportions, from some other country or from each other, the course of modification in the two areas will inevitably have been different.

On this view of migration, with subsequent modification, we see why oceanic islands are inhabited by only few species, but of these, why many are peculiar or endemic forms. We clearly see why species belonging to those groups of animals which cannot cross wide spaces of the ocean, as frogs and terrestrial mammals, do not inhabit oceanic islands; and why, on the other hand, new and peculiar species of bats, animals which can traverse the ocean, are found on islands far distant from any continent. Such cases as the presence of peculiar species of bats on oceanic islands and the absence of all other terrestrial mammals, are facts utterly inexplicable on the theory of independent acts of creation.

The existence of closely allied or representative species in any two areas, implies, on the theory of descent with modification, that the same parent-forms formerly inhabited both areas; and we almost invariably find that wherever many closely allied species inhabit two areas, some identical species are still common to both. Wherever many closely allied yet distinct species occur, doubtful forms and varieties belonging to the same groups likewise occur. It is a rule of high generality that the inhabitants of each area are related to the inhabitants of the nearest source whence immigrants might have been derived. We see this in the striking relation of nearly all plants and animals of the Galapagos Archipelago, of Juan Fernandez, and of the other American islands, to the plants and animals of the neighbouring American mainland; and of those of the Cape de Verde Archipelago, and of the other African islands to the African mainland. It must be admitted that these facts receive no explanation on the theory of creation.

The fact, as we have seen, that all past and present organic beings can be arranged within a few great classes, in groups subordinate to groups, and with the extinct groups often falling in between the recent groups, is intelligible on the theory of natural selection with its contingencies of extinction and divergence of character. On these same principles we see how it is, that the mutual affinities of the forms within each class are so complex and circuitous. We see why certain characters are far more serviceable than others for classification;—why adaptive characters, though of paramount importance to the beings, are of hardly any importance in classification; why characters derived from rudimentary parts, though of no service to the beings, are often of high classificatory value; and why embryological characters are often the most valuable of all. The real affinities of all organic beings, in contradistinction to their adaptive resemblances, are due to inheritance or community of descent. The Natural System is a genealogical arrangement, with the acquired grades of difference, marked by the terms, varieties, species, genera, families, &c.; and we have to discover the lines of descent by the most permanent characters whatever they may be and of however slight vital importance.

The similar framework of bones in the hand of a man, wing of a bat, fin of the porpoise, and leg of the horse,—the same number of vertebræ forming the neck of the giraffe and of the elephant,—and innumerable other such facts, at once explain themselves on the theory of descent with slow and slight successive modifications. The similarity of pattern in the wing and in the leg of a bat, though used for such different purpose,—in the jaws and legs of a crab,—in the petals, stamens, and pistils of a flower, is likewise, to a large extent, intelligible on the view of the gradual modification of parts or organs, which were aboriginally alike in an early progenitor in each of these classes. On the principle of successive variations not always supervening at an early age, and being inherited at a corresponding not early period of life, we clearly see why the embryos of mammals, birds, reptiles, and fishes should be so closely similar, and so unlike the adult forms. We may cease marvelling at the embryo of an air-breathing mammal or bird having branchial slits and arteries running in loops, like those of a fish which has to breathe the air dissolved in water by the aid of well-developed branchiæ.

Disuse, aided sometimes by natural selection, will often have reduced organs when rendered useless under changed habits or conditions of life; and we can understand on this view the meaning of rudimentary organs. But disuse and selection will generally act on each creature, when it has come to maturity and has to play its full part in the struggle for existence, and will thus have little power on an organ during early life; hence the organ will not be reduced or rendered rudimentary at this early age. The calf, for instance, has inherited teeth, which never cut through the gums of the upper jaw, from an early progenitor having well-developed teeth; and we may believe, that the teeth in the mature animal were formerly reduced by disuse, owing to the tongue and palate, or lips, having become excellently fitted through natural selection to browse without their aid; whereas in the calf, the teeth have been left unaffected, and on the principle of inheritance at corresponding ages have been inherited from a remote period to the present day. On the view of each organism with all its separate parts having been specially created, how utterly inexplicable is it that organs bearing the plain stamp of inutility, such as the teeth in the embryonic calf or the shrivelled wings under the soldered wing-covers of many beetles, should so frequently occur. Nature may be said to have taken pains to reveal her scheme of modification, by means of rudimentary organs, of embryological and homologous structures, but we are too blind to understand her meaning.

I have now recapitulated the facts and considerations which have thoroughly convinced me that species have been modified, during a long course of descent. This has been effected chiefly through the natural selection of numerous successive, slight, favourable variations; aided in an important manner by the inherited effects of the use and disuse of parts; and in an unimportant manner, that is in relation to adaptive structures, whether past or present, by the direct action of external conditions, and by variations which seem to us in our ignorance to arise spontaneously. It appears that I formerly underrated the frequency and value of these latter forms of variation, as leading to permanent modifications of structure independently of natural selection. But as my conclusions have lately been much misrepresented, and it has been stated that I attribute the modification of species exclusively to natural selection, I may be permitted to remark that in the first edition of this work, and subsequently, I placed in a most conspicuous position—namely, at the close of the Introduction—the following words: 'I am convinced that natural selection has been the main but not the exclusive means of modification.' This has been of no avail. Great is the power of steady misrepresentation; but the history of science shows that fortunately this power does not long endure.

It can hardly be supposed that a false theory would explain, in so satisfactory a manner as does the theory of natural selection, the several large classes of facts above specified. It has recently been objected that this is an unsafe method of arguing; but it is a method used in judging of the common events of life, and has often been used by the greatest natural philosophers. The undulatory theory of light has thus been arrived at; and the belief in the revolution of the earth on its own axis was until lately supported by hardly any direct evidence. It is no valid objection that science as yet throws no light on the far higher problem of the essence or origin of life. Who can explain what is the essence of the attraction of gravity? No one now objects to following out the results consequent on this unknown element of attraction; notwithstanding that Leibnitz formerly accused Newton of introducing 'occult qualities and miracles into philosophy'.

I see no good reason why the views given in this volume should shock the religious feelings of any one. It is satisfactory, as showing how transient such impressions are, to remember that the greatest discovery ever made by man, namely, the law of the attraction of gravity, was also attacked by Leibnitz, 'as subversive of natural, and inferentially of revealed, religion'. A celebrated author and divine has written to me that 'he has gradually learnt to see that it is just as noble a conception of the

Deity to believe that He created a few original forms capable of self-development into other and needful forms, as to believe that He required a fresh act of creation to supply the voids caused by the action of His laws.'

Why, it may be asked, until recently did nearly all the most eminent living naturalists and geologists disbelieve in the mutability of species? It cannot be asserted that organic beings in a state of nature are subject to no variation; it cannot be proved that the amount of variation in the course of long ages is a limited quality; no clear distinction has been, or can be, drawn between species and well-marked varieties. It cannot be maintained that species when intercrossed are invariably sterile, and varieties invariably fertile; or that sterility is a special endowment and sign of creation. The belief that species were immutable productions was almost unavoidable as long as the history of the world was thought to be of short duration; and now that we have acquired some idea of the lapse of time, we are too apt to assume, without proof, that the geological record is so perfect that it would have afforded us plain evidence of the mutation of species, if they had undergone mutation.

But the chief cause of our natural unwillingness to admit that one species has given birth to clear and distinct species, is that we are always slow in admitting great changes of which we do not see the steps. The difficulty is the same as that felt by so many geologists, when Lyell first insisted that long lines of inland cliffs had been formed, and great valleys excavated, by the agencies which we see still at work. The mind cannot possibly grasp the full meaning of the term of even a million years; it cannot add up and perceive the full effects of many slight variations, accumulated during an almost infinite number of generations.

Although I am fully convinced of the truth of the views given in this volume under the form of an abstract, I by no means expect to convince experienced naturalists whose minds are stocked with a multitude of facts all viewed, during a long course of years, from a point of view directly opposite to mine. It is so easy to hide our ignorance under such expressions as the 'plan of creation', 'unity of design', &c., and to think that we give an explanation when we only re-state a fact. Any one whose disposition leads him to attach more weight to unexplained difficulties than to the explanation of a certain number of facts will certainly reject the theory. A few naturalists, endowed with much flexibility of mind, and who have already begun to doubt the immutability of species, may be influenced by this volume; but I look with confidence to the future,—to young and rising naturalists, who will be able to view both sides of the question with impartiality. Whoever is led to believe that species are mutable will do good service by conscientiously expressing his conviction; for thus only can the load of prejudice by which this subject is overwhelmed be removed.

Several eminent naturalists have of late published their belief that a multitude of reputed species in each genus are not real species; but that other species are real, that is, have been independently created. This seems to me a strange conclusion to arrive at. They admit that a multitude of forms, which till lately they themselves thought were special creations, and which are still thus looked at by the majority of naturalists, and which consequently have all the external characteristic features of true species,—they admit that these have been produced by variation, but they refuse to extend the same view to other and slightly different forms. Nevertheless they do not pretend that they can define, or even conjecture, which are the created forms of life, and which are those produced by secondary laws. They admit variation as a *vera causa* in one case, they arbitrarily reject it in another, without assigning any distinction in the two cases. The day will come when this will be given as a curious illustration of the blindness of preconceived opinion. These authors seem no more startled at a miraculous act of creation than at an ordinary birth. But do they really believe that at innumerable periods in the earth's history certain elemental atoms have been commanded suddenly to flash into living tissues? Do they believe that at each supposed act of creation one individual or many were produced? Were all the infinitely numerous kinds of animals and plants created as eggs or seed, or as full grown? and in the case of mammals, were they created bearing the false marks of nourishment from the mother's womb? Undoubtedly some of these same questions cannot be answered by those who believe in the appearance of creation of only a few forms of life, or of some one form alone. It has been maintained by several authors that it is as easy to believe in the creation of a million beings as of one; but Maupertuis' philosophical axiom 'of least action' leads the mind more willingly to admit the smaller number; and certainly we ought not to believe that innumerable beings within each great class have been created with plain, but deceptive, marks of descent from a single parent.

As a record of a former state of things, I have retained in the foregoing paragraphs, and elsewhere, several sentences which imply that naturalists believe in the separate creation of each species; and I have been much censured for having thus expressed myself. But undoubtedly this was the general belief when the first edition of the present work appeared. I formerly spoke to very many naturalists on the subject of evolution, and never once met with any sympathetic agreement. It is probable that some did then believe in evolution, but they were either silent, or expressed themselves so ambiguously that it was not easy to understand their meaning. Now things are wholly changed, and almost every naturalist admits the great principle of evolution. There are, however, some who still think that species have suddenly given birth, through quite unexplained means, to new and totally different forms: but, as I have attempted to show, weighty evidence can be opposed to the admission of great and abrupt modifications. Under a scientific point of view, and as leading to further investigation, but little advantage is gained by believing that new forms are suddenly developed in an inexplicable manner from old and widely different forms, over the old belief in the creation of species from the dust of the earth.

It may be asked how far I extend the doctrine of the modification of species. The question is difficult to answer, because the more distinct the forms are which we consider, by so much the arguments in favour of community of descent become fewer in number and less in force. But some arguments of the greatest weight extend very far. All the members of whole classes are connected together by a chain of affinities, and all can be classed on the same principle, in groups subordinate to groups. Fossil remains sometimes tend to fill up very wide intervals between existing orders.

Organs in a rudimentary condition plainly show that an early progenitor had the organ in a fully developed condition; and this in some cases implies an enormous amount of modification in the descendants. Throughout whole classes various structures are formed on the same pattern, and at a very early age the embryos closely resemble each other. Therefore I cannot doubt that the theory of descent with modification embraces all the members of the same great class or kingdom. I believe that animals are descended from at most only four or five progenitors, and plants from an equal or lesser number.

Analogy would lead me one step farther, namely, to the belief that all animals and plants are descended from some one prototype. But analogy may be a deceitful guide. Nevertheless all living things have much in common, in their chemical composition, their cellular structure, their laws of growth, and their liability to injurious influences. We see this even in so trifling a fact as that the same poison often similarly affects plants and animals; or that the poison secreted by the gall-fly produces monstrous growths on the wild rose or oak-tree. With all organic beings excepting perhaps some of the very lowest, sexual production seems to be essentially similar. With all, as far as is at present known the germinal vesicle is the same; so that all organisms start from a common origin. If we look even to the two main divisions—namely, to the animal and vegetable kingdoms—certain low forms are so far intermediate in character that naturalists have disputed to which kingdom they should be referred. As Professor Asa Gray has remarked, 'the spores and other reproductive bodies of many of the lower algæ may claim to have first a characteristically animal, and then an unequivocally vegetable existence.' Therefore, on the principle of natural selection with divergence of character, it does not seem incredible that, from such low and intermediate form, both animals and plants may have been developed; and, if we admit this, we must likewise admit that all the organic beings which have ever lived on this earth may be descended from some one primordial form. But this inference is chiefly grounded on analogy and it is immaterial whether or not it be accepted. No doubt it is possible, as Mr. G. H. Lewes has urged, that at the first commencement of life many different forms were evolved; but if so we may conclude that only a very few have left modified descendants. For, as I have recently remarked in regard to the members of each great kingdom, such as the Vertebrata Articulata &c., we have distinct evidence in their embryological, homologous, and rudimentary structures, that within each kingdom all the members are descended from a single progenitor.

When the views advanced by me in this volume, and by Mr. Wallace, or when analogous views on the origin of species are generally admitted, we can dimly foresee that there will be a considerable revolution in natural history. Systematists will be able to pursue their labours as at present; but they will not be incessantly haunted by the shadowy doubt whether this or that form be a true species. This, I feel sure and I speak after experience, will be no slight relief. The endless disputes whether or not some fifty species of British brambles are good species will cease. Systematists will have only to decide (not that this will be easy) whether any form be sufficiently constant and distant from other forms, to be capable of definition; and if definable, whether the differences be sufficiently important to deserve a specific name. This latter point will become a far more essential consideration than it is at present; for differences, however slight, between any two forms if not blended by intermediate gradations, are looked at by most naturalists as sufficient to raise both forms to the rank of species.

Hereafter we shall be compelled to acknowledge that the only distinction between species and well-marked varieties is, that the latter are known, or believed, to be connected at the present day by intermediate gradations, whereas species were formerly thus connected. Hence, without rejecting the consideration of the present existence of intermediate gradations between any two forms we shall be led to weigh more carefully and to value higher the actual amount of difference between them. It is quite possible that forms now generally acknowledged to be merely varieties may hereafter be thought worthy of specific names; and in this case scientific and common language will come into accordance. In short, we shall have to treat species in the same manner as those naturalists treat genera, who admit that genera are merely artificial combinations made for convenience. This may not be a cheering prospect; but we shall at least be free from the vain search for the undiscovered and undiscoverable essence of the term species.

The other and more general departments of natural history will rise greatly in interest. The terms used by naturalists, of affinity, relationship, community of type, paternity, morphology, adaptive characters, rudimentary and aborted organs, &c., will cease to be metaphorical, and will have a plain signification. When we no longer look at an organic being as a savage looks at a ship, as something wholly beyond his comprehension; when we regard every production of nature as one which has had a long history; when we contemplate every complex structure and instinct as the summing up of many contrivances, each useful to the possessor, in the same way as any great mechanical invention is the summing up of the labour, the experience, the reason, and even the blunders of numerous workmen; when we thus view each organic being, how far more interesting—I speak from experience—does the study of natural history become!

A grand and almost untrodden field of inquiry will be opened, on the causes and laws of variation, on correlation, on the effects of use and disuse, on the direct action of external conditions, and so forth. The study of domestic productions will rise immensely in value. A new variety raised by man will be a more important and interesting subject for study than one more species added to the infinitude of already recorded species. Our classifications will come to be, as far as they can be so made, genealogies; and will then truly give what may be called the plan of creation. The rules for classifying will no doubt become simpler when we have a definite object in view. We possess no pedigrees or armorial bearings; and we have to discover and trace the many diverging lines of descent in our natural genealogies, by characters of any kind which have long been inherited. Rudimentary organs will speak infallibly with respect to the nature of long-lost structures. Species and groups of species which are called aberrant, and which may fancifully be called living fossils, will aid us in forming a picture of the ancient forms of life. Embryology will often reveal to us the structure, in some degree obscured, of the prototype of each great class.

When we feel assured that all the individuals of the same species, and all the closely allied species of most genera, have within a not very remote period descended from one parent, and have migrated from some one birth-place; and when we better know the many means of migration, then, by the light which geology now throws, and will continue to throw, on former changes of climate and of the level of the land, we shall surely be enabled to trace in an admirable manner the former migrations of the inhabitants of the whole world. Even at present, by comparing the differences between the inhabitants of the sea on the opposite sides of a continent, and the nature of the various inhabitants on that continent, in relation to their apparent means of immigration, some light can be thrown on ancient geography.

The noble science of Geology loses glory from the extreme imperfection of the record. The crust of the earth with its imbedded remains must not be looked at as a well-filled museum, but as a poor collection made at hazard and at rare intervals. The accumulation of each great fossiliferous formation will be recognised as having depended on an unusual concurrence of favourable circumstances, and the blank intervals between the successive stages as having been of vast duration. But we shall be able to gauge with some security the duration of these intervals by a comparison of the preceding and succeeding organic forms. We must be cautious in attempting to correlate as strictly contemporaneous two formations, which do not include many identical species, by the general succession of the forms of life. As species are produced and exterminated by slowly acting and still existing causes, and not by miraculous acts of creation; and as the most important of all causes of organic change is one which is almost independent of altered and perhaps suddenly altered physical conditions, namely, the mutual relation of organism to organism,—the improvement of one organism entailing the improvement or the extermination of others; it follows, that the amount of organic change in the fossils of consecutive formations probably serves as a fair measure of the relative though not actual lapse of time. A number of species, however, keeping in a body might remain for a long period unchanged, whilst within the same period several of these species by migrating into new countries and coming into competition with foreign associates, might become modified; so that we must not overrate the accuracy of organic change as a measure of time.

In the future I see open fields for far more important researches. Psychology will be securely based on the foundation already well laid by Mr. Herbert Spencer, that of the necessary acquirement of each mental power and capacity by gradation. Much light will be thrown on the origin of man and his history.

Authors of the highest eminence seem to be fully satisfied with the view that each species has been independently created. To my mind it accords better with what we know of the laws impressed on matter by the Creator, that the production and extinction of the past and present inhabitants of the world should have been due to secondary causes, like those determining the birth and death of the individual. When I view all beings not as special creations, but as the lineal descendants of some few beings which lived long before the first bed of the Cambrian system was deposited, they seem to me to become ennobled. Judging from the past, we may safely infer that not one living species will transmit its unaltered likeness to a distant futurity. And of the species now living very few will transmit progeny of any kind to a far distant futurity; for the manner in which all organic beings are grouped, shows that the greater number of species in each genus, and all the species in many genera, have left no descendants, but have become utterly extinct. We can so far take a prophetic glance into futurity as to foretell that it will be the common and widely-spread species, belonging to the larger and dominant groups within each class, which will ultimately prevail and procreate new and dominant species. As all the living forms of life are the lineal descendants of those which lived long before the Cambrian epoch, we may feel certain that the ordinary succession by generation has never once been broken, and that no cataclysm has desolated the whole world. Hence we may look with some confidence to a secure future of great length. And as natural selection works solely by and for the good of each being, all corporeal and mental endowments will tend to progress towards perfection.

It is interesting to contemplate a tangled bank, clothed with many plants of many kinds, with birds singing on the bushes, with various insects flitting about, and with worms crawling through the damp earth, and to reflect that these elaborately constructed forms, so different from each other, and dependent upon each other in so complex a manner, have all been produced by laws acting around us. These laws, taken in the largest sense, being Growth with Reproduction; Inheritance which is almost implied by reproduction; Variability from the indirect and direct action of the conditions of life, and from use and disuse: a Ratio of Increase so high as to lead to a Struggle for Life, and as a consequence to Natural Selection, entailing Divergence of Character and the Extinction of less improved forms. Thus, from the war of nature, from famine and death, the most exalted object which we are capable of conceiving, namely, the production of the higher animals, directly follows. There is grandeur in this view of life, with its several powers, having been originally breathed by the Creator into a few forms or into one; and that, whilst this planet has gone cycling on according to the fixed law of gravity, from so simple a beginning endless forms most beautiful and most wonderful have been, and are being evolved.

PART FOUR

THE DESCENT OF MAN

CHAPTER 12

OUTLINE OF THE EVIDENCE

[Extracts from the first four chapters of *The Descent of Man and Selection in Relation to Sex*. This book was first published in 1871, in two volumes. Although Darwin had from the first presumed that the ideas of natural selection and evolution would apply to man as well as to the rest of nature, he refrained from mentioning the subject in the *Origin* beyond noting that by this theory 'light would be thrown on the origin of man and his history'. The human implications of the *Origin* were of course self-evident, and the cause of much of the immediate controversy. In 1863, Huxley published his great book, *Evidence of Man's Place in Nature*, in which the implications were spelled out. When Darwin finally got around to writing his own book about man, the ideas were neither surprising nor shocking.

As has often been pointed out, the *Descent* is really two books—a rather short essay on human evolution carrying the burden of a long digression on the secondary sexual characteristics of animals from which a theory of sexual selection is developed. For present purposes, we have cut most of this digression on sexual characters, leaving only the general statement of theory and a few examples from the chapters on birds. The emphasis in the present anthology is thus different from that in the original, but we feel that Darwin's ideas and observations on man hold most interest for the general reader.]

HE who wishes to decide whether man is the modified descendant of some pre-existing form, would probably first enquire whether man varies, however slightly, in bodily structure and in mental faculties; and if so, whether the variations are transmitted to his offspring in accordance with the laws which prevail with the lower animals. Again, are the variations the result, as far as our ignorance permits us to judge, of the same general causes, and are they governed by the same general laws, as in the case of other organisms; for instance, by correlation, the inherited effects of use and disuse, &c.? Is man subject to similar malconformations, the result of arrested development, of reduplication of parts, &c., and does he display in any of his anomalies reversion to some former and ancient type of structure? It might also naturally be enquired whether man, like so many other animals, has given rise to varieties and sub-races, differing but slightly from each other, or to races differing so much that they must be classed as doubtful species? How are such races distributed over the world; and how, when crossed, do they react on each other in the first and succeeding generations? And so with many other points.

The enquirer would next come to the important point, whether man tends to increase at so rapid a rate, as to lead to occasional severe struggles for existence; and consequently to beneficial variations, whether in body or mind, being preserved, and injurious ones eliminated. Do the races or species of men, whichever term may be applied, encroach on and replace one another, so that some finally become extinct? We shall see that all these questions, as indeed is obvious in respect to most of them, must be answered in the affirmative, in the same manner as with the lower animals. But the several considerations just referred to may be conveniently deferred for a time: and we will first see how far the bodily structure of man shows traces, more or less plain, of his descent from some lower form. In succeeding chapters the mental powers of man, in comparison with those of the lower animals, will be considered.

THE BODILY STRUCTURE OF MAN

It is notorious that man is constructed on the same general type or model as other mammals. All the bones in his skeleton can be compared with corresponding bones in a monkey, bat, or seal. So it is with his muscles, nerves, blood-vessels and internal viscera. The brain, the most important of all the organs, follows the same law, as shewn by Huxley and other anatomists. Bischoff, who is a hostile witness, admits that every chief fissure and fold in the brain of man has its analogy in that of the orang; but he adds that at no period of development do their brains perfectly agree; nor could perfect agreement be expected, for otherwise their mental powers would have been the same.

* * * *

It may, however, be worth while to specify a few points, not directly or obviously connected with structure, by which this correspondence or relationship is well shewn.

* * * *

The whole process of that most important function, the reproduction of the species, is strikingly the same in all mammals, from the first act of courtship by the male, to the birth and nurturing of the young. Monkeys are born in almost as helpless a condition as our own infants; and in certain genera the young differ fully as much in appearance from the adults, as do our children from their full-grown parents. It has been urged by some writers, as an important distinction, that with man the young arrive at maturity at a much later age than with any other animal: but if we look to the races of mankind which inhabit tropical countries the difference is not great, for the orang is believed not to be adult till the age of from ten to fifteen years. Man differs from woman in size, bodily strength, hairiness, &c., as well as in mind, in the same manner as do the two sexes of many mammals. So that the correspondence in general structure, in the minute structure of the tissues, in chemical composition and in constitution, between man and the higher animals, especially the anthropomorphous apes, is extremely close.

EMBRYONIC DEVELOPMENT

Man is developed from an ovule, about the 125th of an inch in diameter, which differs in no respect from the ovules of other animals. The embryo itself at a very early period can hardly be distinguished from that of other members of the vertebrate kingdom. At this period the arteries run in arch-like branches, as if to carry the blood to branchiæ which are not present in the higher vertebrata, though the slits on the sides of the neck still remain, marking their former position. At a somewhat later period, when the extremities are developed, 'the feet of lizards and mammals,' as the illustrious Von Baer remarks, 'the wings and feet of birds, no less than the hands and feet of man, all arise from the same fundamental form.' It is, says Prof. Huxley, 'quite in the later stages of development that the young human being presents marked differences from the young ape, while the latter departs as much from the dog in its developments, as the man does. Startling as this last assertion may appear to be, it is demonstrably true.'

* * * *

After the foregoing statements made by such high authorities, it would be superfluous on my part to give a number of borrowed details, shewing that the embryo of man closely resembles that of other mammals. It may, however, be added, that the human embryo likewise resembles certain low forms when adult in various points of structure. For instance, the heart at first exists as a simple pulsating vessel; the excreta are voided through a cloacal passage; and the os coccyx projects like a true tail, 'extending considerably beyond the rudimentary legs'. In the embryos of all air-breathing vertebrates, certain glands, called the corpora Wolffiana, correspond with, and act like the kidneys of mature fishes. Even at a later embryonic period, some striking resemblances between man and the lower animals may be observed. Bischoff says 'that the convolutions of the brain in a human fœtus at the end of the seventh month reach about the same stage of development as in a baboon when adult'. The great toe, as Professor Owen remarks, 'which forms the fulcrum when standing or walking, is perhaps the most characteristic peculiarity in the human structure', but in an embryo, about an inch in length, Prof. Wyman found 'that the great toe was shorter than the others; and, instead of being parallel to them, projected at an angle from the side of the foot, thus corresponding with the permanent condition of this part in the quadrumana'. I will conclude with a quotation from Huxley, who after asking, does man originate in a different way from a dog, bird, frog or fish? says, 'the reply is not doubtful for a moment; without question, the mode of origin, and the early stages of the development of man, are identical with those of the animals immediately below him in the scale: without a doubt in these respects, he is far nearer to apes than the apes are to the dog.'

RUDIMENTS

This subject, though not intrinsically more important than the two last, will for several reasons be treated here more fully. Not one of the higher animals can be named which does not bear some part in a rudimentary condition; and man forms no exception to the rule. Rudimentary organs must be distinguished from those that are nascent; though in some cases the distinction is not easy. The former are either absolutely useless, such as the mammæ of male quadrupeds, or the incisor teeth of ruminants which never cut through the gums; or they are of such slight service to their present possessors, that we can hardly suppose that they were developed under the conditions which now exist. Organs in this latter state are not strictly rudimentary, but they are tending in this direction. Nascent organs, on the other hand, though not fully developed, are of high service to their possessors, and are capable of further development. Rudimentary organs are eminently variable; and this is partly intelligible, as they are useless, or nearly useless, and consequently are no longer subjected to natural selection. They often become wholly suppressed. When this occurs, they are nevertheless liable to occasional reappearance through reversion—a circumstance well worthy of attention. . . .

Rudiments of various muscles have been observed in many parts of the human body; and not a few muscles, which are regularly present in some of the lower animals can occasionally be detected in man in a greatly reduced condition.

★ ★ ★ ★

Some few persons have the power of contracting the superficial muscles on their scalps; and these muscles are in a variable and partially rudimentary condition. M. Alphonse de Candolle has communicated to me a curious instance of the long-continued persistence or inheritance of this power, as well as of its unusual development. He knows a family, in which one member, the present head of the family, could, when a youth, pitch several heavy books from his head by the movement of the scalp alone; and he won wagers by performing this feat. His father, uncle, grandfather, and his three children possess the same power to the same unusual degree. This family became divided eight generations ago into two branches; so that the head of the above-mentioned branch is cousin in the seventh degree to the head of the other branch. This distant cousin resides in another part of France; and on being asked whether he possessed the same faculty, immediately exhibited his power. This case offers a good illustration how persistent may be the transmission of an absolutely useless faculty, probably derived from our remote semi-human progenitors; since many monkeys have, and frequently use the power, of largely moving their scalps up and down.

★ ★ ★ ★

The nictitating membrane, or third eyelid, with its accessory muscles and other structures, is especially well developed in birds, and is of much functional importance to them, as it can be rapidly drawn across the whole eye-ball. It is found in some reptiles and amphibians, and in certain fishes, as in sharks. It is fairly well developed in the two lower divisions of the mammalian series, namely, in the monotremata and marsupials, and in some few of the higher mammals, as in the walrus. But in man, the quadrumana, and most other mammals, it exists, as is admitted by all anatomists, as a mere rudiment, called the semilunar fold.

★ ★ ★ ★

It appears as if the posterior molar or wisdom-teeth were tending to become rudimentary in the more civilised races of man. These teeth are rather smaller than the other molars, as is likewise the case with the corresponding teeth in the chimpanzee and orang; and they have only two separate fangs. They do not cut through the gums till about the seventeenth year, and I have been assured that they are much more liable to decay, and are earlier lost than the other teeth; but this is denied by some eminent dentists. They are also much more liable to vary, both in structure and in the period of their development, than the other teeth. In the Melanian races, on the other hand, the wisdom-teeth are usually furnished with three separate fangs, and are generally sound; they also differ from the other molars in size, less than in the Caucasian races. Prof. Schaaffhausen accounts for this difference between the races by 'the posterior dental portion of the jaw being always shortened' in those that are civilised, and this shortening may, I presume, be attributed to civilised men habitually feeding on soft, cooked food, and thus using their jaws less. I am informed by Mr. Brace that it is becoming quite a common practice in the United States to remove some of the molar teeth of children, as the jaw does not grow large enough for the perfect development of the normal number.

With respect to the alimentary canal, I have met with an account of only a single rudiment, namely the vermiform appendage of the cæcum. The cæcum is a branch or diverticulum of the intestine, ending in a cul-de-sac, and is extremely long in many of the lower vegetable-feeding mammals. In the marsupial koala it is actually more than thrice as long as the whole body. It is sometimes produced into a long gradually-tapering point, and is sometimes constricted in parts. It appears as if, in consequence of changed diet or habits, the cæcum had become much shortened in various animals, the vermiform appendage being left as a rudiment of the shortened part. That this appendage is a rudiment, we may infer from its small size, and from the evidence which Prof. Canestrini has collected of its variability in man. It is occasionally quite absent, or again is largely developed. The passage is sometimes completely closed for half or two-thirds of its length, with the terminal part consisting of a flattened solid expansion. In the orang this appendage is long and convoluted: in man it arises from the end of the short cæcum, and is commonly from four to five inches in length, being only about the third of an inch in diameter. Not only is it useless, but it is sometimes the cause of death, of which fact I have lately heard two instances: this is due to small hard bodies, such as seeds, entering the passage, and causing inflammation.

* * * *

In man, the os coccyx, together with certain other vertebræ hereafter to be described, though functionless as a tail, plainly represent this part in other vertebrate animals. At an early embryonic period it is free, and projects beyond the lower extremities; as may be seen in the drawing of a human embryo. Even after birth it has been known, in certain rare and anomalous cases, to form a small external rudiment of a tail. The os coccyx is short, usually including only four vertebræ, all anchylosed together: and these are in a rudimentary condition, for they consist, with the exception of the basal one, of the centrum alone. They are furnished with some small muscles; one of which, as I am informed by Prof. Turner, has been expressly described by Theile as a rudimentary repetition of the extensor of the tail, a muscle which is so largely developed in many mammals.

* * * *

The bearing of the three great classes of facts now given is unmistakable. But it would be superfluous fully to recapitulate the line of argument given in detail in my *Origin of Species*. The homological construction of the whole frame in the members of the same class is intelligible, if we admit their descent from a common progenitor, together with their subsequent adaptation to diversified conditions. On any other view, the similarity of pattern between the hand of a man or monkey, the foot of a horse, the flipper of a seal, the wing of a bat, &c., is utterly inexplicable. It is no scientific explanation to assert that they have all been formed on the same ideal plan. With respect to development, we can clearly understand, on the principle of variation supervening at a rather late embryonic period, and being inherited at a corresponding period, how it is that the embryos of wonderfully different forms should still retain, more or less perfectly, the structure of their common progenitor. No other explanation has ever been given of the marvellous fact that the embryos of a man, dog, seal, bat, reptile, &c., can at first hardly be distinguished from each other. In order to understand the existence of rudimentary organs, we have only to suppose that a former progenitor possessed the parts in question in a perfect state, and that under changed habits of life they became greatly reduced, either from simple disuse, or through the natural selection of those individuals which were least encumbered with a superfluous part, aided by the other means previously indicated.

Thus we can understand how it has come to pass that man and all other vertebrate animals have been constructed on the same general model, why they pass through the same early stages of development, and why they retain certain rudiments in common. Consequently we ought frankly to admit their community of descent; to take any other view, is to admit that our own structure, and that of all the animals around us, is a mere snare laid to entrap our judgment. This conclusion is greatly strengthened, if we look to the members of the whole animal series, and consider the evidence derived from their affinities or classification, their geographical distribution and geological succession. It is only our natural prejudice, and that arrogance which made our forefathers declare that they were descended from demi-gods, which leads us to demur to this conclusion. But the time will before long come, when it will be thought wonderful that naturalists, who were well acquainted with the comparative structure and development of man, and other mammals, should have believed that each was the work of a separate act of creation.

ON THE MANNER OF DEVELOPMENT OF MAN FROM SOME LOWER FORM

It is manifest that man is now subject to much variability. No two individuals of the same race are quite alike. We may compare millions of faces, and each will be distinct. There is an equally great amount of diversity in the proportions and dimensions of the various parts of the body; the length of the legs being one of the most variable points. Although in some quarters of the world an elongated skull, and in other quarters a short skull prevails, yet there is great diversity of shape even within the limits of the same race, as with the aborigines of America and South Australia—the latter a race 'probably as pure and homogeneous in blood, customs, and language as any in existence'—and even with the inhabitants of so confined an area as the Sandwich Islands. An eminent dentist assures me that there is nearly as much diversity in the teeth as in the features. The chief arteries so frequently run in abnormal courses, that it has been found useful for surgical purposes to calculate from 1040 corpses how often each course prevails. The muscles are eminently variable: thus those of the foot were found by Prof. Turner not to be strictly alike in any two out of fifty bodies; and in some the deviations were considerable. He adds, that the power of performing the appropriate movements must have been modified in accordance with the several deviations. Mr. J. Wood has recorded the occurrence of 295 muscular variations in thirty-six subjects, and in another set of the same number no less than 558 variations, those occurring on both sides of the body being only reckoned as one.

* * * *

The variability or diversity of the mental faculties in men of the same race, not to mention the greater differences between men of distinct races, is so notorious that not a word need here be said. So it is with the lower animals. All who have had charge of menageries admit this fact, and we see it plainly in our dogs and other domestic animals. Brehm especially insists that each individual monkey of those which he kept tame in Africa had its own peculiar disposition and temper: he mentions one baboon remarkable for its high intelligence; and the keepers in the Zoological Gardens pointed out to me a monkey, belonging to the New World division, equally remarkable for intelligence. Rengger, also, insists on the diversity in the various mental characters of the monkeys of the same species which he kept in Paraguay; and this diversity, as he adds, is partly innate, and partly the result of the manner in which they have been treated or educated.

* * * *

With respect to the causes of variability, we are in all cases very ignorant; but we can see that in man as in the lower animals, they stand in some relation to the conditions to which each species has been exposed, during several generations. Domesticated animals vary more than those in a state of nature; and this is apparently due to the diversified and changing nature of the conditions to which they have been subjected. In this respect the different races of man resemble domesticated animals, and so do the individuals of the same race, when inhabiting a very wide area, like that of America. We see the influence of diversified conditions in the more civilised nations; for the members belonging to different grades of rank, and following different occupations, present a greater range of character than do the members of barbarous nations. But the uniformity of savages has often been exaggerated, and in some cases can hardly be said to exist. It is, nevertheless, an error to speak of man, even if we look only to the conditions to which he has been exposed, as 'far more domesticated' than any other animal. Some savage races, such as the Australians, are not exposed to more diversified conditions than are many species which have a wide range. In another and much more important respect, man differs widely from any strictly domesticated animal; for his breeding has never long been controlled, either by methodical or unconscious selection. No race or body of men has been so completely subjugated by other men, as that certain individuals should be preserved, and thus unconsciously selected, from somehow excelling in utility to their masters. Nor have certain male and female individuals been intentionally picked out and matched, except in the well-known case of the Prussian grenadiers; and in this case man obeyed, as might have been expected, the law of methodical selection; for it is asserted that many tall men were reared in the villages inhabited by the grenadiers and their tall wives. In Sparta, also, a form of selection was followed, for it was enacted that all children should be examined shortly after birth; the well-formed and vigorous being preserved, the others left to perish.

[Darwin then goes on to discuss the possible ways in which man could have evolved from some lower form: especially how the erect posture, hairless skin, manipulative skill with the hands, could have developed. The argument is summarized in the final part of Darwin's Chapter II, which follows.]

I have now endeavoured to shew that some of the most distinctive characters of man have in all probability been acquired, either directly, or more commonly indirectly, through natural selection. We should bear in mind that modifications in structure or constitution which do not serve to adapt an organism to its habits of life, to the food which it consumes, or passively to the surrounding conditions, cannot have been thus acquired. We must not, however, be too confident in deciding what modifications are of service to each being: we should remember how little we know about the use of many parts, or what changes in the blood or tissues may serve to fit an organism for a new climate or new kinds of food. Nor must we forget the principle of correlation, by which, as Isidore Geoffroy has shewn in the case of man, many strange deviations of structure are tied together. Independently of correlation, a change in one part often leads, through the increased or decreased use of other parts, to other changes of a quite unexpected nature. It is also well to reflect on such facts, as the wonderful growth of galls on plants caused by the poison of an insect, and on the remarkable changes of colour in the plumage of parrots when fed on certain fishes, or inoculated with the poison of toads; for we can thus see that the fluids of the system, if altered for some special purpose, might induce other changes. We should especially bear in mind that modifications acquired and continually used during past ages for some useful purpose, would probably become firmly fixed, and might be long inherited.

Thus a large yet undefined extension may safely be given to the direct and indirect results of natural selection; but I now admit, after reading the essay by Nägeli on plants, and the remarks by various authors with respect to animals, more especially those recently made by Professor Broca, that in the earlier editions of my *Origin of Species* I perhaps attributed too much to the action of natural selection or the survival of the fittest. I have altered the fifth edition of the *Origin* so as to confine my remarks to adaptive changes of structure; but I am convinced, from the light gained during even the last few years, that very many structures which now appear to us useless, will hereafter be proved to be useful, and will therefore come within the range of natural selection. Nevertheless, I did not formerly consider sufficiently the existence of structures, which, as far as we can at present judge, are neither beneficial nor injurious; and this I believe to be one of the greatest oversights as yet detected in my work. I may be permitted to say, as some excuse, that I had two distinct objects in view; firstly, to shew that species had not been separately created, and secondly, that natural selection had been the chief agent of change, though largely aided by the inherited effects of habit, and slightly by the direct action of the surrounding conditions. I was not, however, able to annul the influence of my former belief, then almost universal, that each species had been purposely created; and this led to my tacit assumption that every detail of structure, excepting rudiments, was of some special, though unrecognised, service. Any one with this assumption in his mind would naturally extend too far the action of natural selection, either during past or present times. Some of those who admit the principle of evolution, but reject natural selection, seem to forget, when criticising my book, that I had the above two objects in view; hence if I have erred in giving to natural selection great power, which I am very far from admitting, or in having exaggerated its power, which is in itself probable, I have at least, as I hope, done good service in aiding to overthrow the dogma of separate creations.

It is, as I can now see, probable that all organic beings, including man, possess peculiarities of structure, which neither are now, nor were formerly of any service to them, and which, therefore, are of no physiological importance. We know not what produces the numberless slight differences between the individuals of each species, for reversion only carries the problem a few steps backwards, but each peculiarity must have had its efficient cause. If these causes, whatever they may be, were to act more uniformly and energetically during a lengthened period (and against this no reason can be assigned), the result would probably be not a mere slight individual difference, but a well-marked and constant modification, though one of no physiological importance. Changed structures, which are in no way beneficial, cannot be kept uniform through natural selection, though the injurious will be thus eliminated. Uniformity of character would, however, naturally follow from the assumed uniformity of the exciting causes, and likewise from the free intercrossing of many individuals. During successive periods, the same organism might in this manner acquire successive modifications, which would be transmitted in a nearly uniform state as long as the exciting causes remained the same and there was free intercrossing. With respect to the exciting causes we can only say, as when speaking of so-called spontaneous variations, that they relate much more closely to the constitution of the varying organism, than to the nature of the conditions to which it has been subjected.

CONCLUSION

In this chapter we have seen that as man at the present day is liable, like every other animal, to multiform individual differences or slight variations, so no doubt were the early progenitors of man; the variations being formerly induced by the same general causes, and governed by the same general and complex laws as at present. As all animals tend to multiply beyond their means of subsistence, so it must have been with the progenitors of man; and this would inevitably lead to a struggle for existence and to natural selection. The latter process would be greatly aided by the inherited effects of the increased use of parts, and these two processes would incessantly react on each other. It appears, also, as we shall hereafter see, that various unimportant characters have been acquired by man through sexual selection. An unexplained residuum of change must be left to the assumed uniform action of those unknown agencies, which occasionally induce strongly marked and abrupt deviations of structure in our domestic productions.

Judging from the habits of savages and of the greater number of the Quadrumana, primeval men, and even their ape-like progenitors, probably lived in society. With strictly social animals, natural selection sometimes acts on the individual, through the preservation of variations which are beneficial to the community. A community which includes a large number of well-endowed individuals increases in number, and is victorious over other less favoured ones; even although each separate member gains no advantage over the others of the same community. Associated insects have thus acquired many remarkable structures, which are of little or no service to the individual, such as the pollen-collecting apparatus, on the sting of the worker-bee, or the great jaws of soldier-ants. With the higher social animals, I am not aware that any structure has been modified solely for the good of the community, though some are of secondary service to it. For instance, the horns of ruminants and the great canine teeth of baboons appear to have been acquired by the males as weapons for sexual strife, but they are used in defence of the herd or troop. In regard to certain mental powers the case, as we shall see in the fifth chapter, is wholly different; for these faculties have been chiefly, or even exclusively, gained for the benefit of the community, and the individuals thereof have at the same time gained an advantage indirectly.

It has often been objected to such views as the foregoing, that man is one of the most helpless and defenceless creatures in the world; and that during his early and less well-developed condition, he would have been still more helpless. The Duke of Argyll, for instance, insists that 'the human frame has diverged from the structure of brutes, in the direction of greater physical helplessness and weakness. That is to say, it is a divergence which of all others it is most impossible to ascribe to mere natural selection.' He adduces the naked and unprotected state of the body, the absence of great teeth or claws for defence, the small strength and speed of man, and his slight power of discovering food or of avoiding danger by smell. To these deficiencies there might be added one still more serious, namely, that he cannot climb quickly, and so escape from enemies. The loss of hair would not have been a great injury to the inhabitants of a warm country. For we know that the unclothed Fuegians can exist under a wretched climate. When we compare the defenceless state of man with that of apes, we must remember that the great canine teeth with which the latter are provided, are possessed in their full development by the males alone, and are chiefly used by them for fighting with their rivals; yet the females, which are not thus provided, manage to survive.

In regard to bodily size or strength, we do not know whether man is descended from some small species, like the chimpanzee, or from one as powerful as the gorilla; and, therefore, we cannot say whether man has become larger and stronger, or smaller and weaker, than his ancestors. We should, however, bear in mind that an animal possessing great size, strength, and ferocity, and which, like the gorilla, could defend itself from all enemies, would not perhaps have become social: and this would most effectually have checked the acquirement of the higher mental qualities, such as sympathy and the love of his fellows. Hence it might have been an immense advantage to man to have sprung from some comparatively weak creature.

The small strength and speed of man, his want of natural weapons, &c., are more than counterbalanced, firstly, by his intellectual powers, through which he has formed for himself weapons, tools, &c., though still remaining in a barbarous state, and, secondly, by his social qualities which lead him to give and receive aid from his fellow-men. No country in the world abounds in a greater degree with dangerous beasts than Southern Africa; no country presents more fearful physical hardships than the Arctic regions; yet one of the puniest of races, that of the Bushmen, maintains itself in Southern Africa, as do the dwarfed Esquimaux in the Arctic regions. The ancestors of man were, no doubt, inferior in intellect, and probably in social disposition, to the lowest existing savages;

but it is quite conceivable that they might have existed, or even flourished, if they had advanced in intellect, whilst gradually losing their brute-like powers, such as that of climbing trees, &c. But these ancestors would not have been exposed to any special danger, even if far more helpless and defenceless than any existing savages, had they inhabited some warm continent or large island, such as Australia, New Guinea, or Borneo, which is now the home of the orang. And natural selection arising from the competition of tribe with tribe, in some such large area as one of these, together with the inherited effects of habit, would, under favourable conditions, have sufficed to raise man to his present high position in the organic scale.

COMPARISON OF THE MENTAL POWERS OF MAN AND THE LOWER ANIMALS

We have [thus] seen that man bears in his bodily structure clear traces of his descent from some lower form; but it may be urged that, as man differs so greatly in his mental power from all other animals, there must be some error in this conclusion. No doubt the difference in this respect is enormous, even if we compare the mind of one of the lowest savages, who has no words to express any number higher than four, and who uses hardly any abstract terms for common objects or for the affections, with that of the most highly organised ape. The difference would, no doubt, still remain immense, even if one of the higher apes had been improved or civilised as much as a dog has been in comparison with its parent-form, the wolf or jackal. The Fuegians rank amongst the lowest barbarians; but I was continually struck with surprise how closely the three natives on board *H.M.S. Beagle*, who had lived some years in England, and could talk a little English, resembled us in disposition and in most of our mental faculties. If no organic being excepting man had possessed any mental power, or if his powers had been of a wholly different nature from those of the lower animals, then we should never have been able to convince ourselves that our high faculties had been gradually developed. But it can be shewn that there is no fundamental difference of this kind. We must also admit that there is a much wider interval in mental power between one of the lowest fishes, as a lamprey or lancelet, and one of the higher apes, than between an ape and man; yet this interval is filled up by numberless gradations.

Nor is the difference slight in moral disposition between a barbarian, such as the man described by the old navigator Byron, who dashed his child on the rocks for dropping a basket of sea-urchins, and a Howard or

Clarkson; and in intellect, between a savage who uses hardly any abstract terms, and a Newton or Shakespeare. Differences of this kind between the highest men of the highest races and the lowest savages, are connected by the finest gradations. Therefore it is possible that they might pass and be developed into each other.

My object in this chapter is to shew that there is no fundamental difference between man and the higher mammals in their mental faculties. Each division of the subject might have been extended into a separate essay, but must here be treated briefly. As no classification of the mental powers has been universally accepted, I shall arrange my remarks in the order most convenient for my purpose; and will select those facts which have struck me most, with the hope that they may produce some effect on the reader.

[Darwin then goes on to compare human intelligence, learning and behaviour with that of other animals. He points out that few human activities seem to be 'instinctive', but that there are many gradations in the degree of instinctive control of behaviour in other animals, instinct becoming less and less important as one ascends the animal scale. Pleasure and pain, happiness and misery, are shared with lower animals, as anyone can tell by watching puppies or kittens. Terror in animals acts in the same way as in man; love and jealousy clearly are not confined to man. Darwin also discusses animal manifestations of *wonder*, *curiosity*, *imitation* and *attention*. He finds evidence of *reason* in many sorts of animal activities.

Darwin discusses the use of tools by animals, and the problem of the origin of language. 'I cannot doubt', he writes, 'that language owes its origin to the imitation and modification of various natural sounds, the voices of other animals, and man's own instinctive cries, aided by signs and gestures.' He point out that no philologist now supposes that any language has been deliberately invented; it has been slowly and unconsciously developed by many steps. He goes on to discuss briefly the possible development of the *sense of beauty* and of *religion* in man. He then takes up, in a separate chapter, the development of the moral sense; we include excerpts from this to indicate the tenor of the argument.]

THE MORAL SENSE

I fully subscribe to the judgment of those writers who maintain that of all the differences between man and the lower animals, the moral sense or conscience is by far the most important. This sense, as Mackintosh remarks, 'has a rightful supremacy over every other principle of human action', it is summed up in that short but imperious word *ought*, so full of high significance. It is the most noble of all the attributes of man, leading him without a moment's hesitation to risk his life for that of a fellow-creature; or after due deliberation, impelled simply by the deep feeling of right or duty, to sacrifice it in some great cause. Immanuel Kant exclaims, 'Duty! Wondrous thought, that workest neither by fond insinuation, flattery, nor by any threat, but merely by holding up thy naked law in the soul, and so extorting for thyself always reverence, if not always obedience; before whom all appetites are dumb, however secretly they rebel; whence thy original?'

* * * *

The following proposition seems to me in a high degree probable—namely, that any animal whatever, endowed with well-marked social instincts, the parental and filial affections being here included, would inevitably acquire a moral sense or conscience, as soon as its intellectual powers had become as well, or nearly as well developed, as in man. For, *firstly*, the social instincts lead an animal to take pleasure in the society of its fellows, to feel a certain amount of sympathy with them, and to perform various services for them. The services may be of a definite and evidently instinctive nature; or there may be only a wish and readiness, as with most of the higher social animals, to aid their fellows in certain general ways. But these feelings and services are by no means extended to all the individuals of the same species, only to those of the same association. *Secondly*, as soon as the mental faculties had become highly developed, images of all past actions and motives would be incessantly passing through the brain of each individual: and that feeling of dissatisfaction, or even misery, which invariably results, as we shall hereafter see, from any unsatisfied instinct, would arise, as often as it was perceived that the enduring and always present social instinct had yielded to some other instinct, at the time stronger, but neither enduring in its nature, nor leaving behind it a very vivid impression. It is clear that many instinctive desires, such as that of hunger, are in their nature of short duration; and after being satisfied, are not readily or vividly recalled. *Thirdly*, after the power of language had been acquired, and the wishes of the community could be expressed, the common opinion how each member ought to act for the public good, would naturally become in a paramount degree the guide to action. But it should be borne in mind that however great weight we may attribute to public opinion, our regard for the approbation and disapprobation of our fellows depends on sympathy, which, as we shall see, forms an essential part of the social instinct, and is indeed its foundation-stone. *Lastly*, habit in the individual would ultimately play a very important part in guiding the conduct of each member; for the social instinct, together with sympathy, is, like any other instinct, greatly strengthened by habit, and so consequently would be obedience to the wishes and judgment of the community. . . .

It may be well first to premise that I do not wish to maintain that any strictly social animal, if its intellectual faculties were to become as active and as highly developed as in man, would acquire exactly the same moral sense as ours. In the same manner as various animals have some sense of beauty, though they admire widely different objects, so they might have a sense of right and wrong, though led by it to follow widely different lines of conduct. If, for instance, to take an extreme case, men were reared under precisely the same conditions as hive-bees, there can hardly be a doubt that our unmarried females would, like the worker-bees, think it a sacred duty to kill their brothers, and mothers would strive to kill their fertile daughters; and no one would think of interfering. Nevertheless, the bee, or any other social animal, would gain in our supposed case, as it appears to me, some feeling of right or wrong, or a conscience. For each individual would have an inward sense of possessing certain stronger or more enduring instincts, and others less strong or enduring; so that there would often be a struggle as to which impulse should be followed; and satisfaction, dissatisfaction, or even misery would be felt, as past impressions were compared during their incessant passage through the mind. In this case an inward monitor would tell the animal that it would have been better to have followed the one impulse rather than the other. The one course ought to have been followed, and the other ought not; the one would have been right and the other wrong; but to these terms I shall recur.

* * * *

MAN A SOCIAL ANIMAL

Every one will admit that man is a social being. We see this in his dislike of solitude, and in his wish for society beyond that of his own family. Solitary confinement is one of the severest punishments which can be inflicted. Some authors suppose that man primevally lived in single families; but at the present day, though single families, or only two or three together, roam the solitudes of some savage lands, they always, as far as I can discover, hold friendly relations with other families inhabiting the same district. Such families occasionally meet in council, and unite for their common defence. It is no argument against savage man being a social animal, that the tribes inhabiting adjacent districts are almost always at war with each other; for the social instincts never extend to all the individuals of the same species. Judging from the analogy of the majority of the Quadrumana, it is probable that the early apelike progenitors of man were likewise social; but this is not of much importance for us. Although man, as he now exists, has few special instincts, having lost any which his early progenitors may have possessed, this is no reason why he should not have retained from an extremely remote period some degree of instinctive love and sympathy for his fellows. We are indeed all conscious that we do possess such sympathetic feelings; but our consciousness does not tell us whether they are instinctive, having originated long ago in the same manner as with the lower animals, or whether they have been acquired by each of us during our early years. As man is a social animal, it is almost certain that he would inherit a tendency to be faithful to his comrades, and obedient to the leader of his tribe; for these qualities are common to most social animals. He would consequently possess some capacity for self-command. He would from an inherited tendency be willing to defend, in concert with others, his fellow-men; and would be ready to aid them in any way, which did not too greatly interfere with his own welfare or his own strong desires.

The social animals which stand at the bottom of the scale are guided almost exclusively, and those which stand higher in the scale are largely guided, by special instincts in the aid which they give to the members of the same community; but they are likewise in part impelled by mutual love and sympathy, assisted apparently by some amount of reason. Although man, as just remarked, has no special instincts to tell him how to aid his fellow-men, he still has the impulse, and with his improved intellectual faculties would naturally be much guided in this respect by reason and experience. Instinctive sympathy would also cause him to value highly the approbation of his fellows; for, as Mr. Bain has clearly shewn, the love of praise and the strong feeling of glory, and the still stronger horror of scorn and infamy, 'are due to the workings of sympathy'. Consequently man would be influenced in the highest degree by the wishes, approbation, and blame of his fellow-men, as expressed by their gestures and language, Thus the social instincts, which must have been acquired by man in a very rude state, and probably even by his early ape-like progenitors, still give the impulse to some of his best actions; but his actions are in a higher degree determined by the expressed wishes and judgment of his fellow-men, and unfortunately very often by his own strong selfish desires. But as love, sympathy and self-command become strengthened by habit, and as the power of reasoning becomes clearer, so that man can value justly the judgments of his fellows, he will feel himself impelled, apart from any transitory pleasure or pain, to certain lines of conduct. He might then declare—not that any barbarian or uncultivated man could thus think—I am the supreme judge of my own conduct, and in the words of Kant, I will not in my own person violate the dignity of humanity.

* * * *

CONCLUDING REMARKS

It was assumed formerly by philosophers of the derivative school of morals that the foundation of morality lay in a form of Selfishness; but more recently the 'Greatest happiness principle' has been brought prominently forward. It is, however, more correct to speak of the latter principle as the standard, and not as the motive of conduct. Nevertheless, all the authors whose works I have consulted, with a few exceptions, write as if there must be a distinct motive for every action, and that this must be associated with some pleasure or displeasure. But man seems often to act impulsively, that is from instinct or long habit, without any consciousness of pleasure, in the same manner as does probably a bee or ant, when it blindly follows its instincts. Under circumstances of extreme peril, as during a fire, when a man endeavours to save a fellow-creature without a moment's hesitation, he can hardly feel pleasure; and still less has he time to reflect on the dissatisfaction which he might subsequently experience if he did not make the attempt. Should he afterwards reflect over his own conduct, he would feel that there lies within him an impulsive power widely different from a search after pleasure or happiness; and this seems to be the deeply planted social instinct.

In the case of the lower animals it seems much more appropriate to speak of their social instincts, as having been developed for the general good rather than for the general happiness of the species. The term, general good, may be defined as the rearing of the greatest number of individuals in full vigour and health, with all their faculties perfect, under the conditions to which they are subjected. As the social instincts both of man and the lower animals have no doubt been developed by nearly the same steps, it would be advisable, if found practicable, to use the same definition in both cases, and to take as the standard of morality, the general good or welfare of the community, rather than the general happiness; but this definition would perhaps require some limitation on account of political ethics.

When a man risks his life to save that of a fellow-creature, it seems also more correct to say that he acts for the general good, rather than for the general happiness of mankind. No doubt the welfare and the happiness of the individual usually coincide; and a contented, happy tribe will flourish better than one that is discontented and unhappy. We have seen that even at an early period in the history of man, the expressed wishes of the community will have naturally influenced to a large extent the conduct of each member; and as all wish for happiness, the 'greatest happiness principle' will have become a most important secondary guide and object; the social instinct, however, together with sympathy (which leads to our regarding the approbation and disapprobation of others), having served as the primary impulse and guide. Thus the reproach is removed of laying the foundation of the noblest part of our nature in the base principle of selfishness; unless, indeed, the satisfaction which every animal feels, when it follows its proper instincts, and the dissatisfaction felt when prevented, be called selfish.

The wishes and opinions of the members of the same community, expressed at first orally, but later by writing also, either form the sole guides of our conduct, or greatly reinforce the social instincts; such opinions, however, have sometimes a tendency directly opposed to these instincts. This latter fact is well exemplified by the *Law of Honour*, that is, the law of the opinion of our equals, and not of all our countrymen. The breach of this law, even when the breach is known to be strictly accordant with true morality, has caused many a man more agony than a real crime. We recognise the same influence in the burning sense of shame which most of us have felt, even after the interval of years, when calling to mind some accidental breach of a trifling, though fixed, rule of etiquette. The judgment of the community will generally be guided by some rude experience of what is best in the long run for all the members; but this judgment will not rarely err from ignorance and weak powers of reasoning. Hence the strangest customs and superstitions, in complete opposition to the true welfare and happiness of mankind, have become all-powerful throughout the world. We see this in the horror felt by a Hindoo who breaks his caste, and in many other such cases. It would be difficult to distinguish between the remorse felt by a Hindoo who has yielded to the temptation of eating unclean food, from that felt after committing a theft; but the former would probably be the more severe.

How so many absurd rules of conduct, as well as so many absurd religious beliefs, have originated, we do not know; nor how it is that they have become, in all quarters of the world, so deeply impressed on the mind of men; but it is worthy of remark that a belief constantly inculcated during the early years of life, whilst the brain is impressible, appears to acquire almost the nature of an instinct; and the very essence of an instinct is that it is followed independently of reason. Neither can we say why certain admirable virtues, such as the love of truth, are much more highly appreciated by some savage tribes than by others; nor, again, why similar differences prevail even amongst highly civilised nations. Knowing how firmly fixed many strange customs and superstitions have become, we need feel no surprise that the self-regarding virtues, supported as they are by reason, should now appear to us so natural as to be thought innate, although they were not valued by man in his early condition.

Notwithstanding many sources of doubt, man can generally and readily distinguish between the higher and lower moral rules. The higher are founded on the social instincts, and relate to the welfare of others. They are supported by the approbation of our fellow-men and by reason. The lower rules, though some of them when implying self-sacrifice hardly deserve to be called lower, relate chiefly to self, and arise from public opinion, matured by experience and cultivation; for they are not practised by rude tribes.

As man advances in civilisation, and small tribes are united into larger communities, the simplest reason would tell each individual that he ought to extend his social instincts and sympathies to all the members of the same nation, though personally unknown to him. This point being once reached, there is only an artificial barrier to prevent his sympathies extending to the men of all nations and races. If, indeed, such men are separated from him by great differences in appearance or habits, experience unfortunately shews us how long it is, before we look at them as our fellow creatures. Sympathy beyond the confines of man, that is, humanity to the lower animals, seems to be one of the latest moral acquisitions. It is apparently unfelt by savages, except towards their pets. How little the old Romans knew of it is shewn by their abhorrent gladiatorial exhibitions. The very idea of humanity, as far as I could observe, was new to most of the Gauchos of the Pampas. This virtue, one of the noblest with which man is endowed, seems to arise incidentally from our sympathies becoming more tender and more widely diffused, until they are extended to all sentient beings. As soon as this virtue is honoured and practised by some few men, it spreads through instruction and example to the young, and eventually becomes incorporated in public opinion.

The highest possible stage in moral culture is when we recognise that we ought to control our thoughts, and 'not even in inmost thought to think again the sins that made the past so pleasant to us'. Whatever makes any bad action familiar to the mind, renders its performance by so much the easier. As Marcus Aurelius long ago said, 'Such as are thy habitual thoughts, such also will be the character of thy mind; for the soul is dyed by the thoughts.'

Our great philosopher, Herbert Spencer, has recently explained his views on the moral sense. He says, 'I believe that the experiences of utility organised and consolidated through all past generations of the human race, have been producing corresponding modifications, which, by continued transmission and accumulation, have become in us certain faculties of moral intuition—certain emotions responding to right and wrong conduct, which have no apparent basis in the individual experiences of utility.' There is not the least inherent improbability, as it seems to me, in virtuous tendencies being more or less strongly inherited; for, not to mention the various dispositions and habits transmitted by many of our domestic animals to their offspring, I have heard of authentic cases in which a desire to steal and a tendency to lie appeared to run in families of the upper ranks; and as stealing is a rare crime in the wealthy classes, we can hardly account by accidental coincidence for the tendency occurring in two or three members of the same family. If bad tendencies are transmitted, it is probable that good ones are likewise transmitted. That the state of the body by affecting the brain, has great influence on the moral tendencies is known to most of those who have suffered from chronic derangements of the digestion or liver. The same fact is likewise shewn by the 'perversion or destruction of the moral sense being often one of the earliest symptoms of mental derangement'; and insanity is notoriously often inherited. Except through the principle of the transmission of moral tendencies, we cannot understand the differences believed to exist in this respect between the various races of mankind.

Even the partial transmission of virtuous tendencies would be an immense assistance to the primary impulse derived directly and indirectly from the social instincts. Admitting for a moment that virtuous tendencies are inherited, it appears probable, at least in such cases as chastity, temperance, humanity to animals, &c., that they become first impressed on the mental organization through habit, instruction and example, continued during several generations in the same family, and in a quite subordinate degree, or not at all, by the individuals possessing such virtues having succeeded best in the struggle for life. My chief source of doubt with respect to any such inheritance, is that senseless customs, superstitions, and tastes, such as the horror of a Hindoo for unclean food, ought on the same principle to be transmitted. I have not met with any evidence in support of the transmission of superstitious customs or senseless habits, although in itself it is perhaps not less probable than that animals should acquire inherited tastes for certain kinds of food or fear of certain foes.

Finally the social instincts, which no doubt were acquired by man as by the lower animals for the good of the community, will from the first have given to him some wish to aid his fellows, some feeling of sympathy, and have compelled him to regard their approbation and disapprobation. Such impulses will have served him at a very early period as a rude rule of right and wrong. But as man gradually advanced in intellectual power, and was enabled to trace the more remote consequences of his actions; as he acquired sufficient knowledge to reject baneful customs and superstitions; as he regarded more and more, not only the welfare, but the happiness of his fellow-men; as from habit, following on beneficial experience, instruction and example, his sympathies became more tender and widely diffused, extending to men of all races, to the imbecile, maimed, and other useless members of society, and finally to the lower animals,—so would the standard of his morality rise higher and higher. And it is admitted by moralists of the derivative school and by some intuitionists, that the standard of morality has risen since an early period in the history of man.

As a struggle may sometimes be seen going on between the various instincts of the lower animals, it is not surprising that there should be a struggle in man between his social instincts, with their derived virtues, and his lower, though momentarily stronger impulses or desires. This, as Mr. Galton has remarked, is all the less surprising, as man has emerged from a state of barbarism within a comparatively recent period. After having yielded to some temptation we feel a sense of dissatisfaction, shame, repentance, or remorse, analogous to the feelings caused by other powerful instincts or desires, when left unsatisfied or baulked. We compare the weakened impression of a past temptation with the ever present social instincts, or with habits, gained in early youth and strengthened during our whole lives, until they have become almost as strong as instincts. If with the temptation still before us we do not yield, it is because either the social instinct or some custom is at the moment predominant, or because we have learnt that it will appear to us hereafter the stronger, when compared with the weakened impression of the temptation, and we realise that its violation would cause us suffering. Looking to future generations, there is no cause to fear that the social instincts will grow weaker, and we may expect that virtuous habits will grow stronger, becoming perhaps fixed by inheritance. In this case the struggle between our higher and lower impulses will be less severe, and virtue will be triumphant.

SUMMARY

There can be no doubt that the difference between the mind of the lowest man and that of the highest animal is immense. An anthropomorphous ape, if he could take a dispassionate view of his own case, would admit that though he could form an artful plan to plunder a garden—though he could use stones for fighting or for breaking open nuts, yet that the thought of fashioning a stone into a tool was quite beyond his scope. Still less, as he would admit, could he follow out a train of metaphysical reasoning, or solve a mathematical problem, or reflect on God, or admire a grand natural scene. Some apes, however, would probably declare that they could and did admire the beauty of the coloured skin and fur of their partners in marriage. They would admit, that though they could make other apes understand by cries some of their perceptions and simpler wants, the notion of expressing definite ideas by definite sounds had never crossed their minds. They might insist that they were ready to aid their fellow-apes of the same troop in many ways, to risk their lives for them, and to take charge of their orphans; but they would be forced to acknowledge that disinterested love for all living creatures, the most noble attribute of man, was quite beyond their comprehension.

Nevertheless the difference in mind between man and the higher animals, great as it is, certainly is one of degree and not of kind. We have seen that the senses and intuitions, the various emotions and faculties, such as love, memory, attention, curiosity, imitation, reason, &c., of which man boasts, may be found in an incipient, or even sometimes in a well-developed condition, in the lower animals. They are also capable of some inherited improvement, as we see in the domestic dog compared with the wolf or jackal. If it could be proved that certain high mental powers, such as the formation of general concepts, self-consciousness, &c., were absolutely peculiar to man, which seems extremely doubtful, it is not improbable that these qualities are merely the incidental results of other highly-advanced intellectual faculties; and these again mainly the result of the continued use of a perfect language. At what age does the new-born infant possess the power of abstraction, or become self-conscious, and reflect on its own existence? We cannot answer; nor can we answer in regard to the ascending organic scale. The half-art, half-instinct of language still bears the stamp of its gradual evolution. The ennobling belief in God is not universal with man; and the belief in spiritual agencies naturally follows from other mental powers. The moral sense perhaps affords the best and highest distinction between man and the lower animals; but I need say nothing on this head, as I have so lately endeavoured to shew that the social instincts,—the prime principle of man's moral constitution—with the aid of active intellectual powers and the effects of habit, naturally lead to the golden rule, 'As ye would that men should do to you, do ye to them likewise', and this lies at the foundation of morality.

CHAPTER 13

THE RACES OF MAN

[Based on Chapter VII of the *Descent*. We have not included any material from Chapter V, 'On the development of the intellectual and moral faculties during primeval and civilized times', because the development of the science of anthropology has greatly modified our understanding of the evolution of human institutions. We have similarly neglected Darwin's Chapter VI, 'On the affinities and genealogy of man', because modern fossil evidence has made much of his reasoning obsolete, interesting though it is from the point of view of the history of thought.]

IT IS not my intention here to describe the several so-called races of men; but I am about to enquire what is the value of the differences between them under a classificatory point of view, and how they have originated. In determining whether two or more allied forms ought to be ranked as species or varieties, naturalists are practically guided by the following considerations; namely, the amount of difference between them, and whether such differences relate to few or many points of structure, and whether they are of physiological importance; but more especially whether they are constant. Constancy of character is what is chiefly valued and sought for by naturalists. Whenever it can be shewn, or rendered probable, that the forms in question have remained distinct for a long period, this becomes an argument of much weight in favour of treating them as species. Even a slight degree of sterility between any two forms when first crossed, or in their offspring, is generally considered as a decisive test of their specific distinctness; and their continued persistence without blending within the same area, is usually accepted as sufficient evidence, either of some degree of mutual sterility, or in the case of animals of some mutual repugnance to pairing.

Independently of fusion from intercrossing, the complete absence, in a well-investigated region, of varieties linking together any two closely-allied forms, is probably the most important of all the criterions of their specific distinctness; and this is a somewhat different consideration from mere constancy of character, for two forms may be highly variable and yet not yield intermediate varieties. Geographical distribution is often brought into play unconsciously and sometimes consciously; so that forms living in two widely separated areas, in which most of the other inhabitants are specifically distinct, are themselves usually looked at as distinct; but in truth this affords no aid in distinguishing geographical races from so-called good or true species.

Now let us apply these generally-admitted principles to the races of man, viewing him in the same spirit as a naturalist would any other animal. In regard to the amount of difference between the races, we must make some allowance for our nice powers of discrimination gained by the long habit of observing ourselves. . . . There is, however, no doubt that the various races, when carefully compared and measured, differ much from each other,—as in the texture of the hair, the relative proportions of all parts of the body, the capacity of the lungs, the form and capacity of the skull, and even in the convolutions of the brain. But it would be an endless task to specify the numerous points of difference. The races differ also in constitution, in acclimatisation and in liability to certain diseases. Their mental characteristics are likewise very distinct; chiefly as it would appear in their emotional, but partly in their intellectual faculties. Every one who has had the opportunity of comparison, must have been struck with the contrast between the taciturn, even morose, aborigines of S. America and the light-hearted, talkative negroes. There is a nearly similar contrast between the Malays and the Papuans, who live under the same physical conditions, and are separated from each other only by a narrow space of sea.

We will first consider the arguments which may be advanced in favour of classing the races of man as distinct species, and then the arguments on the other side. If a naturalist, who had never before seen a Negro, Hottentot, Australian, or Mongolian, were to compare them, he would at once perceive that they differed in a multitude of characters, some of slight and some of considerable importance. On enquiry he would find that they were adapted to live under widely different climates, and that they differed somewhat in bodily constitution and mental disposition. If he were then told that hundreds of similar specimens could be brought from the same countries, he would assuredly declare that they were as good species as many to which he had been in the habit of affixing specific names. This conclusion would be greatly strengthened as soon as he had ascertained that these forms had all retained the same character for many centuries; and that negroes, apparently identical with existing negroes, had lived at least 4000 years ago. He would also hear, on the authority of an excellent observer, Dr. Lund, that the human skulls found in the caves of Brazil, entombed with many extinct mammals, belonged to the same type as that now prevailing throughout the American Continent.

Our naturalist would then perhaps turn to geographical distribution, and he would probably declare that those forms must be distinct species, which differ not only in appearance, but are fitted for hot, as well as damp or dry countries, and for the Arctic regions. He might appeal to the fact that no species in the group next to man—namely, the Quadrumana, can resist a low temperature, or any considerable change of climate; and that the species which come nearest to man have never been reared to maturity, even under the temperate climate of Europe. He would be deeply impressed with the fact, first noticed by Agassiz, that the different races of man are distributed over the world in the same zoological provinces as those inhabited by undoubtedly distinct species and genera of mammals. This is manifestly the case with the Australian, Mongolian, and Negro races of man; in a less well-marked manner with the Hottentots; but plainly with the Papuans and Malays, who are separated, as Mr. Wallace has shewn, by nearly the same line which divides the great Malayan and Australian zoological provinces. The Aborigines of America range throughout the Continent; and this at first appears opposed to the above rule, for most of the productions of the Southern and Northern halves, differ widely: yet some few living forms, as the opossum, range from the one into the other, as did formerly some of the gigantic Edentata. The Esquimaux, like other Arctic animals, extend round the whole polar regions. It should be observed that the amount of difference between the mammals of the several zoological provinces does not correspond with the degree of separation between the latter; so that it can hardly be considered as an anomaly that the Negro differs more, and the American much less than the other races of man, than do the mammals of the African and American continents from the mammals of the other provinces. Man, it may be added, does not appear to have aboriginally inhabited any oceanic island; and in this respect, he resembles the other members of his class.

In determining whether the supposed varieties of the same kind of domestic animal should be ranked as such, or as specifically distinct, that is, whether any of them are descended from distinct wild species, every naturalist would lay much stress on the fact of their external parasites being specifically distinct. All the more stress would be laid on this fact, as it would be an exceptional one; for I am informed by Mr. Denny that the most different kinds of dogs, fowls, and pigeons, in England, are infested by the same species of Pediculi or lice. Now Mr. A. Murray has carefully examined the Pediculi collected in different countries from the different races of man; and he finds that they differ, not only in colour, but in the structure of their claws and limbs. In every case in which many specimens were obtained the differences were constant. The surgeon of a whaling ship in the Pacific assured me that when the Pediculi, with which some Sandwich Islanders on board swarmed, strayed on to the bodies of the English sailors, they died in the course of three or four days. These Pediculi were darker coloured, and appeared different from those proper to the natives of Chiloe in South America, of which he gave me specimens. These, again, appeared larger and much softer than European lice. Mr. Murray procured four kinds from Africa, namely, from the Negroes of the Eastern and Western coasts, from the Hottentots and Kaffirs; two kinds from the natives of Australia; two from North and two from South America. In these latter cases it may be presumed that the Pediculi came from natives inhabiting different districts. With insects slight structural differences, if constant, are generally esteemed of specific value: and the fact of the races of man being infested by parasites, which appear to be specifically distinct, might fairly be urged as an argument that the races themselves ought to be classed as distinct species.

Our supposed naturalist having proceeded thus far in his investigation, would next enquire whether the races of men, when crossed, were in any degree sterile. He might consult the work of Professor Broca, a cautious and philosophical observer, and in this he would find good evidence that some races were quite fertile together, but evidence of an opposite nature in regard to other races. Thus it has been asserted that the native women of Australia and Tasmania rarely produce children to European men; the evidence, however, on this head has now been shewn to be almost valueless. The half-castes are killed by the pure blacks: and an account has lately been published of eleven half-caste youths murdered and burnt at the same time, whose remains were found by the police. Again, it has often been said that when mulattoes intermarry, they produce few children; on the other hand, Dr. Bachman, of Charleston, positively asserts that he has known mulatto families which have intermarried for several generations, and have continued on an average as fertile as either pure whites or pure blacks. Enquiries formerly made by Sir C. Lyell on this subject led him, as he informs me, to the same conclusion. In the United States the census for the year 1854 included, according to Dr. Bachman, 405,751 mulattoes; and this number, considering all the circumstances of the case, seems small; but it may partly be accounted for by the degraded and anomalous position of the class, and by the profligacy of the women. A certain amount of absorption of mulattoes into negroes must always be in progress; and this would lead to an apparent diminution of the former. The inferior vitality of mulattoes is spoken of in a trustworthy work as a well-known phenomenon; and this, although a different consideration from their lessened fertility, may perhaps be advanced as a proof of the specific distinctness of the parent races. No doubt both animal and vegetable hybrids, when produced from extremely distinct species, are liable to premature death; but the parents of mulattoes cannot be put under the category of extremely distinct species. The common Mule, so notorious for long life and vigour, and yet so sterile, shews how little necessary connection there is in hybrids between lessened fertility and vitality; other analogous cases could be cited.

Even if it should hereafter be proved that all the races of men were perfectly fertile together, he who was inclined from other reasons to rank them as distinct species, might with justice argue that fertility and sterility are not safe criterions of specific distinctness. We know that these qualities are easily affected by changed conditions of life, or by close inter-breeding, and that they are governed by highly complex laws, for instance, that of the unequal fertility of converse crosses between the same two species. With forms which must be ranked as undoubted species, a perfect series exists from those which are absolutely sterile when crossed, to those which are almost or completely fertile. The degrees of sterility do not coincide strictly with the degrees of difference between the parents in external structures or habits of life. Man in many respects may be compared with those animals which have long been domesticated, and a large body of evidence can be advanced in favour of the Pallasian doctrine, that domestication tends to eliminate the sterility which is so general a result of the crossing of species in a state of nature. From these several considerations, it may be justly urged that the perfect fertility of the intercrossed races of man, if established, would not absolutely preclude us from ranking them as distinct species.

Independently of fertility, the characters presented by the offspring from a cross have been thought to indicate whether or not the parent-forms ought to be ranked as species or varieties; but after carefully studying the evidence, I have come to the conclusion that no general rules of this kind can be trusted. The ordinary result of a cross is the production of a blended or intermediate form; but in certain cases some of the offspring take closely after one parent-form, and some after the other. This is especially apt to occur when the parents differ in characters which first appeared as sudden variations or monstrosities. I refer to this point, because Dr. Rohlfs informs me that he has frequently seen in Africa the offspring of negroes crossed with members of other races, either completely black or completely white, or rarely piebald. On the other hand, it is notorious that in America mulattoes commonly present an intermediate appearance.

We have now seen that a naturalist might feel himself fully justified in ranking the races of man as distinct species; for he has found that they are distinguished by many differences in structure and constitution, some being of importance. These differences have, also, remained nearly constant for very long periods of time. Our naturalist will have been in some degree influenced by the enormous range of man, which is a great anomaly in the class of mammals, if mankind be viewed as a single species. He will have been struck with the distribution of the several so-called races, which accords with that of other undoubtedly distinct species of mammals. Finally, he might urge that the mutual fertility of all the races has not as yet been fully proved, and even if proved would not be an absolute proof of their specific identity.

On the other side of the question, if our supposed naturalist were to enquire whether the forms of man keep distinct like ordinary species, when mingled together in large numbers in the same country, he would immediately discover that this was by no means the case. In Brazil he would behold an immense mongrel population of Negroes and Portuguese; in Chiloe, and other parts of South America, he would behold the whole population consisting of Indians and Spaniards blended in various degrees. In many parts of the same continent he would meet with the most complex crosses between Negroes, Indians, and Europeans; and judging from the vegetable kingdom, such triple crosses afford the severest test of the mutual fertility of the parent forms. In one island of the Pacific he would find a small population of mingled Polynesian and English blood; and in the Fiji Archipelago a population of Polynesian and Negritos crossed in all degrees. Many analogous cases could be added; for instance, in Africa. Hence the races of man are not sufficiently distinct to inhabit the same country without fusion; and the absence of fusion affords the usual and best test of specific distinctness.

Our naturalist would likewise be much disturbed as soon as he perceived that the distinctive characters of all the races were highly variable. This fact strikes every one on first beholding the negro slaves in Brazil, who have been imported from all parts of Africa. The same remark holds good with the Polynesians, and with many other races. It may be doubted whether any character can be named which is distinctive of a race and is constant. Savages, even within the limits of the same tribe, are not nearly so uniform in character, as has been often asserted. Hottentot women offer certain peculiarities, more strongly marked than those occurring in any other race, but these are known not to be of constant occurrence. In the several American tribes, colour and hairiness differ considerably; as does colour to a certain degree, and the shape of the features greatly, in the Negroes of Africa. The shape of the skull varies much in some races; and so it is with every other character. Now all naturalists have learnt by dearly bought experience, how rash it is to attempt to define species by the aid of inconstant characters.

But the most weighty of all the arguments against treating the races of man as distinct species, is that they graduate into each other, independently in many cases, as far as we can judge, of their having intercrossed. Man has been studied more carefully than any other animal, and yet there is the greatest possible diversity amongst capable judges whether he should be classed as a single species or race, or as two (Virey), as three (Jacquinot), as four (Kant), five (Blumenbach), six (Buffon), seven (Hunter), eight (Agassiz), eleven (Pickering), fifteen (Bory St. Vincent), sixteen (Desmoulins), twenty-two (Morton), sixty (Crawfurd), or as sixty-three, according to Burke. This diversity of judgment does not prove that the races ought not to be ranked as species, but it shews that they graduate into each other, and that it is hardly possible to discover clear distinctive characters between them.

Every naturalist who has had the misfortune to undertake the description of a group of highly varying organisms, has encountered cases (I speak after experience) precisely like that of man; and if of a cautious disposition, he will end by uniting all the forms which graduate into each other, under a single species; for he will say to himself that he has no right to give names to objects which he cannot define. Cases of this kind occur in the Order which include man, namely in certain genera of monkeys; whilst in other genera, as in Cercopithecus, most of the species can be determined with certainty. In the American genus Cebus, the various forms are ranked by some naturalists as species, by others as mere geographical races. Now if numerous specimens of Cebus were collected from all parts of South America, and those forms which at present appear to be specifically distinct, were found to graduate into each other by close steps, they would usually be ranked as mere varieties or races; and this course has been followed by most naturalists with respect to the races of man. Nevertheless, it must be confessed that there are forms, at least in the vegetable kingdom, which we cannot avoid naming as species, but which are connected together by numberless gradations, independently of intercrossing.

Some naturalists have lately employed the term 'sub-species' to designate forms which possess many of the characteristics of true species, but which hardly deserve so high a rank. Now if we reflect on the weighty arguments above given, for raising the races of man to the dignity of species, and the insuperable difficulties on the other side in defining them, it seems that the term 'sub-species' might here be used with propriety. But from long habit the term 'race' will perhaps always be employed. The choice of terms is only so far important in that it is desirable to use, as far as possible, the same terms for the same degrees of difference. Unfortunately this can rarely be done: for the larger genera generally include closely-allied forms, which can be distinguished only with much difficulty, whilst the smaller genera within the same family include forms that are perfectly distinct; yet all must be ranked equally as species. So again, species within the same large genus by no means resemble each other to the same degree: on the contrary, some of them can generally be arranged in little groups round other species, like satellites round planets.

The question whether mankind consists of one or several species has of late years been much discussed by anthropologists, who are divided into the two schools of monogenists and polygenists. Those who do not admit the principle of evolution, must look at species as separate creations, or as in some manner as distinct entities; and they must decide what forms of man they will consider as species by the analogy of the method commonly pursued in ranking other organic beings as species. But it is a hopeless endeavour to decide this point, until some definition of the term 'species' is generally accepted; and the definition must not include an indeterminate element such as an act of creation. We might as well attempt without any definition to decide whether a certain number of houses should be called a village, town, or city. We have a practical illustration of the difficulty in the never-ending doubts whether many closely-allied mammals, birds, insects, and plants, which represent each other respectively in North America and Europe, should be ranked as species or geographical races; and the like holds true of the productions of many islands situated at some little distance from the nearest continent.

Those naturalists, on the other hand, who admit the principle of evolution, and this is now admitted by the majority of rising men, will feel no doubt that all the races of men are descended from a single primitive stock; whether or not they may think fit to designate the races as distinct species, for the sake of expressing their amount of difference. With our domestic animals the question whether the various races have arisen from one or more species is somewhat different. Although it may be admitted that all the races, as well as all the natural species within the same genus, have sprung from the same primitive stock, yet it is a fit subject for discussion, whether all the domestic races of the dog, for instance, have acquired their present amount of difference since some one species was first domesticated by man; or whether they owe some of their characters to inheritance from distinct species, which had already been differentiated in a state of nature. With man no such question can arise, for he cannot be said to have been domesticated at any particular period.

During an early stage in the divergence of the races of man from a common stock, the differences between the races and their number must have been small; consequently as far as their distinguishing characters are concerned, they then had less claim to rank as distinct species than the existing so-called races. Nevertheless, so arbitrary is the term of species, that such early races would perhaps have been ranked by some naturalists as distinct species, if their differences, although extremely slight, had been more constant than they are at present, and had not graduated into each other.

* * * *

Although the existing races of man differ in many respects, as in colour, hair, shape of skull, proportions of the body, &c., yet if their whole structure be taken into consideration they are found to resemble each other closely in a multitude of points. Many of these are of so unimportant or of so singular a nature, that it is extremely improbable that they should have been independently acquired by aboriginally distinct species or races. The same remark holds good with equal or greater force with respect to the numerous points of mental similarity between the most distinct races of man. The American aborigines, Negroes and Europeans are as different from each other in mind as any three races that can be named; yet I was incessantly struck, whilst living with the Fuegians on board the *Beagle*, with the many little traits of character, shewing how similar their minds were to ours; and so it was with a full-blooded negro with whom I happened once to be intimate.

He who will read Mr. Tylor's and Sir J. Lubbock's interesting works can hardly fail to be deeply impressed with the close similarity between the men of all races in tastes, dispositions and habits. This is shewn by the pleasure which they all take in dancing, rude music, acting, painting, tattooing, and otherwise decorating themselves; in their mutual comprehension of gesture-language, by the same expression in their features, and by the same inarticulate cries, when excited by the same emotions. This similarity, or rather identity, is striking, when contrasted with the different expressions and cries made by distinct species of monkeys. There is good evidence that the art of shooting with bows and arrows has not been handed down from any common progenitor of mankind, yet as Westropp and Nilsson have remarked, the stone arrow-heads, brought from the most distant parts of the world, and manufactured at the most remote periods, are almost identical; and this fact can only be accounted for by the various races having similar inventive or mental powers. The same observation has been made by archæologists with respect to certain widely-prevalent ornaments, such as zig-zags, &c.; and with respect to various simple beliefs and customs, such as the burying of the dead under megalithic structures. I remember observing in South America, that there, as in so many other parts of the world, men have generally chosen the summits of lofty hills, to throw up piles of stones, either as a record of some remarkable event, or for burying their dead.

Now when naturalists observe a close agreement in numerous small details of habits, tastes, and dispositions between two or more domestic races, or between nearly-allied natural forms, they use this fact as an argument that they are descended from a common progenitor who was thus endowed; and consequently that all should be classed under the same species. The same argument may be applied with much force to the races of man.

* * * *

Whether primeval man, when he possessed but few arts, and those of the rudest kind, and when his power of language was extremely imperfect, would have deserved to be called man, must depend on the definition which we employ. In a series of forms graduating insensibly from some ape-like creature to man as he now exists, it would be impossible to fix on any definite point when the term 'man' ought to be used. But this is a matter of very little importance. So again, it is almost a matter of indifference whether the so-called races of man are thus designated, or are ranked as species or sub-species; but the latter term appears the more appropriate. Finally, we may conclude that when the principle of evolution is generally accepted, as it surely will be before long, the dispute between the monogenists and the polygenists will die a silent and unobserved death.

* * * *

ON THE EXTINCTION OF THE RACES OF MAN

The partial or complete extinction of many races and sub-races of man is historically known. Humboldt saw in South America a parrot which was the sole living creature that could speak a word of the language of a lost tribe. Ancient monuments and stone implements found in all parts of the world, about which no tradition has been preserved by the present inhabitants, indicate much extinction. Some small and broken tribes, remnants of former races, still survive in isolated and generally mountainous districts. In Europe the ancient races were all, according to Shaaffhausen, 'lower in the scale than the rudest living savages'; they must therefore have differed, to a certain extent, from any existing race. The remains described by Professor Broca from Les Eyzies, though they unfortunately appear to have belonged to a single family, indicate a race with a most singular combination of low or simious, and of high characteristics. This race is 'entirely different from any other, ancient or modern, that we have heard of'. It differed, therefore, from the quaternary race of the caverns of Belgium.

Man can long resist conditions which appear extremely unfavourable for his existence. He has long lived in the extreme regions of the North, with no wood for his canoes or implements, and with only blubber as fuel, and melted snow as drink. In the southern extremity of America the Fuegians survive without the protection of clothes, or of any building worthy to be called a hovel. In South Africa the aborigines wander over arid plains, where dangerous beasts abound. Man can withstand the deadly influence of the Terai at the foot of the Himalaya, and the pestilential shores of tropical Africa.

Extinction follows chiefly from the competition of tribe with tribe, and race with race. Various checks are always in action, serving to keep down the numbers of each savage tribe,—such as periodical famines, nomadic habits and the consequent deaths of infants, prolonged suckling, wars, accidents, sickness, licentiousness, the stealing of women, infanticide, and especially lessened fertility. If any one of these checks increases in power, even slightly, the tribe thus affected tends to decrease; and when of two adjoining tribes one becomes less numerous and less powerful than the other, the contest is soon settled by war, slaughter, cannibalism, slavery, and absorption. Even when a weaker tribe is not thus abruptly swept away, if it once begins to decrease, it generally goes on decreasing until it becomes extinct.

When civilised nations come into contact with barbarians the struggle is short, except where a deadly climate gives its aid to the native race. Of the causes which lead to the victory of civilised nations, some are plain and simple, others complex and obscure. We can see that the cultivation of the land will be fatal in many ways to savages, for they cannot, or will not, change their habits. New diseases and vices have in some cases proved highly destructive; and it appears that a new disease often causes much death, until those who are most susceptible to its destructive influence are gradually weeded out; and so it may be with the evil effects from spirituous liquors, as well as with the unconquerably strong taste for them shewn by so many savages. It further appears, mysterious as is the fact, that the first meeting of distinct and separated people generates disease. Mr. Sproat, who in Vancouver Island closely attended to the subject of extinction, believed that changed habits of life, consequent on the advent of Europeans, induces much ill health. He lays, also, great stress on the apparently trifling cause that the natives become 'bewildered and dull by the new life around them; they lose the motives for exertion, and get no new ones in their place'.

The grade of their civilisation seems to be a most important element in the success of competing nations. A few centuries ago Europe feared the inroads of Eastern barbarians; now any such fear would be ridiculous. It is a more curious fact, as Mr. Bagehot has remarked, that savages did not formerly waste away before the classical nations, as they now do before modern civilised nations; had they done so, the old moralists would have mused over the event; but there is no lament in any writer of that period over the perishing barbarians. The most potent of all the causes of extinction, appears in many cases to be lessened fertility and ill-health, especially amongst the children, arising from changed conditions of life, notwithstanding that the new conditions may not be injurious in themselves. I am much indebted to Mr. H. H. Howorth for having called my attention to this subject, and for having given me information respecting it. I have collected the following cases.

When Tasmania was first colonised the natives were roughly estimated by some at 7000 and by others at 20,000. Their number was soon greatly reduced, chiefly by fighting with the English and with each other. After the famous hunt by all the colonists, when the remaining natives delivered themselves up to the government, they consisted only of 120 individuals, who were in 1832 transported to Flinders Island. This island, situated between Tasmania and Australia, is forty miles long, and from twelve to eighteen miles broad: it seems healthy, and the natives were well treated. Nevertheless, they suffered greatly in health. In 1834 they consisted . . . of forty-seven adult males, forty-eight adult females, and sixteen children, or in all of 111 souls. In 1835 only one hundred were left. As they continued rapidly to decrease, and as they themselves thought that they should not perish so quickly elsewhere, they were removed in 1847 to Oyster Cove in the southern part of Tasmania. They then consisted (Dec. 20th, 1847) of fourteen men, twenty-two women and ten children. But the change of site did no good. Disease and death still pursued them, and in 1864 one man (who died in 1869), and three elderly women alone survived. The infertility of the women is even a more remarkable fact than the liability of all to ill-health and death. At the time when only nine women were left at Oyster Cove, they told Mr. Bonwick . . . , that only two had ever borne children: and these two had together produced only three children!

With respect to the cause of this extraordinary state of things, Dr. Story remarks that death followed the attempts to civilise the natives. 'If left to themselves to roam as they were wont and undisturbed, they would have reared more children, and there would have been less mortality.' Another careful observer of the natives, Mr. Davis, remarks, 'The births have been few and the deaths numerous. This may have been in a great measure owing to their change of living and food; but more so to their banishment from the mainland of Van Diemen's Land, and consequent depression of spirits.' . .

[Darwin goes on to review the history of population decline among the native Australians, the Maoris of New Zealand, and the natives of the Sandwich Islands (Hawaii).]

We thus see that many of the wilder races of man are apt to suffer much in health when subjected to changed conditions or habits of life, and not exclusively from being transported to a new climate. Mere alterations in habits, which do not appear injurious in themselves, seem to have this same effect; and in several cases the children are particularly liable to suffer. It has often been said, as Mr. Macnamara remarks, that man can resist with impunity the greatest diversities of climate and other changes; but this is true only of the civilised races. Man in his wild condition seems to be in this respect almost as susceptible as his nearest allies, the anthropoid apes, which have never yet survived long, when removed from their native country.

Lessened fertility from changed conditions, as in the case of the Tasmanians, Maoris, Sandwich Islanders, and apparently the Australians, is still more interesting than their liability to ill-health and death; for even a slight degree of infertility, combined with those other causes which tend to check the increase of every population, would sooner or later lead to extinction. The diminution of fertility may be explained in some cases by the profligacy of the women (as until lately with the Tahitians), but Mr. Fenton has shewn that this explanation by no means suffices with the New Zealanders, nor does it with the Tasmanians.

In the paper above quoted, Mr. Macnamara gives reasons for believing that the inhabitants of districts subject to malaria are apt to be sterile; but this cannot apply in several of the above cases. Some writers have suggested that the aborigines of islands have suffered in fertility and health from long continued inter-breeding; but in the above cases infertility has coincided too closely with the arrival of Europeans for us to admit this explanation. Nor have we at present any reason to believe that man is highly sensitive to the evil effects of inter-breeding, especially in areas so large as New Zealand, and the Sandwich Archipelago with its diversified stations. On the contrary, it is known that the present inhabitants of Norfolk Island are nearly all cousins or near relations, as are the Todas in India, and the inhabitants of some of the Western Islands of Scotland; and yet they seem not to have suffered in fertility.

A much more probable view is suggested by the analogy of the lower animals. The reproductive system can be shewn to be susceptible to an extraordinary degree (though why we know not) to changed conditions of life; and this susceptibility leads both to beneficial and to evil results. A large collection of facts on this subject is given in chap. xviii. of vol. ii. of my *Variation of Animals and Plants under Domestication*, I can here give only the briefest abstract; and every one interested in the subject may consult the above work. Very slight changes increase the health, vigour, and fertility of most or all organic beings, whilst other changes are known to render a large number of animals sterile. One of the most familiar cases, is that of tamed elephants not breeding in India; though they often breed in Ava, where the females are allowed to roam about the forests to some extent, and are thus placed under more natural conditions. The case of various American monkeys, both sexes of which have been kept for many years together in their own countries, and yet have very rarely or never bred, is a more apposite instance, because of their relationship to man. It is remarkable how slight a change in the conditions often induces sterility in a wild animal when captured; and this is the more strange as all our domesticated animals have become more fertile than they were in a state of nature; and some of them can resist the most unnatural conditions with undiminished fertility. Certain groups of animals are much more liable than others to be affected by captivity; and generally all the species of the same group are affected in the same manner. But sometimes a single species in a group is rendered sterile, whilst the others are not so; on the other hand, a single species may retain its fertility whilst most of the others fail to breed. The males and females of some species when confined, or when allowed to live almost, but not quite free, in their native country, never unite; others thus circumstanced frequently unite but never produce offspring; others again produce some offspring, but fewer than in a state of nature; and as bearing on the above cases of man, it is important to remark that the young are apt to be weak and sickly, or malformed, and to perish at an early age.

Seeing how general is this law of the susceptibility of the reproductive system to changed conditions of life, and that it holds good with our nearest allies, the Quadrumana, I can hardly doubt that it applies to man in his primeval state. Hence if savages of any race are induced suddenly to change their habits of life, they become more or less sterile, and their young offspring suffer in health, in the same manner and from the same cause, as do the elephant and hunting-leopard in India, many monkeys in America, and a host of animals of all kinds, on removal from their natural conditions.

We can see why it is that aborigines, who have long inhabited islands, and who must have been long exposed to nearly uniform conditions, should be specially affected by any change in their habits, as seems to be the case. Civilised races can certainly resist changes of all kinds far better than savages; and in this respect they resemble domesticated animals, for though the latter sometimes suffer in health (for instance European dogs in India), yet they are rarely rendered sterile, though a few such instances have been recorded. The immunity of civilised races and domesticated animals is probably due to their having been subjected to a greater extent, and therefore having grown somewhat more accustomed, to diversified or varying conditions, than the majority of wild animals; and to their having formerly immigrated or been carried from country to country, and to different families or sub-races having intercrossed. It appears that a cross with civilised races at once gives to an aboriginal race an immunity from the evil consequences of changed conditions. Thus the crossed offspring from the Tahitians and English, when settled in Pitcairn Island, increased so rapidly that the Island was soon overstocked; and in June 1856 they were removed to Norfolk Island. They then consisted of 60 married persons and 134 children, making a total of 194. Here they likewise increased so rapidly, that although sixteen of them returned to Pitcairn Island in 1859, they numbered in January 1868, 300 souls; the males and females being in exactly equal numbers. What a contrast does this case present with that of the Tasmanians; the Norfolk Islanders *increased* in only twelve and a half years from 194 to 300; whereas the Tasmanians *decreased* during fifteen years from 120 to 46, of which latter number only ten were children.

* * * *

Finally, although the gradual decrease and ultimate extinction of the races of man is a highly complex problem, depending on many causes which differ in different places and at different times; it is the same problem as that presented by the extinction of one of the higher animals—of the fossil horse, for instance, which disappeared from South America, soon afterwards to be replaced, within the same districts, by countless troups of the Spanish horse. The New Zealander seems conscious of this parallelism, for he compares his future fate with that of the native rat now almost exterminated by the European rat. Though the difficulty is great to our imagination, and really great, if we wish to ascertain the precise causes and their manner of action, it ought not to be so to our reason, as long as we keep steadily in mind that the increase of each species and each race is constantly checked in various ways; so that if any new check, even a slight one, be superadded, the race will surely decrease in number; and decreasing numbers will sooner or later lead to extinction; the end, in most cases, being promptly determined by the inroads of conquering tribes.

ON THE FORMATION OF THE RACES OF MAN

In some cases the crossing of distinct races has led to the formation of a new race. The singular fact that the Europeans and Hindoos, who belong to the same Aryan stock, and speak a language fundamentally the same, differ widely in appearance, whilst Europeans differ but little from Jews, who belong to the Semitic stock, and speak quite another language, has been accounted for by Broca, through certain Aryan branches having been largely crossed by indigenous tribes during their wide diffusion. When two races in close contact cross, the first result is a heterogeneous mixture: thus Mr. Hunter, in describing the Santali or hill-tribes of India, says that hundreds of imperceptible gradations may be traced 'from the black, squat tribes of the mountains to the tall olive-coloured Brahman, with his intellectual brow, calm eyes, and high but narrow head'; so that it is necessary in courts of justice to ask the witnesses whether they are Santalis or Hindoos. Whether a heterogeneous people, such as the inhabitants of some of the Polynesian Islands, formed by the crossing of two distinct races, with few or no pure members left, would ever become homogeneous, is not known from direct evidence. But as with our domesticated animals, a cross-breed can certainly be fixed and made uniform by careful selection in the course of a few generations, we may infer that the free intercrossing of a heterogeneous mixture during a long descent would supply the place of selection, and overcome any tendency to reversion; so that the crossed race would ultimately become homogeneous, though it might not partake in an equal degree of the characters of the two parent-races.

Of all the differences between the races of man, the colour of the skin is the most conspicuous and one of the best marked. It was formerly thought that differences of this kind could be accounted for by long exposure to different climates; but Pallas first shewed that this is not tenable, and he has since been followed by almost all anthropologists. This view has been rejected chiefly because the distribution of the variously coloured races, most of whom must have long inhabited their present homes, does not coincide with corresponding differences of climate. Some little weight may be given to such cases as that of the Dutch families, who, as we hear on excellent authority, have not undergone the least change of colour after residing for three centuries in South Africa. An argument on the same side may likewise be drawn from the uniform appearance in various parts of the world of gipsies and Jews, though the uniformity of the latter has been somewhat exaggerated. A very damp or a very dry atmosphere has been supposed to be more influential in modifying the colour of the skin than mere heat; but as D'Orbigny in South America, and Livingstone in Africa, arrived at diametrically opposite conclusions with respect to dampness and dryness, any conclusion on this head must be considered as very doubtful.

* * * *

Dr. Sharpe remarks, that a tropical sun, which burns and blisters a white skin, does not injure a black one at all; and, as he adds, this is not due to habit in the individual, for children only six or eight months old are often carried about naked, and are not affected. I have been assured by a medical man, that some years ago during each summer, but not during the winter, his hands became marked with light brown patches, like, although larger than freckles, and that these patches were never affected by sun-burning, whilst the white parts of his skin have on several occasions been much inflamed and blistered. With the lower animals there is, also, a constitutional difference in liability to the action of the sun between those parts of the skin clothed with white hair and other parts. Whether the saving of the skin from being thus burnt is of sufficient importance to account for a dark tint having been gradually acquired by man through natural selection, I am unable to judge. If it be so, we should have to assume that the natives of tropical America have lived there for a much shorter time than the negroes in Africa, or the Papuans in the southern parts of the Malay Archipelago, just as the lighter-coloured Hindoos have resided in India for a shorter time than the darker aborigines of the central and southern parts of the peninsula.

Although with our present knowledge we cannot account for the differences of colour in the races of man, through any advantage thus gained, or from the direct action of climate; yet we must not quite ignore the latter agency, for there is good reason to believe that some inherited effect is thus produced.

We have seen in the second chapter that the conditions of life affect the development of the bodily frame in a direct manner, and that the effects are transmitted. Thus, as is generally admitted, the European settlers in the United States undergo a slight but extraordinary rapid change of appearance. Their bodies and limbs become elongated; and I hear from Col. Bernys that during the late war in the United States, good evidence was afforded of this fact by the ridiculous appearance presented by the German regiments, when dressed in ready-made clothes manufactured for the American market, and which were much too long for the men in every way. There is, also, a considerable body of evidence shewing that in the Southern States the house-slaves of the third generation present a markedly different appearance from the field-slaves.

If, however, we look to the races of man as distributed over the world, we must infer that their characteristic differences cannot be accounted for by the direct action of different conditions of life, even after exposure to them for an enormous period of time. The Esquimaux live exclusively on animal food; they are clothed in thick fur, and are exposed to intense cold and to prolonged darkness; yet they do not differ in any extreme degree from the inhabitants of Southern China, who live entirely on vegetable food, and are exposed almost naked to a hot, glaring climate. The unclothed Fuegians live on the marine productions of their inhospitable shores; the Botocudos of Brazil wander about the hot forests of the interior and live chiefly on vegetable productions; yet these tribes resemble each other so closely that the Fuegians on board the *Beagle* were mistaken by some Brazilians for Botocudos. The Botocudos again, as well as the other inhabitants of tropical America, are wholly different from the Negroes who inhabit the opposite shores of the Atlantic, are exposed to a nearly similar climate, and follow nearly the same habits of life.

* * * *

We have now seen that the external characteristic differences between the races of man cannot be accounted for in a satisfactory manner by the direct action of the conditions of life, nor by the effects of the continued use of parts, nor through the principle of correlation. We are therefore led to enquire whether slight individual differences, to which man is eminently liable, may not have been preserved and augmented during a long series of generations through natural selection. But here we are at once met by the objection that beneficial variations alone can be thus preserved; and as far as we are enabled to judge, although always liable to err on this head, none of the differences between the races of man are of any direct or special service to him. The intellectual and moral or social faculties must of course be excepted from this remark. The great variability of all the external differences between the races of man, likewise indicates that they cannot be of much importance; for if important, they would long ago have been either fixed and preserved, or eliminated. In this respect man resembles those forms, called by naturalists protean or polymorphic, which have remained extremely variable, owing, as it seems, to such variations being of an indifferent nature, and to their having thus escaped the action of natural selection.

We have thus far been baffled in all our attempts to account for the differences between the races of man; but there remains one important agency, namely Sexual Selection, which appears to have acted powerfully on man, as on many other animals. I do not intend to assert that sexual selection will account for all the differences between the races. An unexplained residuum is left, about which we can only say, in our ignorance, that as individuals are continually born with, for instance, heads a little rounder or narrower, and with noses a little longer or shorter, such slight differences might become fixed and uniform, if the unknown agencies which induced them were to act in a more constant manner, aided by long-continued intercrossing. Such variations come under the provisional class, alluded to in our second chapter, which for want of a better term are often called spontaneous. Nor do I pretend that the effects of sexual selection can be indicated with scientific precision; but it can be shewn that it would be an inexplicable fact if man had not been modified by this agency, which appears to have acted powerfully on innumerable animals. It can further be shewn that the differences between the races of man, as in colour, hairiness, form of features, &c., are of a kind which might have been expected to come under the influence of sexual selection. But in order to treat this subject properly, I have found it necessary to pass the whole animal kingdom in review. I have therefore devoted to it the Second Part of this work. At the close I shall return to man, and, after attempting to shew how far he has been modified through sexual selection, will give a brief summary of the chapters in this First Part.

going, the males and females of some animals differ in structures related to different habits of life, and not at all, or only indirectly, to the reproductive functions. Thus the females of certain flies (Culicidæ and Tabanidæ) are blood-suckers, whilst the males, living on flowers, have mouths destitute of mandibles. The males of certain moths and of some crustaceans (*e.g.* Tanais) have imperfect, closed mouths, and cannot feed. The complemental males of certain Cirripedes live like epiphytic plants either on the female or on the hermaphrodite form, and are destitute of a mouth and of prehensile limbs. In these cases it is the male which has been modified, and has lost certain important organs, which the female possesses. In other cases it is the female which has lost such parts; for instance, the female glow-worm is destitute of wings, as also are many female moths, some of which never leave their cocoons. Many female parasitic crustaceans have lost their natatory legs. In some weevil-beetles (Curculionidæ) there is a great difference between the male and female in the length of the rostrum or snout; but the meaning of this and of many analogous differences, is not at all understood. Differences of structure between the two sexes in relation to different habits of life are generally confined to the lower animals; but with some few birds the beak of the male differs from that of the female. In the Huia of New Zealand the difference is wonderfully great, and we hear from Dr. Buller that the male uses his strong beak in chiselling the larvæ of insects out of decayed wood, whilst the female probes the softer parts with her far longer, much curved and pliant beak: and thus they mutually aid each other. In most cases, differences of structure between the sexes are more or less directly connected with the propagation of the species: thus a female, which has to nourish a multitude of ova, requires more food than the male, and consequently requires special means for procuring it. A male animal, which lives for a very short time, might lose its organs for procuring food through disuse, without detriment; but he would retain his locomotive organs in a perfect state, so that he might reach the female. The female on the other hand, might safely lose her organs for flying, swimming, or walking, if she gradually acquired habits which rendered such powers useless.

We are, however, here concerned only with sexual selection. This depends on the advantage which certain individuals have over others of the same sex and species solely in respect of reproduction. When, as in the cases above mentioned, the two sexes differ in structure in relation to different habits of life, they have no doubt been modified through natural selection, and by inheritance, limited to one and the same sex. So again the primary sexual organs, and those for nourishing or protecting the young, come under the same influence; for those individuals which generated or nourished their offspring best, would leave, *cœteris paribus*, the greatest number to inherit their superiority; whilst those which generated or nourished their offspring badly, would leave but few to inherit their weaker powers. As the male has to find the female, he requires organs of sense and locomotion, but if these organs are necessary for the other purposes of life, as is generally the case, they will have been developed through natural selection. When the male has found the female, he sometimes absolutely requires prehensile organs to hold her; thus Dr. Wallace informs me that the males of certain moths cannot unite with the females if their tarsi or feet are broken. The males of many oceanic crustaceans, when adult, have their legs and antennæ modified in an extraordinary manner for the prehension of the female; hence we may suspect that it is because these animals are washed about by the waves of the open sea, that they require these organs in order to propagate their kind, and if so, their development has been the result of ordinary or natural selection. Some animals extremely low in the scale have been modified for this same purpose; thus the males of certain parasitic worms, when fully grown, have the lower surface of the terminal part of their bodies roughened like a rasp, and with this they coil round and permanently hold the females.

When the two sexes follow exactly the same habits of life, and the male has the sensory or locomotive organs more highly developed than those of the female, it may be that the perfection of these is indispensable to the male for finding the female; but in the vast majority of cases, they serve only to give one male an advantage over another, for with sufficient time, the less well-endowed males would succeed in pairing with the females; and judging from the structure of the female, they would be in all other respects equally well adapted for their ordinary habits of life. Since in such cases the males have acquired their present structure, not from being better fitted to survive in the struggle for existence, but from having gained an advantage over other males, and from having transmitted this advantage to their male offspring alone, sexual selection must here have come into action. It was the importance of this distinction which led me to designate this form of selection as Sexual Selection. So again, if the chief service rendered to the male by his prehensile organs is to prevent the escape of the female before the arrival of other males, or when assaulted by them, these organs will have been perfected through sexual selection, that is by the advantage acquired by certain individuals over their rivals. But in most cases of this kind it is impossible to distinguish between the effects of natural and sexual selection. Whole chapters could be filled with details on the differences between the sexes in their sensory, locomotive, and prehensile organs. As, however, these structures are not more interesting than others adapted for the ordinary purposes of life I shall pass them over almost entirely, giving only a few instances under each class.

There are many other structures and instincts which must have been developed through sexual selection—such as the weapons of offence and the means of defence—of the males for fighting with and driving away their rivals—their courage and pugnacity—their various ornaments—their contrivances for producing vocal or instrumental music—and their glands for emitting odours, most of these latter structures serving only to allure or excite the female. It is clear that these characters are the result of sexual and not of ordinary selection, since unarmed, unornamented, or unattractive males would succeed equally well in the battle for life and in leaving a numerous progeny, but for the presence of better endowed males. We may infer that this would be the case, because the females, which are unarmed and unornamented, are able to survive and procreate their kind. Secondary sexual characters of the kind just referred to, will be fully discussed in the following chapters, as being in many respects interesting, but especially as depending on the will, choice, and rivalry of the individuals of either sex. When we behold two males fighting for the possession of the female, or several male birds displaying their gorgeous plumage, and performing strange antics before an assembled body of females, we cannot doubt that, though led by instinct, they know what they are about, and consciously exert their mental and bodily powers.

Just as man can improve the breeds of his game-cocks by the selection of those birds which are victorious in the cock-pit, so it appears that the strongest and most vigorous males, or those provided with the best weapons, have prevailed under nature, and have led to the improvement of the natural breed or species. A slight degree of variability leading to some advantage, however slight, in reiterated deadly contests would suffice for the work of sexual selection; and it is certain that secondary sexual characters are eminently variable. Just as man can give beauty, according to his standard of taste, to his male poultry, or more strictly can modify the beauty originally acquired by the parent species, can give to the Sebright bantam a new and elegant plumage, an erect and peculiar carriage—so it appears that female birds in a state of nature, have by a long selection of the more attractive males, added to their beauty or other attractive qualities. No doubt this implies powers of discrimination and taste on the part of the female which will at first appear extremely improbable; but by the facts to be adduced hereafter, I hope to be able to shew that the females actually have these powers. When, however, it is said that the lower animals have a sense of beauty, it must not be supposed that such sense is comparable with that of a cultivated man, with his multiform and complex associated ideas. A more just comparison would be between the taste for the beautiful in animals, and that in the lowest savages, who admire and deck themselves with any brilliant, glittering or curious object.

From our ignorance on several points, the precise manner in which sexual selections acts is somewhat uncertain. Nevertheless if those naturalists who already believe in the mutability of species, will read the following chapters, they will, I think, agree with me, that sexual selection has played an important part in the history of the organic world. It is certain that amongst almost all animals there is a struggle between the males for the possession of the female. This fact is so notorious that it would be superfluous to give instances. Hence the females have the opportunity of selecting one out of several males, on the supposition that their mental capacity suffices for the exertion of a choice. In many cases special circumstances tend to make the struggle between the males particularly severe. Thus the males of our migratory birds generally arrive at their places of breeding before the females, so that many males are ready to contend for each female. I am informed by Mr. Jenner Weir, that the bird-catchers assert that this is invariably the case with the nightingale and blackcap, and with respect to the latter he can himself confirm the statement.

⋆ ⋆ ⋆ ⋆

Our difficulty in regard to sexual selection lies in understanding how it is that the males which conquer other males, or those which prove the most attractive to the females, leave a greater number of offspring to inherit their superiority than their beaten and less attractive rivals. Unless this result does follow, the characters which give to certain males an advantage over others, could not be perfected and augmented through sexual selection. When the sexes exist in exactly equal numbers, the worst-endowed males will (except where polygamy prevails), ultimately find females, and leave as many offspring, as well fitted for their general habits of life, as the best-endowed males. From various facts and considerations, I formerly inferred that with most animals, in which secondary sexual characters are well developed, the males considerably exceeded the females in number; but this is not by any means always true. If the males were to the females as two to one, or as three to two, or even in a somewhat lower ratio, the whole affair would be simple; for the better-armed or more attractive males would leave the largest number of offspring. But after investigating, as far as possible, the numerical proportion of the sexes, I do not believe that any great inequality in number commonly exists. In most cases sexual selection appears to have been effective in the following manner.

Let us take any species, a bird for instance, and divide the females inhabiting a district into two equal bodies, the one consisting of the more vigorous and better-nourished individuals, and the other of the less vigorous and healthy. The former, there can be little doubt, would be ready to breed in the spring before the others; and this is the opinion of Mr. Jenner Weir, who has carefully attended to the habits of birds during many years. There can also be no doubt that the most vigorous, best-nourished and earliest breeders would on an average succeed in rearing the largest number of fine offspring. The males, as we have seen, are generally ready to breed before the females; the strongest, and with some species the best armed of the males, drive away the weaker; and the former would then unite with the more vigorous and better-nourished females, because they are the first to breed. Such vigorous pairs would surely rear a larger number of offspring than the retarded females, which would be compelled to unite with the conquered and less powerful males, supposing the sexes to be numerically equal; and this is all that is wanted to add, in the course of successive generations, to the size, strength and courage of the males, or to improve their weapons.

But in very many cases the males which conquer their rivals, do not obtain possession of the females, independently of the choice of the latter. The courtship of animals is by no means so simple and short an affair as might be thought. The females are most excited by, or prefer pairing with, the more ornamented males, or those which are the best songsters, or play the best antics; but it is obviously probable that they would at the same time prefer the more vigorous and lively males, and this has in some cases been confirmed by actual observation. Thus the more vigorous females, which are the first to breed, will have the choice of many males; and though they may not always select the strongest or best armed, they will select those which are vigorous and well armed, and in other respects the most attractive. Both sexes, therefore, of such early pairs would as above explained, have an advantage over others in rearing offspring; and this apparently has sufficed during a long course of generations to add not only to the strength and fighting powers of the males, but likewise to their various ornaments or other attractions.

In the converse and much rarer case of the males selecting particular females, it is plain that those which were the most vigorous and had conquered others, would have the freest choice; and it is almost certain that they would select vigorous as well as attractive females. Such pairs would have an advantage in rearing offspring, more especially if the male had the power to defend the female during the pairing-season as occurs with some of the higher animals, or aided her in providing for the young. The same principles would apply if each sex preferred and selected certain individuals of the opposite sex; supposing that they selected not only the more attractive, but likewise the more vigorous individuals.

* * * *

To sum up on the means through which, as far as we can judge, sexual selection has led to the development of secondary sexual characters. It has been shewn that the largest number of vigorous offspring will be reared from the pairing of the strongest and best-armed males, victorious in contests over other males, with the most vigorous and best-nourished females, which are the first to breed in the spring. If such females select the more attractive, and at the same time vigorous males, they will rear a larger number of offspring than the retarded females, which must pair with the less vigorous and less attractive males. So it will be if the more vigorous males select the more attractive and at the same time healthy and vigorous females; and this will especially hold good if the male defends the female, and aids in providing food for the young. The advantage thus gained by the more vigorous pairs in rearing a larger number of offspring has apparently sufficed to render sexual selection efficient. But a large numerical preponderance of males over females will be still more efficient; whether the preponderance is only occasional and local, or permanent; whether it occurs at birth, or afterwards from the greater destruction of the females; or whether it indirectly follows from the practice of polygamy.

* * * *

Sexual selection acts in a less rigorous manner than natural selection. The latter produces its effects by the life or death at all ages of the more or less successful individuals. Death, indeed, not rarely ensues from the conflicts of rival males. But generally the less successful male merely fails to obtain a female, or obtains a retarded and less vigorous female later in the season, or, if polygamous, obtains fewer females; so that they leave fewer, less vigorous, or no offspring. In regard to structures acquired through ordinary or natural selection, there is in most cases, as long as the conditions of life remain the same, a limit to the amount of advantageous modification in relation to certain special purposes; but in regard to structures adapted to make one male victorious over another, either in fighting or in charming the female, there is no definite limit to the amount of advantageous modification; so that as long as the proper variations arise the work of sexual selection will go on. This circumstance may partly account for the frequent and extraordinary amount of variability presented by secondary sexual characters. Nevertheless, natural selection will determine that such characters shall not be acquired by the victorious males, if they would be highly injurious, either by expending too much of their vital powers, or by exposing them to any great danger. The development, however, of certain structures—of the horns, for instance, in certain stags—has been carried to a wonderful extreme; and in some cases to an extreme which, as far as the general conditions of life are concerned, must be slightly injurious to the male. From this fact we learn that the advantages which favoured males derive from conquering other males in battle or courtship, and thus leaving a numerous progeny, are in the long run greater than those derived from rather more perfect adaptation to their conditions of life. We shall further see, and it could never have been anticipated, that the power to charm the females has sometimes been more important than the power to conquer other males in battle.

* * * *

SUMMARY AND CONCLUDING REMARKS

From the foregoing discussion on the various laws of inheritance, we learn that the characters of the parents often, or even generally, tend to become developed in the offspring of the same sex, at the same age, and periodically at the same season of the year, in which they first appeared in the parents. But these rules, owing to unknown causes, are far from being fixed. Hence during the modification of a species, the successive changes may readily be transmitted in different ways; some to one sex, and some to both; some to the offspring at one age, and some to the offspring at all ages. Not only are the laws of inheritance extremely complex, but so are the causes which induce and govern variability. The variations thus induced are preserved and accumulated by sexual selection, which is in itself an extremely complex affair, depending, as it does, on the ardour in love, the courage, and the rivalry of the males, as well as on the powers of perception, the taste, and will of the female. Sexual selection will also be largely dominated by natural selection tending towards the general welfare of the species. Hence the manner in which the individuals of either or both sexes have been affected through sexual selection cannot fail to be complex in the highest degree.

When variations occur late in life in one sex, and are transmitted to the same sex at the same age, the other sex and the young are left unmodified. When they occur late in life, but are transmitted to both sexes at the same age, the young alone are left unmodified. Variations, however, may occur at any period of life in one sex or in both, and be transmitted to both sexes at all ages, and then all the individuals of the species are similarly modified. In the following chapters it will be seen that all these cases frequently occur in nature.

Sexual selection can never act on any animal before the age for reproduction arrives. From the great eagerness of the male it has generally acted on this sex and not on the females. The males have thus become provided with weapons for fighting with their rivals, with organs for discovering and securely holding the female, and for exciting or charming her. When the sexes differ in these respects, it is also, as we have seen, an extremely general law that the adult male differs more or less from the young male; and we may conclude from this fact that the successive variations, by which the adult male became modified, did not generally occur much before the age for reproduction. Whenever some or many of the variations occurred early in life, the young males would partake more or less of the characters of the adult males; and differences of this kind between the old and young males may be observed in many species of animals.

It is probable that young male animals have often tended to vary in a manner which would not only have been of no use to them at an early age, but would have been actually injurious—as by acquiring bright colours, which would render them conspicuous to their enemies, or by acquiring structures, such as great horns, which would expend much vital force in their development. Variations of this kind occurring in the young males would almost certainly be eliminated through natural selection. With the adult and experienced males, on the other hand, the advantages derived from the acquisition of such characters, would more than counterbalance some exposure to danger, and some loss of vital force.

As variations which give to the male a better chance of conquering other males, or of finding, securing, or charming the opposite sex, would, if they happened to arise in the female, be of no service to her, they would not be preserved in her through sexual selection. We have also good evidence with domesticated animals, that variations of all kinds are, if not carefully selected, soon lost through intercrossing and accidental deaths. Consequently in a state of nature, if variations of the above kind chanced to arise in the female line, and be transmitted exclusively in this line, they would be extremely liable to be lost. If, however, the females varied and transmitted their newly acquired characters to their offspring of both sexes, the characters which were advantageous to the males would be preserved by them through sexual selection, and the two sexes would in consequence be modified in the same manner, although such characters were of no use to the females: but I shall hereafter have to recur to these more intricate contingencies. Lastly, the females may acquire, and apparently have often acquired by transference, characters from the male sex.

As variations occurring later in life, and transmitted to one sex alone, have incessantly been taken advantage of and accumulated through sexual selection in relation to the reproduction of the species; therefore it appears, at first sight, an unaccountable fact that similar variations have not frequently been accumulated through natural selection, in relation to the ordinary habits of life. If this had occurred, the two sexes would often have been differently modified, for the sake, for instance, of capturing prey or of escaping from danger. Differences of this kind between the two sexes do occasionally occur, especially in the lower classes. But this implies that the two sexes follow different habits in their struggles for existence, which is a rare circumstance with the higher animals. The case, however, is widely different with the reproductive functions, in which respect the sexes necessarily differ. For variations in structure which are related to these functions, have often proved of value to one sex, and from having arisen at a late period of life, have been transmitted to one sex alone; and such variations, thus preserved and transmitted, have given rise to secondary sexual characters.

In the following chapters, I shall treat of the secondary sexual characters in animals of all classes, and shall endeavour in each case to apply the principles explained in the present chapter. The lowest classes will detain us for a very short time, but the higher animals, especially birds, must be treated at considerable length. It should be borne in mind that for reasons already assigned, I intend to give only a few illustrative instances of the innumerable structures by the aid of which the male finds the female, or, when found, holds her. On the other hand, all structures and instincts by the aid of which the male conquers other males, and by which he allures or excites the female, will be fully discussed, as these are in many ways the most interesting.

CHAPTER 15

SECONDARY SEXUAL CHARACTERS OF BIRDS

[Chapters IX–XVIII of the *Descent* are devoted to a review of secondary sexual characters in the different classes of the animal kingdom. The worms, molluscs, crustacea and the like are treated rather briefly. The insects are covered in more detail, since the differences betweeen the sexes are often remarkable: among other things, Darwin describes the elaborate sound-producing organs of the males of many crickets, katydids and grasshoppers; the exaggerated horns and jaws of many male beetles; the great differences in colour and form between the males and females of many butterflies and moths. Sexual differences in fish, amphibians and reptiles are the subject of another chapter, and here also there are numerous examples of gaudy males associated with dull-coloured or conservative females. Birds, however, show the most frequent and extreme development of sexual divergence in appearance, and Darwin devotes four chapters to these animals. Finally, mammals are discussed in two chapters: the elaborate horns of many ruminants; the tusks of boars; scent organs sometimes limited to the male, sometimes shared by both sexes; and the sexual differences in voice, hair pattern or colour found in several different groups of mammals.

As examples of Darwin's treatment, we include here a few excerpts from the four chapters on birds.]

SECONDARY sexual characters are more diversified and conspicuous in birds, though not perhaps entailing more important changes of structure, than in any other class of animals. I shall, therefore, treat the subject at considerable length. Male birds sometimes, though rarely, possess special weapons for fighting with each other. They charm the female by vocal or instrumental music of the most varied kinds. They are ornamented by all sorts of combs, wattles, protuberances, horns, air-distended sacks, topknots, naked shafts, plumes and lengthened feathers gracefully springing from all parts of the body. The beak and naked skin about the head, and the feathers, are often gorgeously coloured. The males sometimes pay their court by dancing, or by fantastic antics performed either on the ground or in the air. In one instance, at least, the male emits a musky odour, which we may suppose serves to charm or excite the female; for that excellent observer, Mr. Ramsay, says of the

Australian musk-duck (*Biziura lobata*) that 'the smell which the male emits during the summer months is confined to that sex, and in some individuals is retained throughout the year; I have never, even in the breeding-season, shot a female which had any smell of musk.' So powerful is this odour during the pairing-season, that it can be detected long before the bird can be seen. On the whole, birds appear to be the most æsthetic of all animals, excepting of course man, and they have nearly the same taste for the beautiful as we have. This is shown by our enjoyment of the singing of birds, and by our women, both civilised and savage, decking their heads with borrowed plumes, and using gems which are hardly more brilliantly coloured than the naked skin and wattles of certain birds. In man, however, when cultivated, the sense of beauty is manifestly a far more complex feeling, and is associated with various intellectual ideas.

Before treating of the sexual characters with which we are here more particularly concerned, I may just allude to certain differences between the sexes which apparently depend on differences in their habits of life; for such cases, though common in the lower, are rare in the higher classes. Two humming-birds belonging to the genus Eustephanus, which inhabit the island of Juan Fernandez, were long thought to be specifically distinct, but are now known, as Mr. Gould informs me, to be the male and female of the same species, and they differ slightly in the form of the beak. In another genus of humming-birds (*Grypus*), the beak of the male is serrated along the margin and hooked at the extremity, thus differing much from that of the female. In the Neomorpha of New Zealand, there is, as we have seen, a still wider difference in the form of the beak in relation to the manner of feeding of the two sexes. Something of the same kind has been observed with the goldfinch (*Carduelis elegans*), for I am assured by Mr. J. Jenner Weir that the bird-catchers can distinguish the males by their slightly longer beaks. The flocks of males are often found feeding on the seeds of the teazle (Dipsacus), which they can reach with their elongated beaks, whilst the females more commonly feed on the seeds of the betony or Scrophularia. With a slight difference of this kind as a foundation, we can see how the beaks of the two sexes might be made to differ greatly through natural selection. In some of the above cases, however, it is possible that the beaks of the males may have been first modified in relation to their contests with other males; and that this afterwards led to slightly changed habits of life.

★ ★ ★ ★

The males of many birds are larger than the females, and this no doubt is the result of the advantage gained by the larger and stronger males over their rivals during many generations. The difference in size between the two sexes is carried to an extreme point in several Australian species; thus the male musk-duck (Biziura), and the male *Cincloramphus cruralis* (allied to our pipits) are by measurement actually twice as large as their respective females. With many other birds the females are larger than the males; and, as formerly remarked, the explanation often given, namely, that the females have most of the work in feeding their young, will not suffice. In some few cases, as we shall hereafter see, the females apparently have acquired their greater size and strength for the sake of conquering other females and obtaining possession of the males.

* * * *

Even with the most pugnacious species it is probable that the pairing does not depend exclusively on the mere strength and courage of the male; for such males are generally decorated with various ornaments, which often become more brilliant during the breeding-season, and which are sedulously displayed before the females. The males also endeavour to charm or excite their mates by love-notes, songs, and antics; and the courtship is, in many instances, a prolonged affair. Hence it is not probable that the females are indifferent to the charms of the opposite sex, or that they are invariably compelled to yield to the victorious males. It is more probable that the females are excited, either before or after the conflict, by certain males, and thus unconsciously prefer them.

* * * *

DECORATION

I will first discuss the cases in which the males are ornamented either exclusively or in a much higher degree than the females, and in a succeeding chapter those in which both sexes are equally ornamented, and finally the rare cases in which the female is somewhat more brightly-coloured than the male. As with the artificial ornaments used by savage and civilised men, so with the natural ornaments of birds, the head is the chief seat of decoration. The ornaments, as mentioned at the commencement of this chapter, are wonderfully diversified. The plumes on the front or back of the head consist of variously-shaped feathers, sometimes capable of erection or expansion, by which their beautiful colours are fully displayed. Elegant ear-tufts are occasionally present. The head is sometimes covered with velvety down, as with the pheasant; or is naked and vividly coloured. The throat, also, is sometimes ornamented with a beard, wattles, or caruncles. Such appendages are generally brightly-coloured, and no doubt serve as ornaments, though not always ornamental in our eyes; for whilst the male is in the act of courting the female, they often swell and assume vivid tints, as in the male turkey. At such times the fleshy appendages about the head of the male Tragopan pheasant (*Ceriornis Temminckii*) swell into a large lappet on the throat and into two horns, one on each side of the splendid top-knot; and these are then coloured of the most intense blue which I have ever beheld. The African hornbill (*Bucorax abyssinicus*) inflates the scarlet bladder-like wattle on its neck, and with its wings drooping and tail expanded 'makes quite a grand appearance'. Even the iris of the eye is sometimes more brightly-coloured in the male than in the female; and this is frequently the case with the beak, for instance, in our common blackbird. In *Buceros corrugatus*, the whole beak and immense casque are coloured more conspicuously in the male than in the female; and 'the oblique grooves upon the sides of the lower mandible are peculiar to the male sex'.

The head, again, often supports fleshy appendages, filaments, and solid protuberances. These, if not common to both sexes, are always confined to the males. The solid protuberances have been described in detail by Dr. W. Marshall, who shews that they are formed either of cancellated bone coated with skin, or of dermal and other tissues. With mammals true horns are always supported on the frontal bones, but with birds various bones have been modified for this purpose; and in species of the same group the protuberances may have cores of bone, or be quite destitute of them, with intermediate gradations connecting these two extremes. Hence, as Dr. Marshall justly remarks, variations of the most different kinds have served for the development through sexual selection of these ornamental appendages. Elongated feathers or plumes spring from almost every part of the body. The feathers on the throat and breast are sometimes developed into beautiful ruffs and collars. The tail-feathers are frequently increased in length; as we see in the tail-coverts of the peacock, and in the tail itself of the Argus pheasant. With the peacock even the bones of the tail have been modified to support the heavy tail-coverts. The body of the Argus is not larger than that of a fowl; yet the length from the end of the beak to the extremity of the tail is no less than five feet three inches, and that of the beautifully ocellated secondary wing-feathers nearly three feet. In a small African night-jar (*Cosmetornis vexillarius*) one of the primary wing-feathers, during the breeding-season, attains a length of twenty-six inches, whilst the bird itself is only ten inches in length. In another closely-allied genus of night-jars, the shafts of the elongated wing-feathers are naked, except at the extremity, where there is a disc. Again, in another genus of night-jars, the tail-feathers are even still more prodigiously developed. In general the feathers of the tail are more often elongated than those of the wings, as any great elongation of the latter impedes flight. We thus see that in closely-allied birds ornaments of the same kind have been gained by the males through the development of widely different feathers.

It is a curious fact that the feathers of species belonging to very distinct groups have been modified in almost exactly the same peculiar manner. Thus the wing-feathers in one of the above-mentioned night-jars are bare along the shaft, and terminate in a disc; or are, as they are sometimes called, spoon- or racket-shaped. Feathers of this kind occur in the tail of a motmot (*Eumomota superciliaris*), of a king-fisher, finch, humming-bird, parrot, several Indian drongos (Dicrurus and Edolius, in one of which the disc stands vertically), and in the tail of certain birds of paradise. In these latter birds, similar feathers, beautifully ocellated, ornament the head, as is likewise the case with some gallinaceous birds. In an Indian bustard (*Sypheotides auritus*) the feathers forming the ear-tufts, which are about four inches in length, also terminate in discs. It is a most singular fact that the motmots, as Mr. Salvin has clearly shewn, give to their tail feathers the racket-shape by biting off the barbs, and, further, that this continued mutilation has produced a certain amount of inherited effect.

★ ★ ★ ★

I will mention only one other bird, remarkable from the extreme contrast in colour between the sexes, namely the famous bell-bird (*Chasmorhynchus niveus*) of S. America, the note of which can be distinguished at the distance of nearly three miles, and astonishes every one when first hearing it. The male is pure white, whilst the female is dusky-green; and white is a very rare colour in terrestrial species of moderate size and inoffensive habits. The male, also, as described by Waterton, has a spiral tube, nearly three inches in length, which rises from the base of the beak. It is jet-black, dotted over with minute downy feathers. This tube can be inflated with air, through a communication with the palate; and when not inflated hangs down on one side. The genus consists of four species, the male of which are very distinct, whilst the female, as described by Mr. Sclater in a very interesting paper, closely resemble each other, thus offering an excellent instance of the common rule that within the same group the males differ much more from each other than do the females. In a second species (*C. nudicollis*) the male is likewise snow-white, with the exception of a large space of naked skin on the throat and round the eyes, which during the breeding-season is of a fine green colour. In a third species (*C. tricarunculatus*) the head and neck alone of the male are white, the rest of the body being chestnut-brown, and the male of this species is provided with free filamentous projections half as long as the body—one rising from the base of the beak, and the two others from the corners of the mouth.

The coloured plumage and certain other ornaments of the adult males are either retained for life, or are periodically renewed during the summer and breeding-season. At this same season the beak and naked skin about the head frequently change colour, as with some herons, ibises, gulls, one of the bell-birds just noticed, &c. In the white ibis, the cheeks, the inflatable skin of the throat, and the basal portion of the beak then become crimson. In one of the rails, *Gallicrex cristatus*, a large red caruncle is developed during this period on the head of the male. So it is with a thin horny crest on the beak of one of the pelicans, *P. erythrorhynchus*; for, after the breeding-season, these horny crests are shed, like horns from the heads of stags, and the shore of an island in a lake in Nevada was found covered with these curious exuviæ.

Changes of colour in the plumage according to the season depend, firstly on a double annual moult, secondly on an actual change of colour in the feathers themselves, and thirdly on their dull-coloured margins being periodically shed, or on these three processes more or less combined. The shedding of the deciduary margins may be compared with the shedding of their down by very young birds; for the down in most cases arises from the summits of the first true feathers.

With respect to the birds which annually undergo a double moult, there are, firstly, some kinds, for instance snipes, swallow-plovers (Glareolæ), and curlews, in which the two sexes resemble each other, and do not change colour at any season. I do not know whether the winter plumage is thicker and warmer than the summer plumage, but warmth seems the most probable end attained of a double moult, where there is no change of colour. Secondly, there are birds, for instance, certain species of Totanus and other Grallatores, the sexes of which resemble each other, but in which the summer and winter plumage differ slightly in colour. The difference, however, in these cases is so small that it can hardly be an advantage to them; and it may, perhaps, be attributed to the direct action of the different conditions to which the birds are exposed during the two seasons. Thirdly, there are many other birds the sexes of which are alike, but which are widely different in their summer and winter plumage. Fourthly, there are birds the sexes of which differ from each other in colour; but the females, though moulting twice, retain the same colours throughout the year, whilst the males undergo a change of colour, sometimes a great one, as with certain bustards. Fifthly and lastly, there are birds the sexes of which differ from each other in both their summer and winter plumage; but the male undergoes a greater amount of change at each recurrent season than the female—of which the ruff (*Machetes pugnax*) offers a good instance.

With respect to the cause or purpose of the differences in colour between the summer and winter plumage, this may in some instances, as with the ptarmigan, serve during both seasons as a protection. When the difference between the two plumages is slight it may perhaps be attributed, as already remarked, to the direct action of the conditions of life.

* * * *

From the foregoing facts, more especially from neither sex of certain birds changing colour during either annual moult, or changing so slightly that the change can hardly be of any service to them, and from the females of other species moulting twice yet retaining the same colours throughout the year, we may conclude that the habit of annually moulting twice has not been acquired in order that the male should assume an ornamental character during the breeding-season; but that the double moult, having been originally acquired for some distinct purpose, has subsequently been taken advantage of in certain cases for gaining a nuptial plumage.

It appears at first sight a surprising circumstance that some closely-allied species should regularly undergo a double annual moult, and others only a single one. The ptarmigan, for instance, moults twice or even thrice in the year, and the blackcock only once: some of the splendidly coloured honey-suckers (Nectariniæ) of India and some sub-genera of obscurely coloured pipits (Anthus) have a double, whilst others have only a single annual moult. But the gradations in the manner of moulting, which are known to occur with various birds, shew us how species, or whole groups, might have originally acquired their double annual moult, or having once gained the habit, have again lost it. With certain bustards and plovers the vernal moult is far from complete, some feathers being renewed, and some changed in colour. There is also reason to believe that with certain bustards and rail-like birds, which properly undergo a double moult, some of the older males retain their nuptial plumage throughout the year.

* * * *

Some male birds, as before stated, become more brightly coloured in the spring, not by a vernal moult, but either by an actual change of colour in the feathers, or by their obscurely-coloured deciduary margins being shed. Changes of colour thus caused may last for a longer or shorter time. In the *Pelecanus onocrotalus* a beautiful rosy tint, with lemon-coloured marks on the breast, overspreads the whole plumage in the spring; but these tints, as Mr. Sclater states, 'do not last long, disappearing generally in about six weeks or two months after they have been attained.' Certain finches shed the margins of their feathers in the spring, and then become brighter coloured, while other finches undergo no such change. Thus the *Fringilla tristis* of the United States (as well as many other American species) exhibits its bright colours only when the winter is past, whilst our goldfinch, which exactly represents this bird in habits, and our siskin, which represents it still more closely in structure, undergo no such annual change. But a difference of this kind in the plumage of allied species is not surprising, for with the common linnet, which belongs to the same family, the crimson forehead and breast are displayed only during the summer in England, whilst in Madeira these colours are retained throughout the year.

DISPLAY BY MALE BIRDS OF THEIR PLUMAGE

Ornaments of all kinds, whether permanently or temporarily gained, are sedulously displayed by the males, and apparently serve to excite, attract, or fascinate the females. But the males will sometimes display their ornaments, when not in the presence of the females, as occasionally occurs with grouse at their balz-places, and as may be noticed with the peacock; this latter bird, however, evidently wishes for a spectator of some kind, and, as I have often see, will show off his finery before poultry, or even pigs. All naturalists who have closely attended to the habits of birds, whether in a state of nature or under confinement, are unanimously of opinion that the males take delight in displaying their beauty. Audubon frequently speaks of the male as endeavouring in various ways to charm the female. Mr. Gould, after describing some peculiarities in a male humming-bird, says he has no doubt that it has the power of displaying them to the greatest advantage before the female. Dr. Jerdon insists that the beautiful plumage of the male serves 'to fascinate and attract the female'. Mr. Bartlett, at the Zoological Gardens, expressed himself to me in the strongest terms to the same effect.

* * * *

The Gold and Amherst pheasants during their courtship not only expand and raise their splendid frills, but twist them, as I have myself seen, obliquely towards the female on whichever side she may be standing,

Polyplectron chinquis, male (T. W. Wood).

obviously in order that a large surface may be displayed before her. They likewise turn their beautiful tails and tail-coverts a little towards the same side. Mr. Bartlett has observed a male Polyplectron in the act of courtship, and has shown me a specimen stuffed in the attitude then assumed. The tail and wing-feathers of this bird are ornamented with beautiful ocelli, like those on the peacock's train. Now when the peacock displays himself, he expands and erects his tail transversely to his body, for he stands in front of the female, and has to shew off, at the same time, his rich blue throat and breast. But the breast of the Polyplectron is obscurely coloured, and the ocelli are not confined to the tail-feathers. Consequently the Polyplectron does not stand in front of the female; but he erects and expands his tail-feathers a little obliquely, lowering the expanded wing on the same side, and raising that on the opposite side. In this attitude the ocelli over the whole body are exposed at the same time before the eyes of the admiring female in one grand bespangled expanse. To which ever side she may turn, the expanded wings and the obliquely-held tail are turned towards her. The male Tragopan pheasant acts in nearly the same manner, for he raises the feathers of the body, though not the wing itself, on the side which is opposite to the female, and which would otherwise be concealed, so that nearly all the beautifully spotted feathers are exhibited at the same time.

The Argus pheasant affords a much more remarkable case. The immensely developed secondary wing-feathers are confined to the male; and each is ornamented with a row of from twenty to twenty-three ocelli, above an inch in diameter. These feathers are also elegantly marked with oblique stripes and rows of spots of a dark colour, like those on the skin of a tiger and leopard combined. These beautiful ornaments are hidden until the male shows himself off before the female. He then erects his tail, and expands his wing-feathers into a great, almost upright, circular fan or shield, which is carried in front of the body. The neck and head are held on one side, so that they are concealed by the fan; but the bird in order to see the female, before whom he is displaying himself, sometimes pushes his head between two of the long wing-feathers (as Mr. Bartlett has seen), and then presents a grotesque appearance. This must be a frequent habit with the bird in a state of nature, for Mr. Bartlett and his son on examining some perfect skins sent from the East, found a place between two of the feathers which was much frayed, as if the head had here frequently been pushed through. Mr. Wood thinks that the male can also peep at the female on one side, beyond the margin of the fan.

The ocelli on the wing-feathers are wonderful objects; for they are so shaded that, as the Duke of Argyll remarks, they stand out like balls lying

Side view of male Argus pheasant, whilst displaying before the female. Observed and sketched from nature by Mr. T. W. Wood.

loosely within sockets. When I looked at the specimen in the British Museum, which is mounted with the wings expanded and trailing downwards, I was however greatly disappointed, for the ocelli appeared flat, or even concave. But Mr. Gould soon made the case clear to me, for he held the feathers erect, in the position in which they would naturally be displayed, and now from the light shining on them from above each ocellus at once resembled the ornament called a ball and socket. These feathers have been shown to several artists, and all have expressed their admiration at the perfect shading. It may well be asked, could such artistically shaded ornaments have been formed by means of sexual selection? But it will be convenient to defer giving an answer to this question until we treat in the next chapter of the principle of gradation.

The foregoing remarks relate to the secondary wing-feathers, but the primary wing-feathers, which in most gallinaceous birds are uniformly coloured, are in the Argus pheasant equally wonderful. They are of a soft brown tint with numerous dark spots, each of which consists of two or three black dots with a surrounding dark zone. But the chief ornament is a space parallel to the dark-blue shaft, which in outline forms a perfect second feather lying within the true feather. This inner part is coloured of a lighter chestnut, and is thickly dotted with minute white points. I have shewn this feather to several persons, and many have admired it even more than the ball and socket feathers, and have declared that it was more like a work of art than of nature. Now these feathers are quite hidden on all ordinary occasions, but are fully displayed, together with the long secondary feathers, when they are all expanded together so as to form the great fan or shield.

The case of the male Argus pheasant is eminently interesting, because it affords good evidence that the most refined beauty may serve as a sexual charm, and for no other purpose. We must conclude that this is the case, as the secondary and primary wing-feathers are not at all displayed, and the ball and socket ornaments are not exhibited in full perfection until the male assumes the attitude of courtship. The Argus pheasant does not possess brilliant colours, so that his success in love appears to depend on the great size of his plumes, and on the elaboration of the most elegant patterns. Many will declare that it is utterly incredible that a female bird should be able to appreciate fine shading and exquisite patterns. It is undoubtedly a marvellous fact that she should possess this almost human degree of taste. He who thinks that he can safely gauge the discrimination and taste of the lower animals may deny that the female Argus pheasant can appreciate such refined beauty; but he will then be compelled to admit that the extraordinary attitudes assumed by the male during the act of courtship, by which the wonderful beauty of his plumage is fully displayed, are purposeless; and this is a conclusion which I for one will never admit.

* * * *

The various ornaments possessed by the males are certainly of the highest importance to them, for in some cases they have been acquired at the expense of greatly impeded powers of flight or of running. The African night-jar (Cosmetornis), which during the pairing-season has one of its primary wing-feathers developed into a streamer of very great length, is thereby much retarded in its flight, although at other times remarkable for its swiftness. The 'unwieldy size' of the secondary wing-feathers of the male Argus pheasant is said 'almost entirely to deprive the bird of flight'. The fine plumes of male birds of paradise trouble them during a high wind. The extremely long tail-feathers of the male widow-birds (Vidua) of Southern Africa render 'their flight heavy'; but as soon as these are cast off they fly as well as the females. As birds always breed when food is abundant, the males probably do not suffer much inconvenience in searching for food from their impeded powers of movement; but there can hardly be a doubt that they must be much more liable to be struck down by birds of prey. Nor can we doubt that the long train of the peacock and the long tail and wing-feathers of the Argus pheasant must render them an easier prey to any prowling tiger-cat than would otherwise be the case. Even the bright colours of many male birds cannot fail to make them conspicuous to their enemies of all kinds. Hence, as Mr. Gould has remarked, it probably is that such birds are generally of a shy disposition, as if conscious that their beauty was a source of danger, and are much more difficult to discover or approach, than the sombre coloured and comparatively tame females or than the young and as yet unadorned males.

It is a more curious fact that the males of some birds which are provided with special weapons for battle, and which in a state of nature are so pugnacious that they often kill each other, suffer from possessing certain ornaments. Cock-fighters trim the hackles and cut off the combs and gills of their cocks; and the birds are then said to be dubbed. An undubbed bird, as Mr. Tegetmeier insists, 'is at a fearful disadvantage; the comb and gills offer an easy hold to his adversary's beak, and as a cock always strikes where he holds, when once he has seized his foe, he has him entirely in his power. Even supposing that the bird is not killed, the loss of blood suffered by an undubbed cock is much greater than that sustained by one that has been trimmed.' Young turkey-cocks in fighting always seize hold of each other's wattles; and I presume that the old birds fight in the same manner. It may perhaps be objected that the comb and wattles are not ornamental, and cannot be of service to the birds in this way; but even to our eyes, the beauty of the glossy black Spanish cock is much enhanced by his white face and crimson comb; and no one who has ever seen the splendid blue wattles of the male Tragopan pheasant distended in courtship can for a moment doubt that beauty is the object gained. From the foregoing facts we clearly see that the plumes and other ornaments of the males must be of the highest importance to them; and we further see that beauty is even sometimes more important than success in battle.

★ ★ ★ ★

With respect to female birds feeling a preference for particular males, we must bear in mind that we can judge of choice being exerted only by analogy. If an inhabitant of another planet were to behold a number of young rustics at a fair courting a pretty girl, and quarrelling about her like birds at one of their places of assemblage, he would, by the eagerness of the wooers to please her and to display their finery, infer that she had the power of choice. Now with birds the evidence stands thus: they have acute powers of observation, and they seem to have some taste for the beautiful both in colour and sound. It is certain that the females occasionally exhibit, from unknown causes, the strongest antipathies and preferences for particular males. When the sexes differ in colour or in other ornaments the males with rare exceptions are the more decorated, either permanently or temporarily during the breeding-season. They sedulously display their various ornaments, exert their voices, and perform strange antics in the presence of the females. Even well-armed males, who, it might be thought, would altogether depend for success on the law of battle, are in most cases highly ornamented; and their ornaments have been acquired at the expense of some loss of power. In other cases ornaments have been acquired, at the cost of increased risk from birds and beasts of prey. With various species many individuals of both sexes congregate at the same spot, and their courtship is a prolonged affair. There is even reason to suspect that the males and females within the same district do not always succeed in pleasing each other and pairing.

What then are we to conclude from these facts and considerations? Does the male parade his charms with so much pomp and rivalry for no purpose? Are we not justified in believing that the female exerts a choice, and that she receives the addresses of the male who pleases her most? It is not probable that she consciously deliberates; but she is most excited or attracted by the most beautiful, or melodious, or gallant males. Nor need it be supposed that the female studies each stripe or spot of colour; that the peahen, for instance, admires each detail in the gorgeous train of the peacock—she is probably struck only by the general effect. Nevertheless, after hearing how carefully the male Argus pheasant displays his elegant primary wing-feathers, and erects his ocellated plumes in the right position for their full effect; or again, how the male goldfinch alternately displays his gold-bespangled wings, we ought not to feel too sure that the female does not attend to each detail of beauty. We can judge, as already remarked, of choice being exerted, only from analogy; and the mental powers of birds do not differ fundamentally from ours. From these various considerations we may conclude that the pairing of birds is not left to chance; but that those males, which are best able by their various charms to please or excite the female, are under ordinary circumstances accepted. If this be admitted, there is not much difficulty in understanding how male birds have gradually acquired their ornamental characters. All animals present individual differences, and as man can modify his domesticated birds by selecting the individuals which appear to him the most beautiful, so the habitual or even occasional preference by the female of the more attractive males would almost certainly lead to their modification; and such modifications might in the course of time be augmented to almost any extent, compatible with the existence of the species.

VARIABILITY OF BIRDS, AND ESPECIALLY OF THEIR SECONDARY SEXUAL CHARACTERS

Variability and inheritance are the foundations for the work of selection. That domesticated birds have varied greatly, their variations being inherited, is certain. That birds in a state of nature have been modified into distinct races is now universally admitted. Variations may be divided into two classes; those which appear to our ignorance to arise spontaneously, and those which are directly related to the surrounding conditions, so that all or nearly all the individuals of the same species are similarly modified. Cases of the latter kind have recently been observed with care by Mr. J. A. Allen, who shews that in the United States many species of birds gradually become more strongly coloured in proceeding southward, and more lightly coloured in proceeding westward to the arid plains of the interior. Both sexes seem generally to be affected in a like manner, but sometimes one sex more than the other. This result is not incompatible with the belief that the colours of birds are mainly due to the accumulation of successive variations through sexual selection; for even after the sexes have been greatly differentiated, climate might produce an equal effect on both sexes, or a greater effect on one sex than on the other, owing to some constitutional difference.

Individual differences between the members of the same species are admitted by every one to occur under a state of nature. Sudden and strongly marked variations are rare; it is also doubtful whether if beneficial they would often be preserved through selection and transmitted to succeeding generations. Nevertheless, it may be worth while to give the few cases which I have been able to collect, relating chiefly to colour,—simple albinism and melanism being excluded. Mr. Gould is well known to admit the existence of few varieties, for he esteems very slight differences as specific; yet he states that near Bogotá certain humming-birds belonging to the genus Cynanthus are divided into two or three races or varieties, which differ from each other in the colouring of the tail—'some having the whole of the feathers blue, while others have the eight central ones tipped with beautiful green.' It does not appear that intermediate gradations have been observed in this or the following cases. In the males alone of one of the Australian parrakeets 'the thighs in some are scarlet, in others grass-green'. In another parrakeet of the same country 'some individuals have the band across the wing-coverts bright-yellow, while in others the same part is tinged with red'. In the United States some few of the males of the Scarlet Tanager (*Tanagra rubra*) have 'a beautiful transverse band of glowing red on the smaller wing-coverts'; but this variation seems to be somewhat rare, so that its preservation through sexual selection would follow only under unusually favourable circumstances. In Bengal the Honey buzzard (*Pernis cristata*) has either a small rudimental crest on its head, or none at all: so slight a difference, however, would not have been worth notice, had not this same species possessed in Southern India 'a well-marked occipital crest formed of several graduated feathers'.

* * * *

With respect to the slight individual differences which are common, in a greater or less degree, to all the members of the same species, we have every reason to believe that they are by far the most important for the work of selection. Secondary sexual characters are eminently liable to vary, both with animals in a state of nature and under domestication. There is also reason to believe . . . that variations are more apt to occur in the male than in the female sex.

* * * *

SUMMARY ON BIRDS

Most male birds are highly pugnacious during the breeding-season, and some possess weapons adapted for fighting with their rivals. But the most pugnacious and the best armed males rarely or never depend for success solely on their power to drive away or kill their rivals, but have special means for charming the female. With some it is the power of song, or of giving forth strange cries, or instrumental music, and the males in consequence differ from the females in their vocal organs, or in the structure of certain feathers. From the curiously diversified means for producing various sounds, we gain a high idea of the importance of this means of courtship. Many birds endeavour to charm the females by love-dances or antics, performed on the ground or in the air, and sometimes at prepared places. But ornaments of many kinds, the most brilliant tints, combs and wattles, beautiful plumes, elongated feathers, top-knots, and so forth, are by far the commonest means. In some cases mere novelty appears to have acted as a charm. The ornaments of the males must be highly important to them, for they have been acquired in not a few cases at the cost of increased danger from enemies, and even at some loss of power in fighting with their rivals. The males of very many species do not assume their ornamental dress until they arrive at maturity, or they assume it only during the breeding-season, or the tints then become more vivid. Certain ornamental appendages become enlarged, turgid, and brightly coloured during the act of courtship. The males display their charms with elaborate care and to the best effect; and this is done in the presence of the females. The courtship is sometimes a prolonged affair, and many males and females congregate at an appointed place. To suppose that the females do not appreciate the beauty of the males, is to admit that their splendid decorations, all their pomp and display, are useless; and this is incredible. Birds have fine powers of discrimination, and in some few instances it can be shewn that they have a taste for the beautiful. The females, moreover, are known occasionally to exhibit a marked preference or antipathy for certain individual males.

If it be admitted that the females prefer, or are unconsciously excited by the more beautiful males, then the males would slowly but surely be rendered more and more attractive through sexual selection. That it is this sex which has been chiefly modified, we may infer from the fact that, in almost every genus where the sexes differ, the males differ much more from one another than do the females; this is well shewn in certain closely-allied representative species, in which the females can hardly be distinguished, whilst the males are quite distinct. Birds in a state of nature offer individual differences which would amply suffice for the work of sexual selection; but we have seen that they occasionally present more strongly marked variations which recur so frequently that they would immediately be fixed, if they served to allure the female. The laws of variation must determine the nature of the initial changes, and will have largely influenced the final result. The gradations, which may be observed between the males of allied species, indicate the nature of the steps through which they have passed. They explain also in the most interesting manner how certain characters have originated, such as the indented ocelli on the tail-feathers of the peacock, and the ball-and-socket ocelli on the wing-feathers of the Argus pheasant. It is evident that the brilliant colours, top-knots, fine plumes, &c., of many male birds cannot have been acquired as a protection, indeed they sometimes lead to danger. That they are not due to the direct and definite action of the conditions of life, we may feel assured, because the females have been exposed to the same conditions, and yet often differ from the males to an extreme degree. Although it is probable that changed conditions acting during a lengthened period have in some cases produced a definite effect on both sexes, or sometimes on one sex alone, the more important result will have been an increased tendency to vary or to present more strongly-marked individual differences; and such differences will have afforded an excellent ground-work for the action of sexual selection.

The laws of inheritance, irrespectively of selection, appear to have determined whether the characters acquired by the males for the sake of ornament, for producing various sounds, and for fighting together, have been transmitted to the males alone or to both sexes, either permanently, or periodically during certain seasons of the year. Why various characters should have been transmitted sometimes in one way and sometimes in another, is not in most cases known; but the period of variability seems often to have been the determining cause. When the two sexes have inherited all characters in common they necessarily resemble each other; but as the successive variations may be differently transmitted, every possible gradation may be found, even within the same genus, from the closest similarity to the widest dissimilarity between the sexes. With many closely-allied species, following nearly the same habits of life, the males have come to differ from each other chiefly through the action of sexual selection; whilst the females have come to differ chiefly from partaking more or less of the characters thus acquired by the males. The effects, moreover, of the definite action of the conditions of life, will not have been masked in the females, as in the males, by the accumulation through sexual selection of strongly-pronounced colours and other ornaments.

The individuals of both sexes, however affected, will have been kept at each successive period nearly uniform by the free intercrossing of many individuals.

With species, in which the sexes differ in colour, it is possible or probable that some of the successive variations often tended to be transmitted equally to both sexes; but that when this occurred the females were prevented from acquiring the bright colours of the males, by the destruction which they suffered during incubation. There is no evidence that it is possible by natural selection to convert one form of transmission into another. But there would not be the least difficulty in rendering a female dull-coloured, the male being still kept bright-coloured, by the selection of successive variations, which were from the first limited in their transmission to the same sex. Whether the females of many species have actually been thus modified, must at present remain doubtful. When, through the law of the equal transmission of characters to both sexes, the females were rendered as conspicuously coloured as the males, their instincts appear often to have been modified so that they were led to build domed or concealed nests.

In one small and curious class of cases the characters and habits of the two sexes have been completely transposed, for the females are larger, stronger, more vociferous and brighter coloured than the males. They have, also, become so quarrelsome that they often fight together for the possession of the males, like the males of other pugnacious species for the possession of the females. If, as seems probable, such females habitually drive away their rivals, and by the display of their bright colours or other charms endeavour to attract the males, we can understand how it is that they have gradually been rendered, by sexual selection and sexually-limited transmission, more beautiful than the males—the latter being left unmodified or only slightly modified.

* * * *

CHAPTER 16

SECONDARY SEXUAL CHARACTERS OF MAN

[From Chapter XIX of the *Descent.*]

WITH mankind the differences between the sexes are greater than in most of the Quadrumana, but not so great as in some, for instance, the mandrill. Man on an average is considerably taller, heavier, and stronger than woman, with squarer shoulders and more plainly-pronounced muscles. Owing to the relation which exists between muscular development and the projection of the brows, the superciliary ridge is generally more marked in man than in woman. His body, and especially his face, is more hairy, and his voice has a different and more powerful tone. In certain races the women are said to differ slightly in tint from the men. For instances, Schweinfurth, in speaking of a negress belonging to the Monbuttoos, who inhabit the interior of Africa a few degrees north of the Equator, says, 'Like all her race, she had a skin several shades lighter than her husband's, being something of the colour of half-roasted coffee.' As the women labour in the fields and are quite unclothed, it is not likely that they differ in colour from the men owing to less exposure to the weather. European women are perhaps the brighter coloured of the two sexes, as may be seen when both have been equally exposed.

Man is more courageous, pugnacious and energetic than woman, and has a more inventive genius. His brain is absolutely larger, but whether or not proportionately to his larger body, has not, I believe, been fully ascertained. In woman the face is rounder; the jaws and the base of the skull smaller; the outlines of the body rounder, in parts more prominent; and her pelvis is broader than in man; but this latter character may perhaps be considered rather as a primary than a secondary sexual character. She comes to maturity at an earlier age than man.

As with animals of all classes, so with man, the distinctive characters of the male sex are not fully developed until he is nearly mature; and if emasculated they never appear. The beard, for instance, is a secondary sexual character, and male children are beardless, though at an early age they have abundant hair on the head. It is probably due to the rather late appearance in life of the successive variations whereby man has acquired his masculine characters, that they are transmitted to the male sex alone. Male and female children resemble each other closely, like the young of so many other animals in which the adult sexes differ widely; they likewise resemble the mature females much more closely than the mature male. The female, however, ultimately assumes certain distinctive characters, and in the formation of her skull, is said to be intermediate between the child and the man. Again, as the young of closely allied though distinct species do not differ nearly so much from each other as do the adults, so it is with the children of the different races of man. Some have even maintained that race-differences cannot be detected in the infantile skull. In regard to colour, the new-born negro child is reddish nut-brown, which soon becomes slaty-grey; the black colour being fully developed within a year in the Soudan, but not until three years in Egypt. The eyes of the negro are at first blue, and the hair chestnut-brown rather than black, being curled only at the ends. The children of the Australians immediately after birth are yellowish-brown, and become dark at a later age. Those of the Guaranys of Paraguay are whitish-yellow, but they acquire in the course of a few weeks the yellowish-brown tint of their parents. Similar observations have been made in other parts of America.

All the secondary sexual characters of man are highly variable, even within the limits of the same race; and they differ much in the several races. These two rules hold good generally throughout the animal kingdom. In the excellent observations made on board the *Novara*, the male Australians were found to exceed the females by only 65 millim. in height, whilst with the Javans the average excess was 218 millim.; so that in this latter race the difference in height between the sexes is more than thrice as great as with the Australians. Numerous measurements were carefully made of the stature, the circumference of the neck and chest, the length of the back-bone and of the arms, in various races; and nearly all these measurements shew that the males differ much more from one another than do the females. This fact indicates that, as far as these characters are concerned, it is the male which has been chiefly modified, since the several races diverged from their common stock.

The development of the beard and the hairiness of the body differ remarkably in the men of distinct races, and even in different tribes or families of the same race. We Europeans see this amongst ourselves. In the Island of St. Kilda, according to Martin, the men do not acquire beards until the age of thirty or upwards, and even then the beards are very thin. On the Europæo-Asiatic continent, beards prevail until we pass beyond India; though with the natives of Ceylon they are often absent, as was noticed in ancient times by Diodorus. Eastward of India beards disappear, as with the Siamese, Malays, Kalmucks, Chinese, and Japanese; nevertheless, the Ainos, who inhabit the northernmost islands of the Japan Archipelago, are the hairiest men in the world. With negroes the beard is scanty or wanting, and they rarely have whiskers; in both sexes the body is frequently almost destitute of fine down. On the other hand, the Papuans of the Malay Archipelago, who are nearly as black as negroes, possess well-developed beards. In the Pacific Ocean the inhabitants of the Fiji Archipelago have large bushy beards, whilst those of the not distant archipelagoes of Tonga and Samoa are beardless; but these men belong to distinct races. In the Ellice group all the inhabitants belong to the same race; yet on one island alone, namely Nunemaya, 'the men have splendid beards'; whilst on the other islands 'they have, as a rule, a dozen straggling hairs for a beard'.

Throughout the great American continent the men may be said to be beardless; but in almost all the tribes a few short hairs are apt to appear on the face, especially in old age. With the tribes of North America, Catlin estimates that eighteen out of twenty men are completely destitute by nature of a beard; but occasionally there may be seen a man, who has neglected to pluck out the hairs at puberty, with a soft beard an inch or two in length. The Guaranys of Paraguay differ from all the surrounding tribes in having a small beard, and even some hair on the body, but no whiskers. I am informed by Mr. D. Forbes, who particularly attended to this point, that the Aymaras and Quichuas of the Cordillera are remarkably hairless, yet in old age a few straggling hairs occasionally appear on the chin. The men of these two tribes have very little hair on the various parts of the body where hair grows abundantly in Europeans, and the women have none on the corresponding parts. The hair on the head, however, attains an extraordinary length in both sexes, often reaching almost to the ground; and this is likewise the case with some of the N. American tribes. In the amount of hair, and in the general shape of the body, the sexes of the American aborigines do not differ so much from each other, as in most other races. This fact is analogous with what occurs with some closely allied monkeys; thus the sexes of the chimpanzee are not as different as those of the orang or gorilla.

* * * *

DIFFERENCE IN THE MENTAL POWERS OF THE TWO SEXES

With respect to differences of this nature between man and woman, it is probable that sexual selection has played a highly important part. I am aware that some writers doubt whether there is any such inherent difference; but this is at least probable from the analogy of the lower animals which present other secondary sexual characters. No one disputes that the bull differs in disposition from the cow, the wild-boar from the sow, the stallion from the mare, and, as is well known to the keepers of menageries, the males of the larger apes from the females. Woman seems to differ from man in mental disposition, chiefly in her greater tenderness and less selfishness; and this holds good even with savages, as shewn by a well-known passage in Mungo Park's *Travels*, and by statements made by many other travellers. Woman, owing to her maternal instincts, displays these qualities towards her infants in an eminent degree; therefore it is likely that she would often extend them towards her fellow-creatures. Man is the rival of other men; he delights in competition, and this leads to ambition which passes too easily into selfishness. These latter qualities seem to be his natural and unfortunate birthright. It is generally admitted that with woman the powers of intuition, of rapid perception, and perhaps of imitation, are more strongly marked than in man; but some, at least, of these faculties are characteristic of the lower races, and therefore of a past and lower state of civilisation.

The chief distinction in the intellectual powers of the two sexes is shewn by man's attaining to a higher eminence, in whatever he takes up, than can woman—whether requiring deep thought, reason, or imagination, or merely the use of the senses and hands. If two lists were made of the most eminent men and women in poetry, painting, sculpture, music (inclusive both of composition and performance), history, science, and philosophy, with half-a-dozen names under each subject, the two lists would not bear comparison. We may also infer, from the law of the deviation from averages, so well illustrated by Mr. Galton, in his work on *Hereditary Genius*, that if men are capable of a decided pre-eminence over women in many subjects, the average of mental power in man must be above that of woman.

Amongst the half-human progenitors of man, and amongst savages, there have been struggles between the males during many generations for the possession of the females. But mere bodily strength and size would do little for victory, unless associated with courage, perseverance, and determined energy. With social animals, the young males have to pass through many a contest before they win a female, and the older males have to retain their females by renewed battles. They have, also, in the case of mankind, to defend their females, as well as their young, from enemies of all kinds, and to hunt for their joint subsistence, But to avoid enemies or to attack them with success, to capture wild animals, and to fashion weapons, requires the aid of the higher mental faculties, namely, observation, reason, invention, or imagination. These various faculties will thus have been continually put to the test and selected during manhood; they will, moreover, have been strengthened by use during this same period of life. Consequently in accordance with the principle often alluded to, we might expect that they would at least tend to be transmitted chiefly to the male offspring at the corresponding period of manhood.

Now, when two men are put into competition, or a man with a woman, both possessed of every mental quality in equal perfection, save that one has higher energy, perseverance, and courage, the latter will generally become more eminent in every pursuit, and will gain the ascendancy. He may be said to possess genius—for genius has been declared by a great authority to be patience; and patience, in this sense, means unflinching, undaunted perseverance. But this view of genius is perhaps deficient; for without the higher powers of the imagination and reason, no eminent success can be gained in many subjects. These latter faculties, as well as the former, will have been developed in man, partly through sexual selection,—that is, through the contest of rival males, and partly through natural selection,—that is, from success in the general struggle for life; and as in both cases the struggle will have been during maturity, the characters gained will have been transmitted more fully to the male than to the female offspring. It accords in a striking manner with this view of the modification and re-inforcement of many of our mental faculties by sexual selection, that, firstly, they notoriously undergo a considerable change at puberty, and, secondly, that eunuchs remain throughout life inferior in these same qualities. Thus man has ultimately become superior to woman. It is, indeed, fortunate that the law of the equal transmission of characters to both sexes prevails with mammals; otherwise it is probable that man would have become as superior in mental endowment to woman, as the peacock is in ornamental plumage to the peahen.

It must be borne in mind that the tendency in characters acquired by either sex late in life, to be transmitted to the same sex at the same age, and of early acquired characters to be transmitted to both sexes, are rules which, though general, do not always hold. If they always held good, we might conclude (but I here exceed my proper bounds) that the inherited effects of the early education of boys and girls would be transmitted equally to both sexes; so that the present inequality in mental power between the sexes would not be effaced by a similar course of early training; nor can it have been caused by their dissimilar early training. In order that woman should reach the same standard as man, she ought, when nearly adult, to be trained to energy and perseverance, and to have her reason and imagination exercised to the highest point; and then she would probably transmit these qualities chiefly to her adult daughters. All women, however, could not be thus raised, unless during many generations those who excelled in the above robust virtues were married, and produced offspring in larger numbers than other women. As before remarked of bodily strength, although men do not now fight for their wives, and this form of selection has passed away, yet during manhood, they generally undergo a severe struggle in order to maintain themselves and their families; and this will tend to keep or even increase their mental powers, and, as a consequence, the present inequality between the sexes.

★ ★ ★ ★

THE INFLUENCE OF BEAUTY IN DETERMINING THE MARRIAGES OF MANKIND

In civilised life man is largely, but by no means exclusively, influenced in the choice of his wife by external appearance; but we are chiefly concerned with primeval times, and our only means of forming a judgment on this subject is to study the habits of existing semi-civilised and savage nations. If it can be shewn that the men of different races prefer women having various characteristics, or conversely with the women, we have then to enquire whether such choice, continued during many generations, would produce any sensible effect on the race, either on one sex or both according to the form of inheritance which has prevailed.

It will be well first to shew in some detail that savages pay the greatest attention to their personal appearance. That they have a passion for ornament is notorious; and an English philosopher goes so far as to maintain, that clothes were first made for ornament and not for warmth. As Professor Waitz remarks, 'however poor and miserable man is, he finds a pleasure in adorning himself.' The extravagance of the naked Indians of South America in decorating themselves is shown 'by a man of large stature gaining with difficulty enough by the labour of a fortnight to procure in exchange the *chica* necessary to paint himself red'. The ancient barbarians of Europe during the Reindeer period brought to their caves any brilliant or singular objects which they happened to find. Savages at the present day everywhere deck themselves with plumes, necklaces, armlets, earrings, &c. They paint themselves in the most diversified manner. 'If painted nations', as Humboldt observes, 'had been examined with the same attention as clothed nations, it would have been perceived that the most fertile imagination and the most mutable caprice have created the fashions of painting, as well as those of garments.'

In one part of Africa the eyelids are coloured black; in another the nails are coloured yellow or purple. In many places the hair is dyed of various tints. In different countries the teeth are stained black, red, blue, &c., and in the Malay Archipelago it is thought shameful to have white teeth 'like those of a dog'. Not one great country can be named, from the Polar regions in the north to New Zealand in the south, in which the aborigines do not tattoo themselves. This practice was followed by the Jews of old, and by the ancient Britons. In Africa some of the natives tattoo themselves, but it is a much more common practice to raise protuberances by rubbing salt into incisions made in various parts of the body; and these are considered by the inhabitants of Kordofan and Darfur 'to be great personal attractions'. In the Arab countries no beauty can be perfect until the cheeks 'or temples have been gashed'. In South America, as Humboldt remarks, 'a mother would be accused of culpable indifference towards her children, if she did not employ artificial means to shape the calf of the leg after the fashion of the country.' In the Old and New Worlds the shape of the skull was formerly modified during infancy in the most extraordinary manner, as is still the case in many places, and such deformities are considered ornamental. For instance, the savages of Colombia deem a much flattened head 'an essential point of beauty'.

The hair is treated with especial care in various countries; it is allowed to grow to full length, so as to reach to the ground, or is combed into 'a compact frizzled mop, which is the Papuan's pride and glory.' In Northern Africa 'a man requires a period of from eight to ten years to perfect his coiffure.' With other nations the head is shaved, and in parts of South America and Africa even the eyebrows and eyelashes are eradicated. The natives of the Upper Nile knock out the four front teeth, saying that they do not wish to resemble brutes. Further south, the Bakotas knock out only the two upper incisors, which, as Livingstone remarks, gives the face a hideous appearance, owing to the prominence of the lower jaw; but these people think the presence of the incisors most unsightly, and on beholding some Europeans, cried out, 'Look at the great teeth!' The chief Sebituani tried in vain to alter this fashion. In various parts of Africa and in the Malay Archipelago the natives file the incisors into points like those of a saw, or pierce them with holes, into which they insert studs.

As the face with us is chiefly admired for its beauty, so with savages it is the chief seat of mutilation. In all quarters of the world the septum, and more rarely the wings of the nose are pierced; rings, sticks, feathers, and other ornaments being inserted into the holes. The ears are everywhere pierced and similarly ornamented, and with the Botocudos and Lenguas of South America the hole is gradually so much enlarged that the lower edge touches the shoulder. In North and South America and in Africa either the upper or lower lip is pierced; and with the Botocudos the hole in the lower lip is so large that a disc of wood, four inches in diameter, is placed in it. Mantegazza gives a curious account of the shame felt by a South American native, and of the ridicule which he excited, when he sold his *tembeta*,—the large coloured piece of wood which is passed through the hole. In Central Africa the women perforate the lower lip and wear a crystal, which, from the movement of the tongue, has 'a wriggling motion, indescribably ludicrous during conversation'. The wife of the chief of Latooka told Sir S. Baker that Lady Baker 'would be much improved if she would extract her four front teeth from the lower jaw, and wear the long pointed polished crystal in her under lip'. Further south with the Makalolo, the upper lip is perforated, and a large metal and bamboo ring called a *pelelé*, is worn in the hole. 'This caused the lip in one case to project two inches beyond the tip of the nose; and when the lady smiled, the contraction of the muscles elevated it over her eyes. "Why do the women wear these things?" the venerable chief, Chinsurdi, was asked. Evidently surprised at such a stupid question, he replied, "For beauty! They are the only beautiful things women have; men have beards, women have none. What kind of a person would she be without the pelelé? She would not be a woman at all with a mouth like a man, but no beard." '

Hardly any part of the body, which can be unnaturally modified, has escaped. The amount of suffering thus caused must have been extreme, for many of the operations require several years for their completion, so that the idea of their necessity must be imperative. The motives are various; the men paint their bodies to make themselves appear terrible in battle; certain mutilations are connected with religious rites, or they mark the age of puberty, or the rank of the man, or they serve to distinguish the tribes. Amongst savages the same fashions prevail for long periods, and thus mutilations, from whatever cause first made, soon come to be valued as distinctive marks, But self-adornment, vanity, and the admiration of others, seem to be the commonest motives. In regard to tattooing,

I was told by the missionaries in New Zealand that when they tried to persuade some girls to give up the practice, they answered, 'We must just have a few lines on our lips; else when we grow old we shall be so very ugly.' With the men of New Zealand, a most capable judge says, 'to have fine tattooed faces was the great ambition of the young, both to render themselves attractive to the ladies, and conspicuous in war.' A star tattooed on the forehead and a spot on the chin are thought by the women in one part of Africa to be irresistible attractions. In most, but not all parts of the world, the men are more ornamented than the women, and often in a different manner; sometimes, though rarely, the women are hardly at all ornamented. As the women are made by savages to perform the greatest share of the work, and as they are not allowed to eat the best kinds of food, so it accords with the characteristic selfishness of man that they should not be allowed to obtain, or use the finest ornaments. Lastly, it is a remarkable fact, as proved by the foregoing quotations, that the same fashions in modifying the shape of the head, in ornamenting the hair, in painting, tattooing, in perforating the nose, lips, or ears, in removing or filing the teeth, &c., now prevail, and have long prevailed, in the most distant quarters of the world. It is extremely improbable that these practices, followed by so many distinct nations, should be due to tradition from any common source. They indicate the close similarity of the mind of man, to whatever race he may belong, just as do the almost universal habits of dancing, masquerading, and making rude pictures.

Having made these preliminary remarks on the admiration felt by savages for various ornaments, and for deformities most unsightly in our eyes, let us see how far the men are attracted by the appearance of their women, and what are their ideas of beauty. I have heard it maintained that savages are quite indifferent about the beauty of their women, valuing them solely as slaves; it may therefore be well to observe that this conclusion does not at all agree with the care which the women take in ornamenting themselves, or with their vanity. Burchell gives an amusing account of a Bush-woman who used as much grease, red ochre, and shining powder 'as would have ruined any but a very rich husband'. She displayed also 'much vanity and too evident a consciousness of her superiority'. Mr. Winwood Reade informs me that the negroes of the West Coast often discuss the beauty of their women. Some competent observers have attributed the fearfully common practice of infanticide partly to the desire felt by the women to retain their good looks. In several regions the women wear charms and use love-philters to gain the affections of the men; and Mr. Brown enumerates four plants used for this purpose by the women of North-Western America.

* * * *

It is well known that with many Hottentot women the posterior part of the body projects in a wonderful manner; they are steatopygous; and Sir Andrew Smith is certain that this peculiarity is greatly admired by the men. He once saw a woman who was considered a beauty, and she was so immensely developed behind, that when seated on level ground she could not rise, and had to push herself along until she came to a slope. Some of the women in various negro tribes have the same peculiarity; and, according to Burton, the Somal men 'are said to choose their wives by ranging them in a line, and by picking her out who projects farthest *a tergo*. Nothing can be more hateful to a negro than the opposite form.'

With respect to colour, the negroes rallied Mungo Park on the whiteness of his skin and the prominence of his nose, both of which they considered as 'unsightly and unnatural conformations'. He in return praised the glossy jet of their skins and the lovely depression of their noses; this they said was 'honeymouth', nevertheless they gave him food. The African Moors, also, 'knitted their brows and seemed to shudder' at the whiteness of his skin. On the eastern coast, the negro boys when they saw Burton, cried out, 'Look at the white man; does he not look like a white ape?' On the western coast, as Mr. Winwood Reade informs me, the negroes admire a very black skin more than one of a lighter tint. But their horror of whiteness may be attributed, according to this same traveller, partly to the belief held by most negroes that demons and spirits are white, and partly to their thinking it a sign of ill-health.

* * * *

The senses of man and of the lower animals seem to be so constituted that brilliant colours and certain forms, as well as harmonious and rhythmical sounds, give pleasure and are called beautiful; but why this should be so we know not. It is certainly not true that there is in the mind of man any universal standard of beauty with respect to the human body. It is, however, possible that certain tastes may in the course of time become inherited, though there is no evidence in favour of this belief; and if so, each race would possess its own innate ideal standard of beauty. It has been argued that ugliness consists in an approach to the structure of the lower animals, and no doubt this is partly true with the more civilised nations, in which intellect is highly appreciated; but this explanation will hardly apply to all forms of ugliness. The men of each race prefer what they are accustomed to; they cannot endure any great change; but they like variety, and admire each characteristic carried to a moderate extreme. Men accustomed to a nearly oval face, to straight and regular features, and to bright colours, admire, as we Europeans know, these points when strongly developed. On the other hand, men accustomed to a broad face, with high cheek-bones, a depressed nose, and a black skin, admire these peculiarities when strongly marked. No doubt characters of all kinds may be too much developed for beauty. Hence a perfect beauty, which implies many characters modified in a particular manner, will be in every race a prodigy. As the great anatomist Bichat long ago said, if every one were cast in the same mould, there would be no such thing as beauty. If all our women were to become as beautiful as the Venus de' Medici, we should for a time be charmed; but we should soon wish for variety; and as soon as we had obtained variety, we should wish to see certain characters a little exaggerated beyond the then existing common standard.

* * * *

SUMMARY

We may conclude that the greater size, strength, courage, pugnacity, and energy of man, in comparison with woman, were acquired during primeval times, and have subsequently been augmented, chiefly through the contests of rival males for the possession of the females. The greater intellectual vigour and power of invention in man is probably due to natural selection, combined with the inherited effects of habit, for the most able men will have succeeded best in defending and providing for themselves and for their wives and offspring. As far as the extreme intricacy of the subject permits us to judge, it appears that our male ape-like progenitors acquired their beards as an ornament to charm or excite the opposite sex, and transmitted them only to their male offspring. The females apparently first had their bodies denuded of hair, also as a sexual ornament; but they transmitted this character almost equally to both sexes. It is not improbable that the females were modified in other respects for the same purpose and by the same means; so that women have acquired sweeter voices and become more beautiful than men.

It deserves attention that with mankind the conditions were in many respects much more favourable for sexual selection during a very early period, when man had only just attained to the rank of manhood, than during later times. For he would then, as we may safely conclude, have been guided more by his instinctive passions, and less by foresight or reason. He would have jealously guarded his wife or wives. He would not have practised infanticide; nor valued his wives merely as useful slaves; nor have been betrothed to them during infancy. Hence we may infer that the races of men were differentiated, as far as sexual selection is concerned, in chief part at a very remote epoch; and this conclusion throws light on the remarkable fact that at the most ancient period, of which we have as yet any record, the races of man had already come to differ nearly or quite as much as they do at the present day.

The views here advanced, on the part which sexual selection has played in the history of man, want scientific precision. He who does not admit this agency in the case of the lower animals, will disregard all that I have written in the later chapters on man. We cannot positively say that this character, but not that, has been thus modified; it has however, been shewn that the races of man differ from each other and from their nearest allies, in certain characters which are of no service to them in their daily habits of life, and which it is extremely probable would have been modified through sexual selection. We have seen that with the lowest savages the people of each tribe admire their own characteristic qualities,—the shape of the head and face, the squareness of the cheek-bones, the prominence or depression of the nose, the colour of the skin, the length of the hair on the head, the absence of hair on the face and body, or the presence of a great beard, and so forth. Hence these and other such points could hardly fail to be slowly and gradually exaggerated, from the more powerful and able men in each tribe, who would succeed in rearing the largest number of offspring, having selected during many generations for their wives the most strongly characterised and therefore most attractive women. For my own part I conclude that of all the causes which have led to the differences in external appearance between the races of man, and to a certain extent between man and the lower animals, sexual selection has been the most efficient.

CHAPTER 17

GENERAL SUMMARY AND CONCLUSION

[Chapter XXI of the *Descent*.]

A BRIEF summary will be sufficient to recall to the reader's mind the more salient points in this work. Many of the views which have been advanced are highly speculative, and some no doubt will prove erroneous; but I have in every case given the reasons which have led me to one view rather than to another. It seemed worth while to try how far the principle of evolution would throw light on some of the more complex problems in the natural history of man. False facts are highly injurious to the progress of science, for they often endure long; but false views, if supported by some evidence, do little harm, for every one takes a salutary pleasure in proving their falseness: and when this is done, one path towards error is closed and the road to truth is often at the same time opened.

The main conclusion here arrived at, and now held by many naturalists who are well competent to form a sound judgment is that man is descended from some less highly organised form. The grounds upon which this conclusion rests will never be shaken, for the close similarity between man and the lower animals in embryonic development, as well as in innumerable points of structure and constitution, both of high and of the most trifling importance,—the rudiments which he retains, and the abnormal reversions to which he is occasionally liable,—are facts which cannot be disputed. They have long been known, but until recently they told us nothing with respect to the origin of man. Now when viewed by the light of our knowledge of the whole organic world, their meaning is unmistakable. The great principle of evolution stands up clear and firm, when these groups or facts are considered in connection with others, such as the mutual affinities of the members of the same group, their geographical distribution in past and present times, and their geological succession. It is incredible that all these facts should speak falsely. He who is not content to look, like a savage, at the phenomena of nature as disconnected, cannot any longer believe that man is the work of a separate act of creation. He will be forced to admit that the close resemblance of the embryo of man to that, for instance, of a dog—the construction of his skull, limbs and whole frame on the same plan with that of other mammals, independently of the uses to which the parts may be put—the occasional re-appearance of various structures, for instance of several muscles, which man does not normally possess, but which are common to the Quadrumana—and a crowd of analogous facts—all point in the plainest manner to the conclusion that man is the co-descendant with other mammals of a common progenitor.

We have seen that man incessantly presents individual differences in all parts of his body and in his mental faculties. These differences or variations seem to be induced by the same general causes, and to obey the same laws as with the lower animals. In both cases similar laws of inheritance prevail. Man tends to increase at a greater rate than his means of subsistence; consequently he is occasionally subjected to a severe struggle for existence, and natural selection will have effected whatever lies within its scope. A succession of strongly-marked variations of a similar nature is by no means requisite; slight fluctuating differences in the individual suffice for the work of natural selection; not that we have any reason to suppose that in the same species, all parts of the organisation tend to vary to the same degree. We may feel assured that the inherited effects of the long-continued use or disuse of parts will have done much in the same direction with natural selection. Modifications formerly of importance, though no longer of any special use, are long-inherited. When one part is modified, other parts change through the principle of correlation, of which we have instances in many curious cases of correlated monstrosities. Something may be attributed to the direct and definite action of the surrounding conditions of life, such as abundant food, heat or moisture; and lastly, many characters of slight physiological importance, some indeed of considerable importance, have been gained through sexual selection.

* * * *

Through the means just specified, aided perhaps by others as yet undiscovered, man has been raised to his present state. But since he attained to the rank of manhood, he has diverged into distinct races, or as they may be more fitly called, sub-species. Some of these, such as the Negro and European, are so distinct that, if specimens had been brought to a naturalist without any further information, they would undoubtedly have been considered by him as good and true species. Nevertheless all the races agree in so many unimportant details of structure and in so many mental peculiarities that these can be accounted for only by inheritance from a common progenitor; and a progenitor thus characterised would probably deserve to rank as man.

* * * *

By considering the embryological structure of man,—the homologies which he presents with the lower animals,—the rudiments which he retains,—and the reversions to which he is liable, we can partly recall in imagination the former condition of our early progenitors; and can approximately place them in their proper place in the zoological series. We thus learn that man is descended from a hairy, tailed quadruped, probably arboreal in its habits, and an inhabitant of the Old World. This creature, if its whole structure had been examined by a naturalist, would have been classed amongst the Quadrumana, as surely as the still more ancient progenitor of the Old and New World monkeys. The Quadrumana and all the higher mammals are probably derived from an ancient marsupial animal, and this through a long series of diversified forms, from some amphibian-like creature, and this again from some fish-like animal. In the dim obscurity of the past we can see that the early progenitor of all the Vertebrata must have been an aquatic animal provided with branchiæ, with the two sexes united in the same individual, and with the most important organs of the body (such as the brain and heart) imperfectly or not at all developed. This animal seems to have been more like the larvæ of the existing marine Ascidians than any other known form.

The high standard of our intellectual power and moral disposition is the greatest difficulty which presents itself, after we have been driven to this conclusion on the origin of man. But every one who admits the principle of evolution, must see that the mental powers of the higher animals, which are the same in kind with those of man, though so different in degree, are capable of advancement. Thus the interval between the mental powers of one of the higher apes and of a fish, or between those of an ant and scale-insect, is immense; yet their development does not offer any special difficulty; for with our domesticated animals, the mental faculties are certainly variable, and the variations are inherited. No one doubts that they are of the utmost importance to animals in a state of nature. Therefore the conditions are favourable for their development through natural selection. The same conclusion may be extended to man; the intellect must have been all-important to him, even at a very remote period, as enabling him to invent and use language, to make weapons, tools, traps, &c., whereby with the aid of his social habits, he long ago became the most dominant of all living creatures.

A great stride in the development of the intellect will have followed, as soon as the half-art and half-instinct of language came into use; for the continued use of language will have reacted on the brain and produced an inherited effect; and this again will have reacted on the improvement of language. As Mr. Chauncey Wright has well remarked, the largeness of the brain in man relatively to his body, compared with the lower animals, may be attributed in chief part to the early use of some simple form of language,—that wonderful engine which affixes signs to all sorts of objects and qualities, and excites trains of thought which would never arise from the mere impression of the senses, or if they did arise could not be followed out. The higher intellectual powers of man, such as those of ratiocination, abstraction, self-consciousness, &c., probably follow from the continued improvement and exercise of the other mental faculties.

The development of the moral qualities is a more interesting problem. The foundation lies in the social instincts, including under this term the family ties. These instincts are highly complex, and in the case of the lower animals give special tendencies towards certain definite actions; but the more important elements are love, and the distinct emotion of sympathy. Animals endowed with the social instincts take pleasure in one another's company, warn one another of danger, defend and aid one another in many ways. These instincts do not extend to all the individuals of the species, but only to those of the same community. As they are highly beneficial to the species, they have in all probability been acquired through natural selection.

A moral being is one who is capable of reflecting on his past actions and their motives—of approving of some and disapproving of others; and the fact that man is the one being who certainly deserves this designation, is the greatest of all distinctions between him and the lower animals. But in the fourth chapter I have endeavoured to shew that the moral sense follows, firstly, from the enduring and ever-present nature of the social instincts; secondly, from man's appreciation of the approbation and disapprobation of his fellows; and thirdly, from the high activity of his mental faculties, with past impressions extremely vivid; and in these latter respects he differs from the lower animals. Owing to this condition of mind, man cannot avoid looking both backwards and forwards, and comparing past impressions. Hence after some temporary desire or passion has mastered his social instincts, he reflects and compares the now weakened impression of such past impulses with the ever-present social instincts; and he then feels that sense of dissatisfaction which all unsatisfied instincts leave behind them, he therefore resolves to act differently for the future,—and this is conscience. Any instinct, permanently stronger or more enduring than another, gives rise to a feeling which we express by saying that it ought to be obeyed. A pointer dog, if able to reflect on his past conduct, would say to himself, I ought (as indeed we say of him) to have pointed at that hare and not have yielded to the passing temptation of hunting it.

Social animals are impelled partly by a wish to aid the members of their community in a general manner, but more commonly to perform certain definite actions. Man is impelled by the same general wish to aid his fellows; but has few or no special instincts. He differs also from the lower animals in the power of expressing his desires by words, which thus become a guide to the aid required and bestowed. The motive to give aid is likewise much modified in man: it no longer consists solely of a blind instinctive impulse, but is much influenced by the praise or blame of his fellows. The appreciation and the bestowal of praise and blame both rest on sympathy; and this emotion, as we have seen, is one of the most important elements of the social instincts. Sympathy, though gained as an instinct, is also much strengthened by exercise or habit. As all men desire their own happiness, praise or blame is bestowed on actions and motives, according as they lead to this end; and as happiness is an essential part of the general good, the greatest-happiness principle indirectly serves as a nearly safe standard of right and wrong. As the reasoning powers advance and experience is gained, the remoter effects of certain lines of conduct on the character of the individual, and on the general good, are perceived; and then the self-regarding virtues come within the scope of public opinion, and receive praise, and their opposites blame. But with the less civilised nations reason often errs, and many bad customs and base superstitions come within the same scope, and are then esteemed as high virtues, and their breach as heavy crimes.

The moral faculties are generally and justly esteemed as of higher value than the intellectual powers. But we should bear in mind that the activity of the mind in vividly recalling past impressions is one of the fundamental though secondary bases of conscience. This affords the strongest argument for educating and stimulating in all possible ways the intellectual faculties of every human being. No doubt a man with a torpid mind, if his social affections and sympathies are well developed, will be led to good actions, and may have a fairly sensitive conscience. But whatever renders the imagination more vivid and strengthens the habit of recalling and comparing past impressions, will make the conscience more sensitive, and may even somewhat compensate for weak social affections and sympathies.

The moral nature of man has reached its present standard, partly through the advancement of his reasoning powers and consequently of a just public opinion, but especially from his sympathies having been rendered more tender and widely diffused through the effects of habit, example, instruction, and reflection. It is not improbable that after long practice virtuous tendencies may be inherited. With the more civilised races, the conviction of the existence of an all-seeing Deity has had a potent influence on the advance of morality. Ultimately man does not accept the praise or blame of his fellows as his sole guide, though few escape this influence, but his habitual convictions, controlled by reason, afford him the safest rule. His conscience then becomes the supreme judge and monitor. Nevertheless the first foundation or origin of the moral sense lies in the social instincts, including sympathy; and these instincts no doubt were primarily gained, as in the case of the lower animals, through natural selection.

The belief in God has often been advanced as not only the greatest, but the most complete of all the distinctions between man and the lower animals. It is however impossible, as we have seen, to maintain that this belief is innate or instinctive in man. On the other hand a belief in all-pervading spiritual agencies seems to be universal; and apparently follows from a considerable advance in man's reason, and from a still greater advance in his faculties of imagination, curiosity and wonder. I am aware that the assumed instinctive belief in God has been used by many persons as an argument for His existence. But this is a rash argument, as we should thus be compelled to believe in the existence of many cruel and malignant spirits, only a little more powerful than man; for the belief in them is far more general than in a beneficent Deity. The idea of a universal and beneficent Creator does not seem to arise in the mind of man, until he has been elevated by long-continued culture.

* * * *

Sexual selection has been treated at great length in this work; for, as I have attempted to shew, it has played an important part in the history of the organic world. I am aware that much remains doubtful, but I have endeavoured to give a fair view of the whole case. In the lower divisions of the animal kingdom, sexual selection seems to have done nothing: such animals are often affixed for life to the same spot, or have the sexes combined in the same individual, or what is still more important, their perceptive and intellectual faculties are not sufficiently advanced to allow of the feelings of love and jealousy, or of the exertion of choice. When, however, we come to the Arthropoda and Vertebrata, even to the lowest classes in these two great Sub-Kingdoms, sexual selection has effected much.

In the several great classes of the animal kingdom,—in mammals, birds, reptiles, fishes, insects, and even crustaceans,—the differences between the sexes follow nearly the same rules. The males are almost always the wooers; and they alone are armed with special weapons for fighting with their rivals. They are generally stronger and larger than the females, and are endowed with the requisite qualities of courage and pugnacity. They are provided, either exclusively or in a much higher degree than the females, with organs for vocal or instrumental music, and with odoriferous glands. They are ornamental with infinitely diversified appendages, and with the most brilliant or conspicuous colours, often arranged in elegant patterns, whilst the females are unadorned. When the sexes differ in more important structures, it is the male which is provided with special sense-organs for discovering the female, with locomotive organs for reaching her, and often with prehensile organs for holding her. These various structures for charming or securing the female are often developed in the male during only part of the year, namely the breeding-season. They have in many cases been more or less transferred to the females; and in the latter case they often appear in her as mere rudiments. They are lost or never gained by the males after emasculation. Generally they are not developed in the male during early youth, but appear a short time before the age for reproduction. Hence in most cases the young of both sexes resemble each other; and the female somewhat resembles her young offspring throughout life. In almost every great class a few anomalous cases occur, where there has been an almost complete transposition of the characters proper to the two sexes; the females assuming characters which properly belong to the males. This surprising uniformity in the laws regulating the differences between the sexes in so many and such widely separated classes, is intelligible if we admit the action of one common cause, namely sexual selection.

Sexual selection depends on the success of certain individuals over others of the same sex, in relation to the propagation of the species; whilst natural selection depends on the success of both sexes, at all ages, in relation to the general conditions of life. The sexual struggle is of two kinds; in the one it is between individuals of the same sex, generally the males, in order to drive away or kill their rivals, the females remaining passive; whilst in the other, the struggle is likewise between the individuals of the same sex, in order to excite or charm those of the opposite sex, generally the females, which no longer remain passive, but select the more agreeable partners. This latter kind of selection is closely analogous to that which man unintentionally, yet effectually, brings to bear on his domesticated productions, when he preserves during a long period the most pleasing or useful individuals, without any wish to modify the breed.

The laws of inheritance determine whether characters gained through sexual selection by either sex shall be transmitted to the same sex, or to both; as well as the age at which they shall be developed. It appears that variations arising late in life are commonly transmitted to one and the same sex. Variability is the necessary basis for the action of selection, and is wholly independent of it. It follows from this, that variations of the same general nature have often been taken advantage of and accumulated through sexual selection in relation to the propagation of the species, as well as through natural selection in relation to the general purposes of life. Hence secondary sexual characters, when equally transmitted to both sexes can be distinguished from ordinary specific characters only by the light of analogy. The modifications acquired through sexual selection are often so strongly pronounced that the two sexes have frequently been ranked as distinct species, or even as distinct genera. Such strongly-marked differences must be in some manner highly important; and we know that they have been acquired in some instances at the cost not only of inconvenience, but of exposure to actual danger.

The belief in the power of sexual selection rests chiefly on the following considerations. Certain characters are confined to one sex; and this alone renders it probable that in most cases they are connected with the act of reproduction. In innumerable instances these characters are fully developed only at maturity, and often during only a part of the year, which is always the breeding-season. The males (passing over a few exceptional cases) are the more active in courtship; they are the better armed, and are rendered the more attractive in various ways. It is to be especially observed that the males display their attractions with elaborate care in the presence of the females; and that they rarely or never display them excepting during the season of love. It is incredible that all this should be purposeless. Lastly we have distinct evidence with some quadrupeds and birds, that the individuals of one sex are capable of feeling a strong antipathy or preference for certain individuals of the other sex.

* * * *

The reader who has taken the trouble to go through the several chapters devoted to sexual selection, will be able to judge how far the conclusions at which I have arrived are supported by sufficient evidence. If he accepts these conclusions he may, I think, safely extend them to mankind; but it would be superfluous here to repeat what I have so lately said on the manner in which sexual selection apparently has acted on man, both on the male and female side, causing the two sexes to differ in body and mind, and the several races to differ from each other in various characters, as well as from their ancient and lowly-organized progenitors.

* * * *

Man scans with scrupulous care the character and pedigree of his horses, cattle, and dogs before he matches them; but when he comes to his own marriage he rarely, or never, takes any such care. He is impelled by nearly the same motives as the lower animals, when they are left to their own free choice, though he is in so far superior to them that he highly values mental charms and virtues. On the other hand he is strongly attracted by mere wealth or rank. Yet he might by selection do something not only for the bodily constitution and frame of his offspring, but for their intellectual and moral qualities. Both sexes ought to refrain from marriage if they are in any marked degree inferior in body or mind; but such hopes are Utopian and will never be even partially realised until the laws of inheritance are thoroughly known. Everyone does good service, who aids towards this end. When the principles of breeding and inheritance are better understood, we shall not hear ignorant members of our legislature rejecting with scorn a plan for ascertaining whether or not consanguineous marriages are injurious to man.

The advancement of the welfare of mankind is a most intricate problem: all ought to refrain from marriage who cannot avoid abject poverty for their children; for poverty is not only a great evil, but tends to its own increase by leading to recklessness in marriage. On the other hand, as Mr. Galton has remarked, if the prudent avoid marriage, whilst the reckless marry, the inferior members tend to supplant the better members of society. Man, like every other animal, has no doubt advanced to his present high condition through a struggle for existence consequent on his rapid multiplication; and if he is to advance still higher, it is to be feared that he must remain subject to a severe struggle. Otherwise he would sink into indolence, and the more gifted men would not be more successful in the battle of life than the less gifted. Hence our natural rate of increase, though leading to many and obvious evils, must not be greatly diminished by any means. There should be open competition for all men; and the most able should not be prevented by laws or customs from succeeding best and rearing the largest number of offspring. Important as the struggle for existence has been and even still is, yet as far as the highest part of man's nature is concerned there are other agencies more important. For the moral qualities are advanced, either directly or indirectly, much more through the effects of habit, the reasoning powers, instruction, religion, &c., than through natural selection; though to this latter agency may be safely attributed the social instincts, which afforded the basis for the development of the moral sense.

The main conclusion arrived at in this work, namely, that man is descended from some lowly organised form, will, I regret to think, be highly distasteful to many. But there can hardly be a doubt that we are descended from barbarians. The astonishment which I felt on first seeing a party of Fuegians on a wild and broken shore will never be forgotten by me, for the reflection at once rushed into my mind—such were our ancestors. These men were absolutely naked and bedaubed with paint, their long hair was tangled, their mouths frothed with excitement, and their expression was wild, startled, and distrustful. They possessed hardly any arts, and like wild animals lived on what they could catch; they had no government, and were merciless to every one not of their own small tribe. He who has seen a savage in his native land will not feel much shame, if forced to acknowledge that the blood of some more humble creature flows in his veins. For my own part I would as soon be descended from that heroic little monkey, who braved his dreaded enemy in order to save the life of his keeper, or from that old baboon, who descending from the mountains, carried away in triumph his young comrade from a crowd of astonished dogs—as from a savage who delights to torture his enemies, offers up bloody sacrifices, practises infanticide without remorse, treats his wives like slaves, knows no decency, and is haunted by the grossest superstitions.

Man may be excused for feeling some pride at having risen, though not through his own exertions, to the very summit of the organic scale; and the fact of his having thus risen, instead of having been aboriginally placed there, may give him hope for a still higher destiny in the distant future. But we are not here concerned with hopes or fears, only with the truth as far as our reason permits us to discover it; and I have given the evidence to the best of my ability. We must, however, acknowledge, as it seems to me, that man with all his noble qualities, with sympathy which feels for the most debased, with benevolence which extends not only to other men but to the humblest living creature, with his god-like intellect which has penetrated into the movements and constitution of the solar system—with all these exalted powers—Man still bears in his bodily frame the indelible stamp of his lowly origin.

PART FIVE

THE EXPRESSION OF THE EMOTIONS

CHAPTER 18

THE EXPRESSION OF THE EMOTIONS IN MONKEYS

[Based on Chapter V of the *Expression of the Emotions in Man and Animals*. Darwin started making notes on human expressions in 1839, with the birth of his first child. He intended to include a chapter on this subject in the *Descent of Man*, but when he started actual writing, he found he had too much material—enough material, in fact, for a whole book by itself. So on January 17th, 1871, two days after finishing the correction of the last proofs of *Descent*, he started writing the *Expression of the Emotions*. The book was published in November, 1872.

In his introduction to the book, Darwin points out that he has found six different means profitable in the study of emotional expression. In the first place, to study infants. In the second place, to study the insane 'as they are liable to the strongest passions, and give uncontrolled vent to them'. Third, to study photographs, and to get the reaction of different people to particular photographs. Fourth, to study painting and sculpture—though in practice, Darwin found this approach to be disappointing. Fifth, it seemed to him 'highly important to ascertain whether the same expressions and gestures prevail, as has so often been asserted without much evidence, with all of the races of mankind, especially with those who have associated but little with Europeans'. Lastly, he attended, 'as closely as I could, to the expression of the several passions in some of the common animals; and this I believe to be of paramount importance . . . as affording the safest basis for generalization on the causes, or origin, of the various movements of Expression. In observing animals, we are not so likely to be biased by our imagination; and we may feel safe that their expressions are not conventional.'

Darwin devotes the first three chapters of his book to a discussion of the three general principles that seem to him 'to account for most of the expressions and gestures involuntarily used by man and the lower animals, under the influence of various emotions and sensations'. These he calls 'the principle of serviceable associated habits, the principle of antithesis, and the principle of the direct action of the nervous system'. These principles are discussed again in the concluding chapter of the book, which is included in the present anthology.

After these general chapters, Darwin takes up the expression of emotion in animals, giving special attention to dogs, cats, horses and monkeys.

The body of the book, eight chapters, is given over to 'special expressions of man'. The list of chapter headings is interesting, in that it reflects a rough classification of human emotions. The headings are: 'Suffering and Weeping'; 'Low Spirits, Anxiety, Grief, Dejection, Despair'; 'Joy, High Spirits, Love, Tender Feelings, Devotion'; 'Reflection—Meditation—Ill-temper—Sulkiness—Determination'; 'Hatred and Anger'; 'Disdain—Contempt—Disgust—Guilt—Pride, etc.—Helplessness—Patience—Affirmation and Negation'; 'Surprise—Astonishment—Fear—Horror'; 'Self-attention—Shame—Shyness—Modesty: Blushing'.

As samples of the book, we have included here the sections on monkeys from Chapter V, and all of Chapter XIII which Darwin entitled 'Self-attention—Shame—Shyness—Modesty: Blushing'. We have also included the last chapter, 'Concluding Remarks and Summary.'

It seemed to us appropriate, in connection with this aspect of Darwin's work, to reprint the 'Biographical sketch of an Infant' which he published in 1877, in *Mind, A Quarterly Review of Psychology and Philosophy*.]

THE various species and genera of monkeys express their feelings in many different ways; and this fact is interesting, as in some degree bearing on the question, whether the so-called races of man should be ranked as distinct species or varieties; for, as we shall see in the following chapters, the different races of man express their emotions and sensations with remarkable uniformity throughout the world. Some of the expressive actions of monkeys are interesting in another way, namely from being closely analogous to those of man. As I have had no opportunity of observing any one species of the group under all circumstances, my miscellaneous remarks will be best arranged under different states of the mind.

PLEASURE, JOY, AFFECTION

It is not possible to distinguish in monkeys, at least without more experience than I have had, the expression of pleasure or joy from that of affection. Young chimpanzees make a kind of barking noise, when pleased by the return of any one to whom they are attached. When this noise, which the keepers call a laugh, is uttered, the lips are protruded; but so they are under various other emotions. Nevertheless I could perceive that when they were pleased the form of the lips differed a little from that assumed when they were angered. If a young chimpanzee be tickled—and the armpits are particularly sensitive to tickling, as in the case of our children,—a more decided chuckling or laughing sound is uttered; though the laughter is sometimes noiseless. The corners of the mouth are then drawn backwards; and this sometimes causes the lower eyelids to be slightly wrinkled. But this wrinkling, which is so characteristic of our own laughter, is more plainly seen in some other monkeys. The teeth in the upper jaw in the chimpanzee are not exposed when they utter their laughing noise, in which respect they differ from us. But their eyes sparkle and grow brighter, as Mr. W. L. Martin, who has particularly attended to their expression, states.

Young Orangs, when tickled, likewise grin and make a chuckling sound; and Mr. Martin says that their eyes grow brighter. As soon as their laughter ceases, an expression may be detected passing over their faces, which, as Mr. Wallace remarked to me, may be called a smile. I have also noticed something of the same kind with the chimpanzee. Dr. Duchenne—and I cannot quote a better authority—informs me that he kept a very tame monkey in his house for a year; and when he gave it during meal-times some choice delicacy, he observed that the corners of its mouth were slightly raised; thus an expression of satisfaction, partaking of the nature of an incipient smile, and resembling that often seen on the face of man, could be plainly perceived in this animal.

The *Cebus azaræ*, when rejoiced at again seeing a beloved person, utters a peculiar tittering (*kichernden*) sound. It also expresses agreeable sensations, by drawing back the corners of its mouth, without producing any sound. Rengger calls this movement laughter, but it would be more appropriately called a smile. The form of the mouth is different when either pain or terror is expressed, and high shrieks are uttered. Another species of *Cebus* in the Zoological Gardens (*C. hypoleucus*) when pleased, makes a reiterated shrill note, and likewise draws back the corners of its mouth, apparently through the contraction of the same muscles as with us. So does the Barbary ape (*Inuus ecaudatus*) to an extraordinary degree; and I observed in this monkey that the skin of the lower eyelids then became much wrinkled. At the same time it rapidly moved its lower jaw or lips in a spasmodic manner, the teeth being exposed; but the noise produced was hardly more distinct than that which we sometimes call silent laughter. Two of the keepers affirmed that this slight sound was the animal's laughter, and when I expressed some doubt on this head (being at the time quite inexperienced), they made it attack or rather threaten a hated Entellus monkey, living in the same compartment. Instantly the whole expression of the face of the Inuus changed; the mouth was opened much more widely, the canine teeth were more fully exposed, and a hoarse barking noise was uttered.

The Anubis baboon (*Cynocephalus anubis*) was first insulted and put into a furious rage, as was easily done, by his keeper, who then made friends with him and shook hands. As the reconciliation was effected the baboon rapidly moved up and down his jaws and lips, and looked pleased. When we laughed heartily, a similar movement, or quiver, may be observed more or less distinctly in our jaws; but with man the muscles of the chest are more particularly acted on, whilst with this baboon, and with some other monkeys, it is the muscles of the jaws and lips which are spasmodically affected.

I have already had occasion to remark on the curious manner in which two or three species of Macacus and the *Cynopithecus niger* draw back their ears and utter a slight jabbering noise, when they are pleased by being caressed. With the Cynopithecus, the corners of the mouth are at the same time drawn backwards and upwards, so that the teeth are exposed. Hence this expression would never be recognized by a stranger as one of pleasure. The crest of long hairs on the forehead is depressed, and apparently the whole skin of the head drawn backwards. The eyebrows are thus raised a little, and the eyes assume a staring appearance. The lower eyelids also become slightly wrinkled; but this wrinkling is not conspicuous, owing to the permanent transverse furrows on the face.

PAINFUL EMOTIONS AND SENSATIONS

With monkeys the expression of slight pain, or of any painful emotion, such as grief, vexation, jealousy, &c., is not easily distinguished from that of moderate anger; and these states of mind readily and quickly pass into each other. Grief, however, with some species is certainly exhibited by weeping. A woman, who sold a monkey to the Zoological Society, believed to have come from Borneo (*Macacus maurus* or *M. inornatus* of Gray), said that it often cried; and Mr. Bartlett, as well as the keeper Mr. Sutton, have repeatedly seen it, when grieved, or even when much pitied, weeping so copiously that the tears rolled down its cheeks. There is, however, something strange about this case, for two specimens subsequently kept in the Gardens, and believed to be the same species, have never been seen to weep, though they were carefully observed by the keeper and myself when much distressed and loudly screaming. Rengger states that the eyes of the *Cebus azaræ* fill with tears, but not sufficiently to overflow, when it is prevented getting some much desired object, or is much frightened. Humboldt also asserts that the eyes of the *Callithrix sciureus* 'instantly fill with tears when it is seized with fear'; but when this pretty little monkey in the Zoological Gardens was teased, so as to cry out loudly, this did not occur. I do not, however, wish to throw the least doubt on the accuracy of Humboldt's statement.

Cynopithecus niger, in a placid condition. Drawn from life by Mr. Wolf.

The same, when pleased by being caressed.

The appearance of dejection in young orangs and chimpanzees, when out of health, is as plain and almost as pathetic as in the case of our children. This state of mind and body is shown by their listless movements, fallen countenances, dull eyes, and changed complexion.

ANGER

This emotion is often exhibited by many kinds of monkeys, and is expressed, as Mr. Martin remarks, in many different ways. 'Some species, when irritated, pout the lips, gaze with a fixed and savage glare on their foe, and make repeated short starts as if about to spring forward, uttering at the same time inward guttural sounds. Many display their anger by suddenly advancing, making abrupt starts, at the same time opening the mouth and pursing up the lips, so as to conceal the teeth, while the eyes are daringly fixed on the enemy, as if in savage defiance. Some again, and principally the long-tailed monkeys, or Guenons, display their teeth, and accompany their malicious grins with a sharp, abrupt, reiterated cry.' Mr. Sutton confirms the statement that some species uncover their teeth when enraged, whilst others conceal them by the protrusion of their lips; and some kinds draw back their ears. The *Cynopithecus niger*, lately referred to, acts in this manner, at the same time depressing the crest of hair on its forehead, and showing its teeth; so that the movements of the features from anger are nearly the same as those from pleasure; and the two expressions can be distinguished only by those familiar with the animal.

Baboons often show their passion and threaten their enemies in a very odd manner, namely, by opening their mouths widely as in the act of yawning. Mr. Bartlett has often seen two baboons, when first placed in the same compartment, sitting opposite to each other and thus alternately opening their mouths; and this action seems frequently to end in a real yawn. Mr. Bartlett believes that both animals wish to show to each other that they are provided with a formidable set of teeth, as is undoubtedly the case. As I could hardly credit the reality of this yawning gesture, Mr. Bartlett insulted an old baboon and put him into a violent passion; and he almost immediately thus acted. Some species of Macacus and of Ceropithecus behave in the same manner. Baboons likewise show their anger, as was observed by Brehm with those which he kept alive in Abyssinia, in another manner, namely, by striking the ground with one hand, 'like an angry man striking the table with his fist.' I have seen this movement with the baboons in the Zoological Gardens; but sometimes the action seems rather to represent the searching for a stone or other object in their beds of straw.

Mr. Sutton has often observed the face of the *Macacus rhesus*, when much enraged, growing red. As he was mentioning this to me, another monkey attacked a *rhesus*, and I saw its face redden as plainly as that of a man in a violent passion. In the course of a few minutes, after the battle, the face of this monkey recovered its natural tint. At the same time that the face reddened, the naked posterior part of the body, which is always

Chimpanzee disappointed and sulky. Drawn from life by Mr. Wood.

red, seemed to grow still redder; but I cannot positively assert that this was the case. When the Mandrill is in any way excited, the brilliantly coloured, naked parts of the skin are said to become still more vividly coloured.

With several species of baboons the ridge of the forehead projects much over the eyes, and is studded with a few long hairs, representing our eyebrows. These animals are always looking about them, and in order to look upwards they raise their eyebrows. They have thus, as it would appear, acquired the habit of frequently moving their eyebrows. However this may be, many kinds of monkeys, especially the baboons, when angered or in any way excited, rapidly and incessantly move their eyebrows up and down, as well as the hairy skin of their foreheads. As we associate in the case of man the raising and lowering of the eyebrows with definite states of the mind, the almost incessant movement of the eyebrows by monkeys gives them a senseless expression. I once observed a man who had a trick of continually raising his eyebrows without any corresponding emotion, and this gave to him a foolish appearance; so it is with some persons who keep the corners of their mouths a little drawn backwards and upwards, as if by an incipient smile, though at the time they are not amused or pleased.

A young orang, made jealous by her keeper attending to another monkey, slightly uncovered her teeth, and, uttering a peevish noise like *tish-shist*, turned her back on him. But orangs and chimpanzees, when a little more angered, protrude their lips greatly, and make a harsh barking noise. A young female chimpanzee, in a violent passion, presented a curious resemblance to a child in the same state. She screamed loudly with widely open mouth, the lips being retracted so that the teeth were fully exposed. She threw her arms wildly about, sometimes clasping them over her head. She rolled on the ground, sometimes on her back, sometimes on her belly, and bit everything within reach. A young gibbon (*Hylobates syndactylus*) in a passion has been described as behaving in almost exactly the same manner.

The lips of young orangs and chimpanzees are protruded, sometimes to a wonderful degree, under various circumstances. They act thus, not only when slightly angered, sulky, or disappointed, but when alarmed at anything—in one instance, at the sight of a turtle,—and likewise when pleased. But neither the degree of protrusion nor the shape of the mouth is exactly the same, as I believe, in all cases; and the sounds which are then uttered are different. The accompanying drawing represents a chimpanzee made sulky by an orange having been offered him, and then taken away. A similar protrusion or pouting of the lips, though to a much slighter degree, may be seen in sulky children.

Many years ago, in the Zoological Gardens, I placed a looking-glass on the floor before two young orangs, who, as far as it was known, had never before seen one. At first they gazed at their own images with the most steady surprise, and often changed their point of view. They then approached close and protruded their lips towards the image, as if to kiss it, in exactly the same manner as they had previously done towards each other, when first placed, a few days before, in the same room. They next made all sorts of grimaces, and put themselves in various attitudes before the mirror; they pressed and rubbed the surface; they placed their hands at different distances behind it; looked behind it; and finally seemed almost frightened, started a little, became cross, and refused to look any longer.

When we try to perform some little action which is difficult and requires precision, for instance, to thread a needle, we generally close our lips firmly, for the sake, I presume, of not disturbing our movements by breathing; and I noticed the same action in a young Orang. The poor little creature was sick, and was amusing itself by trying to kill the flies on the window-panes with its knuckles; this was difficult as the flies buzzed about, and at each attempt the lips were firmly compressed, and at the same time slightly protruded.

Although the countenances, and more especially the gestures, of orangs and chimpanzees are in some respects highly expressive, I doubt whether on the whole they are so expressive as those of some other kinds of monkeys. This may be attributed in part to their ears being immovable, and in part to the nakedness of their eyebrows, of which the movements are thus rendered less conspicuous. When, however, they raise their eyebrows their foreheads become, as with us, transversely wrinkled. In comparison with man, their faces are inexpressive, chiefly owing to their not frowning under any emotion of the mind—that is, as far as I have been able to observe, and I carefully attended to this point. Frowning, which is one of the most important of all the expressions in man, is due to the contraction of the corrugators by which the eyebrows are lowered and brought together, so that vertical furrows are formed on the forehead. Both the orang and chimpanzee are said to possess this muscle, but it seems rarely brought into action, at least in a conspicuous manner. I made my hands into a sort of cage, and placing some tempting fruit within, allowed both a young orang and chimpanzee to try their utmost to get it out; but although they grew rather cross, they showed not a trace of a frown. Nor was there any frown when they were enraged. Twice I took two chimpanzees from their rather dark room suddenly into bright sunshine, which would certainly have caused us to frown; they blinked and winked their eyes, but only once did I see a very slight frown. On another occasion, I tickled the nose of a chimpanzee with a straw, and as it crumpled up its face, slight vertical furrows appeared between the eyebrows. I have never seen a frown on the forehead of the orang.

The gorilla, when enraged, is described as erecting its crest of hair, throwing down its under lip, dilating its nostrils, and uttering terrific yells. Messrs. Savage and Wyman state that the scalp can be freely moved backwards and forwards, and that when the animal is excited it is strongly contracted; but I presume that they mean by this latter expression that the scalp is lowered; for they likewise speak of the young chimpanzee, when crying out, 'as having the eyebrows strongly contracted.' The great power of movement in the scalp of the gorilla, of many baboons and other monkeys, deserves notice in relation to the power possessed by some few men, either through reversion or persistence, of voluntarily moving their scalps.

ASTONISHMENT, TERROR

A living fresh-water turtle was placed at my request in the same compartment in the Zoological Gardens with many monkeys; and they showed unbounded astonishment, as well as some fear. This was displayed by their remaining motionless, staring intently with widely opened eyes, their eyebrows being often moved up and down. Their faces seemed somewhat lengthened. They occasionally raised themselves on their hind-legs to get a better view. They often retreated a few feet, and then turning their heads over one shoulder, again stared intently. It was curious to observe how much less afraid they were of the turtle than of a living snake which I had formerly placed in their compartment; for in the course of a few minutes some of the monkeys ventured to approach and touch the turtle. On the other hand, some of the larger baboons were greatly terrified, and grinned as if on the point of screaming out. When I showed a little dressed-up doll to the *Cynopithecus niger*, it stood motionless, stared intently with widely opened eyes, and advanced its ears a little forwards. But when the turtle was placed in its compartment, this monkey also moved its lips in an odd, rapid, jabbering manner, which the keeper declared was meant to conciliate or please the turtle.

I was never able clearly to perceive that the eyebrows of astonished monkeys were kept permanently raised, though they were frequently moved up and down. Attention, which precedes astonishment, is expressed by man by a slight raising of the eyebrows; and Dr. Duchenne informs me that when he gave to the monkey formerly mentioned some quite new article of food, it elevated its eyebrows a little, thus assuming an appearance of close attention. It then took the food in its fingers, and, with lowered or rectilinear eyebrows, scratched, smelt, and examined it, —an expression of reflection being thus exhibited. Sometimes it would throw back its head a little, and again with suddenly raised eyebrows re-examine and finally taste the food.

In no case did any monkey keep its mouth open when it was astonished. Mr. Sutton observed for me a young orang and chimpanzee during a considerable length of time; and however much they were astonished, or whilst listening intently to some strange sound, they did not keep their mouths open. This fact is surprising, as with mankind hardly any expression is more general than a widely opened mouth under the sense of astonishment. As far as I have been able to observe, monkeys breathe more freely through their nostrils than men do; and this may account for their not opening their mouths when they are astonished; for, as we shall see in a future chapter, man apparently acts in this manner when startled, at first for the sake of quickly drawing a full inspiration, and afterwards for the sake of breathing as quietly as possible.

Terror is expressed by many kinds of monkeys by the utterance of shrill screams; the lips being drawn back, so that the teeth are exposed. The hair becomes erect, especially when some anger is likewise felt. Mr. Sutton has distinctly seen the face of the *Macacus rhesus* grow pale from fear. Monkeys also tremble from fear; and sometimes they void their excretions. I have seen one which, when caught, almost fainted from an excess of terror.

CHAPTER 19

SPECIAL EXPRESSIONS OF MAN: BLUSHING

[Chapter XIII of *Expression of the Emotions.*]

BLUSHING is the most peculiar and most human of all expressions. Monkeys redden from passion, but it would require an overwhelming amount of evidence to make us believe that any animal could blush. The reddening of the face from a blush is due to the relaxation of the muscular coats of the small arteries, by which the capillaries become filled with blood; and this depends on the proper vaso-motor centre being affected. No doubt if there be at the same time much mental agitation, the general circulation will be affected; but it is not due to the action of the heart that the network of minute vessels covering the face becomes under a sense of shame gorged with blood. We can cause laughing by tickling the skin, weeping or frowning by a blow, trembling from the fear of pain, and so forth; but we cannot cause a blush, as Dr. Burgess remarks, by any physical means,—that is by any action on the body. It is the mind which must be affected. Blushing is not only involuntary; but the wish to restrain it, by leading to self-attention actually increases the tendency.

The young blush much more freely than the old, but not during infancy, which is remarkable, as we know that infants at a very early age redden from passion. I have received authentic accounts of two little girls blushing at the ages of between two and three years; and of another sensitive child, a year older, blushing, when reproved for a fault. Many children, at a somewhat more advanced age, blush in a strongly marked manner. It appears that the mental powers of infants are not as yet sufficiently developed to allow of their blushing. Hence, also, it is that idiots rarely blush. Dr. Crichton Browne observed for me those under his care, but never saw a genuine blush, though he has seen their faces flush, apparently from joy, when food was placed before them, and from anger. Nevertheless some, if not utterly degraded, are capable of blushing. A microcephalous idiot, for instance, thirteen years old, whose eyes brightened a little when he was pleased or amused, has been described by

Dr. Behn, as blushing and turning to one side, when undressed for medical examination.

Women blush much more than men. It is rare to see an old man, but not nearly so rare to see an old woman blushing. The blind do not escape. Laura Bridgman, born in this condition, as well as completely deaf, blushes. The Rev. R. H. Blair, Principal of the Worcester College, informed me that three children born blind, out of seven or eight then in the Asylum, are great blushers. The blind are not at first conscious that they are observed, and it is a most important part of their education, as Mr. Blair informs me, to impress this knowledge on their minds; and the impression thus gained would greatly strengthen the tendency to blush, by increasing the habit of self-attention.

The tendency to blush is inherited. Dr. Burgess gives the case of a family consisting of a father, mother, and ten children, all of whom, without exception, were prone to blush to a most painful degree. The children were grown up; 'and some of them were sent to travel in order to wear away this diseased sensibility, but nothing was of the slightest avail.' Even peculiarities in blushing seem to be inherited. Sir James Paget, whilst examining the spine of a girl, was struck at her singular manner of blushing; a big splash of red appeared first on one cheek, and then other splashes, variously scattered over the face and neck. He subsequently asked the mother whether her daughter always blushed in this peculiar manner; and was answered, 'Yes, she takes after me.' Sir J. Paget then perceived that by asking this question he had caused the mother to blush; and she exhibited the same peculiarity as her daughter.

In most cases the face, ears and neck are the sole parts which redden; but many persons, whilst blushing intensely, feel that their whole bodies grow hot and tingle; and this shows that the entire surface must be in some manner affected. Blushes are said sometimes to commence on the forehead, but more commonly on the cheeks, afterwards spreading to the ears and neck. In two Albinos examined by Dr. Burgess, the blushes commenced by a small circumsribed spot on the cheeks, over the parotidean plexus of nerves, and then increased into a circle; between this blushing circle and the blush on the neck there was an evident line of demarcation; although both arose simultaneously. The retina, which is naturally red in the Albino, invariably increased at the same time in redness. Every one must have noticed how easily after one blush fresh blushes chase each other over the face. Blushing is preceded by a peculiar sensation in the skin. According to Dr. Burgess the reddening of the skin is generally succeeded by a slight pallor, which shows that the capillary vessels contract after dilating. In some rare cases paleness instead of redness is caused under conditions which would naturally induce a blush. For instance, a young lady told me that in a large and crowded party she caught her hair so firmly on the button of a passing servant, that it took some time before she could be extricated; from her sensations she imagined that she had blushed crimson; but was assured by a friend that she had turned extremely pale.

I was desirous to learn how far down the body blushes extend; and Sir J. Paget, who necessarily has frequent opportunities for observation, has kindly attended to this point for me during two or three years. He finds that with women who blush intensely on the face, ears, and nape of neck, the blush does not commonly extend any lower down the body. It is rare to see it as low down as the collar-bones and shoulder-blades; and he has never himself seen a single instance in which it extended below the upper part of the chest. He has also noticed that blushes sometimes die away downwards, not gradually and insensibly, but by irregular ruddy blotches. Dr. Langstaff has likewise observed for me several women whose bodies did not in the least redden while their faces were crimsoned with blushes. With the insane, some of whom appear to be particularly liable to blushing, Dr. J. Crichton Browne has several times seen the blush extend as far down as the collar-bones, and in two instances to the breasts. He gives me the case of a married woman, aged twenty-seven, who suffered from epilepsy. On the morning after her arrival in the Asylum, Dr. Browne, together with his assistants, visited her whilst she was in bed. The moment that he approached, she blushed deeply over her cheeks and temples; and the blush spread quickly to her ears. She was much agitated and tremulous. He unfastened the collar of her chemise in order to examine the state of her lungs; and then a brilliant blush rushed over her chest, in an arched line over the upper third of each breast, and extended downwards between the breasts nearly to the ensiform cartilage of the sternum. This case is interesting, as the blush did not thus extend downwards until it became intense by her attention being drawn to this part of her person. As the examination proceeded she became composed, and the blush disappeared; but on several subsequent occasions the same phenomena were observed.

The foregoing facts show that, as a general rule, with English women, blushing does not extend beneath the neck and upper part of the chest. Nevertheless Sir J. Paget informs me that he has lately heard of a case, on which he can fully rely, in which a little girl, shocked by what she imagined to be an act of indelicacy, blushed all over her abdomen and the upper parts of her legs. Moreau also relates, on the authority of a celebrated painter, that the chest, shoulders, arms, and whole body of a girl, who unwillingly consented to serve as a model, reddened when she was first divested of her clothes.

It is a rather curious question why, in most cases the face, ears, and neck alone redden, inasmuch as the whole surface of the body often tingles and grows hot. This seems to depend, chiefly, on the face and adjoining parts of the skin having been habitually exposed to the air, light, and alternations of temperature, by which the small arteries not only have acquired the habit of readily dilating and contracting, but appear to have become unusually developed in comparison with other parts of the surface. It is probably owing to this same cause, as M. Moreau and Dr. Burgess have remarked, that the face is so liable to redden under various circumstances, such as a fever-fit, ordinary heat, violent exertion, anger, a slight blow, &c.; and on the other hand that it is liable to grow pale from cold and fear, and to be discoloured during pregnancy. The face is also particularly liable to be affected by cutaneous complaints, by small-pox, erysipelas, &c. This view is likewise supported by the fact that the men of certain races, who habitually go nearly naked, often blush over their arms and chests and even down to their waists. A lady, who is a great blusher, informs Dr. Crichton Browne, that when she feels ashamed or is agitated, she blushes over her face, neck, wrists, and hands,—that is, over all the exposed portions of her skin. Nevertheless it may be doubted whether the habitual exposure of the skin of the face and neck, and its consequent power of reaction under stimulants of all kinds, is by itself sufficient to account for the much greater tendency in English women of these parts than of others to blush; for the hands are well supplied with nerves and small vessels, and have been as much exposed to the air as the face or neck, and yet the hands rarely blush. We shall presently see that the attention of the mind having been directed much more frequently and earnestly to the face than to any other part of the body, probably affords a sufficient explanation.

BLUSHING IN THE VARIOUS RACES OF MAN

The small vessels of the face become filled with blood, from the emotion of shame, in almost all the races of man, though in the very dark races no distinct change of colour can be perceived. Blushing is evident in all the Aryan nations of Europe, and to a certain extent with those of India. But Mr. Erskine has never noticed that the necks of the Hindoos are decidedly affected. With the Lepchas of Sikhim, Mr. Scott has often observed a faint blush on the cheeks, base of the ears, and sides of the neck, accompanied by sunken eyes and lowered head. This has occurred when he has detected them in a falsehood, or has accused them of ingratitude. The pale, sallow complexions of these men render a blush much more conspicuous than in most of the other natives of India. With the latter, shame, or it may be in part fear, is expressed, according to Mr. Scott, much more plainly by the head being averted or bent down, with the eyes wavering or turned askant, than by any change of colour in the skin.

The Semitic races blush freely, as might have been expected, from their general similitude to the Aryans. Thus with the Jews, it is said in the Book of Jeremiah (chap. vi. 15), 'Nay, they were not at all ashamed, neither could they blush.' Mrs. Asa Gray saw an Arab managing his boat clumsily on the Nile, and when laughed at by his companions, 'he blushed quite to the back of his neck.' Lady Duff Gordon remarks that a young Arab blushes on coming into her presence.

Mr. Swinhoe has seen the Chinese blushing, but he thinks it is rare; yet they have the expression 'to redden with shame'. Mr. Geach informs me that the Chinese settled in Malacca and the native Malays of the interior both blush. Some of these people go nearly naked, and he particularly attended to the downward extension of the blush. Omitting the cases in which the face alone was seen to blush, Mr. Geach observed that the face, arms, and breast of a Chinaman, aged 24 years, reddened from shame; and with another Chinese, when asked why he had not done his work in better style, the whole body was similarly affected. In two Malays he saw the face, neck, breast, and arms blushing; and in a third Malay (a Bugis) the blush extended down to the waist.

The Polynesians blush freely. The Rev. Mr. Stack has seen hundreds of instances with the New Zealanders. The following case is worth giving, as it relates to an old man who was unusually dark-coloured and partly tattooed. After having let his land to an Englishman for a small yearly rental, a strong passion seized him to buy a pig, which had lately become the fashion with the Maoris. He consequently wished to draw all the rent for four years from his tenant, and consulted Mr. Stack whether he could do so. The man was old, clumsy, poor, and ragged, and the idea of his driving himself about in his carriage for display amused Mr. Stack so much that he could not help bursting out into a laugh; and then 'the old man blushed up to the roots of his hair'. Forster says that 'you may easily distinguish a spreading blush' on the cheeks of the fairest women in Tahiti. The natives also of several of the other archipelagoes in the Pacific have been seen to blush.

Mr. Washington Matthews has often seen a blush on the faces of the young squaws belonging to various wild Indian tribes of North America.

At the opposite extremity of the continent in Tierra del Fuego, the natives, according to Mr. Bridges, 'blush much, but chiefly in regard to women; but they certainly blush also at their own personal appearance.' This latter statement agrees with what I remember of the Fuegian, Jemmy Button, who blushed when he was quizzed about the care which he took in polishing his shoes, and in otherwise adorning himself. With respect to the Aymara Indians on the lofty plateaus of Bolivia, Mr. Forbes says, that from the colour of their skins it is impossible that their blushes should be as clearly visible as in the white race; still under such circumstances as would raise a blush in us, 'there can always be seen the same expression of modesty or confusion; and even in the dark, a rise of temperature of the skin of the face can be felt, exactly as occurs in the European.' With the Indians who inhabit the hot, equable, and damp parts of South America, the skin apparently does not answer to mental excitement so readily as with the natives of the northern and southern parts of the continent, who have long been exposed to great vicissitudes of climate; for Humboldt quotes without a protest the sneer of the Spaniard, 'How can those be trusted, who know not how to blush?' Von Spix and Martius, in speaking of the aborigines of Brazil, assert that they cannot properly be said to blush; 'it was only after long intercourse with the whites, and after receiving some education, that we perceived in the Indians a change of colour expressive of the emotions of their minds.' It is, however, incredible that the power of blushing could have thus originated; but the habit of self-attention, consequent on their education and new course of life, would have much increased any innate tendency to blush.

Several trustworthy observers have assured me that they have seen on the faces of negroes an appearance resembling a blush, under circumstances which would have excited one in us, though their skins were of an ebony-black tint. Some describe it as blushing brown, but most say that the blackness becomes more intense. An increased supply of blood in the skin seems in some manner to increase its blackness; thus certain exanthematous diseases cause the affected places in the negro to appear blacker, instead of, as with us, redder. The skin, perhaps, from being rendered more tense by the filling of the capillaries, would reflect a somewhat different tint to what it did before. That the capillaries of the face in the negro become filled with blood, under the emotion of shame, we may feel confident; because a perfectly characterized albino negress, described by Buffon, showed a faint tinge of crimson on her cheeks when she exhibited herself naked. Cicatrices of the skin remain for a long time white in the negro, and Dr. Burgess, who had frequent opportunities of observing a scar of this kind on the face of a negress, distinctly saw that it 'invariably became red whenever she was abruptly spoken to, or charged with any trivial offence'. The blush could be seen proceeding from the circumference of the scar towards the middle, but it did not reach the centre. Mulattoes are often great blushers, blush succeeding blush over their faces. From these facts there can be no doubt that negroes blush, although no redness is visible on the skin.

I am assured by Gaika and by Mrs. Barber that the Kafirs of South Africa never blush; but this may only mean that no change of colour is distinguishable. Gaika adds that under the circumstances which would make a European blush, his countrymen 'look ashamed to keep their heads up'.

It is asserted by four of my informants that the Australians, who are almost as black as negroes, never blush. A fifth answers doubtfully, remarking that only a very strong blush could be seen, on account of the dirty state of their skins. Three observers state that they do blush; Mr. S. Wilson adding that this is noticeable only under a strong emotion, and when the skin is not too dark from long exposure and want of cleanliness. Mr. Lang answers, 'I have noticed that shame almost always excites a blush, which frequently extends as low as the neck.' Shame is also shown, as he adds, 'by the eyes being turned from side to side.' As Mr. Lang was a teacher in a native school, it is probable that he chiefly observed children, and we know that they blush more than adults. Mr. G. Taplin has seen half-castes blushing, and he says that the aborigines have a word expressive of shame. Mr. Hagenauer, who is one of those who has never observed the Australians to blush, says that he has 'seen them looking down to the ground on account of shame', and the missionary, Mr. Bulmer, remarks that though 'I have not been able to detect anything like shame in the adult aborigines, I have noticed that the eyes of the children, when ashamed, present a restless, watery appearance, as if they did not know where to look'.

The facts now given are sufficient to show that blushing, whether or not there is any change of colour, is common to most, probably to all, of the races of man.

MOVEMENTS AND GESTURES WHICH ACCOMPANY BLUSHING

Under a keen sense of shame there is a strong desire for concealment. We turn away the whole body, more especially the face, which we endeavour in some manner to hide. An ashamed person can hardly endure to meet the gaze of those present, so that he almost invariably casts down his eyes or looks askant. As there generally exists at the same time a strong wish to avoid the appearance of shame, a vain attempt is made to look direct at the person who causes this feeling; and the antagonism between these opposite tendencies leads to various restless movements in the eyes. I have noticed two ladies who, whilst blushing, to which they are very liable, have thus acquired, as it appears, the oddest trick of incessantly blinking their eyelids with extraordinary rapidity. An intense blush is sometimes accompanied by a slight effusion of tears; and this, I presume, is due to the lacrymal glands partaking of the increased supply of blood, which we know rushes into the capillaries of the adjoining parts, including the retina.

Many writers, ancient and modern, have noticed the foregoing movements; and it has already been shown that the aborigines in various parts of the world often exhibit their shame by looking downwards or askant, or by restless movements of their eyes. Ezra cries out (ch. ix. 6), 'O, my God! I am ashamed, and blush to lift up my head to thee, my God.' In *Isaiah* (ch. I. 6) we meet with the words, 'I hid not my face from shame.' Seneca remarks (*Epist. xi.* 5) 'that the Roman players hang down their heads, fix their eyes on the ground and keep them lowered, but are unable to blush in acting shame'. According to Macrobius, who lived in the fifth century ('*Saturnalia*,' B. vii. c. 11), 'Natural philosophers assert that nature being moved by shame spreads the blood before herself as a veil, as we see any one blushing often puts his hands before his face.' Shakespeare makes Marcus ('*Titus Andronicus*,' act ii, sc. 5) say to his niece, 'Ah! now thou turn'st away thy face for shame.' A lady informs me that she found in the Lock Hospital a girl whom she had formerly known, and who had become a wretched castaway, and the poor creature, when approached, hid her face under the bed-clothes, and could not be persuaded to uncover it. We often see little children, when shy or ashamed, turn away, and still standing up, bury their faces in their mother's gown; or they throw themselves face downwards on her lap.

CONFUSION OF MIND

Most persons, whilst blushing intensely, have their mental powers confused. This is recognized in such common expressions as 'she was covered with confusion'. Persons in this condition lose their presence of mind, and utter singularly inappropriate remarks. They are often much distressed, stammer, and make awkward movements or strange grimaces. In certain cases involuntary twitchings of some of the facial muscles may be observed. I have been informed by a young lady, who blushes excessively, that at such times she does not even know what she is saying. When it was suggested to her that this might be due to her distress from the consciousness that her blushing was noticed, she answered that this could not be the case, 'as she had sometimes felt quite as stupid when blushing at a thought in her own room.'

I will give an instance of the extreme disturbance of mind to which some sensitive men are liable. A gentleman, on whom I can rely, assured me that he had been an eye-witness of the following scene:—A small dinner-party was given in honour of an extremely shy man, who, when he rose to return thanks, rehearsed the speech, which he had evidently learnt by heart, in absolute silence, and did not utter a single word; but he acted as if he were speaking with much emphasis. His friends, perceiving how the case stood, loudly applauded the imaginary bursts of eloquence, whenever his gestures indicated a pause, and the man never discovered that he had remained the whole time completely silent. On the contrary, he afterwards remarked to my friend, with much satisfaction, that he thought he had succeeded uncommonly well.

When a person is much ashamed or very shy, and blushes intensely, his heart beats rapidly and his breathing is disturbed. This can hardly fail to affect the circulation of the blood within the brain, and perhaps the mental powers. It seems however doubtful, judging from the still more powerful influence of anger and fear on the circulation, whether we can thus satisfactorily account for the confused state of mind in persons whilst blushing intensely.

The true explanation apparently lies in the intimate sympathy which exists between the capillary circulation of the surface of the head and face, and that of the brain. On applying to Dr. J. Crichton Browne for information, he has given me various facts bearing on this subject. When the sympathetic nerve is divided on one side of the head, the capillaries on this side are relaxed and become filled with blood, causing the skin to redden and to grow hot, and at the same time the temperature within the cranium on the same side rises. Inflammation of the membranes of the brain leads to the engorgement of the face, ears, and eyes with blood. The first stage of an epileptic fit appears to be the contraction of the vessels of the brain, and the first outward manifestation is an extreme pallor of countenance. Erysipelas of the head commonly induces delirium. Even the relief given to a severe headache by burning the skin with strong lotion, depends, I presume, on the same principle.

Dr. Browne has often administered to his patients the vapour of the nitrite of amyl, which has the singular property of causing vivid redness of the face in from thirty to sixty seconds. This flushing resembles blushing in almost every detail: it begins at several distinct points on the face, and spreads till it involves the whole surface of the head, neck, and front of the chest; but has been observed to extend only in one case to the abdomen. The arteries in the retina become enlarged; the eyes glisten, and in one instance there was a slight effusion of tears. The patients are at first pleasantly stimulated, but, as the flushing increases, they become confused and bewildered. One woman to whom the vapour had often been administered asserted that, as soon as she grew hot, she grew *muddled*. With persons just commencing to blush it appears, judging from their bright eyes and lively behaviour, that their mental powers are somewhat stimulated. It is only when the blushing is excessive that the mind grows confused. Therefore it would seem that the capillaries of the face are affected, both during the inhalation of the nitrite of amyl and during blushing, before that part of the brain is affected on which the mental powers depend.

Conversely when the brain is primarily affected, the circulation of the skin is so in a secondary manner. Dr. Browne has frequently observed, as he informs me, scattered red blotches and mottlings on the chests of epileptic patients. In these cases, when the skin on the thorax or abdomen is gently rubbed with a pencil or other object, or, in strongly-marked cases, is merely touched by the finger, the surface becomes suffused in less than half a minute with bright red marks, which spread to some distance on each side of the touched point, and persist for several minutes. These are the *cerebral maculæ* of Trousseau; and they indicate, as Dr. Browne remarks, a highly modified condition of the cutaneous vascular system. If, then, there exists, as cannot be doubted, an intimate sympathy between the capillary circulation in that part of the brain on which our mental powers depend, and in the skin of the face, it is not surprising that the moral causes which induce intense blushing should likewise induce, independently of their own disturbing influence, much confusion of mind.

THE NATURE OF THE MENTAL STATES WHICH INDUCE BLUSHING

These consist of shyness, shame, and modesty; the essential element in all being self-attention. Many reasons can be assigned for believing that originally self-attention directed to personal appearance, in relation to the opinion of others, was the exciting cause; the same effect being subsequently produced, through the force of association, by self-attention in relation to moral conduct. It is not the simple act of reflecting on our own appearance, but the thinking what others think of us, which excites a blush. In absolute solitude the most sensitive person would be quite indifferent about his appearance. We feel blame or disapprobation more acutely than approbation; and consequently depreciatory remarks or ridicule, whether of our appearance or conduct, causes us to blush much more readily than does praise. But undoubtedly praise and admiration are highly efficient: a pretty girl blushes when a man gazes intently at her, though she may know perfectly well that he is not depreciating her. Many children, as well as old and sensitive persons, blush when they are much praised. Hereafter the question will be discussed, how it has arisen that the consciousness that others are attending to our personal appearance should have led to the capillaries, especially those of the face, instantly becoming filled with blood.

My reasons for believing that attention directed to personal appearance, and not to moral conduct, has been the fundamental element in the acquirement of the habit of blushing, will now be given. They are separately light, but combined possess, as it appears to me, considerable weight. It is notorious that nothing makes a shy person blush so much as any remark, however slight, on his personal appearance. One cannot notice even the dress of a woman much given to blushing, without causing her face to crimson. It is sufficient to stare hard at some persons to make them, as Coleridge remarks, blush,—'account for that he who can.'

With the two albinos observed by Dr. Burgess, 'the slightest attempt to examine their peculiarities invariably' caused them to blush deeply. Women are much more sensitive about their personal appearance than men are, especially elderly women in comparison with elderly men, and they blush much more freely. The young of both sexes are much more sensitive on this same head than the old, and they also blush much more freely than the old. Children at a very early age do not blush; nor do they show those other signs of self-consciousness which generally accompany blushing; and it is one of their chief charms that they think nothing about what others think of them. At this early age they will stare at a stranger with a fixed gaze and unblinking eyes, as on an inanimate object, in a manner which we elders cannot imitate.

It is plain to every one that young men and women are highly sensitive to the opinion of each other with reference to their personal appearance; and they blush incomparably more in the presence of the opposite sex than in that of their own. A young man, not very liable to blush, will blush intensely at any slight ridicule of his appearance from a girl whose judgment on any important subject he would disregard. No happy pair of young lovers, valuing each other's admiration and love more than anything else in the world, probably ever courted each other without many a blush. Even the barbarians of Tierra del Fuego, according to Mr. Bridges, blush 'chiefly in regard to women, but certainly also at their own personal appearance'.

Of all parts of the body, the face is most considered and regarded, as is natural from its being the chief seat of expression and the source of the voice. It is also the chief seat of beauty and of ugliness, and throughout the world is the most ornamented. The face, therefore, will have been subjected during many generations to much closer and more earnest self-attention than any other part of the body; and in accordance with the principle here advanced we can understand why it should be the most liable to blush. Although exposure to alternations of temperature, &c., has probably much increased the power of dilatation and contraction in the capillaries of the face and adjoining parts, yet this by itself will hardly account for these parts blushing much more than the rest of the body; for it does not explain the fact of the hands rarely blushing. With Europeans the whole body tingles slightly when the face blushes intensely; and with the races of men who habitually go nearly naked, the blushes extend over a much larger surface than with us. These facts are, to a certain extent, intelligible, as the self-attention of primeval man, as well as of the existing races which still go naked, will not have been so exclusively confined to their faces, as is the case with the people who now go clothed.

We have seen that in all parts of the world persons who feel shame for some moral delinquency, are apt to avert, bend down, or hide their faces, independently of any thought about their personal appearance. The object can hardly be to conceal their blushes, for the face is thus averted or hidden under circumstances which exclude any desire to conceal shame, as when guilt is fully confessed and repented of. It is, however, probable that primeval man before he had acquired much moral sensitiveness would have been highly sensitive about his personal appearance, at least in reference to the other sex, and he would consequently have felt distress at any depreciatory remarks about his appearance; and this is one form of shame. And as the face is the part of the body which is most regarded, it is intelligible that any one ashamed of his personal appearance would desire to conceal this part of his body. The habit having been thus acquired, would naturally be carried on when shame from strictly moral causes was felt; and it is not easy otherwise to see why under these circumstances there should be a desire to hide the face more than any other part of the body.

The habit, so general with every one who feels ashamed, of turning away, or lowering his eyes, or restlessly moving them from side to side, probably follows from each glance directed towards those present, bringing home the conviction that he is intently regarded; and he endeavours, by not looking at those present, and especially not at their eyes, momentarily to escape from this painful conviction.

SHYNESS

This odd state of mind, often called shamefacedness, or false shame, or *mauvaise honte*, appears to be one of the most efficient of all the causes of blushing. Shyness is, indeed, chiefly recognized by the face reddening, by the eyes being averted or cast down, and by awkward, nervous movements of the body. Many a woman blushes from this cause, a hundred, perhaps a thousand times, to once that she blushes from having done anything deserving blame, and of which she is truly ashamed. Shyness seems to depend on sensitiveness to the opinion, whether good or bad, of others, more especially with respect to external appearance. Strangers neither know nor care anything about our conduct or character, but they may, and often do, criticize our appearance: hence shy persons are particularly apt to be shy and to blush in the presence of strangers. The consciousness of anything peculiar, or even new, in the dress, or any slight blemish on the person, and more especially on the face—points which are likely to attract the attention of strangers—makes the shy intolerably shy. On the other hand, in those cases in which conduct and not personal appearance is concerned, we are much more apt to be shy in the presence of acquaintances, whose judgment we in some degree value, than in that of strangers. A physician told me that a young man, a wealthy duke, with whom he had travelled as medical attendant, blushed like a girl, when he paid him his fee; yet this young man probably would not have blushed and been shy, had he been paying a bill to a tradesman. Some persons, however, are so sensitive, that the mere act of speaking to almost any one is sufficient to rouse their self-consciousness, and a slight blush is the result.

Disapprobation or ridicule, from our sensitiveness on this head, causes shyness and blushing much more readily than does approbation; though the latter with some persons is highly efficient. The conceited are rarely shy; for they value themselves much too highly to expect depreciation. Why a proud man is often shy, as appears to be the case, is not so obvious, unless it be that, with all his self-reliance, he really thinks much about the opinion of others, although in a disdainful spirit. Persons who are exceedingly shy are rarely shy in the presence of those with whom they are quite familiar, and of whose good opinion and sympathy they are perfectly assured;—for instance, a girl in the presence of her mother. I neglected to inquire in my printed paper whether shyness can be detected in the different races of man; but a Hindoo gentleman assured Mr. Erskine that it is recognizable in his countrymen.

Shyness, as the derivation of the word indicates in several languages, is closely related to fear; yet it is distinct from fear in the ordinary sense. A shy man no doubt dreads the notice of strangers, but can hardly be said to be afraid of them; he may be as bold as a hero in battle, and yet have no self-confidence about trifles in the presence of strangers. Almost every one is extremely nervous when first addressing a public assembly, and most men remain so throughout their lives; but this appears to depend on the consciousness of a great coming exertion, with its associated effects on the system, rather than on shyness; although a timid or shy man no doubt suffers on such occasions infinitely more than another. With very young children it is difficult to distinguish between fear and shyness; but this latter feeling with them has often seemed to me to partake of the character of the wildness of an untamed animal. Shyness comes on at a very early age. In one of my own children, when two years and three months old, I saw a trace of what certainly appears to be shyness, directed towards myself after an absence from home of only a week. This was shown not by a blush, but by the eyes being for a few minutes slightly averted from me. I have noticed on other occasions that shyness or shamefacedness and real shame are exhibited in the eyes of young children before they have acquired the power of blushing.

As shyness apparently depends on self-attention, we can perceive how right are those who maintain that reprehending children for shyness, instead of doing them any good, does much harm, as it calls their attention still more closely to themselves. It has been well urged that 'nothing hurts young people more than to be watched continually about their feelings, to have their countenances scrutinized, and the degrees of their sensibility measured by the surveying eye of the unmerciful spectator. Under the constraint of such examinations they can think of nothing but that they are looked at, and feel nothing but shame or apprehension.'

MORAL CAUSES: GUILT

With respect to blushing from strictly moral causes, we meet with the same fundamental principle as before, namely, regard for the opinion of others. It is not the conscience which raises a blush, for a man may sincerely regret some slight fault committed in solitude, or he may suffer the deepest remorse for an undetected crime, but he will not blush. 'I blush', says Dr. Burgess, 'in the presence of my accusers.' It is not the sense of guilt, but the thought that others think or know us to be guilty which crimsons the face. A man may feel thoroughly ashamed at having told a small falsehood, without blushing; but if he even suspects that he is detected he will instantly blush, especially if detected by one whom he reveres.

On the other hand, a man may be convinced that God witnesses all his actions, and he may feel deeply conscious of some fault and pray for forgiveness; but this will not, as a lady who is a great blusher believes, ever excite a blush. The explanation of this difference between the knowledge by God and man of our actions lies, I presume, in man's disapprobation of immoral conduct being somewhat akin in nature to his depreciation of our personal appearance, so that through association both lead to similar results; whereas the disapprobation of God brings up no such association.

Many a person has blushed intensely when accused of some crime, though completely innocent of it. Even the thought, as the lady before referred to has observed to me, that others think that we have made an unkind or stupid remark, is amply sufficient to cause a blush, although we know all the time that we have been completely misunderstood. An action may be meritorious or of an indifferent nature, but a sensitive person, if he suspects that others take a different view of it, will blush. For instance, a lady by herself may give money to a beggar without a trace of a blush, but if others are present, and she doubts whether they approve, or suspects that they think her influenced by display, she will blush. So it will be, if she offers to relieve the distress of a decayed gentlewoman, more particularly of one whom she had previously known under better circumstances, as she cannot then feel sure how her conduct will be viewed. But such cases as these blend into shyness.

BREACHES OF ETIQUETTE

The rules of *etiquette* always refer to conduct in the presence of, or towards others. They have no necessary connection with the moral sense, and are often meaningless. Nevertheless as they depend on the fixed custom of our equals and superiors, whose opinion we highly regard, they are considered almost as binding as are the laws of honour to a gentleman. Consequently the breach of the laws of etiquette, that is, any impoliteness or *gaucherie*, any impropriety, or an inappropriate remark, though quite accidental, will cause the most intense blushing of which a man is capable. Even the recollection of such an act, after an interval of many years, will make the whole body to tingle. So strong, also, is the power of sympathy that a sensitive person, as a lady has assured me, will sometimes blush at a flagrant breach of etiquette by a perfect stranger, though the act may in no way concern her.

MODESTY

This is another powerful agent in exciting blushes; but the word modesty includes very different states of the mind. It implies humility, and we often judge of this by persons being greatly pleased and blushing at slight praise, or by being annoyed at praise which seems to them too high according to their own humble standard of themselves. Blushing here has the usual significance of regard for the opinion of others. But modesty frequently relates to acts of indelicacy; and indelicacy is an affair of etiquette, as we clearly see with the nations that go altogether or nearly naked. He who is modest, and blushes easily at acts of this nature, does so because they are breaches of a firmly and wisely established etiquette. This is indeed shown by the derivation of the word *modest* from *modus*, a measure or standard of behaviour. A blush due to this form of modesty is, moreover, apt to be intense, because it generally relates to the opposite sex; and we have seen how in all cases our liability to blush is thus increased. We apply the term 'modest', as it would appear, to those who have an humble opinion of themselves, and to those who are extremely sensitive about an indelicate word or deed, simply because in both cases blushes are readily excited, for these two frames of mind have nothing else in common. Shyness also, from this same cause, is often mistaken for modesty in the sense of humility.

Some persons flush up, as I have observed and have been assured, at any sudden and disagreeable recollection. The commonest cause seems to be the sudden remembrance of not having done something for another person which had been promised. In this case it may be that the thought passes half unconsciously through the mind, 'What will he think of me?' and then the flush would partake of the nature of a true blush. But whether such flushes are in most cases due to the capillary circulation being affected, is very doubtful; for we must remember that almost every strong emotion, such as anger or great joy, acts on the heart, and causes the face to redden.

The fact that blushes may be excited in absolute solitude seems opposed to the view here taken, namely that the habit originally arose from thinking about what others think of us. Several ladies, who are great blushers, are unanimous in regard to solitude; and some of them believe that they have blushed in the dark. From what Mr. Forbes has stated with respect to the Aymaras, and from my own sensations, I have no doubt that this latter statement is correct. Shakespeare, therefore, erred when he made Juliet, who was not even by herself, say to Romeo (act ii. sc. 2):

> 'Thou know'st the mask of night is on my face;
> Else would a maiden blush bepaint my cheek,
> For that which thou hast heard me speak to-night.'

But when a blush is excited in solitude, the case almost always relates to the thoughts of others about us—to acts done in their presence, or suspected by them; or again when we reflect what others would have thought of us had they known of the act. Nevertheless one or two of my informants believe that they have blushed from shame at acts in no way relating to others. If this be so, we must attribute the result to the force of inveterate habit and association, under a state of mind closely analogous to that which ordinarily excites a blush; nor need we feel surprise at this, as even sympathy with another person who commits a flagrant breach of etiquette is believed, as we have just seen, sometimes to cause a blush.

Finally, then, I conclude that blushing,—whether due to shyness—to shame for a real crime—to shame from a breach of the laws of etiquette—to modesty from humility—to modesty from an indelicacy—depends in all cases on the same principle; this principle being a sensitive regard for the opinion, more particularly for the depreciation of others, primarily in relation to our personal appearance, especially of our faces; and secondarily, through the force of association and habit, in relation to the opinion of others on our conduct.

THEORY OF BLUSHING

We have now to consider, why should the thought that others are thinking about us affect our capillary circulation? Sir C. Bell insists that blushing 'is a provision for expression, as may be inferred from the colour extending only to the surface of the face, neck, and breast, the parts most exposed. It is not acquired; it is from the beginning'. Dr. Burgess believes that it was designed by the Creator in 'order that the soul might have sovereign power of displaying in the cheeks the various internal emotions of the moral feelings;' so as to serve as a check on ourselves, and as a sign to others, that we were violating rules which ought to be held sacred. Gratiolet merely remarks,—'Or, comme il est dans l'ordre de la nature que l'être social le plus intelligent soit aussi le plus intelligible, cette faculté de rougeur et de pâleur qui distingue l'homme, est un signe naturel de sa haute perfection.'

The belief that blushing was *specially* designed by the Creator is opposed to the general theory of evolution, which is now so largely accepted; but it forms no part of my duty here to argue on the general question. Those who believe in design, will find it difficult to account for shyness being the most frequent and efficient of all the causes of blushing, as it makes the blusher to suffer and the beholder uncomfortable, without being of the least service to either of them. They will also find it difficult to account for negroes and other dark-coloured races blushing, in whom a change of colour in the skin is scarcely or not at all visible.

No doubt a slight blush adds to the beauty of a maiden's face; and the Circassian women who are capable of blushing, invariably fetch a higher price in the seraglio of the Sultan than less susceptible women. But the firmest believer in the efficacy of sexual selection will hardly suppose that blushing was acquired as a sexual ornament. This view would also be opposed to what has just been said about the dark-coloured races blushing in an invisible manner.

The hypothesis which appears to me the most probable, though it may at first seem rash, is that attention closely directed to any part of the body tends to interfere with the ordinary and tonic contraction of the small arteries of that part. These vessels, in consequence, become at such times more or less relaxed, and are instantly filled with arterial blood. This tendency will have been much strengthened, if frequent attention has been paid during many generations to the same part, owing to nerve-force readily flowing along accustomed channels, and by the power of inheritance. Whenever we believe that others are depreciating or even considering our personal appearance, our attention is vividly directed to the outer and visible parts of our bodies; and of all such parts we are most sensitive about our faces, as no doubt has been the case during many past generations. Therefore, assuming for the moment that the capillary vessels can be acted on by close attention, those of the face will have become eminently susceptible. Through the force of association, the same effects will tend to follow whenever we think that others are considering or censuring our actions or character.

As the basis of this theory rests on mental attention having some power to influence the capillary circulation, it will be necessary to give a considerable body of details, bearing more or less directly on this subject. Several observers, who from their wide experience and knowledge are eminently capable of forming a sound judgment, are convinced that attention or consciousness (which latter term Sir H. Holland thinks the more explicit) concentrated on almost any part of the body produces some direct physical effect on it. This applies to the movements of the involuntary muscles, and of the voluntary muscles when acting involuntarily,—to the secretion of the glands,—to the activity of the senses and sensations,—and even to the nutrition of parts.

It is known that the involuntary movements of the heart are affected if close attention be paid to them. Gratiolet gives the case of a man, who by continually watching and counting his own pulse, at last caused one beat out of every six to intermit. On the other hand, my father told me of a careful observer, who certainly had heart-disease and died from it, and who positively stated that his pulse was habitually irregular to an extreme degree; yet to his great disappointment it invariably became regular as soon as my father entered the room. Sir H. Holland remarks, that 'the effect upon the circulation of a part from the consciousness suddenly directed and fixed upon it, is often obvious and immediate'. Professor Laycock, who has particularly attended to phenomena of this nature, insists that 'when the attention is directed to any portion of the body, innervation and circulation are excited locally, and the functional activity of that portion developed'.

It is generally believed that the peristaltic movements of the intestines are influenced by attention being paid to them at fixed recurrent periods; and these movements depend on the contraction of unstriped and involuntary muscles. The abnormal action of the voluntary muscles in epilepsy, chorea, and hysteria is known to be influenced by the expectation of an attack, and by the sight of other patients similarly affected. So it is with the involuntary acts of yawning and laughing.

Certain glands are much influenced by thinking of them, or of the conditions under which they have been habitually excited. This is familiar to every one in the increased flow of saliva, when the thought, for instance, of intensely acid fruit is kept before the mind. It was shown in our sixth chapter, that an earnest and long-continued desire either to repress, or to increase, the action of the lacrymal glands is effectual. Some curious cases have been recorded in the case of women, of the power of the mind on the mammary glands; and still more remarkable ones in relation to the uterine functions.

When we direct our whole attention to any one sense, its acuteness is increased; and the continued habit of close attention, as with blind people to that of hearing, and with the blind and deaf to that of touch, appears to improve the sense in question permanently. There is, also, some reason to believe, judging from the capacities of different races of man, that the effects are inherited. Turning to ordinary sensations, it is well known that pain is increased by attending to it; and Sir B. Brodie goes so far as to believe that pain may be felt in any part of the body to which attention is closely drawn. Sir H. Holland also remarks that we become not only conscious of the existence of a part subjected to concentrated attention, but we experience in it various odd sensations, as of weight, heat, cold, tingling, or itching.

Lastly, some physiologists maintain that the mind can influence the nutrition of parts. Sir J. Paget has given a curious instance of the power, not indeed of the mind, but of the nervous system, on the hair. A lady 'who is subject to attacks of what is called nervous headache, always finds in the morning after such an one, that some patches of her hair are white, as if powdered with starch. The change is effected in a night, and in a few days after, the hairs gradually regain their dark brownish colour.'

We thus see that close attention certainly affects various parts and organs, which are not properly under the control of the will. By what means attention—perhaps the most wonderful of all the wondrous powers of the mind—is effected, is an extremely obscure subject. According to Müller, the process by which the sensory cells of the brain are rendered, through the will, susceptible of receiving more intense and distinct impressions, is closely analogous to that by which the motor cells are excited to send nerve-force to the voluntary muscles. There are many points of analogy in the action of the sensory and motor nerve-cells; for instance, the familiar fact that close attention to any one sense causes fatigue, like the prolonged exertion of any one muscle. When therefore we voluntarily concentrate our attention on any part of the body, the cells of the brain which receive impressions or sensations from that part are, it is probable, in some unknown manner stimulated into activity. This may account, without any local change in the part to which our attention is earnestly directed, for pain or odd sensations being there felt or increased.

If, however, the part is furnished with muscles, we cannot feel sure, as Mr. Michael Foster has remarked to me, that some slight impulse may not be unconsciously sent to such muscles; and this would probably cause an obscure sensation in the part.

In a large number of cases, as with the salivary and lacrymal glands, intestinal canal, &c., the power of attention seems to rest, either chiefly, or as some physiologists think, exclusively, on the vaso-motor system being affected in such a manner that more blood is allowed to flow into the capillaries of the part in question. This increased action of the capillaries may in some cases be combined with the simultaneously increased activity of the sensorium.

The manner in which the mind affects the vaso-motor system may be conceived in the following manner. When we actually taste sour fruit, an impression is sent through the gustatory nerves to a certain part of the sensorium; this transmits nerve-force to the vaso-motor centre, which consequently allows the muscular coats of the small arteries that permeate the salivary glands to relax. Hence more blood flows into these glands, and they secrete a copious supply of saliva. Now it does not seem an improbable assumption, that, when we reflect intently on a sensation, the same part of the sensorium, or a closely connected part of it, is brought into a state of activity, in the same manner as when we actually perceive the sensation. If so, the same cells in the brain will be excited, though, perhaps, in a less degree, by vividly thinking about a sour taste, as by perceiving it; and they will transmit in the one case, as in the other, nerve-force to the vaso-motor centre with the same results.

To give another, and, in some respects, more appropriate illustration. If a man stands before a hot fire, his face reddens. This appears to be due, as Mr. Michael Foster informs me, in part to the local action of the heat, and in part to a reflex action from the vaso-motor centres. In this latter case, the heat affects the nerves of the face; these transmit an impression to the sensory cells of the brain, which act on the vaso-motor centre, and this reacts on the small arteries of the face, relaxing them and allowing them to become filled with blood. Here, again, it seems not improbable that if we were repeatedly to concentrate with great earnestness our attention on the recollection of our heated faces, the same part of the sensorium which gives us the consciousness of actual heat would be in some slight degree stimulated, and would in consequence tend to transmit some nerve-force to the vaso-motor centres, so as to relax the capillaries of the face. Now as men during endless generations have had their attention often and earnestly directed to their personal appearance, and especially to their faces, any incipient tendency in the facial capillaries to be thus affected will have become in the course of time greatly strengthened through the principles just referred to, namely, nerve-force passing readily along accustomed channels, and inherited habit. Thus, as it appears to me, a plausible explanation is afforded of the leading phenomena connected with the act of blushing.

RECAPITULATION

Men and women, and especially the young, have always valued, in a high degree, their personal appearance; and have likewise regarded the appearance of others. The face has been the chief object of attention, though, when man aboriginally went naked, the whole surface of his body would have been attended to. Our self-attention is excited almost exclusively by the opinion of others, for no person living in absolute solitude would care about his appearance. Every one feels blame more acutely than praise. Now, whenever we know, or suppose, that others are depreciating our personal appearance, our attention is strongly drawn towards ourselves, more especially to our faces. The probable effect of this will be, as has just been explained, to excite into activity that part of the sensorium which receives the sensory nerves of the face; and this will react through the vaso-motor system on the facial capillaries. By frequent reiteration during numberless generations, the process will have become so habitual, in association with the belief that others are thinking of us, that even a suspicion of their depreciation suffices to relax the capillaries, without any conscious thought about our faces. With some sensitive persons it is enough even to notice their dress to produce the same effect. Through the force, also, of association and inheritance our capillaries are relaxed, whenever we know, or imagine, that any one is blaming, though in silence, our actions, thoughts, or character; and, again, when we are highly praised.

On this hypothesis we can understand how it is that the face blushes much more than any other part of the body, though the whole surface is somewhat affected, more especially with the races which still go nearly naked. It is not at all surprising that the dark-coloured races should blush, though no change of colour is visible in their skins. From the principle of inheritance it is not surprising that persons born blind should blush. We can understand why the young are much more affected than the old, and women more than men; and why the opposite sexes especially excite each other's blushes. It becomes obvious why personal remarks should be particularly liable to cause blushing, and why the most powerful of all the causes is shyness; for shyness relates to the presence and opinion of others, and the shy are always more or less self-conscious. With respect to real shame from moral delinquencies, we can perceive why it is not guilt, but the thought that others think us guilty, which raises a blush. A man reflecting on a crime committed in solitude, and stung by his conscience, does not blush; yet he will blush under the vivid recollection of a detected fault, or of one committed in the presence of others, the degree of blushing being closely related to the feeling of regard for those who have detected, witnessed, or suspected his fault. Breaches of conventional rules of conduct, if they are rigidly insisted on by our equals or superiors, often cause more intense blushes even than a detected crime; and an act which is really criminal, if not blamed by our equals, hardly raises a tinge of colour on our cheeks. Modesty from humility, or from an indelicacy, excites a vivid blush, as both relate to the judgment or fixed customs of others.

From the intimate sympathy which exists between the capillary circulation of the surface of the head and of the brain, whenever there is intense blushing, there will be some, and often great, confusion of mind. This is frequently accompanied by awkward movements, and sometimes by the involuntary twitching of certain muscles.

As blushing, according to this hypothesis, is an indirect result of attention, originally directed to our personal appearance, that is to the surface of the body, and more especially to the face, we can understand the meaning of the gestures which accompany blushing throughout the world. These consist in hiding the face, or turning it towards the ground, or to one side. The eyes are generally averted or are restless, for to look at the man who causes us to feel shame or shyness, immediately brings home in an intolerable manner the consciousness that his gaze is directed on us. Through the principle of associated habit, the same movements of the face and eyes are practised, and can, indeed, hardly be avoided, whenever we know or believe that others are blaming, or too strongly praising, our moral conduct.

CHAPTER 20

CONCLUDING REMARKS ON EMOTIONS

[Chapter XIV of *Expression of the Emotions.*]

I HAVE now described, to the best of my ability, the chief expressive actions in man, and in some few of the lower animals. I have also attempted to explain the origin or development of these actions through the three principles given in the first chapter. The first of these principles is, that movements which are serviceable in gratifying some desire, or in relieving some sensation, if often repeated, become so habitual that they are performed, whether or not of any service, whenever the same desire or sensation is felt, even in a very weak degree.

Our second principle is that of antithesis. The habit of voluntarily performing opposite movements under opposite impulses has become firmly established in us by the practice of our whole lives. Hence, if certain actions have been regularly performed, in accordance with our first principle, under a certain frame of mind, there will be a strong and involuntary tendency to the performance of directly opposite actions, whether or not these are of any use, under the excitement of an opposite frame of mind.

Our third principle is the direct action of the excited nervous system on the body, independently of the will, and independently, in large part, of habit. Experience shows that nerve-force is generated and set free whenever the cerebro-spinal system is excited. The direction which this nerve-force follows is necessarily determined by the lines of connection between the nerve-cells, with each other and with various parts of the body. But the direction is likewise much influenced by habit; inasmuch as nerve-force passes readily along accustomed channels.

The frantic and senseless actions of an enraged man may be attributed in part to the undirected flow of nerve-force, and in part to the effects of habit, for these actions often vaguely represent the act of striking. They thus pass into gestures included under our first principle; as when an indignant man unconsciously throws himself into a fitting attitude for attacking his opponent, though without any intention of making an actual attack. We see also the influence of habit in all the emotions and sensations which are called exciting; for they have assumed this character from having habitually led to energetic action; and action affects, in an indirect manner, the respiratory and circulatory system; and the latter reacts on the brain. Whenever these emotions or sensations are even slightly felt by us, though they may not at the time lead to any exertion, our whole system is nevertheless disturbed through the force of habit and association. Other emotions and sensations are called depressing, because they have not habitually led to energetic action, excepting just at first, as in the case of extreme pain, fear, and grief, and they have ultimately caused complete exhaustion; they are consequently expressed chiefly by negative signs and by prostration. Again, there are other emotions, such as that of affection, which do not commonly lead to action of any kind, and consequently are not exhibited by any strongly marked outward signs. Affection indeed, in as far as it is a pleasurable sensation, excites the ordinary signs of pleasure.

On the other hand, many of the effects due to the excitement of the nervous system seem to be quite independent of the flow of nerve-force along the channels which have been rendered habitual by former exertions of the will. Such effects, which often reveal the state of mind of the person thus affected, cannot at present be explained; for instance, the change of colour in the hair from extreme terror or grief,—the cold sweat and the trembling of the muscles from fear,—the modified secretions of the intestinal canal,—and the failure of certain glands to act.

Notwithstanding that much remains unintelligible in our present subject, so many expressive movements and actions can be explained to a certain extent through the above three principles, that we may hope hereafter to see all explained by these or by closely analogous principles.

Actions of all kinds, if regularly accompanying any state of the mind, are at once recognized as expressive. These may consist of movements of any part of the body, as the wagging of a dog's tail, the shrugging of a man's shoulders, the erection of the hair, the exudation of perspiration, the state of the capillary circulation, laboured breathing, and the use of the vocal or other sound-producing instruments. Even insects express anger, terror, jealousy, and love by their stridulation. With man the respiratory organs are of especial importance in expression, not only in a direct, but in a still higher degree in an indirect manner.

Few points are more interesting in our present subject than the extraordinarily complex chain of events which lead to certain expressive movements. Take, for instance, the oblique eyebrows of a man suffering from grief or anxiety. When infants scream loudly from hunger or pain, the circulation is affected, and the eyes tend to become gorged with blood: consequently the muscles surrounding the eyes are strongly contracted as a protection: this action, in the course of many generations, has become firmly fixed and inherited: but when, with advancing years and culture, the habit of screaming is partially repressed, the muscles round the eyes still tend to contract, whenever even slight distress is felt: of these muscles, the pyramidals of the nose are less under the control of the will than are the others, and their contraction can be checked only by that of the central fasciæ of the frontal muscle: these latter fasciæ draw up the inner ends of the eyebrows, and wrinkle the forehead in a peculiar manner, which we instantly recognize as the expression of grief or anxiety. Slight movements, such as these just described, or the scarcely perceptible drawing down of the corners of the mouth, are the last remnants or rudiments of strongly marked and intelligible movements. They are as full of significance to us in regard to expression, as are ordinary rudiments to the naturalist in the classification and genealogy of organic beings.

That the chief expressive actions, exhibited by man and by the lower animals, are now innate or inherited,—that is, have not been learnt by the individual,—is admitted by every one. So little has learning or imitation to do with several of them that they are from the earliest days and throughout life quite beyond our control; for instance, the relaxation of the arteries of the skin in blushing, and the increased action of the heart in anger. We may see children, only two or three years old, and even those born blind, blushing from shame; and the naked scalp of a very young infant reddens from passion. Infants scream from pain directly after birth, and all their features then assume the same form as during subsequent years. These facts alone suffice to show that many of our most important expressions have not been learnt; but it is remarkable that some, which are certainly innate, require practice in the individual, before they are performed in a full and perfect manner; for instance, weeping and laughing. The inheritance of most of our expressive actions explains the fact that those born blind display them, as I hear from the Rev. R. H. Blair, equally well with those gifted with eyesight. We can thus also understand the fact that the young and the old of widely different races, both with man and animals, express the same state of mind by the same movements.

We are so familiar with the fact of young and old animals displaying their feelings in the same manner, that we hardly perceive how remarkable it is that a young puppy should wag its tail when pleased, depress its ears and uncover its canine teeth when pretending to be savage, just like an old dog; or that a kitten should arch its little back and erect its hair when frightened and angry, like an old cat. When, however, we turn to less common gestures in ourselves, which we are accustomed to look at as artificial or conventional,—such as shrugging the shoulders, as a sign of impotence, or the raising the arms with open hands and extended fingers, as a sign of wonder,—we feel perhaps too much surprise at finding that they are innate. That these and some other gestures are inherited, we may infer from their being performed by very young children, by those born blind, and by the most widely distinct races of man. We should also bear in mind that new and highly peculiar tricks, in association with certain states of the mind, are known to have arisen in certain individuals, and to have been afterwards transmitted to their offspring, in some cases, for more than one generation.

Certain other gestures, which seem to us so natural that we might easily imagine that they were innate, apparently have been learnt like the words of a language. This seems to be the case with the joining of the uplifted hands, and the turning up of the eyes, in prayer. So it is with kissing as a mark of affection; but this is innate, in so far as it depends on the pleasure derived from contact with a beloved person. The evidence with respect to the inheritance of nodding and shaking the head, as signs of affirmation and negation, is doubtful; for they are not universal, yet seem too general to have been independently acquired by all the individuals of so many races.

We will now consider how far the will and consciousness have come into play in the development of the various movements of expression. As far as we can judge, only a few expressive movements, such as those just referred to, are learnt by each individual; that is, were consciously and voluntarily performed during the early years of life for some definite object, or in imitation of others, and then became habitual. The far greater number of the movements of expression, and all the more important ones, are, as we have seen, innate or inherited; and such cannot be said to depend on the will of the individual. Nevertheless, all those included under our first principle were at first voluntarily performed for a definite object,—namely, to escape some danger, to relieve some distress, or to gratify some desire. For instance, there can hardly be a doubt that the animals which fight with their teeth, have acquired the habit of drawing back their ears closely to their heads, when feeling savage, from their progenitors having voluntarily acted in this manner in order to protect their ears from being torn by their antagonists; for those animals which do not fight with their teeth do not thus express a savage state of mind. We may infer as highly probable that we ourselves have acquired the habit of contracting the muscles round the eyes, whilst crying gently, that is, without the utterance of any loud sound, from our progenitors, especially during infancy, having experienced, during the act of screaming, an uncomfortable sensation in their eyeballs. Again, some highly expressive movements result from the endeavour to check or prevent other expressive movements; thus the obliquity of the eyebrows and the drawing down of the corners of the mouth follow from the endeavour to prevent a screaming-fit from coming on, or to check it after it has come on. Here it is obvious that the consciousness and will must at first have come into play; not that we are conscious in these or in other such cases what muscles are brought into action, any more than when we perform the most ordinary voluntary movements.

With respect to the expressive movements due to the principle of antithesis, it is clear that the will has intervened, though in a remote and indirect manner. So again with the movements coming under our third principle; these, in as far as they are influenced by nerve-force readily passing along habitual channels, have been determined by former and repeated exertions of the will. The effects indirectly due to this latter agency are often combined in a complex manner, through the force of habit and association, with those directly resulting from the excitement of the cerebro-spinal system. This seems to be the case with the increased action of the heart under the influence of any strong emotion. When an animal erects its hair, assumes a threatening attitude, and utters fierce sounds, in order to terrify an enemy, we see a curious combination of movements which were originally voluntary with those that are involuntary. It is, however, possible that even strictly involuntary actions, such as the erection of the hair, may have been affected by the mysterious power of the will.

Some expressive movements may have arisen spontaneously, in association with certain states of the mind, like the tricks lately referred to, and afterwards been inherited. But I know of no evidence rendering this view probable.

The power of communication between the members of the same tribe by means of language has been of paramount importance in the development of man; and the force of language is much aided by the expressive movements of the face and body. We perceive this at once when we converse on an important subject with any person whose face is concealed. Nevertheless there are no grounds, as far as I can discover, for believing that any muscle has been developed or even modified exclusively for the sake of expression. The vocal and other sound-producing organs, by which various expressive noises are produced, seem to form a partial exception; but I have elsewhere attempted to show that these organs were first developed for sexual purposes, in order that one sex might call or charm the other. Nor can I discover grounds for believing that any inherited movement, which now serves as a means of expression, was at first voluntarily and consciously performed for this special purpose,—like some of the gestures and the finger-language used by the deaf and dumb. On the contrary, every true or inherited movement of expression seems to have had some natural and independent origin. But when once acquired, such movements may be voluntarily and consciously employed as a means of communication. Even infants, if carefully attended to, find out at a very early age that their screaming brings relief, and they soon voluntarily practise it. We may frequently see a person voluntarily raising his eyebrows to express surprise, or smiling to express pretended satisfaction and acquiescence. A man often wishes to make certain gestures conspicuous or demonstrative, and will raise his extended arms with widely opened fingers above his head, to show astonishment, or lift his shoulders to his ears, to show that he cannot or will not do something. The tendency to such movements will be strengthened or increased by their being thus voluntarily and repeatedly performed; and the effects may be inherited.

It is perhaps worth consideration whether movements at first used only by one or a few individuals to express a certain state of mind may not sometimes have spread to others, and ultimately have become universal, through the power of conscious and unconscious imitation. That there exists in man a strong tendency to imitation, independently of the conscious will, is certain. This is exhibited in the most extraordinary manner in certain brain diseases, especially at the commencement of inflammatory softening of the brain, and has been called the 'echo sign'. Patients thus affected imitate, without understanding, every absurd gesture which is made, and every word which is uttered near them, even in a foreign language. In the case of animals, the jackal and wolf have learnt under confinement to imitate the barking of the dog. How the barking of the dog, which serves to express various emotions and desires, and which is so remarkable from having been acquired since the animal was domesticated, and from being inherited in different degrees by different breeds, was first learnt, we do not know; but may we not suspect that imitation has had something to do with its acquisition, owing to dogs having long lived in strict association with so loquacious an animal as man?

In the course of the foregoing remarks and throughout this volume, I have often felt much difficulty about the proper application of the terms, will, consciousness, and intention. Actions, which were at first voluntary, soon became habitual, and at last hereditary, and may then be performed even in opposition to the will. Although they often reveal the state of the mind, this result was not at first either intended or expected. Even such words as that 'certain movements serve as a means of expression' are apt to mislead, as they imply that this was their primary purpose or object. This, however, seems rarely or never to have been the case; the movements having been at first either of some direct use, or the indirect effect of the excited state of the sensorium. An infant may scream either intentionally or instinctively to show that it wants food; but it has no wish or intention to draw its features into the peculiar form which so plainly indicates misery; yet some of the most characteristic expressions exhibited by man are derived from the act of screaming, as has been explained.

Although most of our expressive actions are innate or instinctive, as is admitted by everyone, it is a different question whether we have any instinctive power of recognizing them. This has generally been assumed to be the case; but the assumption has been strongly controverted by M. Lemoine. Monkeys soon learn to distinguish, not only the tones of voice of their masters, but the expression of their faces, as is asserted by a careful observer. Dogs well know the difference between caressing and threatening gestures or tones; and they seem to recognize a compassionate tone. But as far as I can make out, after repeated trials, they do not understand any movement confined to the features, excepting a smile or laugh; and this they appear, at least in some cases, to recognize. This limited amount of knowledge has probably been gained, both by monkeys and dogs, through their associating harsh or kind treatment with our actions; and the knowledge certainly is not instinctive. Children, no doubt, would soon learn the movements of expression in their elders in the same manner as animals learn those of man. Moreover; when a child cries or laughs, he knows in a general manner what he is doing and what he feels; so that a very small exertion of reason would tell him what crying or laughing meant in others. But the question is, do our children acquire their knowledge of expression solely by experience through the power of association and reason?

As most of the movements of expression must have been gradually acquired, afterwards becoming instinctive, there seems to be some degree of *a priori* probability that their recognition would likewise have become instinctive. There is, at least, no greater difficulty in believing this than in admitting that, when a female quadruped first bears young, she knows the cry of distress of her offspring, or than in admitting that many animals instinctively recognize and fear their enemies; and of both these statements there can be no reasonable doubt. It is however extremely difficult to prove that our children instinctively recognize any expression. I attended to this point in my first-born infant, who could not have learnt anything by associating with other children, and I was convinced that he understood a smile and received pleasure from seeing one, answering it by another, at much too early an age to have learnt anything by experience. When this child was about four months old, I made in his presence many odd noises and strange grimaces, and tried to look savage; but the noises, if not too loud, as well as the grimaces, were all taken as good jokes; and I attributed this at the time to their being preceded or accompanied by smiles. When five months old, he seemed to understand a compassionate expression and tone of voice. When a few days over six months old, his nurse pretended to cry, and I saw that his face instantly assumed a melancholy expression, with the corners of the mouth strongly depressed; now this child could rarely have seen any other child crying, and never a grown-up person crying, and I should doubt whether at so early an age he could have reasoned on the subject. Therefore it seems to me that an innate feeling must have told him that the pretended crying of his nurse expressed grief; and this through the instinct of sympathy excited grief in him.

* * * *

I have endeavoured to show in considerable detail that all the chief expressions exhibited by man are the same through the world. This fact is interesting, as it affords a new argument in favour of the several races being descended from a single parent-stock, which must have been almost completely human in structure, and to a large extent in mind, before the period at which the races diverged from each other. No doubt similar structures, adapted for the same purpose, have often been independently acquired through variation and natural selection by distinct species; but this view will not explain close similarity between distinct species in a multitude of unimportant details. Now if we bear in mind the numerous points of structure having no relation to expression, in which all the races of man closely agree, and then add to them the numerous points, some of the highest importance and many of the most trifling value, on which the movements of expression directly or indirectly depend, it seems to me improbable in the highest degree that so much similarity, or rather identity of structure, could have been acquired by independent means. Yet this must have been the case if the races of man are descended from several aboriginally distinct species. It is far more probable that the many points of close similarity in the various races are due to inheritance from a single parent-form, which had already assumed a human character.

It is a curious, though perhaps an idle speculation, how early in the long line of our progenitors the various expressive movements, now exhibited by man, were successively acquired. The following remarks will at least serve to recall some of the chief points discussed in this volume. We may confidently believe that laughter, as a sign of pleasure or enjoyment, was practised by our progenitors long before they deserved to be called human; for very many kinds of monkeys, when pleased, utter a reiterated sound, clearly analogous to our laughter, often accompanied by vibratory movements of their jaws or lips, with the corners of the mouth drawn backwards and upwards, by the wrinkling of the cheeks, and even by the brightening of the eyes.

We may likewise infer that fear was expressed from an extremely remote period, in almost the same manner as it now is by man; namely, by trembling, the erection of the hair, cold perspiration, pallor, widely opened eyes, the relaxation of most of the muscles, and by the whole body cowering downwards or held motionless.

Suffering, if great, will from the first have caused screams or groans to be uttered, the body to be contorted, and the teeth to be ground together. But our progenitors will not have exhibited those highly expressive movements of the features which accompany screaming and crying until their circulatory and respiratory organs, and the muscles surrounding the eyes, had acquired their present structure. The shedding of tears appears to have originated through reflex action from the spasmodic contraction of the eyelids, together perhaps with the eyeballs becoming gorged with blood during the act of screaming. Therefore weeping probably came on rather late in the line of our descent; and this conclusion agrees with the fact that our nearest allies, the anthropomorphous apes, do not weep. But we must here exercise some caution, for as certain monkeys, which are not closely related to man, weep, this habit might have been developed long ago in a sub-branch of the group from which man is derived. Our early progenitors, when suffering from grief or anxiety, would not have made their eyebrows oblique, or have drawn down the corners of their mouth, until they had acquired the habit of endeavouring to restrain their screams. The expression, therefore, of grief and anxiety is eminently human.

Rage will have been expressed at a very early period by threatening or frantic gestures, by the reddening of the skin, and by glaring eyes, but not by frowning. For the habit of frowning seems to have been acquired chiefly from the corrugators being the first muscles to contract round the eyes, whenever during infancy pain, anger, or distress is felt, and there consequently is a near approach to screaming; and partly from a frown serving as a shade in difficult and intent vision. It seems probable that this shading action would not have become habitual until man had assumed a completely upright position, for monkeys do not frown when exposed to a glaring light. Our early progenitors, when enraged, would probably have exposed their teeth more freely than does man, even when giving full vent to his rage, as with the insane. We may, also, feel almost certain that they would have protruded their lips, when sulky or disappointed, in a greater degree than is the case with our own children, or even with the children of existing savage races.

Our early progenitors, when indignant or moderately angry, would not have held their heads erect, opened their chests, squared their shoulders, and clenched their fists, until they had acquired the ordinary carriage and upright attitude of man, and had learnt to fight with their fists or clubs. Until this period had arrived the antithetical gesture of shrugging the shoulders, as a sign of impotence or of patience, would not have been developed. From the same reason astonishment would not then have been expressed by raising the arms with open hands and extended fingers. Nor, judging from the actions of monkeys, would astonishment have been exhibited by a widely opened mouth; but the eyes would have been opened and the eyebrows arched. Disgust would have been shown at a very early period by movements round the mouth, like those of vomiting,—that is, if the view which I have suggested respecting the source of the expression is correct, namely, that our progenitors had the power, and used it, of voluntarily and quickly rejecting any food from their stomachs which they disliked. But the more refined manner of showing contempt or disdain, by lowering the eyelids, or turning away the eyes and face, as if the despised person were not worth looking at, would not probably have been acquired until a much later period.

Of all expressions, blushing seems to be the most strictly human; yet it is common to all or nearly all the races of man, whether or not any change of colour is visible in their skin. The relaxation of the small arteries of the surface, on which blushing depends, seems to have primarily resulted from earnest attention directed to the appearance of our own persons, especially of our faces, aided by habit, inheritance, and the ready flow of nerve-force along accustomed channels; and afterwards to have been extended by the power of association to self-attention directed to moral conduct. It can hardly be doubted that many animals are capable of appreciating beautiful colours and even forms, as is shown by the pains which the individuals of one sex take in displaying their beauty before those of the opposite sex. But it does not seem possible that any animal, until its mental powers had been developed to an equal or nearly equal degree with those of man, would have closely considered and been sensitive about its own personal appearance. Therefore we may conclude that blushing originated at a very late period in the long line of our descent.

From the various facts just alluded to, and given in the course of this volume, it follows that, if the structure of our organs of respiration and circulation had differed in only a slight degree from the state in which they now exist, most of our expressions would have been wonderfully different. A very slight change in the course of the arteries and veins which run to the head, would probably have prevented the blood from accumulating in our eyeballs during violent expiration; for this occurs in extremely few quadrupeds. In this case we should not have displayed some of our most characteristic expressions. If man had breathed water by the aid of external branchiæ (though the idea is hardly conceivable), instead of air through his mouth and nostrils, his features would not have expressed his feelings much more efficiently than now do his hands or limbs. Rage and disgust, however, would still have been shown by movements about the lips and mouth, and the eyes would have become brighter or duller according to the state of the circulation. If our ears had remained movable, their movements would have been highly expressive, as is the case with all the animals which fight with their teeth; and we may infer that our early progenitors thus fought, as we still uncover the canine tooth on one side when we sneer at or defy any one, and we uncover all our teeth when furiously enraged.

The movements of expression in the face and body, whatever their origin may have been, are in themselves of much importance for our welfare. They serve as the first means of communication between the mother and her infant; she smiles approval, and thus encourages her child on the right path, or frowns disapproval. We readily perceive sympathy in others by their expression; our sufferings are thus mitigated and our pleasures increased; and mutual good feeling is thus strengthened. The movements of expression give vividness and energy to our spoken words. They reveal the thoughts and intentions of others more truly than do words, which may be falsified. Whatever amount of truth the so-called science of physiognomy may contain, appears to depend, as Haller long ago remarked, on different persons bringing into frequent use different facial muscles, according to their dispositions; the development of these muscles being perhaps thus increased, and the lines or furrows on the face, due to their habitual contraction, being thus rendered deeper and more conspicuous. The free expression by outward signs of an emotion intensifies it. On the other hand, the repression, as far as this is possible, of all outward signs softens our emotions. He who gives way to violent gestures will increase his rage; he who does not control the signs of fear will experience fear in a greater degree; and he who remains passive when overwhelmed with grief loses his best chance of recovering elasticity of mind. These results follow partly from the intimate relation which exists between almost all the emotions and their outward manifestations; and partly from the direct influence of exertion on the heart, and consequently on the brain. Even the simulation of an emotion tends to arouse it in our minds. Shakespeare, who from his wonderful knowledge of the human mind ought to be an excellent judge, says:

> 'Is it not monstrous that this player here,
> But in a fiction, in a dream of passion,
> Could force his soul so to his own conceit,
> That, from her working, all his visage wann'd;
> Tears in his eyes, distraction in 's aspect,
> A broken voice, and his whole function suiting
> With forms to his conceit? And all for nothing!'
>
> *Hamlet*, act ii. sc. 2.

We have seen that the study of the theory of expression confirms to a certain limited extent the conclusion that man is derived from some lower animal form, and supports the belief of the specific or sub-specific unity of the several races; but as far as my judgment serves, such confirmation was hardly needed. We have also seen that expression in itself, or the language of the emotions, as it has sometimes been called, is certainly of importance for the welfare of mankind. To understand, as far as possible, the source or origin of the various expressions which may be hourly seen on the faces of the men around us, not to mention our domesticated animals, ought to possess much interest for us. From these several causes, we may conclude that the philosophy of our subject has well deserved the attention which it has already received from several excellent observers, and that it deserves still further attention, especially from any able physiologist.

CHAPTER 21

BIOGRAPHICAL SKETCH OF AN INFANT

[An article published in the July 1877 issue of *Mind, A Quarterly Review of Psychology and Philosophy*.]

M. TAINE'S very interesting account of the mental development of an infant, translated in the last number of *Mind* (p. 252), has led me to look over a diary which I kept thirty-seven years ago with respect to one of my own infants. I had excellent opportunities for close observation, and wrote down at once whatever was observed. My chief object was expression, and my notes were used in my book on this subject; but as I attended to some other points, my observations may possibly possess some little interest in comparison with those by M. Taine, and with others which hereafter no doubt will be made. I feel sure, from what I have seen with my own infants, that the period of development of the several faculties will be found to differ considerably in different infants.

During the first seven days various reflex actions, namely sneezing, hickuping, yawning, stretching, and of course sucking and screaming, were well performed by my infant. On the seventh day, I touched the naked sole of his foot with a bit of paper, and he jerked it away, curling at the same time his toes, like a much older child when tickled. The perfection of these reflex movements shows that the extreme imperfection of the voluntary ones is not due to the state of the muscles or of the coordinating centres, but to that of the seat of the will. At this time, though so early, it seemed clear to me that a warm soft hand applied to his face excited a wish to suck. This must be considered as a reflex or an instinctive action, for it is impossible to believe that experience and association with the touch of his mother's breast could so soon have come into play. During the first fortnight he often started on hearing any sudden sound, and blinked his eyes. The same fact was observed with some of my other infants within the first fortnight. Once, when he was 66 days old, I happened to sneeze and he started violently, frowned, looked frightened, and cried rather badly: for an hour afterwards he was in a state which would be called nervous in an older person, for every slight noise made him start. A few days before this same date, he first started at an object suddenly seen; but for a long time afterwards sounds made him start and wink his eyes much more frequently than did sight; thus when 114 days old, I shook a paste-board box with comfits in it near his face and he started, whilst the same box when empty or any other object shaken as near or much nearer to his face produced no effect. We may infer from these several facts that the winking of the eyes, which manifestly serves to protect them, had not been acquired through experience. Although so sensitive to sound in a general way, he was not able even when 124 days old easily to recognise whence a sound proceeded, so as to direct his eyes to the source.

With respect to vision,—his eyes were fixed on a candle as early as the 9th day, and up to the 45th day nothing else seemed thus to fix them; but on the 49th day his attention was attracted by a bright-coloured tassel, as was shown by his eyes becoming fixed and the movements of his arms ceasing. It was surprising how slowly he acquired the power of following with his eyes an object if swinging at all rapidly; for he could not do this well when seven and a half months old. At the age of 32 days he perceived his mother's bosom when three or four inches from it, as was shown by the protrusion of his lips and his eyes becoming fixed; but I much doubt whether this had any connection with vision; he certainly had not touched the bosom. Whether he was guided through smell or the sensation of warmth or through association with the position in which he was held, I do not at all know.

The movements of his limbs and body were for a long time vague and purposeless, and usually performed in a jerking manner; but there was one exception to this rule, namely, that from a very early period, certainly long before he was 40 days old, he could move his hands to his own mouth. When 77 days old, he took the sucking bottle (with which he was partly fed) in his right hand, whether he was held on the left or right arm of his nurse, and he would not take it in his left hand until a week later although I tried to make him do so; so that the right hand was a week in advance of the left. Yet this infant afterwards proved to be left-handed, the tendency being no doubt inherited—his grandfather, mother, and a brother having been or being left-handed. When, between 80 and 90 days old, he drew all sorts of objects into his mouth, and in two or three weeks' time could do this with some skill; but he often first touched his nose with the object and then dragged it down into his mouth. After grasping my finger and drawing it to his mouth, his own hand prevented him from sucking it; but on the 114th day, after acting in this manner, he slipped his own hand down so that he could get the end of my finger into his mouth. This action was repeated several times, and evidently was not a chance but a rational one. The intentional movements of the hands and arms were thus much in advance of those of the body and legs; though the purposeless movements of the latter were from a very early period usually alternate as in the act of walking. When four months old, he often looked intently at his own hands and other objects close to him, and in doing so the eyes were turned much inwards, so that he often squinted frightfully. In a fortnight after this time (*i.e.* 132 days old) I observed that if an object was brought as near to his face as his own hands were, he tried to seize it, but often failed; and he did not try to do so in regard to more distant objects. I think there can be little doubt that the convergence of his eyes gave him the clue and excited him to move his arms. Although this infant thus began to use his hands at an early period, he showed no special aptitude in this respect, for when he was 2 years and 4 months old, he held pencils, pens, and other objects far less neatly and efficiently than did his sister who was then only 14 months old, and who showed great inherent aptitude in handling anything.

ANGER

It was difficult to decide at how early an age anger was felt; on his eighth day he frowned and wrinkled the skin round his eyes before a crying fit, but this may have been due to pain or distress, and not to anger. When about ten weeks old, he was given some rather cold milk and he kept a slight frown on his forehead all the time that he was sucking, so that he looked like a grown-up person made cross from being compelled to do something which he did not like. When nearly four months old, and perhaps much earlier, there could be no doubt, from the manner in which the blood gushed into his whole face and scalp, that he easily got into a violent passion. A small cause sufficed; thus, when a little over seven months old, he screamed with rage because a lemon slipped away and he could not seize it with his hands. When eleven months old, if a wrong plaything was given him, he would push it away and beat it; I presume that the beating was an instinctive sign of anger, like the snapping of the jaws by a young crocodile just out of the egg, and not that he imagined he could hurt the plaything. When two years and three months old, he became a great adept at throwing books or sticks, &c., at anyone who offended him; and so it was with some of my other sons. On the other hand, I could never see a trace of such aptitude in my infant daughters; and this makes me think that a tendency to throw objects is inherited by boys.

FEAR

This feeling probably is one of the earliest which is experienced by infants, as shown by their starting at any sudden sound when only a few weeks old, followed by crying. Before the present one was $4\frac{1}{2}$ months old I had been accustomed to make close to him many strange and loud noises, which were all taken as excellent jokes, but at this period I one day made a loud snoring noise which I had never done before; he instantly looked grave and then burst out crying. Two or three days afterwards, I made through forgetfulness the same noise with the same result. About the same time (*viz.* on the 137th day) I approached with my back towards him and then stood motionless: he looked very grave and much surprised, and would soon have cried, had I not turned round; then his face instantly relaxed into a smile. It is well known how intensely older children suffer from vague and undefined fears, as from the dark, or in passing an obscure corner in a large hall, &c. I may give as an instance that I took the child in question, when $2\frac{1}{4}$ years old, to the Zoological Gardens, and he enjoyed looking at all the animals which were like those that he knew, such as deer, antelopes &c., and all the birds, even the ostriches, but was much alarmed at the various larger animals in cages. He often said afterwards that he wished to go again, but not to see 'beasts in houses'; and we could in no manner account for this fear. May we not suspect that the vague but very real fears of children, which are quite independent of experience, are the inherited effects of real dangers and abject superstitions during ancient savage times? It is quite conformable with what we know of the transmission of formerly well-developed characters, that they should appear at an early period of life, and afterwards disappear.

PLEASURABLE SENSATIONS

It may be presumed that infants feel pleasure whilst sucking, and the expression of their swimming eyes seems to show that this is the case. This infant smiled when 45 days, a second infant when 46 days old; and these were true smiles, indicative of pleasure, for their eyes brightened and eyelids slightly closed. The smiles arose chiefly when looking at their mother, and were therefore probably of mental origin; but this infant often smiled then, and for some time afterwards, from some inward pleasurable feeling, for nothing was happening which could have in any way excited or amused him. When 110 days old he was exceedingly amused by a pinafore being thrown over his face and then suddenly withdrawn; and so he was when I suddenly uncovered my own face and approached his.

He then uttered a little noise which was an incipient laugh. Here surprise was the chief cause of the amusement, as is the case to a large extent with the wit of grown-up persons. I believe that for three or four weeks before the time when he was amused by a face being suddenly uncovered, he received a little pinch on his nose and cheeks as a good joke. I was at first surprised at humour being appreciated by an infant only a little above three months old, but we should remember how very early puppies and kittens begin to play. When four months old, he showed in an unmistakable manner that he liked to hear the pianoforte played; so that here apparently was the earliest sign of an æsthetic feeling, unless the attraction of bright colours, which was exhibited much earlier, may be so considered.

AFFECTION

This probably arose very early in life, if we may judge by his smiling at those who had charge of him when under two months old; though I had no distinct evidence of his distinguishing and recognising anyone, until he was nearly four months old. When nearly five months old, he plainly showed his wish to go to his nurse. But he did not spontaneously exhibit affection by overt acts until a little above a year old, namely, by kissing several times his nurse who had been absent for a short time. With respect to the allied feeling of sympathy, this was clearly shown at 6 months and 11 days by his melancholy face, with the corners of his mouth well depressed, when his nurse pretended to cry. Jealousy was plainly exhibited when I fondled a large doll, and when I weighed his infant sister, he being then 15½ months old. Seeing how strong a feeling jealousy is in dogs, it would probably be exhibited by infants at an earlier age than that just specified, if they were tried in a fitting manner.

ASSOCIATION OF IDEAS, REASON, &c.

The first action which exhibited, as far as I observed, a kind of practical reasoning, has already been noticed, namely, the slipping his hand down my finger so as to get the end of it into his mouth; and this happened on the 114th day. When four and a half months old, he repeatedly smiled at my image and his own in a mirror, and no doubt mistook them for real objects; but he showed sense in being evidently surprised at my voice coming from behind him. Like all infants he much enjoyed thus looking at himself, and in less than two months perfectly understood that it was an image; for if I made quite silently any odd grimace, he would suddenly turn round to look at me. He was, however, puzzled at the age of seven months, when being out of doors he saw me on the inside of a large plate-glass window, and seemed in doubt whether or not it was an image. Another of my infants, a little girl, when exactly a year old, was not nearly so acute, and seemed quite perplexed at the image of a person in a mirror approaching her from behind. The higher apes which I tried with a small looking-glass behaved differently; they placed their hands behind the glass, and in doing so showed their sense, but far from taking pleasure in looking at themselves they got angry and would look no more.

When five months old, associated ideas arising independently of any instruction became fixed in his mind; thus as soon as his hat and cloak were put on, he was very cross if he was not immediately taken out of doors. When exactly seven months old, he made the great step of associating his nurse with her name, so that if I called it out he would look round for her. Another infant used to amuse himself by shaking his head laterally: we praised and imitated him, saying 'Shake your head'; and when he was seven months old, he would sometimes do so on being told without any other guide. During the next four months the former infant associated many things and actions with words; thus when asked for a kiss he would protrude his lips and keep still,—would shake his head and say in a scolding voice 'Ah' to the coal-box or a little spilt water, &c., which he had been taught to consider as dirty. I may add that when a few days under nine months old he associated his own name with his image in the looking-glass, and when called by name would turn towards the glass even when at some distance from it. When a few days over nine months, he learnt spontaneously that a hand or other object causing a shadow to fall on the wall in front of him was to be looked for behind. Whilst under a year old, it was sufficient to repeat two or three times at intervals any short sentence to fix firmly in his mind some associated idea. In the infant described by M. Taine (pp. 254–256) the age at which ideas readily became associated seems to have been considerably later, unless indeed the earlier cases were overlooked. The facility with which associated ideas due to instruction and others spontaneously arising were acquired, seemed to me by far the most strongly marked of all the distinctions between the mind of an infant and that of the cleverest full-grown dog that I have ever known. What a contrast does the mind of an infant present to that of the pike, described by Professor Möbius, who during three whole months dashed and stunned himself against a glass partition which separated him from some minnows; and when, after at last learning that he could not attack them with impunity, he was placed in the aquarium with these same minnows, then in a persistent and senseless manner he would not attack them!

Curiosity, as M. Taine remarks, is displayed at an early age by infants, and is highly important in the development of their minds; but I made no special observation on this head. Imitation likewise comes into play. When our infant was only four months old I thought that he tried to imitate sounds; but I may have deceived myself, for I was not thoroughly convinced that he did so until he was ten months old. At the age of $11\frac{1}{2}$ months he could readily imitate all sorts of actions, such as shaking his head and saying 'Ah' to any dirty object, or by carefully and slowly putting his forefinger in the middle of the palm of his other hand, to the childish rhyme of 'Pat it and pat it and mark it with T'. It was amusing to behold his pleased expression after successfully performing any such accomplishment.

I do not know whether it is worth mentioning, as showing something about the strength of memory in a young child, that this one when 3 years and 23 days old on being shown an engraving of his grandfather, whom he had not seen for exactly six months, instantly recognised him and mentioned a whole string of events which had occurred whilst visiting him, and which certainly had never been mentioned in the interval.

MORAL SENSE

The first sign of moral sense was noticed at the age of nearly 13 months: I said 'Doddy (his nickname) won't give poor papa a kiss,—naughty Doddy'. These words, without doubt, made him feel slightly uncomfortable; and at last when I had returned to my chair, he protruded his lips as a sign that he was ready to kiss me; and he then shook his hand in an angry manner until I came and received his kiss. Nearly the same little scene recurred in a few days, and the reconciliation seemed to give him so much satisfaction, that several times afterwards he pretended to be angry and slapped me, and then insisted on giving me a kiss. So that here we have a touch of the dramatic art, which is so strongly pronounced in most young children. About this time it became easy to work on his feelings and make him do whatever was wanted. When 2 years and 3 months old, he gave his last bit of gingerbread to his little sister, and then cried out with high self-approbation 'Oh kind Doddy, kind Doddy'. Two months later, he became extremely sensitive to ridicule, and was so suspicious that he often thought people who were laughing and talking together were laughing at him. A little later (2 years and $7\frac{1}{2}$ months old) I met him coming out of the dining room with his eyes unnaturally bright, and an odd unnatural or affected manner, so that I went into the room to see who was there, and found that he had been taking pounded sugar, which he had been told not to do. As he had never been in any way punished, his odd manner certainly was not due to fear, and I suppose it was pleasurable excitement struggling with conscience. A fortnight afterwards, I met him coming out of the same room, and he was eyeing his pinafore which he had carefully rolled up; and again his manner was so odd that I determined to see what was within his pinafore, notwithstanding that he said there was nothing and repeatedly commanded me to 'go away', and I found it stained with pickle-juice; so that here was carefully planned deceit. As this child was educated solely by working on his good feelings, he soon became as truthful, open, and tender, as anyone could desire.

UNCONSCIOUSNESS, SHYNESS

No one can have attended to very young children without being struck at the unabashed manner in which they fixedly stare without blinking their eyes at a new face; an old person can look in this manner only at an animal or inanimate object. This, I believe, is the result of young children not thinking in the least about themselves, and therefore not being in the least shy, though they are sometimes afraid of strangers. I saw the first symptom of shyness in my child when nearly two years and three months old: this was shown towards myself, after an absence of ten days from home, chiefly by his eyes being kept slightly averted from mine; but he soon came and sat on my knee and kissed me, and all trace of shyness disappeared.

MEANS OF COMMUNICATION

The noise of crying or rather of squalling, as no tears are shed for a long time, is of course uttered in an instinctive manner, but serves to show that there is suffering. After a time the sound differs according to the cause, such as hunger or pain. This was noticed when this infant was eleven weeks old, and I believe at an earlier age in another infant. Moreover, he appeared soon to learn to begin crying voluntarily, or to wrinkle his face in the manner proper to the occasion, so as to show that he wanted something. When 46 days old, he first made little noises without any meaning to please himself, and these soon became varied. An incipient laugh was observed on the 113th day, but much earlier in another infant. At this date I thought, as already remarked, that he began to try to imitate sounds, as he certainly did at a considerably later period. When five and a half months old, he uttered an articulate sound 'da' but without any meaning attached to it. When a little over a year old, he used gestures to explain his wishes; to give a simple instance, he picked up a bit of paper and giving it to me pointed to the fire, as he had often seen and liked to see paper burnt. At exactly the age of a year, he made the great step of inventing a word for food, namely, *mum*, but what led him to it I did not discover. And now instead of beginning to cry when he was hungry, he used this word in a demonstrative manner or as a verb, implying 'Give me food'. This word therefore corresponds with *ham* as used by M. Taine's infant at the later age of 14 months. But he also used *mum* as a substantive of wide signification; thus he called sugar *shu-mum*, and a little later after he had learned the word 'black', he called liquorice *black-shu-mum*,—black-sugar-food.

I was particularly struck with the fact that when asking for food by the word *mum* he gave to it (I will copy the words written down at the time) 'a most strongly marked interrogatory sound at the end'. He also gave to 'Ah', which he chiefly used at first when recognising any person or his own image in a mirror, an exclamatory sound, such as we employ when surprised. I remark in my notes that the use of these intonations seemed to have arisen instinctively, and I regret that more observations were not made on this subject. I record, however, in my notes that at a rather later period, when between 18 and 21 months old, he modulated his voice in refusing peremptorily to do anything by a defiant whine, so as to express 'That I won't'; and again his humph of assent expressed 'Yes, to be sure'. M. Taine also insists strongly on the highly expressive tones of the sounds made by his infant before she had learnt to speak. The interrogatory sound which my child gave to the word *mum* when asking for food is especially curious; for if anyone will use a single word or a short sentence in this manner, he will find that the musical pitch of his voice rises considerably at the close. I did not then see that this fact bears on the view which I have elsewhere maintained that before man used articulate language, he uttered notes in a true musical scale as does the anthropoid ape Hylobates.

Finally, the wants of an infant are at first made intelligible by instinctive cries, which after a time are modified in part unconsciously, and in part, as I believe, voluntarily as a means of communication,—by the unconscious expression of the features,—by gestures and in a marked manner by different intonations,—lastly by words of a general nature invented by himself, then of a more precise nature imitated from those which he hears; and these latter are acquired at a wonderfully quick rate. An infant understands to a certain extent, and as I believe at a very early period, the meaning or feelings of those who tend him, by the expression of their features. There can hardly be a doubt about this with respect to smiling; and it seemed to me that the infant whose biography I have here given understood a compassionate expression at a little over five months old. When 6 months and 11 days old he certainly showed sympathy with his nurse on her pretending to cry. When pleased after performing some new accomplishment, being then almost a year old, he evidently studied the expression of those around him. It was probably due to differences of expression and not merely of the form of the features that certain faces clearly pleased him much more than others, even at so early an age as a little over six months. Before he was a year old, he understood intonations and gestures, as well as several words and short sentences. He understood one word, namely, his nurse's name, exactly five months before he invented his first word *mum*; and this is what might have been expected, as we know that the lower animals easily learn to understand spoken words.

PART SIX

PLANTS AND WORMS

CHAPTER 22

THE MOVEMENTS AND HABITS OF CLIMBING PLANTS

[The strands of interest in botany, zoology and geology interweave through Darwin's career from his student days at Cambridge. He was thus always the true naturalist, observing and describing whatever struck his attention in the natural world about him, without regard to the 'speciality' that might be concerned. This wide interest comes out clearly and early in his narrative of the voyage of the *Beagle*.

Darwin's scientific reputation, however, was first established as a geologist, with his publication of the geological observations and deductions made while on the *Beagle*. After working up these geological notes, he plunged into his long zoological study of the classification of the barnacles, which resulted in four bulky technical volumes, but which found only vague reflection in his general writing. All of this time, he was accumulating notes on the variations and relationships of species and building up the theory of natural selection. For this, he drew not only on animals of all kinds, but also on plants of all kinds.

Darwin's most notable botanical studies, however, were products of his later years. His first book after the *Origin* was *On the Various Contrivances by which British and Foreign Orchids are Fertilized by Insects*, in which he showed how the fantastic forms of these flowers have biological meaning. Darwin had ample opportunity to observe plants on his walks and in his gardens at Down—and he was always observing everything about him. In 1863 he built a hot-house at Down, and wrote to Hooker at Kew asking for plants to stock it. From that time on, the hot-house provided Darwin with an experimental laboratory, and he found relief there, with his plants, from the tedium of writing.

Darwin was in constant correspondence with the American botanist, Asa Gray. A short article by Gray on the movements of tendrils in wild cucumber plants caught Darwin's interest, and led him to watch and measure the movements of climbing plants in general. He was, of course, immediately involved in the problem of the evolution of the climbing habit in plants. His observations and ideas were presently (1865) written up as a long article in the *Journal of the Linnean Society*. This was re-written and published as a book in 1875. Darwin continued to be fascinated by the movements of plants and in 1880, in collaboration with his son Francis, published a general study of *The Power of Movement in Plants*.

To illustrate this aspect of Darwin's interests, we include here the 'Concluding Remarks' from Chapter V of the 1875 edition of *Climbing Plants*.]

PLANTS become climbers, in order, as it may be presumed, to reach the light, and to expose a large surface of their leaves to its action and to that of the free air. This is effected by climbers with wonderfully little expenditure of organized matter, in comparison with trees, which have to support a load of heavy branches by a massive trunk. Hence, no doubt, it arises that there are so many climbing plants in all quarters of the world, belonging to so many different orders. These plants have been arranged under four classes, disregarding those which merely scramble over bushes without any special aid. Hook-climbers are the least efficient of all, at least in our temperate countries, and can climb only in the midst of an entangled mass of vegetation. Roof-climbers are excellently adapted to ascend naked faces of rock or trunks of trees; when, however, they climb trunks they are compelled to keep much in the shade; they cannot pass from branch to branch and thus cover the whole summit of a tree, for their rootlets require long-continued and close contact with a steady surface in order to adhere. The two great classes of twiners and of plants with sensitive organs, namely, leaf-climbers and tendril-bearers taken together, far exceed in number and in the perfection of their mechanism the climbers of the two first classes. Those which have the power of spontaneously revolving and of grasping objects with which they come in contact, easily pass from branch to branch, and securely ramble over a wide, sun-lit surface.

The divisions containing twining plants, leaf-climbers, and tendril-bearers graduate to a certain extent into one another, and nearly all have the same remarkable power of spontaneously revolving. Does this gradation, it may be asked, indicate that plants belonging to one subdivision have actually passed during the lapse of ages, or can pass, from one state to the other? Has, for instance, any tendril-bearing plant assumed its present structure without having previously existed as a leaf-climber or a twiner? If we consider leaf-climbers alone, the idea that they were primordially twiners is forcibly suggested. The internodes of all, without exception, revolve in exactly the same manner as twiners; some few can still twine well, and many others in an imperfect manner. Several leaf-climbing genera are closely allied to other genera which are simple twiners, It should also be observed, that the possession of leaves with sensitive petioles, and with the consequent power of clasping an object, would be of comparatively little use to a plant, unless associated with revolving internodes, by which the leaves are brought into contact with a support; although no doubt a scrambling plant would be apt, as Professor Jaeger has remarked, to rest on other plants by its leaves. On the other hand, revolving internodes, without any other aid, suffice to give the power of climbing; so that it seems probable that leaf-climbers were in most cases at first twiners, and subsequently became capable of grasping a support; and this, as we shall presently see, is a great additional advantage.

From analogous reasons, it is probable that all tendril-bearers were primordially twiners, that is, are the descendants of plants having this power and habit. For the internodes of the majority revolve; and, in a few species, the flexible stem still retains the capacity of spirally twining round an upright stick. Tendril-bearers have undergone much more modification than leaf-climbers; hence it is not surprising that their supposed primordial habits of revolving and twining have been more frequently lost or modified than in the case of leaf-climbers. The three great tendril-bearing families in which this loss has occurred in the most marked manner, are the Cucurbitaceæ, Passifloraceæ, and Vitaceæ. In the first, the internodes revolve; but I have heard of no twining form, with the exception (according to Palm, p. 29. 52) of *Momordica balsamina*, and this is only an imperfect twiner. In the two other families I can hear of no twiners; and the internodes rarely have the power of revolving, this power being confined to the tendrils. The internodes, however, of *Passiflora gracilis* have the power in a perfect manner, and those of the common Vine in an imperfect degree: so that at least a trace of the supposed primordial habit has been retained by some members of all the larger tendril-bearing groups.

On the view here given, it may be asked, Why have the species which were aboriginally twiners been converted in so many groups into leaf-climbers or tendril-bearers? Of what advantage has this been to them? Why did they not remain simple twiners? We can see several reasons. It might be an advantage to a plant to acquire a thicker stem, with short internodes bearing many or large leaves; and such stems are ill fitted for twining. Any one who will look during windy weather at twining plants will see that they are easily blown from their support; not so with tendril-bearers or leaf-climbers, for they quickly and firmly grasp their support by a much more efficient kind of movement. In those plants which still twine, but at the same time possess tendrils or sensitive petioles, as some species of Bignonia, Clematis, and Tropæolum, it can readily be observed how incomparably better they grasp an upright stick than do simple twiners. Tendrils, from possessing this power of grasping an object, can be made long and thin; so that little organic matter is expended in their development, and yet they sweep a wide circle in search of a support. Tendril-bearers can, from their first growth, ascend along the outer branches of any neighbouring bush, and they are thus always fully exposed to the light; twiners, on the contrary, are best fitted to ascend bare stems, and generally have to start in the shade. Within tall and dense tropical forests, twining plants would probably succeed better than most kinds of tendril-bearers; but the majority of twiners, at least in our temperate regions, from the nature of their revolving movement, cannot ascend thick trunks, whereas this can be effected by tendril-bearers if the trunks are branched or bear twigs, and by some species if the bark is rugged.

The advantage gained by climbing is to reach the light and free air with as little expenditure of organic matter as possible; now, with twining plants, the stem is much longer than is absolutely necessary; for instance, I measured the stem of a kidney-bean, which had ascended exactly two feet in height, and it was three feet in length: the stem of a pea, on the other hand, which had ascended to the same height by the aid of its tendrils, was but little longer than the height reached. That this saving of the stem is really an advantage to climbing plants, I infer from the species that still twine but are aided by clasping petioles or tendrils, generally making more open spires than those made by simple twiners. Moreover, the plants thus aided, after taking one or two turns in one direction, generally ascend for a space straight, and then reverse the direction of their spire. By this means they ascend to a considerably greater height, with the same length of stem, than would otherwise have been possible; and they do this with safety, as they secure themselves at intervals by their clasping petioles or tendrils.

We have seen that tendrils consist of various organs in a modified state, namely, leaves, flower-peduncles, branches, and perhaps stipules. With respect to leaves, the evidence of their modification is ample. In young plants of Bignonia the lower leaves often remain quite unchanged, whilst the upper ones have their terminal leaflets converted into perfect tendrils; in *Eccremocarpus* I have seen a single lateral branch of a tendril replaced by a perfect leaflet; in *Vicia sativa*, on the other hand, leaflets are sometimes replaced by tendril-branches; and many other such cases could be given. But he who believes in the slow modification of species will not be content simply to ascertain the homological nature of different kinds of tendrils; he will wish to learn, as far as is possible, by what actual steps leaves, flower-peduncles, &c., have had their functions wholly changed, and have come to serve merely as prehensile organs.

In the whole group of leaf-climbers abundant evidence has been given that an organ, still subserving the functions of a leaf, may become sensitive to a touch, and thus grasp an adjoining object. With several leaf-climbers the true leaves spontaneously revolve; and their petioles, after clasping a support, grow thicker and stronger. We thus see that leaves may acquire all the leading and characteristic qualities of tendrils, namely, sensitiveness, spontaneous movement, and subsequently increased strength. If their blades or laminæ were to abort, they would form true tendrils. And of this process of abortion we can follow every step, until no trace of the original nature of the tendril is left.

* * * *

On the view here given, leaf-climbers were primordially twiners, and tendril-bearers (when formed of modified leaves) were primordially leaf-climbers. The latter, therefore, are intermediate in nature between twiners and tendril-bearers, and ought to be related to both. This is the case: thus the several leaf-climbing species of the Antirrhineæ, of Solanum, Cocculus, and Gloriosa, have within the same family and even within the same genus, relatives which are twiners. In the genus Mikania, there are leaf-climbing and twining species. The leaf-climbing species of Clematis are very closely allied to the tendril-bearing Naravelia. The Fumariaceæ include closely allied genera which are leaf-climbers and tendril-bearers. Lastly, a species of Bignonia is at the same time both a leaf-climber and a tendril-bearer; and other closely allied species are twiners.

Tendrils of another kind consist of modified flower-peduncles. In this case we likewise have many interesting transitional states. The common Vine (not to mention the *Cardiospermum*) gives us every possible gradation between a perfectly developed tendril and a flower-peduncle covered with flowers, yet furnished with a branch, forming the flower-tendril. When the latter itself bears a few flowers, as we know sometimes is the case, and still retains the power of clasping a support, we see an early condition of all those tendrils which have been formed by the modification of flower-peduncles.

According to Mohl and others, some tendrils consist of modified branches: I have not observed any such cases, and know nothing of their transitional states, but these have been fully described by Fritz Müller. The genus Lophospermum also shows us how such a transition is possible; for its branches spontaneously revolve and are sensitive to contact. Hence, if the leaves on some of the branches of the Lophospermum were to abort, these branches would be converted into true tendrils. Nor is there anything improbable in certain branches alone being thus modified, whilst others remained unaltered; for we have seen with certain varieties of *Phaseolus*, that some of the branches are thin, flexible, and twine, whilst other branches on the same plant are stiff and have no such power.

If we inquire how a petiole, a branch or flower-peduncle first became sensitive to a touch, and acquired the power of bending towards the touched side, we get no certain answer. Nevertheless an observation by Hofmeister well deserves attention, namely, that the shoots and leaves of all plants, whilst young, move after being shaken. Kerner also finds, as we have seen, that the flower-peduncles of a large number of plants, if shaken or gently rubbed bend to this side. And it is young petioles and tendrils, whatever their homological nature may be, which move on being touched. It thus appears that climbing plants have utilized and perfected a widely distributed and incipient capacity, which capacity, as far as we can see, is of no service to ordinary plants. If we further inquire how the stems, petioles, tendrils, and flower-peduncles of climbing plants first acquired their power of spontaneously revolving, or, to speak more accurately, of successively bending to all points of the compass, we are again silenced, or at most can only remark that the power of moving, both spontaneously and from various stimulants, is far more common with plants, than is generally supposed to be the case by those who have not attended to the subject. I have given one remarkable instance, namely that of the *Maurandia semperflorens*, the young flower-peduncles of which spontaneously revolve in very small circles, and bend when gently rubbed to the touched side; yet this plant certainly does not profit by these two feebly developed powers. A rigorous examination of other young plants would probably show slight spontaneous movements in their stems, petioles or peduncles, as well as sensitiveness to a touch. We see at least that the *Maurandia* might, by a little augmentation of the powers which it already possesses, come first to grasp a support by its flower-peduncles, and then, by the abortion of some of its flowers (as with *Vitis* or *Cardiospermum*), acquire perfect tendrils.

There is one other interesting point which deserves notice. We have seen that some tendrils owe their origin to modified leaves, and others to modified flower-peduncles; so that some are foliar and others axial in their nature. It might therefore have been expected that they would have presented some difference in function. This is not the case. On the contrary, they present the most complete identity in their several characteristic powers. Tendrils of both kinds spontaneously revolve at about the same rate. Both, when touched, bend quickly to the touched side, and afterwards recover themselves and are able to act again. In both the sensitiveness is either confined to one side or extends all round the tendril. Both are either attracted or repelled by the light. The latter property is seen in the foliar tendrils of *Bignonia capreolata* and in the axial tendrils of *Ampelopsis*. The tips of the tendrils in these two plants become, after contact, enlarged into discs, which are at first adhesive by the secretion of some cement. Tendrils of both kinds, soon after grasping a support, contract spirally; they then increase greatly in thickness and strength. When we add to these several points of identity the fact that the petiole of *Solanum jasminoides*, after it has clasped a support, assumes one of the most characteristic features of the axis, namely, a closed ring of woody vessels, we can hardly avoid asking, whether the difference between foliar and axial organs can be of so fundamental a nature as is generally supposed?

We have attempted to trace some of the stages in the genesis of climbing plants. But, during the endless fluctuations of the conditions of life to which all organic beings have been exposed, it might be expected that some climbing plants would have lost the habit of climbing. In the cases given of certain South African plants belonging to great twining families, which in their native country never twine, but reassume this habit when cultivated in England, we have a case in point. In the leaf-climbing *Clematis flammula*, and in the tendril-bearing Vine, we see no loss in the power of climbing, but only a remnant of the revolving power which is indispensable to all twiners, and is so common as well as so advantageous to most climbers. In *Tecoma radicans*, one of the Bignoniaceæ, we see a last and doubtful trace of the power of revolving.

With respect to the abortion of tendrils, certain cultivated varieties of *Cucurbita pepo* have, according to Naudin, either quite lost these organs or bear semi-monstrous representatives of them. In my limited experience, I have met with only one apparent instance of their natural suppression, namely, in the common bean. All the other species of *Vicia*, I believe, bear tendrils; but the bean is stiff enough to support its own stem, and in this species, at the end of the petiole, where, according to analogy, a tendril ought to have existed, a small pointed filament projects, about a third of an inch in length, and which is probably the rudiment of a tendril. This may be the more safely inferred, as in young and unhealthy specimens of other tendril-bearing plants similar rudiments may occasionally be observed. In the bean these filaments are variable in shape, as is so frequently the case with rudimentary organs; they are either cylindrical, or foliaceous, or are deeply furrowed on the upper surface. They have not retained any vestige of the power of revolving. It is a curious fact, that many of these filaments, when foliaceous, have on their lower surfaces, dark-coloured glands like those on the stipules, which excrete a sweet fluid; so that these rudiments have been feebly utilized.

* * * *

The most interesting point in the natural history of climbing plants is the various kinds of movement which they display in manifest relation to their wants. The most different organs—stems, branches, flower-peduncles, petioles, mid-ribs of the leaf and leaflets, and apparently aërial roots—all possess this power.

The first action of a tendril is to place itself in a proper position. For instance, the tendril of Cobæa first rises vertically up, with its branches divergent and with the terminal hooks turned outwards; the young shoot at the extremity of the stem is at the same time bent to one side, so as to be out of the way. The young leaves of Clematis, on the other hand, prepare for action by temporarily curving themselves downwards, so as to serve as grapnels.

Secondly, if a twining plant or a tendril gets by any accident into an inclined position, it soon bends upwards, though secluded from the light. The guiding stimulus no doubt is the attraction of gravity, as Andrew Knight showed to be the case with germinating plants. If a shoot of any ordinary plant be placed in an inclined position in a glass of water in the dark, the extremity will, in a few hours, bend upwards; and if the position of the shoot be then reversed, the downward-bent shoot reverses its curvature; but if the stolon of a strawberry, which has no tendency to grow upwards, be thus treated, it will curve downwards in the direction of, instead of in opposition to, the force of gravity. As with the strawberry, so it is generally with the twining shoots of the *Hibbertia dentata*, which climbs laterally from bush to bush; for these shoots, if placed in a position inclined downwards, show little and sometimes no tendency to curve upwards.

Thirdly, climbing plants, like other plants, bend towards the light by a movement closely analogous to the incurvation which causes them to revolve, so that their revolving movement is often accelerated or retarded in travelling to or from the light. On the other hand, in a few instances tendrils bend towards the dark.

Fourthly, we have the spontaneous revolving movement which is independent of any outward stimulus, but is contingent on the youth of the part, and on vigorous health; and this again of course depends on a proper temperature and other favourable conditions of life.

Fifthly, tendrils, whatever their homological nature may be, and the petioles or tips of the leaves of leaf-climbers, and apparently certain roots, all have the power of movement when touched, and bend quickly towards the touched side. Extremely slight pressure often suffices. If the pressure be not permanent, the part in question straightens itself and is again ready to bend on being touched.

Sixthly, and lastly, tendrils, soon after clasping a support, but not after a mere temporary curvature, contract spirally. If they have not come into contact with any object, they ultimately contract spirally, after ceasing to revolve; but in this case the movement is useless, and occurs only after a considerable lapse of time.

With respect to the means by which these various movements are effected, there can be little doubt from the researches of Sachs and H. de Vries, that they are due to unequal growth; but from the reasons already assigned, I cannot believe that this explanation applies to the rapid movements from a delicate touch.

Finally, climbing plants are sufficiently numerous to form a conspicuous feature in the vegetable kingdom, more especially in tropical forests. America, which so abounds with arboreal animals, as Mr. Bates remarks, likewise abounds according to Mohl and Palm with climbing plants; and of the tendril-bearing plants examined by me, the highest developed kinds are natives of this grand continent, namely the several species of *Bignonia*, *Eccremocarpus*, *Cobœa*, and *Ampelopsis*. But even in the thickets of our temperate regions the number of climbing species and individuals is considerable, as will be found by counting them. They belong to many and widely different orders. To gain some rude idea of their distribution in the vegetable series, I marked, from the lists given by Mohl and Palm (adding a few myself, and a competent botanist, no doubt, could have added many more), all those families in Lindley's *Vegetable Kingdom* which include twiners, leaf-climbers, or tendril-bearers. Lindley divides Phanerogamic plants into fifty-nine Alliances; of these, no less than thirty-five include climbing plants of the above kinds, hook and root-climbers being excluded. To these a few Cryptogamic plants must be added. When we reflect on the wide separation of these plants in the series, and when we know that in some of the largest, well-defined orders, such as the Compositæ, Rubiaceæ, Scrophulariaceæ, Liliaceæ, &c., species in only two or three genera have the power of climbing, the conclusion is forced on our minds that the capacity of revolving, on which most climbers depend, is inherent, though undeveloped, in almost every plant in the vegetable kingdom.

It has often been vaguely asserted that plants are distinguished from animals by not having the power of movement. It should rather be said that plants acquire and display this power only when it is of some advantage to them; this being of comparatively rare occurrence, as they are affixed to the ground, and food is brought to them by the air and rain. We see how high in the scale of organization a plant may rise, when we look at one of the more perfect tendril-bearers. It first places its tendrils ready for action, as a polypus places its tentacula. If the tendril be displaced, it is acted on by the force of gravity and rights itself. It is acted on by the light, and bends towards or from it, or disregards it, whichever may be most advantageous. During several days the tendrils or internodes, or both, spontaneously revolve with a steady motion. The tendril strikes some object, and quickly curls round and firmly grasps it. In the course of some hours it contracts into a spire, dragging up the stem, and forming an excellent spring. All movements now cease. By growth the tissues soon become wonderfully strong and durable. The tendril has done its work, and has done it in an admirable manner.

CHAPTER 23

INSECTIVOROUS PLANTS

[In the economy of nature, animals live off plants, either directly, or indirectly by eating other animals down some 'chain of foods' to an ultimate base in vegetation. A few plants have turned the tables, however, and taken to living off animals. These are the so-called insectivorous or carnivorous plants. Some of the tropical kinds are rather spectacular, though never remotely approaching the man-eating proportions sometimes pictured by macabre novelists. But all such plants, however inconspicuous, are of great interest to the naturalist, because of their curious and diverse adaptations for attracting and catching the insects that form their prey.

Several sorts of insectivorous plants are found in Europe and North America. One of these, the sun-dew or Drosera, caught Darwin's attention. 'In the summer of 1860', he wrote in his *Autobiography*, 'I was idling and resting near Hartfield, where two species of Drosera abound; and I noticed that numerous insects had been entrapped by the leaves. I carried home some plants, and on giving them insects saw the movements of the tentacles, and this made me think it probable that the insects were caught for some special purpose. Fortunately a crucial test occurred to me, that of placing a large number of leaves in various nitrogenous and non-nitrogenous fluids of equal density; and as soon as I found that the former alone excited energetic movements, it was obvious that here was a fine new field for investigation.'

Darwin became fascinated by these insect-eating plants. In the fall of 1860, he wrote to Lyell that 'at the present moment, I care more about Drosera than the origin of all the species in the world'. He intended to publish his observations next year, after a few more experiments. But one experiment led to another and he kept at Drosera off and on until finally, in 1875, he published a whole book on this and the other insectivorous plants that he was able to observe in his hot-house.

The Darwin of this book seems a quite different character from the Darwin of the other books. Here is the purely experimental scientist, trying everything, even cobra venom, to see how his plants react. This experimental tendency, to be sure, comes out in Darwin's studies of his children and in his studies of plant movements. But with Drosera, he seems to have become fascinated with the experimental game for its own sake, to the extent that he fails even to make any generalizations about the possible evolutionary origin of the strange reactions he is studying.

The experiments are reported in great detail in his book. To give an idea of their nature, and of this side of Darwin's character, it has seemed to us most appropriate to include here the whole of Chapter XI of *Insectivorous Plants*; this chapter, in the original, is entitled 'Recapitulation of the Chief Observations on Drosera rotundifolia'.]

RECAPITULATION OF THE CHIEF OBSERVATIONS ON DROSERA ROTUNDIFOLIA

As summaries have been given to most of the chapters, it will be sufficient here to recapitulate, as briefly as I can, the chief points. In the first chapter a preliminary sketch was given of the structure of the leaves, and of the manner in which they capture insects. This is affected by drops of extremely viscid fluid surrounding the glands and by the inward movement of the tentacles. As the plants gain most of their nutriment by this means, their roots are very poorly developed; and they often grow in places where hardly any other plant except mosses can exist. The glands have the power of absorption, besides that of secretion. They are extremely sensitive to various stimulants, namely repeated touches, the pressure of minute particles, the absorption of animal matter and of various fluids, heat, and galvanic action. A tentacle with a bit of raw meat on the gland has been seen to begin bending in 10 s., to be strongly incurved in 5 m., and to reach the centre of the leaf in half an hour. The blade of the leaf often becomes so much inflected that it forms a cup, enclosing any object placed on it.

A gland, when excited, not only sends some influence down its own tentacle, causing it to bend, but likewise to the surrounding tentacles, which become incurved; so that the bending place can be acted on by an impulse received from opposite directions, namely from the gland on the summit of the same tentacle, and from one or more glands of the neighbouring tentacles. Tentacles, when inflected, re-expand after a time, and during this process the glands secrete less copiously, or become dry. As soon as they begin to secrete again, the tentacles are ready to re-act; and this may be repeated at least three, probably many more times.

It was shown in the second chapter that animal substances placed on the discs cause much more prompt and energetic inflection than do inorganic bodies of the same size, or mere mechanical irritation; but there is a still more marked difference in the greater length of time during which the tentacles remain inflected over bodies yielding soluble and nutritious matter, than over those which do not yield such matter. Extremely minute particles of glass, cinders, hair, thread, precipitated chalk, &c., when placed on the glands of the outer tentacles, cause them to bend. A particle, unless it sinks through the secretion and actually touches the surface of the gland with some one point, does not produce any effect. A little bit of thin human hair $\frac{8}{1000}$ of an inch (.203 mm.) in length, and weighing only $\frac{1}{78740}$ of a grain (.000822 mg.), though largely supported by the dense secretion, suffices to induce movement. It is not probable that the pressure in this case could have amounted to that from the millionth of a grain. Even smaller particles cause a slight movement, as could be seen through a lens. Larger particles than those of which the measurements have been given cause no sensation when placed on the tongue, one of the most sensitive parts of the human body.

Movement ensues if a gland is momentarily touched three or four times; but if touched only once or twice, though with considerable force and with a hard object, the tentacle does not bend. The plant is thus saved from much useless movement, as during a high wind the glands can hardly escape being occasionally brushed by the leaves of surrounding plants. Though insensible to a single touch, they are exquisitely sensitive, as just stated, to the slightest pressure if prolonged for a few seconds; and this capacity is manifestly of service to the plant in capturing small insects. Even gnats, if they rest on the glands with their delicate feet, are quickly and securely embraced. The glands are insensible to the weight and repeated blows of drops of heavy rain, and the plants are thus likewise saved from much useless movement.

The description of the movements of the tentacles was interrupted in the third chapter for the sake of describing the process of aggregation. This process always commences in the cells of the glands, the contents of which first become cloudy; and this has been observed within 10 s. after a gland has been excited. Granules just resolvable under a very high power soon appear, sometimes within a minute, in the cells beneath the glands; and these then aggregate into minute spheres. The process afterwards travels down the tentacles, being arrested for a short time at each transverse partition. The small spheres coalesce into larger spheres, or into oval, club-headed, thread- or necklace-like, or otherwise shaped masses of protoplasm, which, suspended in almost colourless fluid, exhibit incessant spontaneous changes of form. These frequently coalesce and again separate. If a gland has been powerfully excited, all the cells down to the base of the tentacle are affected. In cells, especially if filled with dark red fluid, the first step in the process often is the formation of a dark red, baglike mass of protoplasm, which afterwards divides and undergoes the usual repeated changes of form. Before any aggregation has been excited, a sheet of colourless protoplasm, including granules (the primordial utricle of Mohl), flows round the walls of the cells; and this becomes more distinct after the contents have been partially aggregated into spheres or

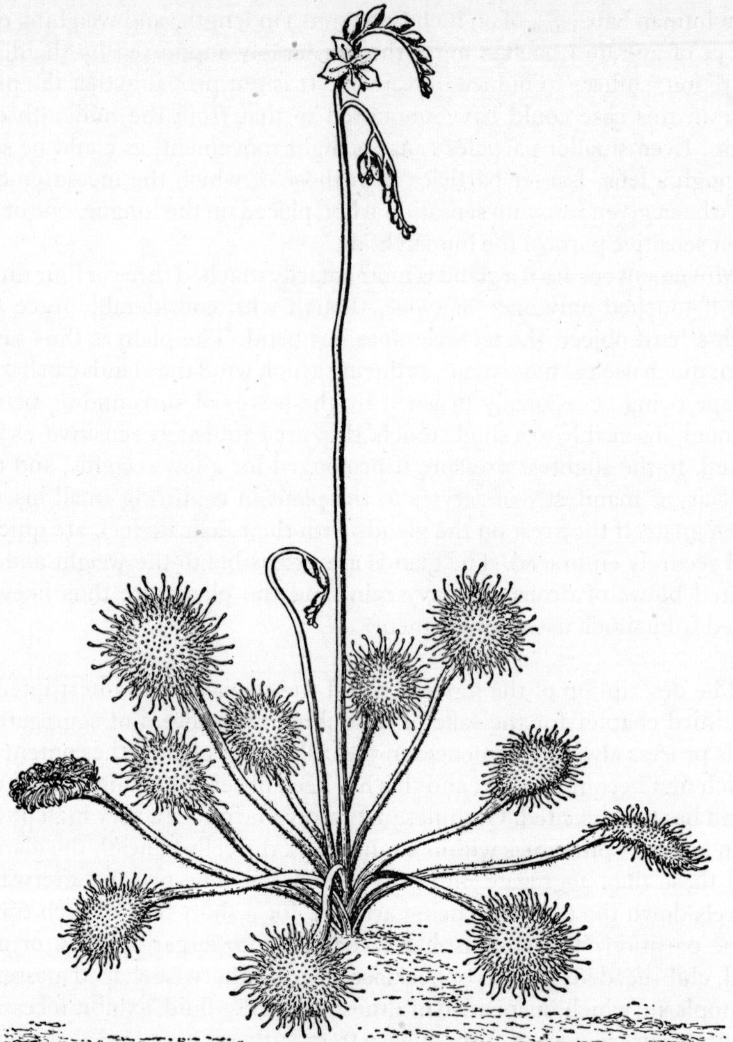

Sun-dew or Drosera

bag-like masses. But after a time the granules are drawn towards the central masses and unite with them; and then the circulating sheet can no longer be distinguished, but there is still a current of transparent fluid within the cells.

Aggregation is excited by almost all the stimulants which induce movement; such as the glands being touched two or three times, the pressure of minute inorganic particles, the absorption of various fluids, even long immersion in distilled water, exosmose, and heat. Of the many stimulants tried, carbonate of ammonia is the most energetic and acts the quickest: a dose of $\frac{1}{134400}$ of a grain (.00048 mg.) given to a single gland suffices to cause in one hour well-marked aggregation in the upper cells of the tentacle. The process goes on only as long as the protoplasm is in a living, vigorous, and oxygenated condition.

The result is in all respects exactly the same, whether a gland has been excited directly, or has received an influence from other and distant glands. But there is one important difference: when the central glands are irritated, they transmit centrifugally an influence up the pedicels of the exterior tentacles to their glands; but the actual process of aggregation travels centripetally, from the glands of the exterior tentacles down their pedicels. The exciting influence, therefore, which is transmitted from one part of the leaf to another must be different from that which actually induces aggregation. The process does not depend on the glands secreting more copiously than they did before; and is independent of the inflection of the tentacles. It continues as long as the tentacles remain inflected, and as soon as these are fully re-expanded, the little masses of protoplasm are all redissolved; the cells becoming filled with homogeneous purple fluid, as they were before the leaf was excited.

As the process of aggregation can be excited by a few touches, or by the pressure of insoluble particles, it is evidently independent of the absorption of any matter, and must be of a molecular nature. Even when caused by the absorption of the carbonate or other salt of ammonia, or an infusion of meat, the process seems to be of exactly the same nature. The protoplasmic fluid must, therefore, be in a singularly unstable condition, to be acted on by such slight and varied causes. Physiologists believe that when a nerve is touched, and it transmits an influence to other parts of the nervous system, a molecular change is induced in it, though not visible to us. Therefore it is a very interesting spectacle to watch the effects on the cells of a gland, of the pressure of a bit of hair, weighing only $\frac{1}{78700}$ of a grain and largely supported by the dense secretion, for this excessively slight pressure soon causes a visible change in the protoplasm, which change is transmitted down the whole length of the tentacle, giving it at last a mottled appearance, distinguishable even by the naked eye.

In the fourth chapter it was shown that leaves placed for a short time in water at a temperature of 110° Fahr. (43°.3 Cent.) become somewhat inflected; they are thus also rendered more sensitive to the action of meat than they were before. If exposed to a temperature of between 115° and 125° (46°.1—51°.6 Cent.), they are quickly inflected, and their protoplasm undergoes aggregation; when afterwards placed in cold water, they re-expand. Exposed to 130° (54°.4 Cent.), no inflection immediately occurs, but the leaves are only temporarily paralysed, for on being left in cold water, they often become inflected and afterwards re-expand. In one leaf thus treated, I distinctly saw the protoplasm in movement. In other leaves, treated in the same manner, and then immersed in a solution of carbonate of ammonia, strong aggregation ensued. Leaves placed in cold water, after an exposure to so high a temperature as 145° (62°.7 Cent.), sometimes become slightly, though slowly, inflected; and afterwards have the contents of their cells strongly aggregated by carbonate of ammonia. But the duration of the immersion is an important element, for if left in water at 145° (62°.7 Cent.), or only at 140° (60° Cent.), until it becomes cool, they are killed, and the contents of the glands are rendered white and opaque. This latter result seems to be due to the coagulation of the albumen, and was almost always caused by even a short exposure to 150° (65°.5 Cent.); but different leaves, and even the separate cells in the same tentacle, differ considerably in their power of resisting heat. Unless the heat has been sufficient to coagulate the albumen, carbonate of ammonia subsequently induces aggregation.

In the fifth chapter, the results of placing drops of various nitrogenous and non-nitrogenous organic fluids on the discs of leaves were given, and it was shown that they detect with almost unerring certainty the presence of nitrogen. A decoction of green peas or of fresh cabbage-leaves acts almost as powerfully as an infusion of raw meat; whereas an infusion of cabbage-leaves made by keeping them for a long time in merely warm water is far less efficient. A decoction of grass-leaves is less powerful than one of green peas or cabbage-leaves.

These results led me to inquire whether Drosera possessed the power of dissolving solid animal matter. The experiments proving that the leaves are capable of true digestion, and that the glands absorb the digested matter, are given in detail in the sixth chapter. These are, perhaps, the most interesting of all my observations on Drosera, as no such power was before distinctly known to exist in the vegetable kingdom. It is likewise an interesting fact that the glands of the disc, when irritated, should transmit some influence to the glands of the exterior tentacles, causing them to secrete more copiously and the secretion to become acid, as if they had been directly excited by an object placed on them. The gastric juice of animals contains, as is well known, an acid and a ferment, both of which are indispensable for digestion, and so it is with the secretion of Drosera.

When the stomach of an animal is mechanically irritated, it secretes an acid, and when particles of glass or other such objects were placed on the glands of Drosera, the secretion, and that of the surrounding and untouched glands, was increased in quantity and became acid. But, according to Schiff, the stomach of an animal does not secrete its proper ferment, pepsin, until certain substances, which he calls peptogenes, are absorbed; and it appears from my experiments that some matter must be absorbed by the glands of Drosera before they secrete their proper ferment. That the secretion does contain a ferment which acts only in the presence of an acid on solid animal matter, was clearly proved by adding minute doses of an alkali, which entirely arrested the process of digestion, this immediately recommencing as soon as the alkali was neutralised by a little weak hydrochloric acid. From trials made with a large number of substances, it was found that those which the secretion of Drosera dissolves completely, or partially, or not at all, are acted on in exactly the same manner by gastric juice. We may, therefore, conclude that the ferment of Drosera is closely analogous to, or identical with, the pepsin of animals.

The substances which are digested by Drosera act on the leaves very differently. Some cause much more energetic and rapid inflection of the tentacles, and keep them inflected for a much longer time, than do others. We are thus led to believe that the former are more nutritious than the latter, as is known to be the case with some of these same substances when given to animals; for instance, meat in comparison with gelatine. As cartilage is so tough a substance and is so little acted on by water, its prompt dissolution by the secretion of Drosera, and subsequent absorption, is, perhaps, one of the most striking cases. But it is not really more remarkable than the digestion of meat, which is dissolved by this secretion in the same manner and by the same stages as by gastric juice. The secretion dissolves bone, and even the enamel of teeth, but this is simply due to the large quantity of acid secreted, owing, apparently, to the desire of the plant for phosphorus. In the case of bone, the ferment does not come into play until all the phosphate of lime has been decomposed and free acid is present, and then the fibrous basis is quickly dissolved. Lastly, the secretion attacks and dissolves matter out of living seeds, which it sometimes kills, or injures, as shown by the diseased state of the seedlings. It also absorbs matter from pollen, and from fragments of leaves.

The seventh chapter was devoted to the action of the salts of ammonia. These all cause the tentacles, and often the blade of the leaf, to be inflected, and the protoplasm to be aggregated. They act with very different power; the citrate being the least powerful, and the phosphate, owing, no doubt, to the presence of phosphorus and nitrogen, by far the most powerful. But the relative efficiency of only three salts of ammonia was carefully determined, namely the carbonate, nitrate, and phosphate. The experiments were made by placing half-minims (.0296 ml.) of solutions of different strengths on the discs of the leaves,—by applying a minute drop (about the $\frac{1}{20}$ of a minim, or .00296 ml.) for a few seconds to three or four glands,—and by the immersion of whole leaves in a measured quantity. In relation to these experiments it was necessary first to ascertain the effects of distilled water, and it was found, as described in detail, that the more sensitive leaves are affected by it, but only in a slight degree.

A solution of the carbonate is absorbed by the roots and induces aggregation in their cells, but does not affect the leaves. The vapour is absorbed by the glands, and causes inflection as well as aggregation. A drop of a solution containing $\frac{1}{960}$ of a grain (.0675 mg.) is the least quantity which, when placed on the glands of the disc, excites the exterior tentacles to bend inwards. But a minute drop, containing $\frac{1}{14400}$ of a grain (.00445 mg.), if applied for a few seconds to the secretion surrounding a gland, causes the inflection of the same tentacle. When a highly sensitive leaf is immersed in a solution, and there is ample time for absorption, the $\frac{1}{268800}$ of a grain (.00024 mg.) is sufficient to excite a single tentacle into movement.

The nitrate of ammonia induces aggregation of the protoplasm much less quickly than the carbonate, but is more potent in causing inflection. a drop containing $\frac{1}{2400}$ of a grain (.027 mg.) placed on the disc acts powerfully on all the exterior tentacles, which have not themselves received any of the solution; whereas a drop with $\frac{1}{2800}$ of a grain caused only a few of these tentacles to bend, but affected rather more plainly the blade. A minute drop applied as before, and containing $\frac{1}{28800}$ of a grain (.0025 mg.), caused the tentacle bearing this gland to bend. By the immersion of whole leaves, it was proved that the absorption by a single gland of $\frac{1}{691200}$ of a grain (.0000937 mg.) was sufficient to set the same tentacle into movement.

The phosphate of ammonia is much more powerful than the nitrate. A drop containing $\frac{1}{3840}$ of a grain (.0169 mg.) placed on the disc of a sensitive leaf causes most of the exterior tentacles to be inflected, as well as the blade of the leaf. A minute drop containing $\frac{1}{153600}$ of a grain (.000423 mg.), applied for a few seconds to a gland, acts, as shown by the movement of the tentacle. When a leaf is immersed in thirty minims (1.7748 ml.) of a solution of one part by weight of the salt to 21,875,000 of water, the absorption by a gland of only the $\frac{1}{19760000}$ of a grain (.00000328 mg.), that is, about the one-twenty-millionth of a grain, is sufficient to cause the tentacle bearing this gland to bend to the centre of the leaf. In this experiment, owing to the presence of the water of crystallisation, less than the one-thirty-millionth of a grain of the efficient elements could have been absorbed. There is nothing remarkable in such minute quantities being absorbed by the glands, for all physiologists admit that the salts of ammonia, which must be brought in still smaller quantity by a single shower of rain to the roots, are absorbed by them. Nor is it surprising that Drosera should be enabled to profit by the absorption of these salts, for yeast and other low fungoid forms flourish in solutions of ammonia, if the other necessary elements are present. But it is an astonishing fact, on which I will not here again enlarge, that so inconceivably minute a quantity as the one-twenty-millionth of a grain of phosphate of ammonia should induce some change in a gland of Drosera, sufficient to cause a motor impulse to be sent down the whole length of the tentacle; this impulse exciting movement often through an angle of above 180°. I know not whether to be most astonished at this fact, or that the pressure of a minute bit of hair, supported by the dense secretion, should quickly cause conspicuous movement. Moreover, this extreme sensitiveness, exceeding that of the most delicate part of the human body, as well as the power of transmitting various impulses from one part of the leaf to another, have been acquired without the intervention of any nervous system.

As few plants are at present known to possess glands specially adapted for absorption, it seemed worth while to try the effects on Drosera of various other salts, besides those of ammonia, and of various acids. Their action, as described in the eighth chapter, does not correspond at all strictly with their chemical affinities, as inferred from the classification commonly followed. The nature of the base is far more influential than that of the acid; and this is known to hold good with animals. For instance, nine salts of sodium all caused well-marked inflection, and none of them were poisonous in small doses; whereas seven of the nine corresponding salts of potassium produced no effect, two causing slight inflection. Small doses, moreover, of some of the latter salts were poisonous. The salts of sodium and potassium, when injected into the veins of animals, likewise differ widely in their action. The so-called earthy salts produce hardly any effect on Drosera. On the other hand, most of the metallic salts cause rapid and strong inflection, and are highly poisonous; but there are some odd exceptions to this rule; thus chloride of lead and zinc, as well as two salts of barium, did not cause inflection, and were not poisonous.

Most of the acids which were tried, though much diluted (one part to

437 of water), and given in small doses, acted powerfully on Drosera; nineteen, out of the twenty-four, causing the tentacles to be more or less inflected. Most of them, even the organic acids, are poisonous, often highly so; and this is remarkable, as the juices of so many plants contain acids. Benzoic acid, which is innocuous to animals, seems to be as poisonous to Drosera as hydrocyanic. On the other hand, hydrochloric acid is not poisonous either to animals or to Drosera, and induces only a moderate amount of inflection. Many acids excite the glands to secrete an extraordinary quantity of mucus; and the protoplasm within their cells seems to be often killed, as may be inferred from the surrounding fluid soon becoming pink. It is strange that allied acids act very differently: formic acid induces very slight inflection, and is not poisonous; whereas acetic acid of the same strength acts most powerfully and is poisonous. Lactic acid is also poisonous, but causes inflection only after a considerable lapse of time. Malic acid acts slightly, whereas citric and tartaric acids produce no effect.

In the ninth chapter the effects of the absorption of various alkaloids and certain other substances were described. Although some of these are poisonous, yet as several, which act powerfully on the nervous system of animals, produce no effect on Drosera, we may infer that the extreme sensibility of the glands, and their power of transmitting an influence to other parts of the leaf, causing movement, or modified secretion, or aggregation, does not depend on the presence of a diffused element, allied to nerve-tissue. One of the most remarkable facts is that long immersion in the poison of the cobra-snake does not in the least check, but rather stimulates, the spontaneous movements of the protoplasm in the cells of the tentacles. Solutions of various salts and acids behave very differently in delaying or in quite arresting the subsequent action of a solution of phosphate of ammonia. Camphor dissolved in water acts as a stimulant, as do small doses of certain essential oils, for they cause rapid and strong inflection. Alcohol is not a stimulant. The vapours of camphor, alcohol, chloroform, sulphuric and nitric ether, are poisonous in moderately large doses, but in small doses serve as narcotics or anæsthetics, greatly delaying the subsequent action of meat. But some of these vapours also act as stimulants, exciting rapid, almost spasmodic movements in the tentacles. Carbonic acid is likewise a narcotic, and retards the aggregation of the protoplasm when carbonate of ammonia is subsequently given. The first access of air to plants which have been immersed in this gas sometimes acts as a stimulant and induces movement. But, as before remarked, a special pharmacopœia would be necessary to describe the diversified effects of various substances on the leaves of Drosera.

In the tenth chapter it was shown that the sensitiveness of the leaves appears to be wholly confined to the glands and to the immediately underlying cells. It was further shown that the motor impulse and other forces or influences, proceeding from the glands when excited, pass through the cellular tissue, and not along the fibro-vascular bundles. A gland sends its motor impulse with great rapidity down the pedicel of the same tentacle to the basal part which alone bends. The impulse, then passing onwards, spreads on all sides to the surrounding tentacles, first affecting those which stand nearest and then those farther off. But by being thus spread out, and from the cells of the disc not being so much elongated as those of the tentacles, it loses force, and here travels much more slowly than down the pedicels. Owing also to the direction and form of the cells, it passes with greater ease and celerity in a longitudinal than in a transverse line across the disc. The impulse proceeding from the glands of the extreme marginal tentacles does not seem to have force enough to affect the adjoining tentacles; and this may be in part due to their length. The impulse from the glands of the next few inner rows spreads chiefly to the tentacles on each side and towards the centre of the leaf; but that proceeding from the glands of the shorter tentacles on the disc radiates almost equally on all sides.

When a gland is strongly excited by the quantity or quality of the substance placed on it, the motor impulse travels farther than from one slightly excited; and if several glands are simultaneously excited, the impulses from all unite and spread still farther. As soon as a gland is excited, it discharges an impulse which extends to a considerable distance; but afterwards, whilst the gland is secreting and absorbing, the impulse suffices only to keep the same tentacle inflected; though the inflection may last for many days.

If the bending place of a tentacle receives an impulse from its own gland, the movement is always towards the centre of the leaf; and so it is with all the tentacles, when their glands are excited by immersion in a proper fluid. The short ones in the middle part of the disc must be excepted, as these do not bend at all when thus excited. On the other hand, when the motor impulse comes from one side of the disc, the surrounding tentacles, including the short ones in the middle of the disc, all bend with precision towards the point of excitement, wherever this may be seated. This is in every way a remarkable phenomenon; for the leaf falsely appears as if endowed with the senses of an animal. It is all the more remarkable, as when the motor impulse strikes the base of a tentacle obliquely with respect to its flattened surface, the contraction of the cells must be confined to one, two, or a very few rows at one end. And different sides of the surrounding tentacles must be acted on, in order that all should bend with precision to the point of excitement.

The motor impulse, as it spreads from one or more glands across the disc, enters the bases of the surrounding tentacles, and immediately acts on the bending place. It does not in the first place proceed up the tentacles to the glands, exciting them to reflect back an impulse to their bases. Nevertheless, some influence is sent up to the glands, as their secretion is soon increased and rendered acid; and then the glands, being thus excited, send back some other influence (not dependent on increased secretion, nor on the inflection of the tentacles), causing the protoplasm to aggregate in cell beneath cell. This may be called a reflex action, though probably very different from that proceeding from the nerve-ganglion of an animal; and it is the only known case of reflex action in the vegetable kingdom.

About the mechanism of the movements and the nature of the motor impulse we know very little. During the act of inflection fluid certainly travels from one part to another of the tentacles. But the hypothesis which agrees best with the observed facts is that the motor impulse is allied in nature to the aggregating process; and that this causes the molecules of the cell-walls to approach each other, in the same manner as do the molecules of the protoplasm within the cells; so that the cell-walls contract. But some strong objections may be urged against this view. The re-expansion of the tentacles is largely due to the elasticity of their outer cells, which comes into play as soon as those on the inner side cease contracting with prepotent force; but we have reason to suspect that fluid is continually and slowly attracted into the outer cells during the act of re-expansion, thus increasing their tension.

I have now given a brief recapitulation of the chief points observed by me, with respect to the structure, movements, constitution, and habits of *Drosera rotundifolia*; and we see how little has been made out in comparison with what remains unexplained and unknown.

CHAPTER 24

THE FORMATION OF VEGETABLE MOULD

[Darwin's last book was about earthworms, but his interest in the subject started in 1837, the first year after his return to England. He had been feeling very unwell. 'My doctors urge me *strongly*', he wrote to Henslow, 'to knock off all work, and go and live in the country for a few weeks.' So he spent about a month at Josiah Wedgwood's house at Maer and there noticed how the worms, by bringing earth to the surface in their castings, slowly undermined any objects lying on the surface, causing an apparent sinking. He read a paper about it to the Geological Society in the fall of 1837.

His interest in the worms revived in the later years at Down, and he put his friends and his children to work making observations for him. Finally, when the *Power of Movement in Plants* was nearly finished, he started writing about the worms. The references to this work in his correspondence are interesting.

He wrote to Professor Carus (Sept. 21, 1880): 'In the intervals of correcting the press, I am writing a very little book, and have done nearly half of it. Its title will be (as at present designed), "The Formation of Vegetable Mould through the Action of Worms". As far as I can judge, it will be a curious little book.' When the proof-sheets were coming in, he again wrote to Professor Carus: 'The subject has been to me a hobby-horse, and I have perhaps treated it in foolish detail.'

The book was published on October 10th, 1881, and it was an immediate success. 'It has been a complete surprise to me how many persons have cared for the subject,' Darwin wrote. And in another letter, 'My book has been received with almost laughable enthusiasm, and 3500 copies have been sold! ! !' Again, 'I have been plagued with an endless stream of letters on the subject; most of them very foolish and enthusiastic; but some containing good facts which I have used in correcting yesterday the "Sixth Thousand" '.

His son, Sir Francis Darwin, has some interesting comments on this success in the *Life and Letters*: 'It is not difficult to account for its success with the non-scientific public. Conclusions so wide and so novel, and so easily understood, drawn from the study of creatures so familiar, and treated with unbated vigour and freshness, may well have attracted many readers. A reviewer remarks: " In the eyes of most men . . . the earthworm is a mere blind, dumb, senseless, and unpleasantly slimy annelid. Mr. Darwin undertakes to rehabilitate his character, and the earthworm steps forth at once as an intelligent and beneficent personage, a worker of vast geological changes, a planer down of mountain sides . . . a friend of man . . . and an ally of the Society for the preservation of ancient monuments." '

The book has seven chapters: two on the habits of worms, one on the amount of earth brought to the surface by worms, one on the part played by worms in the burial of ancient monuments, two on the action of worms in the denudation of land, and final summary and conclusion. To indicate the flavour of the book, we include here extracts from Chapter III, and the whole of the concluding chapter.]

THE AMOUNT OF FINE EARTH BROUGHT UP BY WORMS TO THE SURFACE

We now come to the more immediate subject of this volume, namely, the amount of earth which is brought up by worms from beneath the surface, and is afterwards spread out more or less completely by the rain and wind. The amount can be judged of by two methods,—by the rate at which objects left on the surface are buried, and more accurately by weighing the quantity brought up within a given time. We will begin with the first method, as it was first followed.

Near Maer Hall in Staffordshire, quicklime had been spread about the year 1827 thickly over a field of good pasture-land, which had not since been ploughed. Some square holes were dug in this field in the beginning of October, 1837; and the sections showed a layer of turf formed by the matted roots of the grasses, ½ inch in thickness, beneath which, at a depth of 2½ inches (or 3 inches from the surface), a layer of the lime in powder or in small lumps could be distinctly seen running all round the vertical sides of the holes. The soil beneath the layer of lime was either gravelly or of a coarse sandy nature, and differed considerably in appearance from the overlying dark-coloured fine mould. Coal-cinders had been spread over a part of this same field either in the year 1833 or 1834; and when the above holes were dug, that is after an interval of 3 or 4 years, the cinders formed a line of black spots round the holes, at a depth of 1 inch beneath the surface, parallel to and above the white layer of lime. Over another part of this field cinders had been strewed, only about half-a-year before, and these either still lay on the surface or were entangled among the roots of the grasses; and I here saw the commencement of the burying process, for worm-castings had been heaped on several of the smaller fragments. After an interval of 4¾ years this field was re-examined, and now the two layers of lime and cinders were found almost everywhere at a greater depth than before by nearly 1 inch, we will say by $\frac{3}{4}$ of an inch. Therefore mould to an average thickness of .22 of an inch had been annually brought up by the worms, and had been spread over the surface of this field.

* * * *

ON THE NUMBER OF WORMS WHICH LIVE WITHIN A GIVEN SPACE

We will now show, firstly, what a vast number of worms live unseen by us beneath our feet, and, secondly, the actual weight of the earth which they bring up to the surface within a given space and within a given time. Hensen, who has published so full and interesting an account of the habits of worms, calculates, from the number which he found in a measured space, that there must exist 133,000 living worms in a hectare of land, or 53,767 in an acre. This latter number of worms would weigh 356 pounds, taking Hensen's standard of the weight of a single worm, namely, one gram. It should, however, be noted that this calculation is founded on the numbers found in a garden, and Hensen believes that worms are here twice as numerous as in corn-fields. The above result, astonishing though it be, seems to me credible, judging from the number of worms which I have sometimes seen, and from the number daily destroyed by birds without the species being exterminated. Some barrels of bad ale were left on Mr. Miller's land, in the hope of making vinegar, but the vinegar proved bad, and the barrels were upset. It should be premised that acetic acid is so deadly a poison to worms that Perrier found that a glass rod dipped into this acid and then into a considerable body of water in which worms were immersed, invariably killed them quickly. On the morning after the barrels had been upset, 'the heaps of worms which lay dead on the ground were so amazing, that if Mr. Miller had not seen them, he could not have thought it possible for such numbers to have existed in the space.' As further evidence of the large number of worms which live in the ground, Hensen states that he found in a garden sixty-four open burrows in a space of $14\frac{1}{2}$ square feet, that is, nine in 2 square feet. But the burrows are sometimes much more numerous, for when digging in a grass-field near Maer Hall, I found a cake of dry earth, as large as my two open hands, which was penetrated by seven burrows, as large as goose-quills.

WEIGHT OF THE EARTH EJECTED FROM A SINGLE BURROW, AND FROM ALL THE BURROWS WITHIN A GIVEN SPACE

* * * *

In a field at the bottom of a valley in the chalk . . . , a square yard was measured at a spot where very large castings abounded; they appeared, however, almost equally numerous in a few other places. These castings, which retained perfectly their vermiform shape, were collected; and they weighed when partially dried, 1 lb. 13½ oz. This field had been rolled with a heavy agricultural roller fifty-two days before, and this would certainly have flattened every single casting on the land. The weather had been very dry for two or three weeks before the day of collection, so that not one casting appeared fresh or had been recently ejected. We may therefore assume that those which were weighed had been ejected within, we will say, forty days from the time when the field was rolled,—that is, twelve days short of the whole intervening period. I had examined the same part of the field shortly before it was rolled, and it then abounded with fresh castings. Worms do not work in dry weather during the summer, or in winter during severe frosts. If we assume that they work for only half the year—though this is too low an estimate—then the worms in this field would eject during the year, 8.387 pounds per square yard; or 18.12 tons per acre, assuming the whole surface to be equally productive in castings.

In the foregoing cases some of the necessary data had to be estimated, but in the two following cases the results are much more trustworthy. A lady, on whose accuracy I can implicitly rely, offered to collect during a year all the castings thrown up on two separate square yards, near Leith Hill Place, in Surrey. The amount collected was, however, somewhat less than that originally ejected by the worms; for, as I have repeatedly observed, a good deal of the finest earth is washed away, whenever castings are thrown up during or shortly before heavy rain. Small portions also adhered to the surrounding blades of grass, and it required too much time to detach every one of them. On sandy soil, as in the present instance, castings are liable to crumble after dry weather, and particles were thus often lost. The lady also occasionally left home for a week or two, and at such times the castings must have suffered still greater loss from exposure to the weather. These losses were, however, compensated to some extent by the collections having been made on one of the squares for four days, and on the other square for two days more than the year.

A space was selected (October 9th, 1870) on a broad, grass-covered terrace, which had been mowed and swept during many years. It faced the south, but was shaded during part of the day by trees. It had been formed at least a century ago by a great accumulation of small and large fragments of sandstone, together with some sandy earth, rammed down level. It is probable that it was at first protected by being covered with turf. This terrace, judging from the number of castings on it, was rather unfavourable for the existence of worms, in comparison with the neighbouring fields and an upper terrace. It was indeed surprising that as many worms could live here as were seen; for on digging a hole in this terrace, the black vegetable mould together with the turf was only four inches in thickness, beneath which lay the level surface of light-coloured sandy soil, with many fragments of sandstone. Before any castings were collected all the previously existing ones were carefully removed. The last day's collection was on October 14th, 1871. The castings were then well dried before a fire; and they weighed exactly 3½ lbs. This would give for an acre of similar land 7.56 tons of dry earth annually ejected by worms.

The second square was marked on unenclosed common land, at a height of about 700 ft. above the sea, at some little distance from Leith Hill Tower. The surface was clothed with short, fine turf, and had never been disturbed by the hand of man. The spot selected appeared neither particularly favourable nor the reverse for worms; but I have often noticed that castings are especially abundant on common land, and this may, perhaps, be attributed to the poorness of the soil. The vegetable mould was here between three and four inches in thickness. As this spot was at some distance from the house where the lady lived, the castings were not collected at such short intervals of time as those on the Terrace; consequently the loss of fine earth during rainy weather must have been greater in this than in the last case. The castings moreover were more sandy, and in collecting them during dry weather they sometimes crumbled into dust, and much was thus lost. Therefore it is certain that the worms brought up to the surface considerably more earth than that which was collected. The last collection was made on October 27th, 1871; i.e., 367 days after the square had been marked out and the surface cleared of all pre-existing castings. The collected castings, after being well dried, weighed 7.453 pounds; and this would give, for an acre of the same kind of land, 16.1 tons of annually ejected dry earth.

* * * *

We have no means of judging how great a weight of earth a single full-sized worm ejects during a year. Hensen estimates that 53,767 worms exist in an acre of land; but this is founded on the number found in gardens, and he believes that only about half as many live in corn-fields. How many live in old pasture-land is unknown; but if we assume that half the above number, or 26,886 worms live on such land, then taking from the previous summary 15 tons as the weight of the castings annually thrown up on an acre of land, each worm must annually eject 20 ounces. A full-sized casting at the mouth of a single burrow often exceeds, as we have seen, an ounce in weight; and it is probable that worms eject more than twenty full-sized castings during a year. If they eject annually more than 20 ounces, we may infer that the worms which live in an acre of pasture-land must be less than 26,886 in number.

Worms live chiefly in the superficial mould, which is usually from 4 or 5 to 10 and even 12 inches in thickness; and it is this mould which passes over and over again through their bodies and is brought to the surface. But worms occasionally burrow into the sub-soil to a much greater depth, and on such occasions they bring up earth from this greater depth; and this process has gone on for countless ages. Therefore the superficial layer of mould would ultimately attain, though at a slower and slower rate, a thickness equal to the depth to which worms ever burrow, were there not other opposing agencies at work which carry away to a lower level some of the finest earth which is continually being brought to the surface by worms. How great a thickness vegetable mould ever attains, I have not had good opportunities for observing; but in the next chapter, when we consider the burial of ancient buildings, some facts will be given on this head. In the last two chapters we shall see that the soil is actually increased, though only to a small degree, through the agency of worms; but their chief work is to sift the finer from the coarser particles, to mingle the whole with vegetable débris, and to saturate it with their intestinal secretions.

Finally, no one who considers the facts given in this chapter—on the burying of small objects and on the sinking of great stones left on the surface—on the vast number of worms which live within a moderate extent of ground—on the weight of the castings ejected from the mouth of the same burrow—on the weight of all the castings ejected within a known time on a measured space—will hereafter, as I believe, doubt that worms play an important part in nature.

* * * *

CONCLUSION

Worms have played a more important part in the history of the world than most persons would at first suppose. In almost all humid countries they are extraordinarily numerous, and for their size possess great muscular power. In many parts of England a weight of more than ten tons (10,516 kilogrammes) of dry earth annually passes through their bodies and is brought to the surface on each acre of land; so that the whole superficial bed of vegetable mould passes through their bodies in the course of every few years. From the collapsing of the old burrows the mould is in constant though slow movement, and the particles composing it are thus rubbed together. By these means fresh surfaces are continually exposed to the action of the carbonic acid in the soil, and of the humus-acids which appear to be still more efficient in the decomposition of rocks. The generation of the humus-acids is probably hastened during the digestion by many half-decayed leaves which worms consume. Thus the particles of earth, forming the superficial mould, are subjected to conditions eminently favourable for their decomposition and disintegration. Moreover, the particles of the softer rocks suffer some amount of mechanical trituration in the muscular gizzards of worms, in which small stones serve as millstones.

The finely levigated castings, when brought to the surface in a moist condition, flow during rainy weather down any moderate slope; and the smaller particles are washed far down even a gently inclined surface. Castings when dry often crumble into small pellets, and these are apt to roll down any sloping surface. Where the land is quite level and is covered with herbage, and where the climate is humid so that much dust cannot be blown away, it appears at first sight impossible that there should be any appreciable amount of subaerial denudation; but worm-castings are blown, especially whilst moist and viscid, in one uniform direction by the prevalent winds which are accompanied by rain. By these several means the superficial mould is prevented from accumulating to a great thickness; and a thick bed of mould checks in many ways the disintegration of the underlying rocks and fragments of rock.

The removal of worm-castings by the above means leads to results which are far from insignificant. It has been shown that a layer of earth, .2 of an inch in thickness, is in many places annually brought to the surface per acre; and if a small part of this amount flows, or rolls, or is washed, even for a short distance down every inclined surface, or is repeatedly blown in one direction, a great effect will be produced in the course of ages. It was found by measurements and calculations that on a surface with a mean inclination of 9° 26′, 2.4 cubic inches of earth which had been ejected by worms crossed, in the course of a year, a horizontal line one yard in length; so that 240 cubic inches would cross a line 100 yards in length. This latter amount in a damp state would weigh

$11\frac{1}{2}$ pounds. Thus a considerable weight of earth is continually moving down each side of every valley, and will in time reach its bed. Finally this earth will be transported by the streams flowing in the valleys into the ocean, the great receptacle for all matter denuded from the land. It is known from the amount of sediment annually delivered into the sea by the Mississippi, that its enormous drainage-area must on an average be lowered .00263 of an inch each year; and this would suffice in four and a half million years to lower the whole drainage-area to the level of the seashore. So that, if a small fraction of the layer of fine earth, .2 of an inch in thickness, which is annually brought to the surface by worms, is carried away, a great result cannot fail to be produced within a period which no geologist considers extremely long.

Archæologists ought to be grateful to worms, as they protect and preserve for an indefinitely long period every object, not liable to decay, which is dropped on the surface of the land, by burying it beneath their castings. Thus, also, many elegant and curious tessellated pavements and other ancient remains have been preserved; though no doubt the worms have in these cases been largely aided by earth washed and blown from the adjoining land, especially when cultivated. The old tessellated pavements have, however, often suffered by having subsided unequally from being unequally undermined by the worms. Even old massive walls may be undermined and subside; and no building is in this respect safe, unless the foundations lie 6 or 7 feet beneath the surface, at a depth at which worms cannot work. It is probable that many monoliths and some old walls have fallen down from having been undermined by worms.

Worms prepare the ground in an excellent manner for the growth of fibrous-rooted plants and for seedlings of all kinds. They periodically expose the mould to the air, and sift it so that no stones larger than the particles which they can swallow are left in it. They mingle the whole intimately together, like a gardener who prepares fine soil for his choicest plants. In this state it is well fitted to retain moisture and to absorb all soluble substances, as well as for the process of nitrification. The bones of dead animals, the harder parts of insects, the shells of land-molluscs, leaves, twigs, &c., are before long all buried beneath the accumulated castings of worms, and are thus brought in a more or less decayed state within reach of the roots of plants. Worms likewise drag an infinite number of dead leaves and other parts of plants into their burrows, partly for the sake of plugging them up and partly as food.

The leaves which are dragged into the burrows as food, after being torn into the finest shreds, partially digested, and saturated with the intestinal and urinary secretions, are commingled with much earth. This earth forms the dark-coloured, rich humus which almost everywhere covers the surface of the land with a fairly well-defined layer or mantle. Von Hensen placed two worms in a vessel 18 inches in diameter, which was filled with sand, on which fallen leaves were strewed; and these were soon dragged into their burrows to a depth of 3 inches. After about 6 weeks an almost uniform layer of sand, a centimetre (.4 inch) in thickness, was converted into humus by having passed through the alimentary canals of these two worms. It is believed by some persons that worm-burrows, which often penetrate the ground almost perpendicularly to a depth of 5 or 6 feet, materially aid in its drainage; notwithstanding that the viscid castings piled over the mouths of the burrows prevent or check the rain-water directly entering them. They allow the air to penetrate deeply into the ground. They also greatly facilitate the downward passage of roots of moderate size; and these will be nourished by the humus with which the burrows are lined. Many seeds owe their germination to having been covered by castings; and others buried to a considerable depth beneath accumulated castings lie dormant, until at some future time they are accidentally uncovered and germinate.

Worms are poorly provided with sense-organs, for they cannot be said to see, although they can just distinguish between light and darkness; they are completely deaf, and have only a feeble power of smell; the sense of touch alone is well developed. They can therefore learn little about the outside world, and it is surprising that they should exhibit some skill in lining their burrows with their castings and with leaves, and in the case of some species in piling up their castings into tower-like constructions. But it is far more surprising that they should apparently exhibit some degree of intelligence instead of a mere blind instinctive impulse, in their manner of plugging up the mouths of their burrows. They act in nearly the same manner as would a man, who had to close a cylindrical tube with different kinds of leaves, petioles, triangles of paper, &c., for they commonly seize such objects by their pointed ends. But with thin objects a certain number are drawn in by their broader ends. They do not act in the same unvarying manner in all cases, as do most of the lower animals; for instance, they do not drag in leaves by their foot-stalks, unless the basal part of the blade is as narrow as the apex, or narrower than it.

When we behold a wide, turf-covered expanse, we should remember that its smoothness, on which so much of its beauty depends, is mainly due to all the inequalities having been slowly levelled by worms. It is a

APPENDIX

THE DARWINIAN LITERATURE

DARWIN and Darwin's ideas are the subjects of an enormous literature—understandably, since by any accounting he is one of the great figures who have shaped the thought of the modern Western world. It would be impossible and inappropriate to try to give a guide to that literature here. But a few suggestions may be helpful for the general reader who wishes to look into the matter.

DARWIN'S WRITINGS

In 1887, Darwin's son Francis published *The Life and Letters of Charles Darwin* in three volumes (brought out in 1896 by Appleton and Co. in America in two volumes). In an appendix, Francis Darwin gives a list of his father's writings. This list seems interesting to us because it shows so nicely the range of Darwin's activity, as well as giving some details of the history of his chief books; for these reasons, we reproduce it here in full.

I. LIST OF WORKS BY C. DARWIN

Narrative of the Surveying Voyages of Her Majesty's Ships 'Adventure' and 'Beagle' between the years 1826 and 1836, describing their examination of the Southern shores of South America, and the 'Beagle's' circumnavigation of the globe. Vol. iii. Journal and Remarks, 1832–1836. By Charles Darwin. 8vo. London, 1839.

Journal of Researches into the Natural History and Geology of the countries visited during the Voyage of H.M.S. 'Beagle' round the world, under the command of Capt. Fitz-Roy, R.N. 2nd edition, corrected, with additions, 8vo. London, 1845. (Colonial and Home Library.)

A Naturalist's Voyage. Journal of Researches, &c. 8vo. London, 1860. (Contains a postscript dated Feb. 1, 1860.)

Zoology of the Voyage of H.M.S. 'Beagle'. Edited and superintended by Charles Darwin. Part I. *Fossil Mammalia*, by Richard Owen. With a Geological Introduction, by Charles Darwin. 4to. London, 1840.

— Part II. *Mammalia*, by George R. Waterhouse. With a notice of their habits and ranges, by Charles Darwin. 4to. London, 1839.

— Part III. *Birds*, by John Gould. An 'Advertisement' (2 pp.) states that in consequence of Mr. Gould's having left England for Australia, many descriptions were supplied by Mr. G. R. Gray of the British Museum. 4to. London, 1841.

— Part IV. *Fish*, by Rev. Leonard Jenyns. 4to. London, 1842.

— Part V. *Reptiles*, by Thomas Bell. 4to. London, 1843.

The Structure and Distribution of Coral Reefs. Being the First Part of the Geology of the Voyage of the 'Beagle'. 8vo. London, 1842.

The Structure and Distribution of Coral Reefs. 2nd edition. 8vo. London, 1874.

Geological Observations on the Volcanic Islands, visited during the Voyage of H.M.S. 'Beagle'. Being the Second Part of the Geology of the Voyage of the 'Beagle'. 8vo. London, 1844.

Geological Observations on South America. Being the Third Part of the Geology of the Voyage of the 'Beagle'. 8vo. London, 1846.

Geological Observations on the Volcanic Islands and parts of South America visited during the Voyage of H.M.S. 'Beagle'. 2nd edition. 8vo. London, 1876.

A Monograph of the Fossil Lepadidae; or, Pedunculated Cirripedes of Great Britain. 4to. London, 1851. (Palaeontographical Society.)

A Monograph of the Sub-class Cirripedia, with Figures of all the species. The Lepadidae; or, Pedunculated Cirripedes. 8vo. London, 1851. (Ray Society.)

— *The Balanidae (or Sessile Cirripedes); the Verrucidae, &c.* 8vo. London, 1854. (Ray Society.)

A Monograph of the Fossil Balanidae and Verrucidae of Great Britain. 4to. London, 1854. (Palaeontographical Society.)

On the Origin of Species by means of Natural Selection, or the Preservation of Favoured Races in the Struggle for Life. 8vo. London, 1859. (Dated Oct. 1st, 1859, published Nov. 24, 1859.)

— Fifth thousand. 8vo. London, 1860.

— Third edition, with additions and corrections. (Seventh thousand.) 8vo. London, 1861. (Dated March, 1861.)

— Fourth edition, with additions and corrections. (Eighth thousand.) 8vo. London, 1866. (Dated June, 1866.)

— Fifth edition, with additions and corrections. (Tenth thousand.) 8vo. London, 1869. (Dated May, 1869).

— Sixth edition, with additions and corrections to 1872. (Twenty-fourth thousand.) 8vo. London, 1882. (Dated Jan., 1872.)

On the various contrivances by which Orchids are fertilised by Insects. 8vo. London, 1862.

— Second edition. 8vo. London, 1877. (In the second edition the word 'On' is omitted from the title.)

The Movements and Habits of Climbing Plants. Second edition. 8vo. London, 1875. (First appeared in the ninth volume of the *Journal of the Linnean Society*.)

The Variation of Animals and Plants under Domestication. 2 vols. 8vo. London, 1868.

— Second edition, revised. 2 vols. 8vo. London, 1875.

The Descent of Man, and Selection in Relation to Sex. 2 vols. 8vo. London, 1871.

— Second edition. 8vo. London, 1874. (In 1 vol.)

The Expression of the Emotions in Man and Animals. 8vo. London, 1872.

The Effects of Cross and Self Fertilisation in the Vegetable Kingdom. 8vo. London, 1876.

— Second edition. 8vo. London, 1878.

The different Forms of Flowers on Plants of the same Species. 8vo. London, 1877.
— Second edition. 8vo. London, 1880.

The Power of Movement in Plants. By Charles Darwin, assisted by Francis Darwin. 8vo. London, 1880.

The Formation of Vegetable Mould, through the Action of Worms, with Observations on their Habits. 8vo. London, 1881.

II. LIST OF BOOKS CONTAINING CONTRIBUTIONS BY C. DARWIN

A manual of scientific enquiry; prepared for the use of Her Majesty's Navy: and adapted for travellers in general. Ed. by Sir John F. W. Herschel, Bart. 8vo. London, 1849. (Section VI, 'Geology'. By Charles Darwin.)

Memoir of the Rev. John Stevens Henslow. By the Rev. Leonard Jenyns. 8vo. London, 1862. (In Chapter III., 'Recollections' by C. Darwin.)

A letter (1876) on the 'Drift' near Southampton, published in Prof. J. Geikie's *Prehistoric Europe.*

Flowers and their Unbidden Guests. By A. Kerner. With a Prefatory Letter by Charles Darwin. The translation revised and edited by W. Ogle. 8vo. London, 1878.

Erasmus Darwin. By Ernst Krause. Translated from the German by W. S. Dallas. With a preliminary notice by Charles Darwin. 8vo. London, 1879.

Studies in the Theory of Descent. By Aug. Weismann. Translated and edited by Raphael Meldola. With a Prefatory Notice by Charles Darwin. 8vo. London, 1880—.

The Fertilisation of Flowers. By Hermann Müller. Translated and edited by D'Arcy W. Thompson. With a Preface by Charles Darwin. 8vo. London, 1883.

Mental Evolution in Animals. By G. J. Romanes. With a posthumous essay on instinct by Charles Darwin, 1883. (Also published in the *Journal of the Linnean Society.*)

Some Notes on a curious habit of male humble bees were sent to Prof. Hermann Müller, of Lippstadt, who had permission from Mr. Darwin to make what use he pleased of them. After Müller's death the Notes were given by his son to Dr. E. Krause, who published them under the title, 'Ueber die Wege der Hummel-Männchen' in his book, *Gesammelte kleinere Schriften von Charles Darwin* (1887).

III. LIST OF SCIENTIFIC PAPERS, INCLUDING A SELECTION OF LETTERS AND SHORT COMMUNICATIONS TO SCIENTIFIC JOURNALS

Letters to Professor Henslow, read by him at the meeting of the Cambridge Philosophical Society, held Nov. 16, 1835. 31 pp. 8vo. Privately printed for distribution among the members of the Society.

Geological Notes made during a survey of the East and West Coasts of South America in the years 1832, 1833, 1834, and 1835; with an account of a transverse section of the Cordilleras of the Andes between Valparaiso and Mendoza. (Read Nov. 18, 1835.) *Geol. Soc. Proc.* ii. 1838, pp. 210–212. (This Paper is incorrectly described in *Geol. Soc. Proc.* ii., p. 210 as follows:—'Geological notes, &c., by F. Darwin, Esq., of St. John's College, Cambridge: communicated by Prof. Sedgwick.' It is indexed under C. Darwin.)

Notes upon the Rhea Americana. *Zool. Soc. Proc.*, Part v. 1837, pp. 35–36.

Observations of proofs of recent elevation on the coast of Chili, made during the survey of H.M.S. 'Beagle', commanded by Capt. FitzRoy. (1837.) *Geol. Soc. Proc.* ii. 1838, pp. 446–449.

A sketch of the deposits containing extinct Mammalia in the neighbourhood of the Plata. (1837.) *Geol. Soc. Proc.* ii. 1838, pp. 542–544.

On certain areas of elevation and subsidence in the Pacific and Indian oceans, as deduced from the study of coral formations. (1837.) *Geol. Soc. Proc.* ii. 1838, pp. 552–554.

On the Formation of Mould. (Read Nov. 1, 1837.) *Geol. Soc. Proc.* ii. 1838, pp. 574–576; *Geol. Soc. Trans.* v. 1840, pp. 505–510.

On the Connexion of certain Volcanic Phenomena and on the formation of mountain-chains and the effects of continental elevations. (Read March 7, 1838). *Geol. Soc. Proc.* ii. 1838, pp. 654–660; *Geol. Soc. Trans.* v. 1840, pp. 601–632. (In the Society's Transactions the wording of the title is slightly different.)

Origin of saliferous deposits. Salt Lakes of Patagonia and La Plata. *Geol. Soc. Journ.* ii. (Part ii.), 1838, pp. 127–128.

Note on a Rock seen on an Iceberg in 16° South Latitude. *Geogr. Soc. Journ.* ix. 1839, pp. 528–529.

Observations on the Parallel Roads of Glen Roy, and of other parts of Lochaber in Scotland, with an attempt to prove that they are of marine origin. *Phil. Trans.* 1839, pp. 39–82.

On a remarkable Bar of Sandstone off Pernambuco, on the Coast of Brazil. *Phil. Mag.* xix. 1841, pp. 257–260.

On the Distribution of the Erratic Boulders and on the Contemporaneous Unstratified Deposits of South America. (1841.) *Geol. Soc. Proc.* iii. 1842, pp. 425–430; *Geol. Soc. Trans.* (1841.) vi. 1842, pp. 415–432.

Notes on the Effects produced by the Ancient Glaciers of Caernarvonshire, and on the Boulders transported by Floating Ice. *London Philosoph. Mag.* vol. xxi, p. 180. 1842.

Remarks on the preceding paper, in a Letter from Charles Darwin, Esq., to Mr. Maclaren. Edinb. *New Phil. Journ.* xxxiv. 1843, pp. 47–50. (The 'preceding' paper is: On Coral Islands and Reefs as described by Mr. Darwin. By Charles Maclaren, Esq., F.R.S.E.)

Observations on the Structure and Propagation of the genus Sagitta. *Ann.* and *Mag. Nat. Hist.* xiii. 1844, pp. 1–6.

Brief Descriptions of several Terrestrial Planariae, and of some remarkable Marine Species, with an Account of their Habits. *Ann.* and *Mag. Nat. Hist.* xiv. 1844, pp. 241–251.

An account of the Fine Dust which often falls on Vessels in the Atlantic Ocean. *Geol. Soc. Journ.* ii. 1846, pp. 26–30.

On the Geology of the Falkland Islands. *Geol. Soc. Journ.* ii. 1846, pp. 267–274.

A review of Waterhouse's 'Natural History of the Mammalia'. (Not signed.) *Ann.* and *Mag. of Nat. Hist.* 1847. vol. xix, p. 53.

On the Transportal of Erratic Boulders from a lower to a higher level. *Geol. Soc. Journ.* iv. 1848, pp. 315–323.

On British fossil Lepadidae. *Geol. Soc. Journ.* vi. 1850, pp. 439–440. (The G.C.J. says, 'This paper was withdrawn by the author with the permission of the Council.')

Analogy of the Structure of some Volcanic Rocks with that of Glaciers. *Edinb. Roy. Soc. Proc.* ii. 1851, pp. 17–18.

On the power of Icebergs to make rectilinear, uniformly-directed Grooves across a Submarine Undulatory Surface. *Phil. Mag.* x. 1855, pp. 96–98.

Vitality of Seeds. *Gardeners' Chronicle*, Nov. 17, 1855, p. 758.

On the action of Sea-water on the Germination of Seeds. (1856.) *Linn. Soc. Journ.* i. 1857 (Botany), pp. 130–140.

On the Agency of Bees in the Fertilisation of Papilionaceous Flowers. *Gardeners' Chronicle.* p. 725, 1857.

On the Tendency of Species to form Varieties; and on the Perpetuation of Varieties and Species by Natural Means of Selection. By Charles Darwin, Esq., F.R.S., F.L.S., and F.G.S., and Alfred Wallace, Esq. (Read July 1st, 1858.) *Journ. Linn. Soc.* 1859, vol. iii (Zoology), p. 45.

Special titles of C. Darwin's contributions to the foregoing:—(i) Extract from an unpublished work on Species by C. Darwin, Esq., consisting of a portion of a chapter entitled, 'On the Variation of Organic Beings in a State of Nature; on the Natural Means of Selection; on the Comparison of Domestic Races and true Species.' (ii) Abstract of a Letter from C. Darwin, Esq., to Professor Asa Gray, of Boston, U.S., dated Sept. 5, 1857.

On the Agency of Bees in the Fertilisation of Papilionaceous Flowers, and on the Crossing of Kidney Beans. *Gardeners' Chronicle*, 1858, p. 828 and *Ann. Nat. Hist.* 3rd series ii. 1858, pp. 459–465.

Do the Tineina or other small Moths suck Flowers, and if so what Flowers? *Entom. Weekly Intell.* vol. viii, 1860, p. 103.

Note on the achenia of Pumilio Argyrolepis *Gardeners' Chronicle*, Jan. 5, 1861, p. 4.

Fertilisation of Vincas. *Gardeners' Chronicle*, pp. 552, 831, 832. 1861.

On the Two Forms, or Dimorphic Condition, in the species of Primula, and on their remarkable Sexual Relations. *Linn. Soc. Journ.* vi. 1862 (Botany), pp. 77–96.

On the Three remarkable Sexual Forms of Catasetum tridentatum, an Orchid in the possession of the Linnean Society. *Linn. Soc. Journ.* vi. 1862 (Botany), pp. 151–157.

Yellow Rain. *Gardeners' Chronicle*, July 18, 1863, p. 675.

On the thickness of the Pampean formation near Buenos Ayres. *Geol. Soc. Journ.* xix. 1863, pp. 68–71.

On the so-called 'Auditory-sac' of Cirripedes. *Nat. Hist. Review*, 1863, pp. 115–116.

A review of Mr. Bates' paper on 'Mimetic Butterflies'. *Nat. Hist. Review*, 1863, p. 221—. (Not signed.)

On the existence of two forms, and on their reciprocal sexual relation, in several species of the genus Linum. *Linn. Soc. Journ.* vii. 1864 (Botany), pp. 69–83.

On the Sexual Relations of the Three Forms of Lythrum salicaria. (1864.) *Linn. Soc. Journ.* viii. 1865 (Botany), pp. 169–196.

On the Movement and Habits of Climbing Plants. (1865.) *Linn. Soc. Journ.* ix. 1867 (Botany), pp. 1–118.

Note on the Common Broom (Cytisus scoparius). (1866.) *Linn. Soc. Journ.* ix. 1867 (Botany), p. 358.

Notes on the Fertilization of Orchids. *Ann.* and *Mag. Nat. Hist.* 4th series, iv. 1869, pp. 141–159.

On the Character and Hybrid-like Nature of the Offspring from the Illegitimate Unions of Dimorphic and Trimorphic Plants. (1868.) *Linn. Soc. Journ.* x. 1869 (Botany), pp. 393–437.

On the Specific Difference between Primula veris, Brit. Fl. (var. officinalis, of Linn.), P. vulgaris, Brit. Fl. (var. acaulis, Linn.), and P. elatior, Jacq.; and on the Hybrid Nature of the common Oxlip. With Supplementary Remarks on naturally-produced Hybrids in the genus Verbascum. (1868.) *Linn. Soc. Journ.* x. 1869 (Botany), pp. 437–454.

Note on the Habits of the Pampas Woodpecker (Colaptes campestris). *Zool. Soc. Proc.* Nov. 1, 1870, pp. 705–706.

Fertilisation of Leschenaultia. *Gardeners' Chronicle*, p. 1166, 1871.

The Fertilisation of Winter-flowering Plants. *Nature*, Nov. 18, 1869, vol. i, p. 85.

Pangenesis. *Nature*, April 27, 1871, vol. iii, p. 502.

A new view of Darwinism. *Nature*, July 6, 1871, vol. iv, p. 180.

Bree on Darwinism. *Nature*, Aug. 8, 1872, vol. vi, p. 279.

Inherited Instinct. *Nature*, Feb. 13, 1873, vol. vii, p. 281.

Perception in the Lower Animals. *Nature*, March 13, 1873, vol. vii, p. 360.

Origin of certain instincts. *Nature*, April 3, 1873, vol. vii, p. 417.

Habits of Ants. *Nature*, July 24, 1873, vol. viii, p. 244.

On the Males and Complemental Males of Certain Cirripedes, and on Rudimentary Structures. *Nature*, Sept. 25, 1873, vol. viii, p. 431.

Recent researches on Termites and Honey-bees. *Nature*, Feb. 19, 1874, vol. ix, p. 308.

Fertilisation of the Fumariaceae. *Nature*, April 16, 1874, vol. ix, p. 460.

Fertilisation of the Primrose destroyed by Birds. *Nature*, April 23, 1874, vol. ix, p. 482; May 14, 1874, vol. x, p. 24.

Cherry Blossoms. *Nature*, May 11, 1876, vol. xiv, p. 28.

Sexual Selection in relation to Monkeys. *Nature*, Nov. 2, 1876, vol. xv, p. 18.

Fritz Müller on Flowers and Insects. *Nature*, Nov. 29, 1877, vol. xvii, p. 78.

The Scarcity of Holly Berries and Bees. *Gardeners' Chronicle*, Jan. 20, 1877, p. 83.

Notes on Fertilisation of Plants. *Gardeners' Chronicle*, vol. vii, p. 246, 1877.

A biographical sketch of an infant. *Mind*, No. 7, July, 1877.

Transplantation of Shells. *Nature*, May 30, 1878, vol. xviii, p. 120.

Fritz Müller on a Frog having Eggs on its back—on the abortion of the hairs on the legs of certain Caddis-Flies, &c. *Nature*, March 20, 1879, vol. xix, p. 462.

Rats and Water-Casks. *Nature*, March 27, 1879, vol. xix, p. 481.

Fertility of Hybrids from the common and Chinese Goose. *Nature*, Jan. 1, 1880, vol. xxi, p. 207.

The Sexual Colours of certain Butterflies. *Nature*, Jan. 8, 1880, vol. xxi, p. 237.

The Omori Shell Mounds. *Nature*, April 15, 1880, vol. xxi, p. 561.

Sir Wyville Thomson and Natural Selection. *Nature*, Nov. 11, 1880, vol. xxiii, p. 32.

Black Sheep. *Nature*, Dec. 30, 1880, vol. xxiii, p. 193.

Movements of Plants. *Nature*, March 3, 1881, vol. xxiii, p. 409.

The Movements of Leaves. *Nature*, April 28, 1881, vol. xxiii, p. 603.

Inheritance. *Nature*, July 21, 1881, vol. xxiv, p. 257.

Leaves injured at Night by Free Radiation. *Nature*, Sept. 15, 1881, vol. xxiv, p. 459.

The Parasitic Habits of Molothrus. *Nature*, Nov. 17, 1881, vol. xxv, p. 51.

On the Dispersal of Freshwater Bivalves. *Nature*, April 6, 1882, vol. xxv, p. 529.
The Action of Carbonate of Ammonia on the Roots of certain Plants. (Read March 16, 1882.) *Linn. Soc. Journ.* (Botany), vol. xix, 1882, pp. 239–261.
The Action of Carbonate of Ammonia on Chlorophyll-bodies. (Read March 6, 1882.) *Linn. Soc. Journ.* (Botany), vol. xix, 1882, pp. 262–284.
On the Modification of a Race of Syrian Street-Dogs by means of Sexual Selection. By W. Van Dyck. With a preliminary notice by Charles Darwin. (Read April 18, 1882.) *Proc. Zoolog. Soc.* 1882, pp. 367–370.

All of Darwin's general books were published in the United States by D. Appleton and Company, and copies of the American printings are often available in second-hand bookstores.

The *Origin of Species* has been reprinted in many different series. It is perhaps most easily available currently, along with the *Descent of Man*, as a 'Modern Library Giant'. The *Voyage of the Beagle*, which has had almost as varied a publishing history as the *Origin*, is currently available in 'Everyman's Library'. The *Autobiography* has been reprinted by Watts & Co. of London in a series called 'The Thinker's Library'.

The Hafner Publishing Company, in 1952, put out a facsimile reprint of the *Journal of Researches* of 1839. The *Beagle* story has also been enriched by the publication, in 1934, of Darwin's *Diary of the Voyage of the Beagle*, edited by his grand-daughter, Lady Nora Barlow. In 1946, Lady Barlow published extracts from various notebooks kept by Darwin while on the *Beagle*, and letters written during the voyage, under the title *Charles Darwin and the Voyage of the Beagle* (New York: Philosophical Library).

A facsimile reprint of *The Expression of the Emotions in Man and Animals* was published by the Philosophical Library in 1955. A condensation of this book has been available, since 1934, in the 'Thinker's Library', published by Watts & Co. of London.

DARWIN BIOGRAPHY

Darwin biographers mostly follow the same well-travelled road, using the material of the *Life and Letters* and the *Beagle*, along with the material available in Huxley's *Letters*, Emma Darwin's *Letters*, and the like. There seems no point, then, in giving a catalogue of these biographies here. A few recent biographies, however, seem particularly interesting, and we list these with our comments.

Geoffrey West: *Charles Darwin, The Fragmentary Man* (London: George Routledge & Sons, 1937; published in the United States by Yale University Press in 1938, with the author's name changed to Geoffrey Wells).

This might well be called the 'standard' biography of Darwin. It contains all of the facts, set forth in a prose that holds the reader's interest. But beyond this, the author clearly became fascinated by his subject, and tried to reach an understanding of Charles Darwin, perhaps coming as close as anyone can.

William Irvine: *Apes, Angels and Victorians* (New York: McGraw-Hill Book Company, 1955).

This is the combined story of Charles Darwin and Thomas Henry Huxley, written with a keen awareness of the Victorian background—history, literature and custom. Irvine, like West, tries to understand Darwin's personality; tries to see how this plodding, neurasthenic, shy man could have become the great intellectual force of his century.

Ruth Moore: *Charles Darwin: A Great Life in Brief* (New York: Alfred Knopf, 1955).

Miss Moore has written a straightforward account of the facts of Darwin's life, without attempting to probe into motivations, neuroses and the like; which is perhaps just as well.

Gwen Raverat: *Period Piece* (New York: W. W. Norton & Co., 1953).

Here a Darwin grand-daughter reminisces about her childhood and family. There is little directly about Charles in this book, since he died three years before the author was born, but somehow, in reading this, one comes to feel closer to the Darwins than in reading any of the formal expositions. Even the Darwin cult of illness seems easy, understandable and amusing.

DARWINIAN INFLUENCE

One cannot think about Darwin without thinking about the 'sociology of knowledge', the problem of the mutual relations between the individual and his thinking and the times in which he lives. It is the problem of the nature of genius, of the hero, of the evolution of ideas: here set forth with particular clarity because a date, 1859, a book, the *Origin of Species*, and a man, Charles Darwin, so plainly symbolize a shift in the direction of thought of a whole civilization. The change surely would have occurred, perhaps would have been much the same, if no such individual as Charles Darwin had ever lived—though it is impossible to be certain of this, since we cannot experiment with the pattern of history.

As it is, Darwin stands conveniently as a symbol for this whole intellectual revolution, and the verbiage devoted to the analysis of this situation is correspondingly enormous. We have, perhaps arbitrarily, picked three books which seem to us to constitute the most convenient introduction to this general question of the nature of the Darwinian influence.

Jacques Barzun: *Darwin, Marx, Wagner: Critique of a Heritage* (Boston: Little, Brown & Co., 1947).

Barzun has built his study of roots of the twentieth-century mind quite plausibly around these three figures, as symbols of the change in natural science, social science and the arts. Barzun, as a humanist, is in a particularly happy position for surveying the influence of Darwin and his ideas on our ways of thought.

Richard Hofstadter: *Social Darwinism in American Thought* (Philadelphia: University of Pennsylvania Press, 1944; revised edition, Boston: The Beacon Press, 1955).

Hofstadter is concerned primarily with the American scene, but he has necessarily had to consider the development of Western thought as a whole. His book thus provides the best introduction known to us to the history of the influence of Darwinian ideas on social theory and practice. He includes a well-selected bibliography.

Paul B. Sears: *Charles Darwin: the Naturalist as a Cultural Force* (New York: Charles Scribner's Sons, 1950).

Sears has attempted in this book to give a short, general appraisal of the influence of Darwin's ideas. He has perhaps been most successful in sketching Darwin's place in the development of modern biology, so that the book makes an excellent companion to Hofstadter's differently oriented study.

CONTEMPORARY EVOLUTIONARY THEORY

The reader may wonder what has happened to Darwin's ideas in the science of today: what has been rejected, what has been confirmed, what has been modified. No one has attempted a general appraisal: Darwin's work touched on so many fields that this would be a very difficult task. In general, his ideas have stood the test of time remarkably well. His theory about the origin of coral reefs, for instance, is still essentially the contemporary theory, modified by our greatly increased knowledge of changes in sea level during the recent ice ages. Similarly, his studies of things like movements of plants and habits of earthworms have been modified by increasing knowledge, but not drastically changed. We would deal, now, with the expression of the emotions in terms of a quite different vocabulary, but it could well be argued that our 'progress' since Darwin has not been spectacular.

Perhaps the two greatest changes affecting such writings of Darwin as have been included in this anthology are the developments of genetics on the one hand, and of anthropology and psychology on the other. Our understanding of man has been greatly changed by our recognition of cultural forces, and by the insights given us by the work of Freud and his successors. Our understanding of evolution has changed chiefly through the development of the gene theory and the mutation theories of modern genetics.

Julian Huxley has given some notes on the fate of Darwin's ideas in a little book called *The Living Thoughts of Darwin* (Philadelphia: David McKay Co., 1939). The reader who wants a general survey of present ideas about evolution, however, would probably best consult one of the recent summaries. We would particularly recommend the following:

Julian Huxley: *Evolution, The Modern Synthesis* (New York: Harper & Bros., 1942). This is the most complete recent statement of the theory of biological evolution. Huxley says in his introduction that he is trying mainly to appeal to professional biologists, and he assumes some knowledge of genetics and animal classification in the reader. Still, the book is certainly no more difficult to read than Darwin's *Origin*, since Huxley always manages an easy prose.

Julian Huxley: *Evolution in Action* (New York: Harper & Bros., 1953). Here Huxley is writing for the general reader, but he is not so much trying to survey evolutionary theory, as he is trying to show how this theory can be used for appraising the human situation.

George Gaylord Simpson: *The Meaning of Evolution* (New Haven: Yale University Press, 1949; also published in an abridged form as a 'Mentor' book by the New American Library). Like Huxley's *Evolution in Action*, this book is as much concerned with the implications of evolution for man, as it is with surveying our present state of knowledge.

INDEX

Abingdon Is., 58, 70
Abortion, in plants, 431
Abyssinia, 374
Acacia, 58, 71
Acalypha, 76
Actions, expressive, 405, 408
Adaptation, 108, 147, 152
Adaptations, 24, 136, 184
Adventure, 37, 40
Affection, shown by infant, 419
Africa, 73
Agassiz, Louis, 298, 302
Albemarle Is., 58, 60, 68, 70, 74–77
  description of, 60
Albinos, 381
Allen, J. A., 339
Amblyrhynchus, 65, 68, 71–72, 76, 78
  cristatus, 68–70
  Demarlii, 70–72
Ampelopsis, 433, 435
Anger, 374–378, 411–412
  of infants, 417
Animals, domesticated, 111, 116–118
  land, 72
Anomma, 195
Anthus, 331
Antirrhineae, 431
Antithesis, principle of, 369, 403, 407
Ants, sterile castes of, 194–196
  variation in castes, 131
  working or sterile, 192
Anubis baboon, 371–372
Anxiety, 411
Apes, 411
Aphides, instincts of, 186–187
Apteryx, 170
Arabs, 384
Arctic, 106
Argentina, 37
Argus pheasant, display of, 334–337
Ari-Atoll, 89
Arteries, variability of in man, 278
Articulata, 173
Aryans, 311, 383, 384
Asclepias, 178
Astonishment, 412
  terror, 378–379
Atolls, 79–80, 82–93
  absence of, 91
Audubon, 171, 187, 332
Australia, 37, 55–56, 86, 98
Australians, 39, 297, 298, 308, 386
Autobiography, 37, 103
Aymara Indians, 385, 396

Baboons, 374, 375, 378
Bachman, Dr., 299
Bagehot, W., 307
Bamboos, 72
Barbarian, 97–98
Barbary ape, 371
Barber, Mrs., 386
Barnacles, 23, 427
Barrier-reefs, 79, 81–93
Barrington Is., 58, 70
Bartlett, A. D., 333, 334, 372, 374
Basket, Fuegia, 40, 41, 50, 52, 54
Bates, H. W., 195, 435
Battle, law of, 108
Bay of Good Success, 38
Beagle, 12, 17–22, 24, 284, 304, 313, 427
Beagle Channel, 46–47, 49, 51, 52, 53
Beauty, 253–254, 349–354
  how acquired, 179–181
  sense of, 180, 181
Beech, 43
Beechey, 79
Bees, and clover, 144–145
  instincts of, 187
Beetle collecting, 13–14, 15
Behn, Dr., 381
Bell, Sir C., 29, 68, 72, 396
Bennett, J. J., 104
Bernys, Col., 313
Bibron, M., 68, 74
Bichat, 354
Bignonia, 429, 431, 435
  modified leaves of, 430
  capreolata, 432
Bignoniaceae, 433
Bindloes Is., 58, 70
'Biographical Sketch of an Infant,' 370
Bird Watching, 7
Birds, 59, 62–63, 71, 73, 76, 78, 112–113
  courtship of, 108
  migrating, 113

Birds—*continued*
moult and sexual dimorphism in colour, 330, 331
ornaments of males, disadvantages of, 337, 338
plumage display of males, 332–339
secondary sexual characters of, 325–343
selection of particular males by females, 338–339
sexual dimorphism in colour of, 329–330
sexual dimorphism in decoration of, 327–332
sexual dimorphism in size of, 326–327
sexual dimorphism in fleshy appendages of, 327–328
sexual dimorphism in wing and tail feathers of, 328–329
tameness of, 77–78
variations of domesticated, 339
variability of secondary sexual characters of, 339, 340
Bischoff, Prof., 272, 274
Biziura, 327
lobata, 326
Blair, R. H., 381, 405
Blumenbach, J. F., 302
Blushing, 412
breaches of etiquette, 394–395
in the various races of man, 383–386
mental states which induce, 389–392
modesty, 395–396
moral causes: guilt, 393–394
special expressions of man, 380–402
theory of, 396–400
Bolabola Is., 81, 82, 86
Bolivia, 385
Borreria, 76
Bory St. Vincent, 302
Botany, 72
Henslow's lectures on, 12
Botocudos, 313
Bougainville, L. A. de, 54
Bourbon Is., 65
Bow Atoll, 63, 79
Brace, Mr., 276
Brazil, 37, 46, 94, 385
Brazilians, 313
Brehm, 374
Bridges, 385, 391
Bridgman, Laura, 381
Broca, Prof., 280, 299, 306, 311
Brodie, B., 399
Browne, J. Crichton, 380, 382, 383, 388, 389
Bucaniers, 59, 67, 78
Buceros corrugatus, 328
Bucorax abyssinicus, 328
Buffon, Comte de, 302, 385
Bulmer, Mr., 386
Bulwer, E. Lytton, 23
Burchell, Dr., 352
Burke, 302
Burgess, Dr., 380–383, 385, 390, 394, 396
Burton, Capt., 353
Butterflies, varieties in, 131–132
Button, Jemmy, 40, 41, 45, 47–55, 385
Buzzard, 62, 64, 67
Bynoe, Mr., 45, 50, 60, 67, 69
Byron, Lord, 30

Cactornis, 63, 75
Cactus, 58, 66, 71
Cactus-trees, 63
Caffres, 39
Callithrix sciureus, 373
Camarhynchus, 63, 75
Cambridge, 12–14, 15, 17
Canestrini, 276
Cape de Verd, 73
Cape Horn, 45
Cape St. Diego, 38
Cardiospermum, 431
Carduelis elegans, 326
Carnivora, 112, 115
Carrion-buzzard, 77
Carus, 449
Caterpillar, instincts of, 185
Catlin, G., 346
Cats, 369
instincts of, 188
Cattle, 105
and parasitic insects, 144
Cebus, 302
azarae, 371, 372
hypoleucus, 371
Cephalopoda, eyes of, 179
Ceriornis Temminckii, 328
Cercopithecus, 302, 374
Certhidea, 63
Certhidea olivacea, 63
Chaffinch, 63
Chagos Islands, 90
Chamisso, 80
Charles Is., 58, 59, 60, 70, 72–78
description of, 59, 60
inhabitants of, 59
vegetation of, 59

Chasmorhynchus niveus, 329
nudicollis, 329
tricarunculatus, 329
Chatham Is., 57–59, 62, 70, 74–77
description of, 58, 59
Checks to increase, nature of, 140–143
Chickens, instincts of, 190
Children, 409
Chile, 23, 46, 60, 65, 73
Chimpanzee, 370–371, 374, 375–379
Chinese, 384
Christianity, 98
Church of England, 12
Cicindela, 7
Cincloramphus cruralis, 327
Circassian, 397
Cirripedes, 23, 316
Cirripedia, 19, 23
Classes, 163
Clematis, 429, 434
flammula, 433
Climate, as a check to increase, 141, 142
Climbing plants,
advantage gained, 430
hook-climbers, 428
kinds, 428
leaf-climbers, 428
lost habit of climbing, 433
movements of, 428–436
numbers of, 435
root-climbers, 428
stages in the genesis of, 433
tendril-bearers, 428
Cobaea, 434, 435
Cocculus, 431
Coccus, 131
Cocoa-nuts, 59
Cocos Is., 59
Coleridge, S. T., 30, 390
Collinett, Capt., 68
Communication, 413
infant's means of, 422–424
power of, 407
Competition, 146, 147, 183, 254
as a check to increase, 141, 142
Compositae, 73, 76, 435
Concholepas, 23
Conditions of Existence, law of, 184
Condor, 140
Confusion of Mind, 387–389
Conscience, 286
Consciousness, 408
Cook, Capt. James, 39, 96, 98
Coral formations, 79–93
Coral reefs, 21, 22, 23, 32
theory on the formation of, 85–93
Correlated variation, law of, 124
Cosmetornis, 337
vexillarius, 328
Creation, 172, 262
for the delight of man, 180
independent acts of, 182
Crustacea, 114, 171
Crustaceans, 19
Cryptocerus, 194
Cryptogamic plants, 72, 435
Cucurbita pepo, 433
Cucurbitaceae, 429
Culicidae, 316
Culpepper Is., 58
Curculionidae, 316
Curiosity, displayed by infants, 421
Cuvier, Frederick, 185
Cynanthus, 340
Cynocephalus anubis, 371–372
Cynopithecus niger, 372, 373 (illus.), 374, 378
Cyperus, 61

Dampier, Wm., 78
Darwin, Charles, 103, 104
Autobiography, 37
barbarian, first sight of, 97, 98
barnacles, 23
'Biographical Sketch of an Infant,' 370
biographies, attitude to, 31
bird watching, 7
blunders, attitude to, 28
books, editions of, 31
books, sale of, 31
Cambridge, time wasted at, 13
character of domestic varieties, 120, 121
chemistry, 8
Coral Formations, 90–91
clergyman, training as, 12
controversy, attitude to, 28
Coral Reefs, 23, 32
criticism, attitude to, 28
Descent of Man, 28, 29, 369
Descent of Man and Selection in Relation to Sex, 271
early interest in variability, 4
Expression of the Emotions in Men and Animals, 29, 369
Fellow of Royal Society, 15
first child, 29
first note-book, 24

Darwin—*continued*
'Formation of Vegetable Mould through the Action of Worms,' 449–458
geological books, 23
Geological Observations on South America, 23
geology, attitude to, 10
geology, study of, 16
habits, 32
health, 15
higher aesthetic tastes, loss of, 31
history books, attitude to, 31
hydropathic treatment, 23, 26
hypothesis, attitude to, 32
ill-health, 21–23, 25, 32
insect collecting, 7
Journal of Researches, 37
mathematics, 31
medical training, 8–9
medicine, attitude to, 8–9
memory, 31
metaphysics, 31
methodical habits, 32
mind, 30
mind, change in, 29
mineral collecting, 7
music, attitude to, 30, 31
music, taste for, 13
novels, attitude to, 30–31
Origin of Species, 24, 25–28, 32, 277, 280
poetry, attitude to, 6–7, 30, 31
poor critic, 31
Power of Movement in Plants, 427, 449
publications, 22–23
reasoning, power of, 32
reviewers, 28
scenery, attitude to, 96–97
school life, 4–6
shooting, 7, 11
slavery, attitude to, 94–95
Structure and Distribution of Coral Reefs, 37
success as a man of science, 32–33
superior to the common run of youths, 15
taste for collecting, 4
travel books, attitude to, 31
Variation of Animals and Plants under Domestication, 309
'Variation of Organic Beings in a State of Nature,' 104
Variation of Organic Beings under Domestication and in Their Natural State,' 103
Various Contrivances by which British and Foreign Orchids are Fertilized by Insects, 427
Voyage of the Beagle, 37
voyages, comments on, 95–97
writing, manner of, 29–30
working, method of, 30
Darwin, Erasmus, 9
Darwin, Sir Francis, 3, 449
'Darwinismus,' 26
Davis, Mr., 308
De Candolle, Alphonse, 105, 109, 132, 160, 167, 275
De Laval, Pyrard, 79
Denny, H., 298
Descent of Man, 28, 29, 369
Descent of Man and Selection in Relation to Sex, 271
De Vries, H., 435
Diatomaceae, 180
Dicrurus, 329
Dimorphism, 131
Dipsacus, 326
Direct action, principle of, 403
Disgust, 412
Distress, 411
Disuse, 259
Divergence of character, 158–161
in domestic productions, 158, 159
in grasses, 159, 160
in plants, 159–161
Divergence, principle of, 110
Diversification of structure, advantage of, 161
Dodo, 67
Dogs, 369, 409
instincts of, 188–190
Dolichonyx oryzivorus, 59
Domestic varieties, 117–118
character of, 120–121
origin of, 120–121
Domestic breeds, origin of, 128–129
Domestic productions, variation of, 29
Domestic races, 120–121
adaptation of, 122, 127
production of, 122
Domestication, 148
D'Orbigny, A., 312
Dove, 62, 64, 77–78
Down, 22, 427, 449
Drift-wood, 72
Drosera rotundifolia, 438–448
Duchenne, Dr., 371, 378
Ducklings, 45

East Indian Archipelago, 91
East Indies, 91
Eccremocarpus, 430, 435
Echo sign, 408
Eciton, 194
Edentata, 298
Edinburgh, 10
  University, 8
Edolius, 329
Edwards, Milne, 161
Eggs, numbers of, 139–140
Electric organs and natural selection, 177–178
Elephant, 138–139
Elevation, 157, 249
Embryo, 27
Embryonic development, 273–274
Emotional expression, study of, 369
England, 54, 78
English, 301, 310
Entellus monkey, 371
Epidemics, 141
  as a check to increase, 142
Erratic boulders, 22
Erskine, Mr., 383, 393
Esquimaux, 55, 298, 313
Eumomota superciliaris, 329
Euphorbia, 76
Euphorbiaceae, 58
Europe, 383
European, 385, 386
Europeans, 301, 304, 311, 391
Eustephanus, 326
Evidence of Man's Place in Nature, 271
Evolution, theory of, 37
  effects on Natural History, 265
Expression of the Emotions in Man and Animals, 29, 369
Expression, movements of, 406, 409–410, 413–414
Expressive actions, inheritance of, 405
Expressive movements, 411
Extermination, 167, 168
Extinction, 117, 166, 212–216, 248, 253, 256
  of the races of man, 305–311
Eyes and natural selection, 172–179
Ezra, 387

Fagus, 43
Fagus betuloides, 43
Falconer, 13
Falkland Islands, 38
Families, 163
Fear, 411
  experienced by infants, 418
Fellow of the Royal Society, 15
Fenton, 308
Fernando Noronha Is., 58
Finches, 62, 73, 76, 77
  thick-billed, 71
Fir, growth in heaths, 143
Fitz-Roy, Capt., 17–19, 23, 37, 40, 45, 46, 47, 48, 50–55, 80
Flustra, 10
Fly-catchers, tyrant, 62, 64
Food, as check to increase, 141, 142
Forbes, E., 27, 167, 346, 385, 395
Forests, 97
Formation of new species, 25
'Formation of Vegetable Mould through the Action of Worms,' 449–458
Formica flava, 194
Fossils, 16, 21, 24
Foster, Michael, 399, 400
Fox, W. Darwin, 14
Friendly Archipelago, 92
Fringilla tristis, 332
Fringing-reefs, 79, 83–86, 88, 90–91
Frog, 65, 66
Fucus loreus, 10
Fuegia Basket, *See* Basket, Fuegia
Fuegians, 38–56, 283, 284, 304, 313, 385
  attitudes of, 39
  barter, notion of, 53–54
  beliefs of, 45
  cannibalistic habits of, 44–45
  canoe, 46
  clothing of, 38, 43
  compared with other races, 55–56
  equality, 55
  famine, 44
  firearms, attitude to, 48
  food of, 44
  government of, 45
    and civilization, 55
  insanity of, 45
  language of, 39
  origin of, 46
  power of mimicry, 39
  sight, acute power of, 41
  superstitions of, 45
  tribes of, 45
  wigwams of, 43
  wives of, 53
  'Yammerschooner,' 47–48, 53
Fulmar petrel, 140
Fumariaceae, 431

Gaika, 386
Gaimard, M., 88
Galapagos Archipelago, 20, 24, 37, 57–78, 235–239
botany of, 72
climate of, 57–58
description of, 57
flora of, 72–73, 75–77
geology of, 57
islands of, 57
land-birds of, 62–63, 235–236
mammals of, 62
map of, 55
natural history of, 61–78
reptiles of, 65–72
Galeopithecus, 170
Gallicrex cristatus, 330
Galton, Francis, 6, 293, 364
'*Hereditary Genius*,' 347
Gambier Is., 83
Geach, Mr., 384
Genus, 163
Geoffroy, Isidore, 280
Geographical distribution, 246, 257
Geological books, 23
Geological Observations on South America, 23
Geological record, imperfection of, 166, 207, 248, 256, 266
Geological Society, 22
Geology, 16, 18, 19, 109, 167, 251, 266
attitude to, 10
Geometrical increase, 138–140, 161, 252
Geospiza, 63, 74
Geospiza fortis, 63
Geospiza parvula, 63
Geospiza magnirostris, 63
Gibbon, 376
Glacial period, 109
Glacial phenomena, 16
Glareolae, 330
Gloriosa, 431
Goeree Road, 42, 43, 46
Good Success Bay, 38
Gordon, Lady Duff, 384
Gorilla, 377–378
Gould, J., 62, 63, 326, 332, 336, 337, 340
Gratiolet, Prof., 396, 398
Gray, Asa, 25, 26, 27, 104, 108, 148, 160, 264, 384, 427
Gray, Thomas, 30
'Greatest happiness principle,' and moral sense, 289
Grief, 411
Grypus, 326
Guayavita, 66, 71
Guenons, 374
Gulls, 64
Gymnotus, 177
Gypsies, 312

Habit, and moral sense, 286–287
inherited changes of in domesticated animals, 188–191
Häckel, E., 28
Hagenauer, Mr., 386
Hamlet, 414
Hawfinch, 63
Hawk, 62, 77
Health, 15
Heath, effect of enclosure, 143
Heer, Oswald, 121
Hensen, Dr., 178, 451, 453
Henslow, 12–17, 20–21, 449
Herbert, W., 109
Herbivora, 112
Herbivorous, 72
'*Hereditary Genius*,' 347
Hermaphrodite plant, 132
Herschel, Sir J., 98
Hibbertia dentata, 434
Hindoos, 311, 312, 383, 393
Hive-bees and moral sense, 287
Hogoleu Is., 82
Holland, H., 397–399
Hood Is., 58, 70, 74
Hooker, Joseph D., 21, 25–27, 72–73, 75, 76, 103, 104, 132, 148, 427
Horses, 369
Hottentots, 297–299
Howorth, H. H., 307
Huber, Pierre, 185, 186, 187
Humble-bees, 144–145
Humboldt, Alexander von, 71, 95, 350, 372, 385
Hunter, J., 302, 311
Huxley, T. H., 31, 271–274
Evidence of Man's Place in Nature, 271
Hybrids, 245–246
sterility, 165, 197–199
Hybridism, 197–199
Hydropathic treatment, 23, 26
Hylobates, 423
syndactylus, 376

Ichneumonidae, 197
Ideas, association of, by infant, 419–421

Idiot, microcephalous, 380
Iguana, 68, 72
Illustrations of British Insects, 14
Imitation, 408
Immigration, 157
Indefatigable Is., 58, 70
India, 384
Indian Ocean, 80, 81
Indians, 301, 385
Individual differences, 130–132
Infant,
 biographical sketch of, 415–424
 reflex actions of, 415–417
Infants, 369
Inheritance, 120, 162, 165, 185
 laws of, 322
 of plants, 29
Insane, 369
Insectivora, 170
Insectivorous plants, 438–448
Insects, 64, 73, 75, 77
 collecting, 7
 neuter and sterile, 192–196
Instinct, 165, 184–197, 255–256, 290
 compared with habit, 185
 definition of, 184
 inherited changes of in domesticated animals, 188–191
 loss of in domestic animals, 190–191
 variation in, 186–188
 variations of, 186
Intention, 408
Intercrossing of plants, 29
Introduction, effect of Scotch fir, 143
Inuus ecaudatus, 371
Isaiah, 387

Jaeger, Dr., 428
James Is., 58, 60–61, 70, 74–77
 climate of, 61
 vegetation of, 61
Jealousy, exhibited by infant, 419
Jemmy Button, *See* Button, Jemmy
Jerdon, Dr., 332
Jeremiah, Book of, 384
Jews, 311, 312, 384
Jourdain, M., 173
Journal, 19
Journal of Researches, 23, 37
Juan Fernandez, 73

Kaffirs, 299, 386
Kant, Immanuel, 286, 289, 302
Keeling Atoll, 80, 87
Kichernden, 371
Kidney-bean, 430
King, Capt., 37, 42
Knight, Andrew, 187, 434

Lacerta, 72
Lagoon-islands, 79
Lamarck, Chevalier de, 118, 196
Land-birds, 62–63
Land-shell, 73, 75
Lang, Mr., 386
Langstaff, Dr., 382
Language, 407–408
 of infant, 422–424
 origin of, 285
 power of, and moral sense, 286
La Plata, 105
Laughter, 411
Law of battle, 108
'Laws of Variation,' 165
Laycock, Prof., 398
Leaf-climbers, 428–431
Leaf-climbing plants, advantages of, 429
Leaves, sensitiveness of, 430
Legs, variability of, in man, 278
Leguminosae, 75
Leibnitz, Baron von, 260
Le Maire, Strait of, 38
Lemoine, M., 409
Lepchas, 383
Lepidosiren, 163
Lewes, G. H., 264
Life and Letters, 449
Liliaceae, 435
Linnean Society, 103, 104
Linnaeus, Carolus, 138
Livingstone, Dr., 125, 312
Lizards, 60, 65, 72, 76
London, 21, 22
Lophospermum, 431
Low Archipelago, 63, 80
Lubbock, Sir J., 131, 195, 304
Luminous organs and natural selection, 178
Lund, Dr., 297
Lyell, Charles, 19, 21, 24–26, 28, 103, 104, 109, 156, 261, 299

Macacus, 372, 374
 inornatus, 372
 maurus, 372
 rhesus, 375, 379
Macgillivray, Mr., 10

Machetes pugnax, 331
Mackintosh, Mr., 285
Macnamara, Mr., 308
Macrobius, 387
Madagascar, 65
Magpies, 78
Mahlos-Mahdoo Atoll, 89
Malacca, 384
Malaria, 308
Malays, 297, 298, 384
Maldiva Archipelago, 88–89
Maldiva Atolls, 79, 89
Malthus, T. R., 105, 106
  doctrine of, 138
  on Population, 25
Mammalia, 72
Mammals, 62, 114
Man,
  belief in God by, 361
  bodily structure of, 272–273
  body size of, 283
  brain of, 272
  characters of interracial hybrids of, 300
  embryo of, 273–274
  embryological structure of, 358
  external parasites of races of, 298–299
  extinction of the races of, 305–311
  formation of the races of, 311–314
  geographical distribution of races of, 298
  helplessness of, 283–284
  hybrid fertility of races of, 299–300
  intercrossing of races of, 302
  intergradation of races of, 302
  manner of development from some lower form, 278–282
  mental powers of, 358
    compared to lower animals, 284–285
  moral qualities of, 359–360
  mutable, 28
  natural selection in, 280, 282
  nictitating membrane of, 275
  one or several species of, 302–305
  os coccyx of, 276–277
  population increase of, 138
  races of, 273, 296–314, 370
    blushing in, 412
    as distinct species, 297–302
  rudimentary organs of, 274–278
  rudiments of muscles of, 274–275
  scalp muscles of, 275
  secondary sexual characters of, 344–355
  sexual dimorphism of, 344–349
  sexual dimorphism in mental powers of, 347–349
  skin colour of, 311–313
  social animal, 287–295
  social instincts of, 359
  special expressions of, 369
  superior to woman, 348
  taxonomic characters of, 296–305
  variability of, 278–279, 282
  vermiform appendage of, 276
  wisdom teeth of, 275–276
Mandrill, 375
Mantegazza, Prof., 351
Manual of the Flora of the Northern United States, 160
Maoris, 308, 384
Marshall, W., 328
Martin, W. L., 371–374
Martius, 385
Matteucci, 177
Matthews, R., 40, 50–52
Matthews, Washington, 384
Maupertuis, 262
Maurandia semperflorens, 432
Mauritius, 65, 67
Maurua Is., 83
M'Donnell, R., 177
Medicine, attitude to, 8–9
Memory in a young child, 421
Menchicoff Atoll, 79
Mental faculties, variability of in man, 278
Mental qualities of domestic animals, 188
Mice, 62
  in La Plata, 105, 106
Micropterus, 170
Milton, John, 30
Mimus melanotis, 74
  parvulus, 74
  trifasciatus, 74
Mineral collecting, 7
Minster, York, 40, 41, 45, 50–52, 54
Mivart, Mr., 178
Möbius, Prof., 420
Mocking-thrush, 62, 64, 74–78
Modesty, 389
Modification of species, 24
Mollusca, 114, 171
Momordica balsamina, 429
Mongolians, 297, 298
Monkeys, 369, 370, 380, 409–412
  expression of the emotions in, 369–379
  long-tailed, 374
Monogenist, 303
Monstrosities, 129, 130

Moral sense, 285–287, 292
of infant, 421–422
Moresby, Capt., 90
Mould formation by earthworms, 22
Mouse, 62
Movement of expression, inherited, 407
Movements, expressive, 404, 406, 407
Movements and gestures which accompany blushing, 386–387
Mozart, W. A., 185
Mulattoes, 299, 300, 386
Mule, 300
Müller, Fritz, 28, 131, 173, 196, 399, 431
Murray, A., 298, 299
Murray, John, 37
Mus galapagoensis, 62
Muscles, variability of, 131
in man, 278
Mustela vison, 169
Myrmecocystus, 194
Myrmica, 195

Nägeli, 280
Naravelia, 431
Narborough Is., 58, 60
Narrative of the Surveying Voyage of Her Majesty's Ships 'Adventure' and 'Beagle,' 37
Natural selection, 27, 109, 136–164, 165–169, 172, 175, 195, 244, 251–260, 280–281
circumstances favourable for the production of new forms through, 156–158
conditions of existence embraced by the theory of, 182–184
illustrations of, 153–156
instinct and, 186
intermediate forms of, 247
man and, 280, 282
objections to term, 149
objections to the theory of, 191–196
process of, 182
special difficulties of the theory of, 177–179
theory of, 37
Naturalised plants, 160–161
Naudin, 433
Nectariniae, 331
Negritos, 301
Negro, 297–299, 301, 304, 313, 385
Neomorpha, 326
Nerves, variability of, 131
Nervous system, principle of the direct action of, 369
Neuter and sterile insects, 192–196
New Caledonia, 82, 84, 86, 89
New Zealand, 37, 52
New Zealanders, 55, 311, 384
Newton, Sir Isaac, 260, 285
Nictitating membrane, 275
Nillandoo Atolls, 89
Nilsson, Prof., 304
Norfolk Islanders, 310
North America, 384
North Wales, 11, 16

Oceanic islands, 258
Oens men, 49, 54
Old Testament, 26
Orang-outang, 42, 371, 374, 376–379
Orchis, 178
Orders, 163
Organs of extreme perfection and complication, 172–175
Origin of man, 29
Origin of Species, 9, 22, 24, 25–28, 32, 103, 277, 280
success of, 26
Ornithorhynchus, 163
Os coccyx, 276–277
Ostrich, 50, 140
Otaheite, 55
Owen, 119, 174, 274
Owls, 62, 64
barn, 62
short-eared, 62

Pacific, 37, 55, 57, 65, 73, 384
Pacini, 178
Paget, James, 381, 382, 399
Pain, 411
Painful emotions and sensations, 372, 374
Painting, 369
Pallas, 312
Pallasian doctrine, 300
Palms, 59, 72
Papuans, 297, 298, 312
Park, Mungo, 353
Travels, 347
Parus major, 191
Passenger pigeon, 113
Passiflora gracilis, 429
Passifloraceae, 429
Patagonia, 20, 38, 64, 73, 97
Patagonians, 38
Patience, 412

Pea, 430
Pediculi, 298–299
Pelecanus erythrorhynchus, 330
  onocrotalus, 332
Permanence of species, 27
Pernis cristata, 340
Peru, 46, 60
Phanerogamic plants, 435
Phaseolus, 431
Photographs, 369
Piano playing, example of habit vs. instinct, 185
Pitcairn Island, 310
Plants, 64, 73
  flowering of, 72
  inheritance of, 29
  intercrossing of, 29
  introduced, 139
  movements of, 432
  variation of, 29
Pleasurable sensations of infants, 418–419
Pleasure, joy, affection, 370–372
Plicata, 66
Plinian Society, 10
Pliny, 125, 126
Plymouth, 19–20
Polar current, 57
Polybori, 62, 64
Polygenists, 303
Polynesians, 301, 384
Polyplectron, 334
Ponsonby Sound, 46, 49, 53, 54
Pontobdella muricata, 10
Population, 112–113
  animal, 114
Port Famine, 42
Power of Movement in Plants, 427, 449
Predators, as checks to increase, 142
Principle of Columbus and his egg, 25
Principles of classification, 24
Progne purpurea, 62
Psychology, 266
Pyrocephalus, 62, 64

Quoy, M., 88

Races, 103, 111, 118, 271
Radack Atolls, 80
Radcliffe, Dr., 177
Rage, 411–412
Rail, 64
Ramsay, Mr., 325
Rana Mascariensis, 65
Rat, 62
Reade, Winwood, 352, 353
Reason, exhibited by infant, 419–421
Rengger, 371, 372
Reproduction, in man, 272–273
Reptiles, 65, 73
Richardson, J., 169
Rimsky Atoll, 79
'Rogues,' 124
'Roguing,' 108, 124
Rohlfs, 300
Romeo and Juliet, quoted, 396
Ross Atoll, 89
Rotundifolia, 438–448
Royal Society, Fellow of, 15
Rubiaceae, 435
Rudimentary organs, 274, 277
Sailors, 78
St. Helena, 20, 73
Saliva, inspissated, 191
Sandwich Archipelago, 65, 309
Sandwich Islanders, 299, 308
Santali, 311
Saturnalia, 387
Savage, 377
Scalesia, 76
Scenery, 96
Schaaffhausen, Prof., 276, 306
Schweinfurth, 344
Science, definition of, 16
Scotch fir, 143
Scott, Mr., 383, 384
Screaming, 411
Scrophularia, 326
Scrophulariaceae, 435
Sculpture, 369
Sea-sickness, 96
Sea-turtle, 65
Sea-weed, 69
Sedgwick, 12, 16, 20
Seedlings, destruction of, 141
Seeds, 77
  nutriment in, 147
Selection, 24, 107, 109, 137, 148, 250
  by man, 150–151
  natural, 103
  principle of, 108
  principles of, 122–125
  sexual, 29, 162, 181, 251, 254, 315–324, 361–365, 397
  unconscious, 125–129
Selfishness and morality, 289
Semitic, 384
Seneca, 387

Serviceable associated habits, principle of, 369
Serviceable movements, principle of, 403
Sexes, numerical proportion of, 319
Sexual characters, primary, definition of, 315
Sexual characters, secondary, 108
  definition of, 315
Sexual dimorphism in habits and structures, 316
  birds, 327
Sexual selection, 29, 162, 181, 251, 254, 361–365, 397
  compared with natural selection, 321
  definition of, 316–317
  principles of, 315–324
Seychelles, 65
Shakespeare, Wm., 30, 285, 396, 414
Shame, 389
Sharpe, Dr., 312
Shelley, P. B., 30
Shells, 73
Shooting, 11, 15
Shrewsbury, 3, 5, 8, 10, 12, 16, 18, 19
Shyness, 389–390, 392–393
  of infant, 422
Sikhim, 383
Skull, variability of, in man, 278
Slave, 94
Slavery, 18
Smith, Andrew, 353
Smith, F., 194, 195
Snake, 65
Social animal, man, 287–295
Social instincts, 286, 291, 293
Society Archipelago, 82, 87
Solanum, 431
  jasminoides, 433
Somerville, Lord, 123
South Africa, 55, 386
South America, 37, 55, 64, 71, 106, 385
South Sea Islanders, 55
Spaniards, 60, 61, 66, 67, 301, 385
Species, 103, 106, 109, 110, 112, 114, 115, 120, 121, 133, 136, 138, 146, 150, 152, 158–160, 163, 165–168, 182, 183, 186, 195, 251, 254, 271, 370
  definition of, 129, 264, 303
  how different from varieties, 296
  mutability of, 261
  mutable productions, 28
  permanent invariability of, 111
  separate creation of, 262
  taxonomic treatment of, 302–303
Spencer, Herbert, 137, 266, 292
Squirrels, transitional habits and structures in, 169–170
Stack, Rev. Mr., 384
Starling, 63
Staten-land, 38
Sterility, 245
Story, Dr., 308
Strait of Le Maire, 38
Strait of Magellan, 38, 42
Strawberry, 434
Structure and Distribution of Coral Reefs, 37
Struggle for existence, 25, 111, 114, 136–148, 172, 244, 250
  definition of, 137–138
  individuals, species, varieties, 146
  interrelations of plants and animals, 142, 146
  intrageneric, 146
  intraspecific, 146
Struggle for life, 161
Suadiva Atoll, 79
Sub-classes, 162
Sub-families, 162
Sub-genera, 162
Sub-races, 271
Subsidence, 81, 85, 86, 89, 92, 157, 249
  evidence of, 87
  theory of, 88
  objections to, 90
Sub-species, 110, 136, 251
  taxonomic treatment of, 302–303
Suffering, 411
Survival of the fittest, 137, 148, 149, 162, 280
Sutton, Mr., 375, 378
Swallow, 62, 64
Swimbladder, 176
Swinhoe, Mr., 384
Switzerland, lake inhabitants of, 121
Sympathy, 291, 413
  and moral sense, 287
Sypheotides auritus, 329

Tabanidae, 316
Tahiti, 37, 384
Tahitians, 308, 310
Taine, M., 415, 420, 423
Tanagra rubra, 340
Tanais, 131, 316
Taplin, G., 386
Tasmanians, 308, 310
  extinction of, 307

Taxonomic characters, principles of, 296–297
Taxonomic treatment of species and subspecies, 302–303
Tecoma radicans, 433
Teeth, variability of in man, 278
Tekenika, 49
Tendency of Varieties to depart indefinitely from the Original Type, 25, 104, 111–119
Tendrils,
  movements of, 431–433
  nature of, 430
  origins of, 431–433
  qualities of, 431
Tendril-bearers, 429–431
Tendril-bearing plants, advantages of, 429
Ternate, 103
Testudo nigra, 65
Thompson, William, 249
Tierra del Fuego, 20, 37–56, 126, 385, 391
  climate, 43
Toads and frogs, absence of in Galapagos, 65
Todas, 309
Torpedo, 177
Tortoises, 59–61, 65–67, 69, 71, 76, 77, 78
  variation of, 73–74
Totanus, 64, 330
Tower Is., 58, 70
Tragopan, 334
Transition, modes of, 175, 176
Transitional forms, 165
Transitional habits and structures,
  in allied species, 169
  in Galeopithecus, 170
  in squirrels, 169–170
Transitional varieties, absence or rarity of, 166–169
Transmutation of species, 24
Travels, 347
Tree of life, 163–164
Tree-frog, 24
Trimorphism, 131
Troglodytes, 197
Tropaeolum, 429
Tropics, 20
Trousseau, cerebral maculae of, 389
Tumbler-pigeons, habits of, 189
Turner, Prof. W., 277, 278
Turtle, 72, 376, 378
Turtle-doves, 78
Twiners, 428
Twining plants, disadvantages of, 429
Tylor, E. B., 304
Tyrant-flycatchers, 77

Ulvae, 69
Unconscious selection, 250
Unconsciousness of infant, 422
Unity of type, law of, 182–184
Uruguay, 37
Use and disuse, 129, 250, 254
  inherited effects of, 271
Usnera, 66
Utilitarian Doctrine, 179–181

Vanikoro Is., 82, 83, 87
Variability, 136, 148, 150, 152, 248–251
  causes of, 120, 279
Variation, 137, 165, 175, 244
  intraspecific, 130–135
  of domestic productions, 29
  of organic beings in a state of nature, 104
  of organic beings under domestication and in their natural state, 103, 105
  of organisms, 120–135
  of plants, 29
Variation of Animals and Plants under Domestication, 309
Variations, 25, 108, 115, 116, 148, 149, 161, 168, 188, 252
  in man, 271
Varieties, 103, 110, 111, 115, 116, 117–119, 136, 158, 159, 163, 168, 182, 251, 254, 271, 370
  as incipient species, 134
  fertility of, when intercrossed, 245
Variety, 110, 111, 115–116, 182
  definition of, 129
Various Contrivances by which British and Foreign Orchids are Fertilized by Insects, 427
Vegetation, 59, 61
Verlot, M., 193
Vermiform appendage, 276
Vertebrata, 174
  eyes of, 178–179
Vicia, 433
  sativa, 430
Vidua, 337
Vine, 429, 431, 433
Virchow, Rudolf, 174
Virtue, inheritance of, 292
Vitaceae, 429
Vitis, 432
Volcanic islands, 22

Volcanoes, 91–92
Volute shell, 16
Vomiting, 412
Von Baer, K. E., 273
Von Spix, 385
Voyage of the Beagle, 37–99

Waders, 64
Waitz, Prof., 349
Wallace, Alfred Russel, 25, 26, 27, 103, 104, 111, 131, 174, 196, 264, 317, 371
  On the Tendency of Varieties to depart indefinitely from the Original Type, 25, 104
Warbler, 63
Water-birds, 63
Waterhouse, Mr., 62, 64, 75, 161
Water-rail, 61
Waterton, C., 329
Watson, H. C., 132
Weeds, 73
Weeping, 411
Weir, Jenner, 319, 326
Wenman Is., 58
West Indies, 91
Westropp, H. M., 304
Whalers, 59, 78
Whales, 51, 72
White, Gilbert, *Natural History of Selborne*, 7
Whitsunday Is., 79
Will, 406, 408
Wilson, S., 386
Winter's bark, 43
Wisdom-teeth, 275–276
Wollaston Is., 43
Wood, J., 278, 334
Woodpecker, 24
Woollya, 50, 52, 53, 54
Wordsworth, 30
Worms,
  amount of fine earth brought up to the surface by, 450–451
  archaeology, contributions to, 456
  in the history of the world, 454–455
  number of, 451
    in an acre, 451–454
  sense-organs of, 457
  weight of the earth ejected by, 452–454
Worm-castings, 455–456
Wren, 62, 64, 77
Wyman, Prof., 274, 377

'Yammerschooner,' 47–48, 53
York Minster, *See* Minster, York

Zoology of the Voyage of the Beagle, 22
Zoonomia, 9
Zygaena, 7

PRINTED IN GREAT BRITAIN BY ROBERT MACLEHOSE AND CO. LTD
THE UNIVERSITY PRESS, GLASGOW